ORDINARY DIFFERENTIAL EQUATIONS AND THEIR SOLUTIONS

---

by

GEORGE M. MURPHY

Professor of Chemistry
New York University

D. VAN NOSTRAND COMPANY, INC.

PRINCETON, NEW JERSEY

TORONTO   LONDON

NEW YORK

D. VAN NOSTRAND COMPANY, INC.
120 Alexander St., Princeton, New Jersey (*Principal office*)
24 West 40 Street, New York 18, New York

D. VAN NOSTRAND COMPANY, LTD.
358, Kensington High Street, London, W.14, England

D. VAN NOSTRAND COMPANY (Canada), LTD.
25 Hollinger Road, Toronto 16, Canada

20746
209

PREFACE

Applied mathematicians, chemists, engineers, physicists, and others who use mathematics sometimes need to solve a differential equation. The related problem of evaluating an integral is usually simple, since tables of standard integrals are readily available. A similar tabulation of standard differential equations might be helpful. The idea is not new. As early as 1889, Professor William E. Byerly of Harvard University included "A Key to the Solution of Differential Equations" in the second edition of his text on integral calculus. Parenthetically, it is interesting to note that Peirce's "A Short Table of Integrals" first appeared in the 1881 edition of the same book. More recently, the well-known German treatise of E. Kamke (1940 and subsequent editions) has contained a collection of more than a thousand equations with their general solutions.

Unfortunately, consideration of the problem shows that it is not easy to select the standard equations. The value of an integral, in the usual case, can be presented in terms of parameters, independent of numerical values assigned to them. On the other hand, a change in sign of some term in a differential equation, the transfer of a term from numerator to denominator, or some other simple alteration in its form may convert the equation from one with a solution by elementary methods into a case with no solution in terms of known functions. In spite of these obvious difficulties, I was still of the opinion that it would be useful to have some formal scheme for solving a given equation. The result is the compromise offered in Parts I and II of this book. It is fully explained in the Introduction.

There are no new methods here but the arrangement of the material is original. I believe that the rather complete treatment of singular points is an important feature. Reference to the index will show that the book of E. L. Ince has been a constant source of help to me. In fact, if one were limited to a single book on differential equations, this is the only possible choice. The well-known books of A. R. Forsyth were also informative. Long out of print, his six volume "Theory of Differential Equations" is now available in a handsomely bound reprint. Finally, I would like to mention the recent book of E. A. Coddington and N. Levinson. Its discussion of the modern theory makes it a worthy companion to the two classics just cited.

The equations in Part II were selected from a much larger number which I collected over a period of several years. All of the equations in about fifteen elementary textbooks or other sources given in the Bibliography were first recorded on cards. After converting each to a uniform notation, they could be arranged according to the various types of Part I. In some cases, it was possible to generalize an equation by the introduction of alternative signs or by the replacement of a numerical constant with a literal one. The final selection for Part II was made more or less arbitrarily. An equation with unusually complicated coefficients was often discarded. Others were kept because their solution required some ingenious trick, because the solution had a pleasing form, or for some similar reason. The final set, 2315 in number, includes typical examples of most methods in Part I. Twice as many could easily have been retained, showing how difficult it would really be to choose a standard set. It was fascinating to note, as the work progressed, that many of the equations could be traced back successively from recent textbooks to the English books of the early twentieth century; then to the French or German treatises of the nineteenth century; finally to Euler, the Bernoullis, Lagrange, or Laplace, who, of course, first showed how to solve them.

I have solved each equation in Part II by the methods indicated. This work involved several thousand pages of notes. Subsequent transfer of the equation and solution to the manuscript, the processes of typing, printing, and proof reading have certainly introduced errors, although each step was carefully checked. No one knows better than I the annoyance than can result from a misprint. I hope that the annoyed reader will let me know when he finds one. Perhaps this is the proper place to make the obvious comment that I am a chemist by training and profession. I make no pretense to mathematical elegance in the book and I am well aware of its many faults in this respect. I believe, however, that it will help people who want to solve a differential equation. I might add that I have certainly solved more differential equations than most chemists and more than many mathematicians.

Writing the last paragraph of a preface is always an agreeable task. The chores of typing, proof reading, and preparation of the index are completed. The excitement of planning and organizing the book is over and I can only hope that the user will have a little of the pleasure that I have had in working on it. I have expressed my gratitude to several mathematicians in an earlier paragraph. Similar comments could be made to the authors of many books listed in the Bibliography. Let me now thank the publisher and the printer for all of the arduous detail required to produce the final product. Special thanks go to Mr. William R. Minrath of the D. Van Nostrand Company, Inc., who encouraged me to write the book in the first place. Finally, I am happy to offer genuine and sincere thanks to my colleague, Professor Frederick W. John, formerly in the Department of Mathematics at Washington Square

College, who was always willing to help me when I had troubles with some particular equation.

GEORGE M. MURPHY

New York, N. Y.
March 25, 1960

CONTENTS

INTRODUCTION

This book has been written for anyone who wants to solve an ordinary differential equation. Two alternative procedures are offered.

a. Go to Part I. It contains most of the methods which have been developed for solving ordinary differential equations. If directions are followed, it should be possible to classify the given equation as a special case of one or more general types. When the type has been identified, details of the method for solving it will also be found.

b. Go to Part II. It contains more than two thousand ordinary differential equations, arranged in a systematic order. A solution of each is also given or some directions as to a method. References to the general methods of Part I are included in each case. If the equation to be solved is contained in this collection, a solution of it is thus found. If the equation is not in the collection, one of similar form there may suggest a method that might be tried. Otherwise, it will be necessary to consult Part I and seek a general method which is applicable.

The remainder of this section contains some definitions, some general properties of differential equations, and a description of the symbols used in the book. It should be read before continuing with either Part I or Part II.

1. Some Definitions. A *differential equation* is a relation involving one or more derivatives and an unknown function. The problem of solving it is a search for that unknown function. The *solution* of a differential equation is any relation, free from derivatives, which satisfies the equation identically.

The most general *ordinary differential equation* is

$$f(x, y, y', y'', \ldots, y^{(n)}) = 0 \tag{1}$$

where x is the *independent variable*, y is the *dependent variable*, $y' = dy/dx$, $y'' = d^2y/dx^2$, $y''' = d^3y/dx^3$, $y^{\mathrm{iv}} = d^4y/dx^4$, $\ldots$, $y^{(n)} = d^ny/dx^n$. It will often also contain *parameters* or literal constants. There are other kinds of differential equations involving variables as follows: one dependent variable, two or more independent variables, and partial differential coefficients of the dependent variable with respect to one or more of the

1

independent variables—a *partial differential equation*; two or more dependent variables, a single independent variable which need not appear explicitly, and differential coefficients with respect to this independent variable—a *total differential equation*; one independent variable, two or more dependent variables, and two or more simultaneous equations—a simultaneous *system of differential equations*; variables, derivatives, and an unknown function behind an integral sign—an *integro-differential equation*; variables, derivatives, and finite differences—a *differential-difference equation*. None of these cases are treated in this book.

The *order* of an ordinary differential equation is the order of the highest differential coefficient which it contains. If the equation is a polynomial in all of the differential coefficients, the degree of the highest-order derivative is the *degree* of the differential equation. It is often necessary to rationalize the equation and to clear it of fractions in order to determine the degree. In some cases, a transcendental function of one or more derivatives may occur. Typical examples are $\ln y'$, $\sin y''$, $\cosh y^{(n)}$. In such cases, the equation is of infinite degree.

2. The Solution of a Differential Equation.   Given a function

$$F(x, y, C_1, C_2, \dots, C_n) = 0 \tag{2}$$

where C_1, C_2, $\dots$, C_n are arbitrary constants, differentiate it n times successively, if this be possible, to get

$$\frac{\partial F}{\partial x} + \frac{\partial F}{\partial y}\frac{dy}{dx} = 0$$

$$\frac{\partial^2 F}{\partial x^2} + 2\frac{\partial^2 F}{\partial x \partial y}\frac{dy}{dx} + \frac{\partial^2 F}{\partial y^2}\left(\frac{dy}{dx}\right)^2 + \frac{\partial F}{\partial y}\frac{d^2 y}{dx^2} = 0$$

$$\dots \quad \dots \quad \dots \quad \dots \quad \dots \quad \dots \quad \dots \quad \dots \quad \dots \tag{3}$$

$$\frac{\partial^n F}{\partial x^n} + \quad \dots \quad \dots \quad \dots \quad \dots \quad \dots \quad + \frac{\partial F}{\partial y}\frac{d^n y}{dx^n} = 0$$

Use (2) and the first equation of (3) to eliminate one of the constants C_i. The result is a differential equation of first order containing $(n-1)$ arbitrary parameters. A total of n differential equations could be found in this way, because any one of the constants C_i could be selected for elimination. However, only two of the n equations would be independent since all were formed from two simultaneous equations.

Continue in this way and use 2, 3, $\dots$, $k \le n$ equations from (3) and get $\binom{n}{k}$ differential equations of order k from (2). Each contains $(n-k)$ constants and there are $(k+1)$ independent equations.

Finally, there is only one differential equation (1) of order n and it is free from arbitrary constants. The reverse of this is also true. Given a differential equation of order n, the existence of a function (2), containing n arbitrary constants, is implied. Such a function is the *complete primitive* of (1), its *general* (or *complete*) *solution*, its *general* (or *complete*) *integral*, or its *integral curves*. Some writers use the word integral to designate an implicit relation like (2) and restrict the meaning of solution to an explicit relation for y as a function of x. Others use integral or solution to mean the result obtained when (1) is solved, reserving the word primitive for (2), if the differential equation has resulted from it by differentiation. Such distinctions will not be made here and the words primitive, integral, solution will mean any function that satisfies the differential equation identically.

The n arbitrary constants eliminated from (2) in obtaining (1), or resulting from the latter when it is solved, are the *constants of integration*. It should not be inferred, however, that the process of differentiation and elimination of these constants is the normal way in which differential equations are produced. Nevertheless, if the general solution can be found, the differential equation could have resulted from it by the process described.

In many cases, especially in applied mathematics, it is of interest to find solutions which satisfy certain special conditions required for physical reasons. Such conditions are *initial values* or *boundary conditions*. The required solution can usually be obtained by assigning particular values to one or more of the integration constants in the general solution. The result, containing less than the full number of arbitrary constants, still satisfies the differential equation. It is a *special* (or *particular*) *solution* or *special* (or *particular*) *integral*.

Sometimes a function exists which satisfies the differential equation but which is not a special case of the general solution. It is a *singular solution* or a *singular integral*.

3. Existence Theorems. Statements in the preceding section were based on the assumption that the given differential equation actually has a unique solution. Elementary methods for finding it are successful because both the equation and its solution belong to a relatively simple class of functions. In more general cases, it is not at all obvious that a solution of the equation exists. Mathematicians, since the time of Cauchy, have been interested in this problem and their conclusions are stated in a number of *existence theorems*. The details and proofs of them are lengthy; they will not be given here. For suitable references see Ince-1, Coddington and Levinson, or other sources listed in the Bibliography.

Existence theorems are usually based on the properties of functions of a complex variable. For our purposes, they can be briefly summarized in terms of a real variable. A given function of the variables x, y, z, ... , t is said to be *analytic* in the neighborhood of arbitrarily assigned constants x_0, y_0, z_0, ... , t_0 if it can be developed by Taylor's theorem as an absolutely convergent power series in $x - x_0$, $y - y_0$, $z - z_0$, ... , $t - t_0$. The existence theorems prove that a differential equation

$$y^{(n)} = f(x, y, y', y'', \ldots, y^{(n-1)})$$

will have a unique solution $y = y(x)$, provided that $f(x, y, y', \ldots, y^{(n-1)})$ is analytic in the neighborhood of x_0, y_0, y_0', y_0'', ... , $y_0^{(n-1)}$. The solution of the equation will satisfy the conditions $y(x_0) = y_0$, $y'(x_0) = y_0'$, $y''(x_0) = y_0''$, ... , $y_0^{(n-1)}(x_0) = y_0^{(n-1)}$. Since, within certain limits, these n constants are arbitrary, they are the required integration constants of the general solution. Further comments about existence theorems will be made later in connection with special kinds of differential equations.

4. Notation. The symbols x, y are used for the independent and dependent variables respectively in this book. Derivatives are written as $y' = dy/dx$, $y'' = d^2y/dx^2$, $y''' = d^3y/dx^n$, $y^{\text{iv}} = d^4y/dx^4$, ... , $y^{(n)} = $ $= d^ny/dx^n$. It is often convenient to let $y' = p$. If a new independent variable is introduced it is called z and there is some relation $\phi(x, z) = 0$ connecting the old and new variables. For clarity, the name of the dependent variable will also be changed so that $y(x) = u(z)$. Other variables that may occur are v, w, t, etc. They will be defined when they are used.

The arbitrary constant of integration is C or C_1, C_2, ... , C_n. Other constants are lower-case letters, such as a, b, c, k, q, r, s, with subscripts where needed. The letters m, n mean integers in most cases.

Functions of one or both variables are f, g, h, F, G, H, X, Y, often with subscripts; A, B sometimes are constants but they may be a function of the variables. Greek letters have generally been avoided but they have been used where necessary.

Primes, double primes, etc., always mean derivatives. A subscript letter indicates a partial derivative; thus, $f_x = \partial f/\partial x$, $F_{xy} = \partial^2 F/\partial x \partial y$.

A wide variety of symbols is needed in a book such as this and it is not always easy to be consistent. The general principles just stated will be used, as far as possible. Departures from them will be explained as they occur.

A number in parentheses always refers to an equation. To simplify the notation, if (3) appears in section **7**, for instance, it will mean the third equation in that section. If the reference is to the third equation in section **4**, the symbol would be **4(3)**. If there are subsections, like **7-1, 7-2, 7-2-1**, etc., the equations are numbered consecutively throughout.

Section numbers are indicated in a similar way but without parentheses. Thus, the number **4-1** appearing in any part of **A1** would mean section 4-1. If it referred to section **4-1** of **A2**, it would be given as **A2-4-1**. When further subdivisions of a section are required they are called **a, b, c**, etc. If still another subdivision is wanted, Roman numerals **i, ii, iii**, are used.

References to texts or other books are given with the name or names of the authors. If there are two or more books by the same author a number is added to the author's name. Full details, such as the title of the book, the publisher, date of publication, etc., will be found in the Bibliography.

Part 1

METHODS FOR SOLVING ORDINARY DIFFERENTIAL EQUATIONS

The equation to be solved has the form

$$f(x, y, y', y'', \dots, y^{(n)}) = 0$$

Determine its order and consult the appropriate section.

A. An equation of first order

B. An equation of second order

C. An equation of order higher than two

A. THE DIFFERENTIAL EQUATION
IS OF FIRST ORDER

The general equation is

$$f(x, y, y', a_1, a_2, \ldots, a_n) = 0$$

where x is the independent variable, y is the dependent variable, $y' = dy/dx$, and a_i is a parameter or literal constant. Proceed according to one of the following directions.

a. The equation is a polynomial in y'. The degree of the polynomial is the degree of the differential equation. There are two cases.

i. The degree of the equation is unity; see **A1.**

ii. The degree of the equation is two or greater; see **A2.**

b. The equation is not a polynomial in y'. If the equation is algebraic in y' but not a polynomial or if transcendental functions of y' occur, like $\cos y'$, $\ln y'$, etc., refer to **A2.**

A1. THE EQUATION IS OF FIRST ORDER AND OF FIRST DEGREE

The general equation is

$$y' = f(x, y)$$

If it is not of this form or cannot be converted to it, refer to **A2**. When it is cleared of fractions, an equivalent and more symmetrical equation, used in many textbooks, is

$$f_1(x, y)dx + f_2(x, y)dy = 0$$

It has the advantage that either x or y could be regarded as the independent variable. The form is also useful when two new variables are to be taken.

Compare the given equation with the cases of the following sections. As far as practicable, they have been presented in the order of increasing complexity. Often an equation may be solved by more than one method but it will usually be true that the one with the smaller type number will be simpler.

It should be noted that the general solution of the equation may be given as

$$y = \int \phi(x)dx + C$$

It is then regarded as solved, even though the integral may not be evaluated in terms of known functions. In this form, it is said that a *quadrature* must be completed in order to obtain an explicit solution $y = F(x) + C$. Thus, the problem has become one of integral calculus, not one of differential equations.

In case there is special interest in the behavior of a solution near a *singular point*, where $f(x, y)$ becomes infinite or indeterminate, proceed at once to **10**. Some general properties of the equation and its solution are also described there.

Sometimes two different solutions for the same equation are found by different methods

$$F_1(x, y) = C_1; \quad F_2(x, y) = C_2$$

9

If both satisfy the differential equation, they must be equivalent, which means that

$$\frac{\partial F_1}{\partial x}\frac{\partial F_2}{\partial y} = \frac{\partial F_1}{\partial y}\frac{\partial F_2}{\partial x}$$

Alternatively, eliminate one of the variables. The other will usually also disappear, leaving a relation between C_1 and C_2.

A related situation occurs when two equations are given

$$f_1(x, y, y', a_1) = 0; \quad f_2(x, y, y', a_2) = 0$$

where a_1, a_2 are constants. If both have arisen from a common primitive, each can be differentiated and the two constants eliminated to get a second-order equation containing no constants

$$\phi(x, y, y', y'') = 0$$

If the general solution of the latter can be found it will contain two integration constants, which can be called a_1 and a_2. More directly, this solution would follow by elimination of y' between the two first-order equations.

1. Separable Variables

The general equation is

$$y' = f(x)g(y)$$

If $g(y) = a$, see **1-1**; if $f(x) = a$, see **1-3**; if neither is a constant, see **1-2**. For a special case, see **1-4**.

1-1. Dependent Variable Missing. The equation is

$$y' = af(x)$$

Its solution is

$$y = a\int f(x)dx + C$$

1-2. Neither Variable Missing. The equation is

$$y' = f(x)g(y)$$

The solution is

$$\int \frac{dy}{g(y)} = \int f(x)dx + C$$

The equation is sometimes presented for solution as

$$X(x)Y_1(y)dx + X_1(x)Y(y)dy = 0$$

In the standard form

$$f(x) = \pm X(x)/X_1(x); \quad g(x) = \mp Y_1(y)/Y(y)$$

Care must be taken not to lose a solution, for the roots of $X_1 = 0$ and $Y_1 = 0$ satisfy the new equation but they may not satisfy the equation written in standard form.

If $f(x)$ and $g(y)$ are the square roots of certain polynomials, see **1-4**.

1-3. Independent Variable Missing. The equation is

$$y' = ag(y)$$

and its solution is

$$\int \frac{dy}{g(y)} = ax + C$$

1-4. The Euler Equation. One of several equations known by the name of Euler, see also **B1-3-1**, has the form

$$\sqrt{X}\, y' = \pm \sqrt{Y}$$

$$X(x) = a_0 + a_1 x + a_2 x^2 + a_3 x^3 + a_4 x^4$$

$$Y(y) = a_0 + a_1 y + a_2 y^2 + a_3 y^3 + a_4 y^4$$

a. The equation is separable, see **1-2**, but evaluation of the integrals may cause difficulty; see **c** and **d**.

b. Square the equation to get one of the second degree and try the methods of **A2**, which may be successful when some of the a_i vanish. In most cases, the procedure of **c** or **d** will be preferable.

c. The functions $X(x)$ and $Y(y)$ are quadratics so that $a_3 = a_4 = 0$. If the roots of the quadratic are equal, integration is simple. If they are unequal, integration gives an inverse trigonometric or hyperbolic function; see any table of integrals, that of Peirce and Foster, for example. Such functions can be inverted to give an algebraic solution, but see also **d**.

d. The functions $X(x)$ and $Y(y)$ are of third or fourth degree. The resulting integrals define elliptic functions and their properties can be used to secure an algebraic solution of the differential equation. Convenient references for elliptic integrals and functions are Erdélyi-1, Macrobert, Whittaker and Watson. Elliptic functions can be avoided and the algebraic solution of the equation obtained directly by either of the following methods.

i. The method of Euler (also attributed to Lagrange). Introduce new variables

$$w = x + y; \quad (x - y)\frac{dw}{dt} = \sqrt{X} \pm \sqrt{Y}$$

so that

$$\frac{d^2w}{dt^2} = a_3/2 + a_4 w$$

A first integral of this second-order equation, see **B2-2-1**, is

$$\left(\frac{dw}{dt}\right)^2 = a_3 w + a_4 w^2 + C$$

When the original variables x and y are recovered the solution of the equation is

$$(\sqrt{X} \pm \sqrt{Y})^2 = (x-y)^2[C + a_3(x+y) + a_4(x+y)^2]$$

Alternatively, use new variables $u = 1/x$ and $v = 1/y$ so that the original equation becomes

$$u'(v)\sqrt{V} = \pm\sqrt{U}$$
$$U(u) = a_4 + a_3 u + a_2 u^2 + a_1 u^3 + a_0 u^4$$
$$V(v) = a_4 + a_3 v + a_2 v^2 + a_1 v^3 + a_0 v^4$$

Its solution is like the previous one with u, v, U, V instead of x, y, X, Y, respectively. When the former variables are replaced by the latter, the result is

$$(y^2\sqrt{X} \pm x^2\sqrt{Y})^2 = (x-y)^2[Cx^2y^2 + a_1xy(x+y) + a_0(x+y)^2]$$

The two solutions are equivalent since they are linearly dependent. After some tedious algebra, both can be rationalized. Complete details, including the intermediate steps, are given by Cayley, Chapter XIV. The final algebraic solution of the differential equation is

$$f(x, y) = c_0 + 2c_1(x+y) + 4c_2xy + c_3(x^2+y^2) + 2c_4xy(x+y) + c_5x^2y^2 = 0 \quad (1)$$

Its coefficients are

$$
\begin{aligned}
c_0 &= a_1{}^2 - 4a_0 C \\
c_1 &= a_1(a_2 - C) - 2a_0 a_3 \\
c_2 &= (a_2{}^2 - a_1 a_3 - C^2)/2 - 2a_0 a_4 \\
c_3 &= (a_2 - C)^2 - 4a_0 a_4 \\
c_4 &= a_3(a_2 - C) - 2a_1 a_4 \\
c_5 &= a_3{}^2 - 4a_4 C
\end{aligned}
\qquad (2)
$$

ii. The method of Cauchy (also called the method of Euler). Assume a solution like (1), where the c_i are constants to be determined. Such a solution can be written in either of the two equivalent symmetric forms

$$f(x, y) = X_0 + 2X_1y + X_2y^2 = Y_0 + 2Y_1x + Y_2x^2 = 0 \qquad (3)$$

$$X_0 = c_0 + 2c_1x + c_3x^2; \quad Y_0 = c_0 + 2c_1y + c_3y^2$$
$$X_1 = c_1 + 2c_2x + c_4x^2; \quad Y_1 = c_1 + 2c_2y + c_4y^2$$
$$X_2 = c_3 + 2c_4x + c_5x^2; \quad Y_2 = c_3 + 2c_4y + c_5y^2$$

Differentiate $f(x, y)$ partially with respect to x and eliminate x to get $\partial f/\partial x$; differentiate with respect to y and eliminate y to get $\partial f/\partial y$. The results are

$$\frac{\partial f}{\partial x} = 2(Y_1{}^2 - Y_0Y_2)^{1/2}; \quad \frac{\partial f}{\partial y} = 2(X_1{}^2 - X_0X_2)^{1/2}$$

If $f(x, y)$ is to satisfy the differential equation, it is necessary that

$$\frac{\partial f}{\partial x}dx + \frac{\partial f}{\partial y}dy = 0$$

Comparison of coefficients shows that

$$(X_1{}^2 - X_0X_2)^{1/2}y' + (Y_1{}^2 - Y_0Y_2)^{1/2} = 0 \qquad (4)$$

In order for this differential equation to be the equivalent of $y'\sqrt{X} = \pm\sqrt{Y}$, the corresponding coefficients must be equal, or

$$X = X_1{}^2 - X_0X_2; \quad Y = Y_1{}^2 - Y_0Y_2 \qquad (5)$$

The left-hand side of these equations contains five constants while the right-hand side contains six constants. This means that five c_i can be fixed, the sixth one remains arbitrary, and that an infinite number of polynomials like (1) will satisfy the differential equation. The c_i in (1) could be determined by equating coefficients of equal powers of the two variables. The calculations can be simplified by geometric considerations, as shown by Jacobi, and the general integral of the differential equation can be presented as a fourth-order determinant, as shown by Stieljes. The details are given by Goursat.

Obviously, the coefficients in (2) are also satisfactory. The general integral (1) is a family of curves of the fourth degree, with two double points at infinity on the x and y axes, respectively. The family of curves has an envelope composed of eight straight lines, four each parallel to the x and y axes. These are singular solutions of the differential equation; see A2-10.

2. The Linear Equation

The form of the equation is

$$y' = f(x) + g(x)y$$

Its solution is

$$y = Y_1 + Y_2$$

$$Y_1 = Ce^\phi; \quad Y_2 = e^\phi \int e^{-\phi} f(x) dx; \quad \phi(x) = \int g(x) dx$$

The general solution is linear in the integration constant, for $y = Ce^\phi + Y_2$. An alternative form of the solution is occasionally useful. Let $u = f(x)/g(x)$. The solution is

$$y = e^\phi (C + \int e^{-\phi} du) - u$$

There are some special cases.

a. $g(x) = 0$. See **1-1**.

b. $f(x) = 0$. See **1-2**. The solution is $\ln y = \int g(x) dx + C$ or $y = C_1 e^\phi$.

c. $g(x) = k$, a constant. The solution is

$$y = Ce^{kx} + e^{kx} \int e^{-kx} f(x) dx$$

d. A special solution, y_1 is known. The general solution, found with only one quadrature, is

$$y = y_1 + Ce^\phi$$

Sometimes, a special solution can be found by inspection.

e. Two special solutions, y_1 and y_2, are known. The general solution, obtained without quadrature, is

$$y = y_1 + C(y_2 - y_1)$$

f. Three special solutions are known. Call them $y_i = C_i F(x) + Y_2(x)$; $i = 1, 2, 3$. Eliminate $F(x)$ and $Y_2(x)$ to get

$$\frac{y_3 - y_1}{y_2 - y_1} = \frac{C_3 - C_1}{C_2 - C_1} = \text{const.}$$

g. The general case, where neither $f(x)$ nor $g(x)$ vanish. The solution previously given can be found in several different ways.

i. The method of Lagrange or variation of parameter. Assume temporarily that $f(x) = 0$, so that the equation is case **b**, but write the solution as $y = ue^\phi$. Regard u as a parameter, to be adjusted so that the equation is satisfied when $f(x) \neq 0$. When this result is put into the original equation, $f(x) = e^\phi u'$, which is now case **a** in u and x, with solution $u = \int e^{-\phi} f(x) dx + C$. The general solution follows. See also **B1-12-3**.

ii. The method of Bernoulli. Assume a solution $y = uv$ and get $vu' + (v' - gv)u = f$. Determine $v(x)$ so that the term in parentheses vanishes. This is case **b**. Now find $u(x)$ from $vu' = f$, which is case **a**. The general solution follows when u and v are substituted into $y = uv$.

iii. The integrating factor. The linear equation may be converted into an exact equation, see **7**, by means of an integrating factor. Such a factor in this case must be a function of x alone. Calling it $I(x)$, it is derivable from the equation of type **a**,

$$\frac{dI}{dx} + I(x)g(x) = 0$$

Its solution is $I(x) = e^{-\phi}$, where $\phi(x) = \int g(x)dx$.

3. The Riccati Equation

There are three different types but the one actually studied by Riccati (1724) is a special case, cf. **3-2**, of the generalized Riccati equation, cf. **3-1**. If the coefficients in these equations have certain special properties, they can be solved by quadratures. In general, the solutions define functions more complicated than the elementary transcendental functions; see also **B2-7**. Such functions are logarithmic, exponential, trigonometric, or hyperbolic; and simple combinations of these functions. They are obtained by integration of algebraic functions or by rational processes following such an integration.

The Riccati equation is introduced at this point because its form suggests that it is similar to the linear equation, type **2**. Actually, it is a more difficult equation to solve and it, together with type **4** following, is much more difficult than many of the subsequent cases; see also **11-4**.

3-1. The Generalized Riccati Equation. The form of the equation is

$$y' = f(x) + g(x)y + h(x)y^2 \tag{1}$$

It has considerable theoretical interest, see **10-1**, since its solutions are free from movable branch points and can have only movable poles. It is a special case of the Abel equation; see **4-1** and **11-4**. There are several special cases.

a. f, g, h are constants; see **1-3**.

b. $h(x) = 0$. It is linear; see **2**.

c. $f(x) = 0$. The equation is of Bernoulli type; see **5**.

d. Other special cases. Compare the given equation with the types of **3-2** and **3-3**. If it is one of these, proceed as directed there.

e. The general equation. None of the preceding special cases are applicable. Refer to **3-1-3**, in the hope of transforming the equation to types **3-2** or **3-3**. If this is not successful, go to **3-1-1**.

3-1-1. The General Solution of the Equation. If one or more special solutions of (1) can be found by inspection or otherwise, the general solution is easy to obtain. When a special solution is not obvious, go to **3-1-2**, where some methods for finding one are presented.

a. A special solution y_1 is known. The general solution can be found by quadratures in two different ways.

i. Let $y = y_1 + 1/u$. Then (1) becomes linear, type **2**,

$$u'(x) + h(x) + U(x)u = 0; \quad U(x) = g + 2hy_1$$

The general solution of (1) is

$$(y - y_1)[C - \int h(x)X(x)dx] = X(x);$$
$$X(x) = \exp[\int U(x)dx]$$

ii. Let $y = y_1 + u$ and get a Bernoulli equation, type **5**,

$$u'(x) = (g + 2hy_1)u + hu^2$$

Its solution is identical with that in **i**, when y is introduced.

b. Two special solutions, y_1 and y_2, are known. The general solution is found with only one quadrature. Assume

$$u(y - y_2) = y - y_1$$

where y is the general solution of the equation and get

$$u'(x) = h(y_1 - y_2)u$$

which is separable, type **1-2**. Its solution is $Cu = U(x)$, where

$$U(x) = \exp[\int h(y_1 - y_2)dx]$$

The general solution of (1) becomes

$$y[C - U(x)] = Cy_1 - y_2 U(x)$$

c. Three special solutions are known. Let them be y_1, y_2, y_3 and the general solution, found without quadrature, is

$$(y - y_1)(y_2 - y_3) = C(y - y_2)(y_3 - y_1)$$

d. Four special equations are known. In this case, their cross-ratio is constant,

$$(y_4 - y_2)(y_3 - y_1) = C(y_4 - y_1)(y_3 - y_2)$$

e. Transform the equation into one of second order. Change the dependent variable by the transformation

$$yh(x)u(x) + u'(x) = 0; \quad \ln u(x) + \int yh(x)dx = 0$$

The result is

$$u''(x) + P(x)u' + Q(x)u = 0$$

where $P(x) = -(g + h'/h)$; $Q(x) = f(x)h(x)$. It is linear and of second order; see **B1**. Such equations have been studied extensively and this may be the most suitable procedure unless the given first-order equation has some special property. If two linearly independent solutions of the second-order equation are u_1 and u_2, then the general solution of the Riccati equation is

$$yh(x)[Cu_1 + u_2] + Cu_1' + u'_2 = 0$$

3-1-2. Special Solutions of the Riccati Equation. Sometimes one or more special equations can be found by inspection or by a lucky guess. More formal procedures apply in certain cases. If the present section is not helpful, try **3-1-1e** or some transformation in **3-1-3**.

Let $y = u(x)/h(x)$ and convert (1) into

$$u'(x) = F(x) + G(x)u + u^2 \qquad (2)$$

where $F(x) = f(x)h(x)$; $G(x) = g(x) + h'/h$. If both $F(x)$ and $G(x)$ are polynomials, see **a**, **b**, **c**, in turn. If $f(x)$, $g(x)$, and $h(x)$ are polynomials, it will not necessarily be true that $G(x)$ is a polynomial; hence the methods of those sections may not apply; see, however, **d** for a possible procedure.

a. The equation becomes

$$u'(x) = F(x) + u^2 \qquad (3)$$

and $F(x)$ is a polynomial, with $G(x) = 0$. There are two possibilities.

i. The degree of $F(x)$ is odd. There is no polynomial solution of (3); hence none of (1).

ii. The degree of $F(x)$ is even. Two possible polynomial solutions may exist. To find them, first note that if $P(x)$ were a polynomial of even degree $2n$, then $\sqrt{P(x)}$ could be expanded in a series of the form

$$\sqrt{P(x)} = a_n x^n + a_{n-1} x^{n-1} + \dots + a_0 + b_1/x + b_2/x^2 + \dots$$

Perform such an expansion on $\sqrt{-F(x)}$ but stop the calculation with the constant term. Call this result $X(x)$; it is a polynomial of degree n, if $F(x)$ is of degree $2n$. The coefficients in the polynomial could be found by a simple modification of the square-root extraction method of elementary algebra, by the method of undetermined coefficients, or by expansion in a Maclaurin series.

If the differential equation has special polynomial solutions, they are given by

$$u = \pm X(x)$$

Test both of them, for both, one, or neither may satisfy the differential equation. If neither is a special solution of (3), there are no polynomial solutions of (3) and hence none of (1).

b. $G(x) \neq 0$. Let $u = w - G(x)/2$ and (2) becomes

$$w'(x) = H(x) + w^2$$

where $4H(x) + G^2(x) = 4F(x) + 2G'(x)$. The equation in $w(x)$ is similar to (3); hence, with slight modifications, the procedure is very much like that in **a**. Calculate

$$Q(x) = G^2 - 4F - 2G'$$

There are two cases.

  i. The degree of $Q(x)$ is odd. There is no polynomial solution of either (2) or (1).

  ii. The degree of $Q(x)$ is even. Expand $\sqrt{Q(x)}$ as in **a**, again stopping with the constant term and call the resulting polynomial $X(x)$. There are two possible polynomial solutions of (2)

$$u = -(G \pm X)/2$$

Test both, for neither may satisfy the differential equation. Alternatively, it is possible to state conditions under which both polynomials are solutions of the differential equation; see **c**.

  c. $Q(x)$ is a constant. This is the necessary and sufficient condition that both solutions of **b** satisfy the differential equation. There are two cases.

  i. $X(x) = k \neq 0$. Introduce a new variable with the relation

$$u = -(G+k)/2 + 1/v$$

so that (2) becomes

$$v'(x) = 1 + kv$$

It is separable, type **1-3**, with solution $v = Ce^{kx} + 1/k$ and the corresponding solution of (2) is

$$u = -(G+k)/2 + \left(Ce^{kx} + \frac{1}{k} \right)^{-1}$$

Two special polynomial solutions of it result with $C = 0, \infty$. The general solution of (1) follows.

  ii. $X(x) = k = 0$. The equation in $v(x)$ becomes $v'(x) + 1 = 0$, which is separable, type **1-1**, with solution $v + x = C$. The solution of (2) is

$$u = -\frac{G}{2} + \frac{1}{(C-x)}$$

  d. Polynomial coefficients. Suppose that (1) has the form

$$\phi(x)y' = f(x) + g(x)y + h(x)y^2 \tag{4}$$

where all of the coefficients are polynomials. Assume it to have a special polynomial solution $y_1 = R(x)$ and use a new variable $y = u + y_1$, so that it becomes

$$\phi(x)u' = F(x)u + h(x)u^2$$

where $F(x) = g(x) + 2h(x)R(x)$. If there is a polynomial solution of (4), having the form $u_1 = (x-a)^m$, $m \geq 1$ then $\phi(x)$ will also contain a factor $(x-a)$. This property restricts the possible types of polynomial solutions. Unlike the previous cases, where only two possible polynomials may exist, the more general equation can have a larger number of such solutions. See **e** for further discussion of this case.

e. Several polynomial solutions. Given (4), any specified number of polynomial solutions can be constructed. From **3-1-1b**, the general solution can be taken as

$$y = \frac{Cf_1(x) + f_2(x)}{Cf_3(x) + f_4(x)}$$

If $f_1f_4 - f_2f_3 \neq 0$, then (1) can be written in the form of (4) with $\phi(x) = f_1f_4 - f_2f_3$; $f(x) = f_1f_2' - f_1'f_2$; $g(x) = f_2f_3' - f_2'f_3 + f_4f_1' - f_1f_4'$; $h(x) = f_3f_4' - f_4f_3'$. Now, suppose that the $f_i(x)$ are polynomials. Select $f_1(x) = 0$, choose any polynomials desired as $f_3(x)$ and $f_4(x)$. Assign n special values $C_1, C_2, \ldots, C_n$ to the arbitrary constant and require that

$$f_2(x) = (C_1f_3 + f_4)(C_2f_3 + f_4) \ldots (C_nf_3 + f_4)$$

The differential equation (4) will have $(n+1)$ polynomial solutions, $y = 0$ and $y_i = f_2/(C_if_3 + f_4)$, $i = 1\ 2, \ldots, n$. The special solution $y = 0$ can be avoided and $(n+1)$ special solutions retained if the variables are transformed with the relation $u(x) = y(x) + P(x)$ where $P(x)$ is any polynomial.

The considerations of this section may not be too useful in solving a Riccati equation. They could, however, be very helpful in constructing an equation with a predetermined number of polynomial solutions.

3-1-3. Some Properties of the Riccati Equation. The following properties of (1) sometimes apply in attempting to solve it.

a. Removal of the linear term. The result, which is similar to (3), can be achieved in three different ways. It might then be treated as in **3-1-2**, but see also **b** for a special case.

i. Let $y = u(x)e^\phi$; $\phi(x) = \int g(x)dx$ and (1) becomes

$$u'(x) = F(x) + G(x)u^2 \tag{5}$$

where $F(x) = f(x)e^{-\phi}$; $G(x) = h(x)e^\phi$.

ii. Let $y = u(x) - v(x)$; $v(x) = g(x)/2h(x)$. If g, h are differentiable and $h(x) \neq 0$, the result is again like (5) but now with

$$F(x) = f + v' - g^2/4h; \quad G(x) = h(x)$$

iii. Let $y = u(z)e^\phi$; $\phi(x) = \int g(x)dx$; $z = -\int he^\phi dx$. In this case, (1) becomes

$$u'(z) = F(z) - u^2(z) \tag{6}$$

with $F(z)h(z) = -f(z)e^{-2\phi}$.

b. Relations between the coefficients. When certain relations exist between the coefficients of (1) its solution may be easy to obtain.

i. Look for two constants a, b with $|a|+|b| > 0$ so that

$$(a^2 f + abg + b^2 h) = 0$$

If $a = 0$, then $f(x) = 0$ and the equation is linear, type **2**. If $a \neq 0$, then $y_1 = b/a$ is a special solution of (1) and **3-1-1** can be used to get its general solution. A simple case arises if $f + g + h = 0$, for then $a = b = 1$ and $y_1 = 1$.

ii. Use **a** to remove the linear term in (1). Then, if $F(x)$ is proportional to $G(x)$ in (5), the result is separable, type **1-2**. In the original variables and functions, the requirement is $f(x) = A^2 h(x) \exp [2 \int g(x)dx]$, where A is a constant of proportionality. The solution of (1) is then

$$y = \sqrt{f/h} \tan (\int \sqrt{fh}\, dx + C); \quad fh > 0$$

If $fh < 0$, replace tan by tanh and insert a minus sign under both radicals. See also **3-3**.

iii. Assume that a special solution of (1) exists so that

$$2hy_1 = X(x) - g(x)$$

where $X(x)$ is determined from the relation $f(x) = hy_1{}^2 - X(x)y_1 + y_1'$. The last equation imposes a severe restriction on the form of $f(x)$ but if it is satisfied, y_1 can be found and the general solution of (1) follows from **3-1-1**. A few cases that might be tested are : $X = 0$, $4f = g^2/h - 2(g/h)'$; $X = -h'/h$, $4f = 2(1/h)'' - 2(g/h)' - h(1/h)'^2 + g^2/h$; $X = g - 2\sqrt{fh}$, $2g = 4\sqrt{fh} + f'/f - h'/h$.

3-2. The Riccati Equation. The equation actually studied by Riccati is

$$y' + by^2 = cx^m \tag{7}$$

It is a special case of **3-1** or **3-3**. The constant m need not be an integer; a and c are constants.

Test the equation for integrability in finite form by **a**. If the test is successful, go to **b**. Sometimes, it is helpful to transform the equation into one of second order; see **c**.

a. Integrable cases. Calculate k from the equation

$$m(2k \pm 1) + 4k = 0 \tag{8}$$

If k is zero or a positive integer, there are two cases; see **i** and **ii**. For other values of k, the equation is not integrable in finite terms; return to **3-1**.

i. The sign in (8) is positive. Let $y(x) = u(z)$; $b(m+1)y = c/u$; $z = x^{m+1}$ and (7) becomes

$$u'(z) + bu^2 = \frac{cz^n}{(m+1)^2}$$

where $n(2k-1) + 4k = 0$. This equation is (8) with a negative sign. Go to case **ii**.

ii. The sign in (8) is negative, or case **i** has been transformed into this type. Let $yb = z(1 - bzu)$; $z = 1/x$ and (7) becomes

$$u'(z) + bu^2 = cz^r$$

with $r[2(k-1)+1] + 4(k-1) = 0$. The equation has been transformed back again into case **i**, with k decreased by unity. Successive applications of the transformations in **i** and **ii** will eventually reduce k to zero and (7) will then be separable, type **1-3**. The general solution in such integrable cases is best completed by the method of **3-3**.

b. A transformed equation. The equation has been shown to be integrable by the procedure of **a**. Let $y = w/x$, so that (7) becomes

$$xw'(x) - w + bw^2 = cx^{m+2} \qquad (9)$$

This is a special case of **3-3**, with $a = 1$, $n = m+2$. Given (7) to solve in an integrable case, transform it to (9) and solve it for $w(x)$, according to **3-3**. This is generally easier than the successive reductions described in **a**.

c. A second-order equation. Let $byu(x) = u'(x)$, so that (7) becomes

$$u''(x) + bcx^m u = 0$$

This linear second-order equation can be solved according to **B1**. The result is often expressed in terms of Bessel functions.

3-3. A Special Riccati Equation. This is a special case of the generalized equation of **3-1**

$$xy' - ay + by^2 = cx^n \qquad (10)$$

It is not necessary that n be an integer; a, b, c are constants. Under certain conditions, the equation can be integrated in finite form; see **a**. For the relation between (10) and the Riccati equation of **3-2**, see **b**.

a. Integrable cases. Examine the equation to see if it satisfies one of the following conditions. If it does not, return to **3-1-1**.

i. If $n = 2a$, let $y = x^a u(x)$ and (10) becomes separable, type **1-2**,

$$u'(x) = x^{a-1}(c - bu^2)$$

It can be integrated directly; it becomes exact if the original variable is reintroduced and a common factor $1/x^{2a}$ is removed; or (10) can be made exact with the integrating factor x^{a-1}. The exact equation, see **7-1**, is

$$f(x, y)y' + g(x, y) = 0,$$

with

$$f(x, y) = x^a/F$$
$$g(x, y) = x^{a-1}(1 - ay/F)$$
$$F(x, y) = by^2 - cx^{2a}$$

In any case, the solution of (10) is

$$y = \sqrt{c/b}\, x^a \tanh(C - \sqrt{bc}\, x^a/a); \quad bc > 0$$

An equivalent form of the solution is

$$y(Ce^\phi - 1)\sqrt{b} = x^a(Ce^\phi + 1)\sqrt{c}$$

where $\phi(x) = 2x^a\sqrt{bc}/a$. If $bc < 0$, replace tanh by tan and put a minus sign under both radicals.

    ii. If $(n - 2a)/2n = k$, a positive integer, assume successively,

$$y = a/b + x^n/y_1, \quad y_1 = (a+n)/c + x^n/y_2, \ldots, \quad y_{k-1} = \frac{a + (k-1)n}{[bc]} + \frac{x^n}{y_k}$$

The symbol $[bc]$ is understood to mean that the first letter b is to be used if the integer k is odd, but the second letter c is to be used if k is even. The solution of (10) is a finite continued fraction

$$y = \frac{a}{b} + \cfrac{x^n}{\cfrac{a+n}{c} + \cfrac{x^n}{\cfrac{a+2n}{b} + \ldots}}$$

The last denominator is y_{k-1}. The differential equation which determines y_k is

$$xy'_k - (a+nk)y_k + [cb]y_k^2 = [bc]x^n$$

It has the same form as the equation of case **i** and can be solved as directed there. In the coefficients of the exact equation, and in its solution, replace a by $n/2$ and b, c by $[cb]$, $[bc]$, respectively.

    iii. If $(n+2a) = 2nk$, where k is a positive integer, assume

$$y = \frac{x^n}{y_1}, \quad y_1 = \frac{(n-a)}{c} + \frac{x^n}{y_2}, \quad \ldots, \quad y_{k-1} = \frac{(k-1)n - a}{[bc]} + \frac{x^n}{y_k}$$

The general solution of the equation is a finite continued fraction as in **ii**. The last denominator is y_{k-1} and the differential equation for y_k is the same as that in **ii** with a replaced by $-a$.

b. Conversion to type **3-2.** Let $y = zu(z)$; $z = x^a$ and (10) becomes

$$au'(z) + bu^2 = cz^{(n-2a)/a}$$

It has the same form as (7). Given an equation of that type to solve, convert it to the form of (10) and follow the directions in **a.** Such a procedure is generally simpler than the direct solution of type **3-2.**

4. The Abel Equation

There are two equations of this type. The first, which contains a term in y^3, is an extension of the Riccati equation; see **4-1.** An equation of the second kind is a further generalization; see **4-2.** In either case, finite solutions result only when the equation has certain special properties. Some of these cases are described in the two following sections. In the general case, it may be necessary to use one of the procedures given in **10.**

4-1. Abel Equation of the First Kind. Its general form is

$$y' = f_0(x) + f_1(x)y + f_2(x)y^2 + f_3(x)y^3 \tag{1}$$

Consult the following special cases and properties of it for possible ways of finding a general solution.

a. $f_0 = f_1 = f_2 = f_3 =$ constant. The equation is separable, type **1-3.**
b. $f_2 = f_3 = 0$. The equation is linear, type **2.**
c. $f_3 = 0$. A Riccati equation results; see **3.**
d. $f_0 = 0$, $f_1 \neq 0$ and either $f_2 = 0$, $f_3 \neq 0$ or $f_2 \neq 0$, $f_3 = 0$. The equation is of Bernoulli type; see **5.**
e. Reduction to standard form. Provided that f_2, f_3 are both differentiable and $f_3 \neq 0$, let $y(x) = u(z)v(x) + F(x)$; $v(x) = \exp[\int (f_1 + f_2 F)dx]$; $F(x) = -f_2/3f_3$; $z = \int f_3 v^2(x)dx$.
The result is

$$u'(z) = U(x) + u^3$$

where $f_3 v^3 U = f_0 - F' + f_1 F + 2f_2 F^2/3$. This can be chosen as the canonical or standard form of the Abel equation. See also **g.**

f. $f_0 = 0, f_2 \neq 0$. The equation can be converted into one of the second order. Let

$$y(x) = u(z)v(x); \quad z = \int vf_2 dx; \quad v = \exp \int f_1 dx \tag{2}$$

In the new independent variable,

$$u'(z) = u^2 + g(z)u^3; \quad g(z) = v(x)f_3/f_2$$

Now, let

$$z'(t) + 1/tu(z) = 0 \tag{3}$$

so that

$$t^2 z''(t) + g(z) = 0 \tag{4}$$

If (4) can be solved, see **B2**, then (3) will give $u(z)$ and (2) will give the general solution of (1).

g. Separable equations. There are two cases where a separable equation can be produced by suitable transformation of variables. In both cases an elliptic integral occurs.

i. Suppose that $f_0 = f_1 = 0$ and $F'(x) = Af_2$, where $F(x) = f_3/f_2$ and A is a constant. In that case, let $yF(x) = u(x)$ and get an equation of type **1-2**.

$$F(x)u'(x) = f_2 u(A + u + u^2)$$

ii. In the general case, let $y = u(x)v(x) + F(x)$ and determine $v(x)$, $F(x)$ to get an equation of type **1-2**,

$$u'(x) = X(x)G(u) \tag{5}$$

It is found that

$$f_3 v(x) = U^{1/3}(x)$$
$$3f_3 F(x) + f_2 = 0;$$
$$U(x) = f_0 f_3^2 + (f_2' f_3 - f_2 f_3' - f_1 f_2 f_3)/3 + 2f_2^3/27$$
$$f_3 X(x) = U^{2/3}(x)$$
$$G(u) = 1 - Au + u^3$$

where A is a constant. When (5) has been solved to get $u(x)$, determine A from the Bernoulli equation; see **5**,

$$f_3 U'(x) + (f_2^2 - 3f_1 f_3 - 3f_3')U = 3AU^{5/3}$$

Note that the result is similar to that in **e** and that $U(x)$ in that section is related to the function $U(x)$ in this section.

In the special case where $U(x) = 0$, a solution of (1) is $y_1 = F(x)$. Use the transformation $y = y_1 + w(x)$ and get a Bernoulli equation, type **5**,

$$w'(x) = (f_1 - f_2 y_1)u + f_3 u^3$$

Its general solution will give the general solution of (1).

h. y_1 is a special solution of (1). An Abel equation of the second kind results, see **4-2**,

$$uu'(x) + F(x) + G(x)u = 0 \tag{6}$$

The new functions are determined by the relations

$$u(y - y_1) = e^\phi$$
$$\phi(x) = \int (3f_3 y_1^2 + 2f_2 y_1 + f_1)dx$$
$$F(x) = f_3 e^{2\phi}$$
$$G(x) = (3f_3 y_1 + f_2)e^\phi$$

When $G(x) = 0$, the special solution is easy to get, for it is $y_1 = -f_2/3f_3$. In that case, (6) is separable, type **1-2**, and $y = y_1 + u(x)$ can be used to get the general solution of (1). The conditions required are

$$f_0 = y_1' - y_1(f_1 + 2f_2 y_1/3)$$

and then the general solution of (1) is

$$y = (C - 2 \int f_3 e^{2h} dx)^{-1/2} e^h + y_1$$

where $h(x) = \int (f_1 + f_2 y_1) dx$.

4-2. Abel Equation of the Second Kind.   This is a more complicated case than **4-1**,

$$[g_0(x) + g_1(x)y]y' = f_0(x) + f_1(x)y + f_2(x)y^2 + f_3(x)y^3 \qquad (7)$$

It becomes **4-1**, if $g_0 = 1$, $g_1 = 0$. Try one of the following procedures in the general case.

a. y_1 is a special solution. It is necessary that $g_0 + g_1 y_1 \neq 0$. Make the transformation $g_0 + g_1 y_1 = 1/u(x)$. The result is an Abel equation of the first kind; see **4-1**. The coefficients are rather complicated functions of f_i, g_i, and the derivatives of g_i. It is assumed that $g_1 \neq 0$ and that g_0, g_1 are differentiable.

b. $f_0 = 0$. Let $y = 1/u$ and the term in y^3 can be removed. The result is

$$(g_1 + g_0 u)u' + f_3 + f_2 u + f_1 u^2 = 0 \qquad (8)$$

Comparison of (8) with (7) shows that the order of the subscripts has been interchanged and that the terms in $f_i(x)$ have moved to the other side of the equation. These effects are caused by the variable transformation and (8) is not misprinted.

c. $f_3 = 0$. The general solution of (7) can be found with two quadratures provided that $g_0 \neq 0$, $g_1 \neq 0$, and

$$g_0(2f_2 + g_1') = g_1(f_1 + g_0')$$

Seek an integrating factor, according to **7-2-3**. It is found to be a function of x alone and it has two equivalent forms

$$g_0 I(x) = e^{-\phi_1}; \quad g_1 I(x) = e^{-\phi_2}$$

where $\phi_1 = \int (f_1/g_0) dx$; $\phi_2 = 2 \int (f_2/g_1) dx$. When the exact equation is integrated, the solution of (7) is

$$I(x)[2g_0 y + g_1 y^2] = 2 \int f_0(x) I(x) dx + C$$

d. $f_3 = 0$, $g_1 = 1$. The equation can be converted into one of the first kind, see **4-1**, or into a simpler equation of the second kind.

i. Let $y + g_0 = 1/u(x)$. It is necessary that $y_1 + g_0 \neq 0$, where y_1

is any special solution of the equation. The resulting equation of the first kind, see **4-1**, is

$$u' + u(F_1 + F_2 u + F_3 u^2) = 0$$

where $F_1 = f_2$, $F_2 = f_1 - 2f_2 g_0 + g_0'$, $F_3 = f_0 - f_1 g_0 + f_2 g_0^2$.

ii. To get a simpler equation of the second kind, let $y + g_0 = u(x)e^\phi$, $\phi(x) = \int f_2(x)dx$. The new equation is

$$uu'(x) = F(x) + G(x)u \tag{9}$$

where $F(x) = (f_0 - f_1 g_0 + f_2 g_0^2)e^{-2\phi}$, $G(x) = (f_1 - 2f_2 g_0 + g_0')e^{-\phi}$. Note that F, G here are the same as F_3, F_2 in **i**, except for the exponential factor. This differential equation is a special case of (7), where $g_0 = f_2 = f_3 = 0$, $g_1 = 1$. It can be simplified further; see **e**.

e. $g_0 = f_2 = f_3 = 0, g_1 = 1$. In this case, or for (9), let $y = u(x) + v(x)$, $v(x) = \int f_1(x)dx$. The new equation lacks a term in the dependent variable

$$(u + v)u' = f_0(x)$$

Further simplification arises, if $f_0 \neq 0$. Let $u(x) = w(x)$, $z = \int f_0(x)dx$, and get

$$(w + v)w'(z) = 1$$

5. The Bernoulli Equation

The general case is

$$y' = f(x)y + g(x)y^k \tag{1}$$

There are several special cases.

a. $f(x)$ and $g(x)$ are constants. The equation is separable, type **1-3**.
b. $k = 0$. The equation is linear, type **2**.
c. $k = 1$. The equation is separable, type **1-2**.
d. k is neither zero nor unity; it is not necessarily an integer. The solution is

$$y^{1-k} = Y_1 + Y_2$$

$$Y_1 = Ce^\phi; \quad Y_2 = (1 - k)e^\phi \int e^{-\phi}g(x)dx; \quad \phi(x) = (1 - k)\int f(x)dx \tag{2}$$

This result can be derived in three different ways.

i. Let $y^{1-k} = u$ and get a linear equation, type **2**,

$$u'(x) = (1 - k)[g(x) + f(x)u]$$

When it is solved, the result is (2).

ii. An integrating factor of (1), see **7-2**, is $I(x, y) = y^{-k}e^{-\phi}$. The solution follows with two quadratures.

iii. Let $y = ue^F$, $F(x) = \int f(x)dx$ and get

$$u'(x) = u^k g(x)e^{(k-1)F}$$

This equation is separable, type **1-2**. Restore y after it has been solved and the result is equivalent to (2).

6. Equations Linear in the Variables
There are two different types. For some other equations of similar form, see **8-5**.

6-1. $y' = f(a + bx + cy)$. There are three possibilities; a more general equation is given in **6-2**.
  a. $b = 0, c \neq 0$. The equation is separable, type **1-3**.
  b. $b \neq 0. c = 0$. It is separable, type **1-1**.
  c. $b \neq 0, c \neq 0$. Let $u = a + bx + cy$ and get

$$u'(x) = b + cf(u) = F(u)$$

which is separable, type **1-3**. Its solution is

$$\int \frac{du}{F(u)} = x + C$$

6-2. $y' = f(X_1/X_2)$, $X_i = a_i + b_i x + c_i y$.   Calculate $\Delta = b_1 c_2 - b_2 c_1$. There are three possible cases.
  a. $\Delta \neq 0$. Introduce new variables u, z with the relations $x = h + z$, $y = k + u$, $h\Delta = c_1 a_2 - c_2 a_1$, $k\Delta = a_1 b_2 - a_2 b_1$. The new equation is

$$u'(z) = f(Z_1/Z_2), \quad Z_i = b_i z + c_i u$$

It is homogeneous and can be solved by **8-1**. From that section, and with the symbols used here, let $u = wz$; $f(Z_1/Z_2) = f(w) = f(W_1/W_2)$, $W_i = b_i + c_i w$; $F(w) = f(w) - w$. The solution of the equation is

$$\ln(x - h) = \int \frac{dw}{F(w)} + C$$

When the integral has been evaluated, restore the original variables with the relations

$$w = \frac{u}{z} = \frac{(y-k)}{(x-h)}$$

  b. $\Delta = 0$, $c_1 \neq 0$. Let $u(x) = X_1$; $U_1 = c_1 u/(c_2 u + A)$; $A = c_1 a_2 - c_2 a_1$. The equation which results is separable, type **1-3**.

$$u'(x) = b_1 + c_1 f(U_1)$$

  c. $\Delta = 0$, $c_2 \neq 0$. Let $u(x) = X_2$; $U_2 = (c_1 u - A)/c_2 u$; $A = c_1 a_2 - c_2 a_1$. The new equation is separable, type **1-3**,

$$u'(x) = b_2 + c_2 f(U_2)$$

7. The Exact Equation and the Integrating Factor

Given a function

$$\phi(x, y) = C \tag{1}$$

its *perfect*, *complete*, or *total differential* is

$$d\phi = \frac{\partial \phi}{\partial x}dx + \frac{\partial \phi}{\partial y}dy = 0 \tag{2}$$

An equivalent form of (2) is

$$f(x, y)y' + g(x, y) = 0 \tag{3}$$

Provided that no common factors have been eliminated in the step from (2) to (3), the equation is said to be *exact* and its complete primitive is (1).

To test a differential equation for exactness, see **7-1**, where methods for finding the primitive are also given. If the test for exactness fails, it means that common factors have been removed and an integrating factor is needed. Such factors can always be found, in principle, but not always easily in practice. When they are known or can be found, the equation can be made exact and integrated; see **7-2**.

7-1. The Exact Equation. The given equation to be tested for exactness is

$$f(x, y)y' + g(x, y) = 0 \tag{3}$$

It is exact if Euler's criterion holds

$$\partial f/\partial x = \partial g/\partial y \tag{4}$$

Make this test and proceed as directed. It should be noted that many textbooks use the standard form $M(x, y)dx + N(x, y)dy = 0$, which is equivalent to (3), with $f(x, y) = N(x, y)$; $g(x, y) = M(x, y)$.

a. The equation is exact and also homogeneous, with degree $k \neq -1$. Go to **8**, for the solution can be found without quadrature. If exact and homogeneous with degree $k = -1$, see **b** or use **8-1**.

b. The equation is exact but not homogeneous. The solution can be found in two equivalent ways.

i. Evaluate either one of the following expressions

$$\int_{x_0}^{x} g(x, y)dx + \int_{y_0}^{y} f(x_0, y)dy = C$$

$$\int_{x_0}^{x} g(x, y_0)dx + \int_{y_0}^{y} f(x, y)dy = C$$

The function which results in either case is the general solution of (3). It may be difficult to solve for y as an explicit function of x; hence the solution can be offered in implicit form as $F(x, y, C) = 0$. The quantities x_0, y_0 in the integrals are arbitrary. They are most conveniently chosen to make the integrations easy, frequently as 0 or 1.

ii. Use either of the equivalent expression

$$\int g(x, y)dx + \int \left[f(x, y) - \frac{\partial}{\partial y} \int g(x, y)dx \right] dy = C$$

$$\int f(x, y)dy + \int \left[g(x, y) - \frac{\partial}{\partial x} \int f(x, y)dy \right] dx = C$$

During the integrations, the second variable is considered to be constant. Thus, for example, y is taken as constant in evaluating $\int g(x, y)dx$.

c. The equation is not exact. Proceed to **7-2** in the hope of finding some function that will make (3) exact so that the methods of this section can be used.

7-2. The Integrating Factor. The test for exactness has been made, it does not hold, and a factor $I(x, y)$ is to be sought so that the new equation

$$I(x, y)[f(x, y)y' + g(x, y)] = 0$$

meets the requirements of (4) in the form

$$\frac{\partial F}{\partial x} = \frac{\partial G}{\partial y}; \quad F = If, \quad G = Ig$$

Euler and his followers attempted to solve all first-order differential equations in this way and the integrating factor is often called an *Euler multiplier* or *Euler factor*. A general theory, based on the properties of continuous transformation groups, shows that an integrating factor can be found, at least in principle, for a properly classified equation. The solution of the equation can then be completed by quadratures. The use of group theory for finding the integrating factor will not be described here. For some appropriate references see Cohen, Ince-1, Lie, Page.

Since the integrating factor may not always be easy to find, some other procedure may be simpler. One possibility is a suitable variable transformation, converting the given differential equation to one of the types **1ff** previously considered. See also **8** and **9** for further suggestions. If the methods of this section are preferred, try **7-2-1** to **7-2-3**, in turn. When an integrating factor has been found, calculate

$$F(x, y) = I(x, y)f(x, y), \quad G(x, y) = I(x, y)g(x, y)$$

and use **7-1b**, replacing f, g by F, G, respectively, in the equations of that section.

Some useful properties of the integrating factor are stated in the following.

a. The number of integrating factors. Suppose that $v(x, y) = C$ is the general solution of an inexact differential equation. Then, the expression $F(v)I(x, y)$ includes all possible integrating factors, where $I(x, y)$ is one such factor. Since the function $F(v)$ contains an arbitrary constant, the number of such functions is infinite and the number of integrating factors is also infinite, provided that the unique solution of the equation is $v(x, y) = C$.

b. Two integrating factors. Let I_1 and I_2 be two independent factors, so that one is not a constant multiple of the other. Then, the general solution of the differential equation is $I_1(x, y) = CI_2(x, y)$.

c. An equation for the integrating factor. It satisfies a first-order partial differential equation

$$gI_y - fI_x = I(f_x - g_y)$$

where a subscript designates a partial derivative; thus, $I_y = \partial I/\partial y$, etc. Unfortunately, the partial differential equation may not be easy to solve and, if one must use it to find an integrating factor, another method might be preferred for solving the given ordinary differential equation. However, the general solution of the partial differential equation is not needed; any special solution of it will suffice. In some cases, the partial differential equation becomes an ordinary differential equation and then it may be easy to find an integrating factor. Some examples are given in **7-2-3**.

d. The equation is homogeneous. The equation has been made exact by an integrating factor and it is also homogeneous and of degree $k \neq -1$. The integration may be completed without a quadrature; see **8**.

7-2-1. Integrating Factor by Inspection.

In some cases, an integrating factor is obvious from the form of the given differential equation or it is obtainable after a few lucky guesses. In making such guesses, the following properties may be helpful. If more formal procedures are preferred, go at once to **7-2-2**.

a. If possible, separate the equation into two or more parts, one of which is exact and the others inexact. It is only necessary to find an integrating factor for the single inexact part.

b. Write the inexact part of the function described in **a** as the product of two other functions, $U(x, y)$ and $V(x, y)$. Attempt to show that $U(x, y)$ is the exact differential of another function $u(x, y)$. Then, convert $V(x, y)$ to a function of u. The result is $F(u)du$, which is an exact differential.

c. Examine the differential equation to see if it contains terms like those in Table 1. In more complicated cases, use the methods of **a** or **b**.

7-2-2. Integrating Factors for Special Equations. It is assumed that an integrating factor was not apparent by inspection, as suggested in **7-2-1**, and that more formal procedures are wanted. When the equation is of some special type, the integrating factor can be given at once, as shown in this section. Alternatively, certain tests can be made on the equation and, if they hold, the integrating factor follows. For this case, see **7-2-3**. To some extent, the two procedures duplicate each other.

Proceed with this section or go directly to **7-2-3**, as desired. Take the differential equation in the form

$$f(x, y)y' + g(x, y) = 0$$

and calculate $M(x, y) = xg + yf$; $N(x, y) = xg - yf$. There are a number of special cases.

a. Both M and N cannot vanish. This would be the trivial case of $f(x, y) = g(x, y) = 0$. If either vanishes identically, the reciprocal of the other is an integrating factor.

TABLE 1.   INTEGRATING FACTORS FOR CERTAIN TERMS
IN AN EQUATION

Term	Integrating Factor
$y - xy'$	$1/x^2,\ 1/y^2,\ 1/xy,\ 1/(x^2 \pm y^2)$
$f(x) + y - xy'$	$1/x^2$
$y + [f(y) - x]y'$	$1/y^2$
$y[1 + f(w)] - x[1 - f(w)]y'$	$1/w;\ w = xy$
$[y + xf(w)] \pm [yf(w) \mp x]y'$	$1/w;\ w = x^2 \pm y^2$

b. The equation is homogeneous. In this case, see **8**, the integrating factor is $1/M$. If $M = 0$, the equation is separable, type **1-2**, with solution $y = Cx$. The same situation occurs if $N = 0$, where the solution is $xy = C$.

c. The equation is isobaric. Then, see **8-2**,

$$f(x, y) = 1$$
$$g(x, y) = -x^{n-1}F(u)$$
$$u = y/x^n$$
$$I(x, y) = 1/(xg + nyf)$$

This case is identical with **b**, when $n = 1$. If the denominator of $I(x, y)$ vanishes, the equation is separable, type **1-2**, and its solution is $y = Cx^n$.

d. $f(x, y) = xF(u)$, $g(x, y) = yG(u)$, $u = xy$. The integrating factor is

$I(x, y) = 1/N$. When $N = 0$, the integrating factor is $1/M$, but it was not needed since the differential equation was exact.

e. $f(x, y) = xF(x, y)$, $g(x, y) = yG(x, y)$; $F = a_1x^my^n + b_1x^ry^s$, $G = a_2x^my^n + b_2x^ry^s$. This case is a generalization of **d**. The exponents need not be integers. An integrating factor is $I(x, y) = x^py^q$ where the constants p, q are determined from the simultaneous equations

$$a_2(q+n+1) = a_1(p+m+1)$$
$$b_2(q+s+1) = b_1(p+r+1)$$

The method fails if $b_2/a_2 = b_1/a_1 = k$, but then the equation can be factored into

$$(x^my^n + kx^ry^s)(a_1xy' + a_2y) = 0$$

The second term is separable, type **1-2**; the first term gives a special solution of the differential equation, not always included in the general solution.

f. $vF(w)u' + G(w)u = 0$, $w = uv$. Here u, v are any functions of x and y. Thus, this case is more general than **d**. Its integrating factor is $I(x, y) = 1/w(F - G)$.

g. The equation is linear; see **2**. The integrating factor is $I(x, y) = \exp \int F(x)dx$; $F(x)f(x, y) = g_y - f_x$.

h. Exchange of variables. Sometimes a differential equation becomes linear, see **2**, if x is taken as the dependent variable and y as the independent variable, instead of the reverse. In that case, $I(x, y) = \exp \int F(y)dy$; $F(y)g(x, y) = f_x - g_y$.

i. $f(x, y) = (x - yF)$, $g(x, y) = -(y + xF)$, $F = F(x^2 + y^2)$. The integrating factor is $I(x, y) = 1/(x^2 + y^2)$.

7-2-3. Tests for an Integrating Factor.

If the given equation, $f(x, y)y' + g(x, y) = 0$, is not one of the special types in **7-2-2**, the following procedures may be helpful. They partially duplicate those of **7-2-2**, but offer an alternative method in the search for an integrating factor.

Assume $I(x, y) = \phi(u)$, where u is some predetermined function of one or both variables. A quick test will then show whether or not such an integrating factor exists. If it does, one quadrature will yield $I(x, y)$. From the partial differential equation in **7-2c**, it follows that

$$\frac{\phi'(u)}{\phi(u)} = \frac{f_x - g_y}{gu_y - fu_x}$$

If the assumed integrating factor exists, the right-hand side of this equation will be a function of u alone, say $h(u)$.

To proceed in this way, first select $u(x, y)$ and calculate

$$\frac{f_x - g_y}{gu_y - fu_x} = h(u) \tag{5}$$

The integrating factor is then given by

$$\ln I(x, y) = \int h(u)du \tag{6}$$

because the partial differential equation, which determines the integrating factor, has become an ordinary differential equation with separable variables.

The success of the method depends on the proper choice of $u(x, y)$. A prominent combination of terms in the differential equation might suggest something to be tried. Lacking such hints, take simple forms like x, y, xy, y/x, $x \pm y$, $x^2 \pm y^2$, etc. See also Table 1. Some typical examples follow and others could be found with (5) and (6).

a. The integrating factor depends on only one variable. Calculate $F(x, y) = f_x - g_y$. If the result is that shown in the first column of Table 2, the integrating factor is that given in the second column. The letters a and k are constants. For a more general case, see **b**.

b. Calculate $F(x, y) = f_x - g_y$. Divide it by the function $G(x, y)$, shown in the first column of Table 3. If the result is some function $h(u)$, where u is given in the second column, calculate $I(x, y)$ from (6).

TABLE 2. INTEGRATING FACTORS
DEPENDING ON ONE VARIABLE

$F(x, y) = f_x - g_y$	$I(x, y)$
kf	e^{-kx}
$-kf/x$	x^k
kg/y	y^k
$-af \cot ax$	$\sin ax$
$af \tan ax$	$\cos ax$

TABLE 3. INTEGRATING FACTOR
DEPENDING ON $u(x, y)$

$G(x, y)$	$u(x, y)$
$-f$	x
g	y
$-(f \mp g)$	$x \pm y$
$-2(xf \mp yg)$	$x^2 \pm y^2$
$-(kf \mp g)$	$kx \pm y$
$xg - yf$	xy
$x^{r-1}y^{s-1}(sxg - ryf)$	$x^r y^s$
$-(xg + yf)/y^2$	x/y
$(xg + yf)/x^2$	y/x

The case $u = xy$ applies to the special equation of **7-2-2d**. See, however, Table 3 for $G(x, y)$ in another form. Similarly, the equation in **7-2-2e** is a special case of $u = x^p y^q$, where p, q are constants.

When $u = y/x$, the condition can be generalized; see **c**. Corresponding equations could be found for $u = x/y$.

c. $u = y/x$. The integrating factor, see Table 3, is a homogeneous function of x and y of degree zero; see **8**. The situation can be generalized by requiring that $I(x, y)$ be homogeneous and of degree k. In that case,

$$\frac{x^2 F(x, y) + kfx}{xg + yf} = h(u), \quad u = y/x \tag{7}$$

and the integrating factor is given by

$$I(x, y) = x^k e^\phi; \quad \phi = \int h(u)du$$

If the differential equation itself is homogeneous, (7) will be satisfied independently of the value assigned to k, provided that its denominator does not vanish; see **7-2-2b**. However, in the exceptional case, the integrating factor is unnecessary since the variables are separable. Advantage can be taken of the fact that k is unspecified for a homogeneous equation. Select two different values of k (0 and 1 might be suitable) and find two different integrating factors. The general solution of the equation follows from **7-2b**.

When the differential equation itself is not homogeneous, the method of this section will work if (7) is satisfied for some value of k. When $k = 0$, the necessary condition is the same as the last case of Table 3.

8. Homogeneous Equations and Related Types

The word *homogeneous* is used with two different meanings in the study of differential equations. Here, consider $\phi(x, y)$ and replace x, y by tx, ty, respectively, where t is any multiplier whatever. If t can be factored out of the result in the form

$$\phi(tx, ty) = t^k \phi(x, y) \tag{1}$$

then $\phi(x, y)$ is homogeneous and of degree k in x and y. For the second meaning of homogeneous, see **B1**.

A differential equation

$$P(x, y)y' + Q(x, y) = 0 \tag{2}$$

is homogeneous, in the sense of this section, if $P(x, y)$ and $Q(x, y)$ are homogeneous functions, both of the same degree. The test for homogeneity can usually be made by inspection.

If (2) is also exact, see **7-1**, and if $k \neq -1$, a quadrature is not needed and the solution is

$$x Q(x, y) + y P(x, y) = C$$

A similar solution exists if (2) is made exact by means of an integrating factor; see **7-2**. If $k = -1$, a quadrature is usually necessary. In that case, the methods of **7-1**, **7-2**, or **8-1** may be used. If the equation is homogeneous, but not exact, and an integrating factor is not to be sought, see **8-1**. Some related equations are presented in **8-2ff**.

8-1. The Homogeneous Equation. The given equation has the form (2). Introduce a new dependent variable, $u = y/x$ so that

$$y' = u + x u'(x)$$

A common factor x^k occurs in both $P(x, y)$ and $Q(x, y)$ so that these two coefficients become $P(x, y) = x^k P(1, u)$, $Q(x, y) = x^k Q(1, u)$. The notation means that x is to be replaced in both P and Q by unity and that y is to be replaced by u. When the common factor x^k is removed, the differential equation becomes separable, type **1-2**, with solution

$$\ln x + \int \frac{R(u)}{u R(u) + S(u)} du = C \tag{3}$$

where $R(u) = P(1, u)$, $S(u) = Q(1, u)$.

Alternatively, the equation may be written as

$$y' = f(y/x) = f(u) \tag{4}$$

Define $F(u) = f(u) - u$ and the solution of (4) is

$$\ln x = \int \frac{du}{F(u)} + C \tag{5}$$

If the denominator of either integrand vanishes, some solutions may be lost. Thus, $y = cx$ satisfies (4) if c is a root of $c = f(c)$. This solution might be contained in (5) or it might be a singular solution; see **A2-10**.

In some cases, polar coordinates are useful. With $x = r \cos \theta$, $y = r \sin \theta$, the solution (5) becomes

$$\ln Cr = \int \frac{1 + \tan \theta \, f(\tan \theta)}{f(\tan \theta) - \tan \theta} d\theta$$

When the form of the given equation suggests the substitution $v = x/y$, the resulting integral may be easier to evaluate than for the case with $u = y/x$. When this occurs, $y' = g(x/y) = g(v)$; $G(v) = 1 - vg(v)$;

$$\ln y = \int \frac{g(v)}{G(v)} dv + C$$

8-2. The Isobaric Equation. This is sometimes called one-dimensional, and in German, *gleichgradig*,

$$y' = x^{n-1}f(y/x^n) = x^{n-1}f(u)$$

It is not necessary that n be an integer. Generalize the definition of a homogeneous function, see **8**, so that

$$\phi(tx,\, t^n y,\, t^{n-1}y') = t^k\phi(x,\, y,\, y')$$

defines an isobaric function of weight w. Assign weights of 1, n, $(n-1)$ to x, y, y', respectively. A general term in the differential equation is $x^a y^b y'^c$, with weight $w = a + bn + c(n-1)$. If n has the same value for each term in the equation, let $y = ux^n$. Then, $xu'(x) = f(u) - nu = F(u)$, which is separable, type **1-2**, with solution

$$\ln x = \int \frac{du}{F(u)} + C$$

8-3. $xy' = xf(x)g(u) + y$. Let $y = ux$ and, in the new dependent variable, the equation is separable, type **1-2**, $xu'(x) = f(x)g(u)$. Its solution is

$$\int \frac{du}{g(u)} = \int \frac{f(x)}{x}\,dx + C$$

8-4. $[f(u) + x^n g(u)]y' = [h(u) + x^{n-1}g(u)y]$; $y = ux$. It is not necessary that n be an integer. Take x as the dependent variable and u as the independent variable. The result is a Bernoulli equation, type **5**,

$$x'(u) = F(u)x + G(u)x^{n+1}$$

where $F(u) = f(u)/H(u)$, $G(u) = g(u)/H(u)$, $H(u) = h(u) - uf(u)$.

8-5. The Jacobi Equation. While not strictly of homogeneous type, the equation is convertible to **8-4**,

$$[f_1(x,\, y) + xf_2(x,\, y)]y' = f_3(x,\, y) + yf_2(x,\, y) \tag{6}$$

where $f_i(x,\, y) = a_i + b_i x + c_i y$. A generalization of it is given in **8-6**. For a special case, see **a**. Otherwise, there are three different ways of solving (6); see **b, c, d**.

a. A special case. If $a_1 = a_3$, the equation is of type **8-4**, with $n = 1$, $y = ux$, $f(u) = a_2 + b_1 + c_1 u$, $g(u) = b_2 + c_2 u$, $h(u) = b_3 + (a_2 + c_3)u$.

b. The general case. When the requirements of **a** do not hold, the equation can be converted into type **8-4**, with suitable variable transformations. Let $x = X + r$, $y = Y + s$ and require that

$$A_1 + rA_3 = 0; \quad A_3 + sA_2 = 0$$

where $A_i = a_i + b_i r + c_i s$. The new equation has the same form as (6)

$$[F_1(X, Y) + X F_2(X, Y)] Y'(X) = F_3(X, Y) + Y F_2(X, Y)$$

with

$$F_1 = (b_1 + r b_2) X + (c_1 + r c_2) Y; \quad F_2 = A_2 + b_2 X + c_2 Y$$
$$F_3 = (b_3 + s b_2) X + (c_3 + s c_2) Y$$

Introduce another constant K, which makes the final results more symmetrical

$$A_1 = K, \quad A_2 = rK, \quad A_3 = sK \tag{7}$$

Elimination of r and s from (7) shows that K is a root of a cubic equation, which can be presented as a determinant

$$\begin{vmatrix} a_1 - K & b_1 & c_1 \\ a_2 & b_2 - K & c_2 \\ a_3 & b_3 & c_3 - K \end{vmatrix} = 0$$

The constants r, s can be found as the solution of any pair of the consistent equations

$$(a_1 - K) + b_1 r + c_1 s = 0$$
$$a_2 + (b_2 - K) r + c_2 s = 0$$
$$a_3 + b_3 r + (c_3 - K) s = 0$$

With these tranformations, the final result is type **8-4**, with $n = 1$. The variables are X, u, where $Y = Xu$; $f(u) = \alpha_1 + \alpha_2 u$, $g(u) = b_2 + c_2 u$, $h(u) = \beta_1 + \beta_2 u$; $\alpha_1 = A_2 + b_1 + b_2 r$, $\alpha_2 = c_1 + c_2 r$; $\beta_1 = b_3 + b_2 s$, $\beta_2 = A_2 + c_3 + c_2 s$. Finally, take X as the dependent variable and a Bernoulli equation is obtained; see **5**.

c. An alternative method. The Darboux equation, see **8-6**, is a generalization of the Jacobi equation. Methods of solving the former can also be applied to the latter. Equation numbers here refer to those shown in **8-6**. Let three special solutions of the Darboux equation be

$$F_i(x, y) = A_i + B_i x + C_i y, \quad i = 1, 2, 3$$

so that $G_i(x, y, z) = A_i z + B_i x + C_i y$, where the degree is $k_i = 1$, $m = 1$, $n = 3$. The result corresponding to (8) is

$$B_i g_1 + C_i g_2 + A_i g_3 = K_i G_i$$

but K_i is a constant, since its degree is $(m - 1) = 0$. Equating coefficients of x, y, z in this identity gives

$$B_i(b_1 - K_i) + C_i b_2 + A_i b_3 = 0$$
$$B_i c_1 + C_i(c_2 - K_i) + A_i c_3 = 0$$
$$B_i a_1 + C_i a_2 + A_i(a_3 - K_i) = 0$$

These relations can be used to calculate A_i, B_i, C_i, after the three values of K_i have been found from the determinant

$$\begin{vmatrix} b_1 - K & b_2 & b_3 \\ c_1 & c_2 - K & c_3 \\ a_1 & a_2 & a_3 - K \end{vmatrix} = 0$$

Note that this determinant is not identical with that of **b**; it could be made identical by suitable permutation of the subscripts.

There are additional conditions, as shown in (9)

$$p_1 + p_2 + p_3 = 0$$

$$K_1 p_1 + K_2 p_2 + K_3 p_3 = 0$$

There are three cases, depending on the values of K_i.

    i. All K_i are different. It is satisfactory to take $p_1 = K_2 - K_3$, $p_2 = K_3 - K_1$, $p_3 = K_1 - K_2$. The general solution of the differential equation becomes

$$u(x, y) = G_1^{p_1} G_2^{p_2} G_3^{p_3} + C$$

where $G_i = G_i(x, y, 1) = A_i + B_i x + C_i y$.

    ii. $K_1 = K_2 \neq K_3$. In this case, the solution is

$$u(x, y) = CG_1 + G_3 \exp[(K_1 - K_3)G_2/G_1]$$

    iii. $K_1 = K_2 = K_3$. The general solution is

$$u(x, y) = 2G_1 G_3 - G_2^2 + CG_1^2$$

    d. A third method. This one, quite different from **b** or **c**, depends on solving three simultaneous equations with constant coefficients. Such equations are not treated in this book but the particular one needed here is quite simple. Details can be found in a number of places, for example, Ince-1, Kaplan-1.

Consider three simultaneous equations with independent variable t

$$X'(t) = G_1(X, Y, Z)$$

$$Y'(t) = G_2(X, Y, Z)$$

$$Z'(t) = G_3(X, Y, Z)$$

where $G_i(X, Y, Z) = a_i Z + b_i X + c_i Y$. Let the solution of this system be $U_i(X, Y, Z, t, K_i) = C_i$, which is linear and homogeneous in the variables X, Y, Z. Its characteristic roots are K_i and its arbitrary constants are C_i. Multiply these simultaneous equations by $(Y dZ - Z dY)$, $(Z dX - X dZ)$, $(X dY - Y dX)$, respectively, and add them to get

$$(ZG_2 - YG_3)dX + (XG_3 - ZG_1)dY + (YG_1 - XG_2)dZ = 0$$

The new variables are $X = xZ$, $Y = yZ$, and elimination of Z will produce the Jacobi equation in the form

$$[f_1(x, y) - xf_3(x, y)]y' = f_2(x, y) - yf_3(x, y)$$

where, as before, $f_i(x, y) = a_i + b_ix + c_iy$. Thus, the solution of the simultaneous system of equations will also give the solution of the Jacobi equation. There are three cases. When the variable t is eliminated, they will correspond to the three cases of $\mathbf{c}$.

i. All K_i are different. The solution of the system is

$$u_i(X, Y, Z)e^{-K_it} = C_i$$

where u_i is the previous linear and homogeneous function of X, Y, Z.

ii. $K_1 = K_2 \neq K_3$. The solution of the system is

$$u_1 = C_1e^{K_1t}; \quad (u_2 - tu_1) = C_2e^{K_1t}; \quad u_3 = C_3e^{K_3t}$$

iii. $K_1 = K_2 = K_3$. In this case, the solution is

$$u_1 = C_1e^{Kt}; \quad (u_2 - tu_1) = C_2e^{Kt}; \quad (u_3 - tu_2 + t^2u_3/2) = C_3e^{Kt}$$

8-6. The Darboux Equation. This is a generalization of **8-5**, where the $f_i(x, y)$ are polynomials in x and y of maximum degree m and at least one of them is actually of degree m.

$$[f_1(x, y) + xf_2(x, y)]y' = f_3(x, y) + yf_2(x, y)$$

It is often written in the equivalent differential form

$$Ldy = Mdx + N(xdy - ydx)$$

For purposes of symmetry, introduce a third variable z and replace x, y by x/z, y/z, respectively, so that $f_i(x, y)$ becomes a homogeneous polynomial of maximum degree m,

$$g_i(x, y, z) = z^mf_i(x/z, y/z)$$

If a homogeneous function of degree zero can be found, $u(x, y, z)$ so that the equation in x, y, z is satisfied, then the general solution of the Darboux equation is $u(x, y, 1) = C$. Conversely, $u(x, y, z)$ can be found if the necessary integrals of the original equation are known. The required conditions in the general case were obtained by Darboux. The details may be found in Ince-1 or Goursat. Here, we only state the two conditions which lead to the complete solution of the Darboux equation.

a. Suppose that $n \geqslant m(m+1)/2 + 2$ special solutions of the Darboux equation are known. Let them be $F_i(x, y) = 0$; $i = 1, 2, \ldots, n$, of degree k_i. Convert them into homogeneous polynomials

$$G_i(x, y, z) = z^{k_i}F_i(x/z, y/z)$$

and then calculate

$$g_1 \frac{\partial G_i}{\partial x} + g_2 \frac{\partial G_i}{\partial y} + g_3 \frac{\partial G_i}{\partial z} = K_i G_i \tag{8}$$

where K_i is a polynomial of degree $(m-1)$. The function

$$u(x, y, z) = G_1^{p_1} G_2^{r_2} \ldots G_n^{n}$$

is now to be determined so that it becomes the general solution of the Darboux equation when $z = 1$. It must be a polynomial of degree zero, satisfying the relations

$$k_1 p_1 + k_2 p_2 + \ldots + k_n p_n = 0$$
$$K_1 p_1 + K_2 p_2 + \ldots + K_n p_n = 0 \tag{9}$$

There are enough relations to determine the parameters p_i. The K_i can be found from (8) and the general solution of the differential equation results without quadratures.

b. There are only $n = m(m+1)/2 + 1$ special solutions known. Two cases arise.

i. The determinant of the coefficients of the p_i vanishes. The case has become equivalent to **a.**

ii. The determinant of the coefficients does not vanish. Replace (9) by

$$k_1 p_1 + k_2 p_2 + \ldots + k_n p_n + m + 2 = 0$$

$$K_1 p_1 + K_2 p_2 + \ldots + K_n p_n + \frac{\partial g_1}{\partial x} + \frac{\partial g_2}{\partial y} + \frac{\partial g_3}{\partial z} = 0$$

These equations are sufficient to determine the p_i, and the resulting function $u(x, y, 1)$ is an integrating factor for the Darboux equation.

9. Change of Variable

When an equation does not fit into one of the previous types, it can often be made to do so by a suitable transformation of variables. In fact, some of the preceding methods were based on a variable change. It was stated in **7-2a** that if an equation has a unique solution it will have an infinite number of integrating factors. Similarly, if it has a unique solution it can be solved by a change of variable. In practice, it may not always be easy to find either an integrating factor or the proper new variable. Sometimes, one method is preferred; at other times, the second method is successful. The following sections contain a few suggestions that might be helpful if one or two new variables are sought. Intuition, thorough familiarity with the basic principles of calculus, and experience are probably the mose useful aids. Many examples of this type will be found in Part II.

9-1. New Independent Variable. There are two possibilities.

a. Interchange x and y. The former becomes the new dependent variable and the latter, the new independent variable. This is an especially simple trick for it requires little calculation and it is easy to see whether the equation is so converted into a known type. Two examples, where this method was successful, were given; see **7-2-2h** and **8-4**.

b. Define a new variable $z = f(x)$. For convenience, rename the dependent variable so that $y(x) = u(z)$. It follows that

$$y'(x) = \frac{dz}{dx}u'(z)$$

With the proper choice of z, the transformed equation may be recognizable as one of the types of preceding sections.

9-2. New Dependent Variable. No general rules can be given, but a conspicuous function in the given equation is often suggestive. Three rather general equations of no previous type, where this procedure works, are given in **b, c, d**. Some hints are presented in **a**. It is not necessary that m and n be integers in this section.

a. The new variable is $u(x)$. Try the following cases.

i. $y = f(x) + g(u)$. If a special solution of the equation is known, or can be found, call it y_1. Then $f(x)$ can often be taken as $y_1(x)$. Otherwise, it might be chosen as some function of x which appears in the original equation. For $g(u)$, try u, $1/u$, $ue^{\phi(x)}$, e^{ϕ}/u, u^k, etc. Examples of this case will be found in **3-1, 4-1, 4-2**; see also Part II.

ii. $y = f(x)g(u)$. For $f(x)$, try $e^{\phi(x)}$, x^k, $F(x)$, $1/F(x)$, where $F(x)$ is some term in the given differential equation. See **iii** for some possible forms of the new variable or take u, $1/u$. See also **2, 3-1-2, 3-1-3, 3-2, 3-3, 4-1, 7-2-2, 8-1, 8-2, 8-3, 8-4**, and Part II.

iii. $u = f(y)$ or $u = g(x, y)$. In the first case, try $y^{\pm k}$ or trigonometric functions like $\sin ay$, $\cos ay$, $\tan ay$, etc. In the second case, test $(a + bx + cy)$, $(x^m + y^n)$, $x^m y^n$, or some trigonometric function of both variables. For examples, see **4-2, 5, 6**, and Part II.

b. $y' = f(x) + g(x)y + h(x)y^n$. This equation is reminiscent of several types from other sections.

i. If $h(x) = 0$, it is linear, type **2**.

ii. If $n = 2$, it is a Riccati equation; see **3-1**.

iii. If $n = 3$, it is a special case of the Abel equation, with $f_2(x) = 0$; see **4-1**.

iv. When $f(x) = 0$, a Bernoulli equation results; see **5**.

v. None of the preceding special cases occur. Let $y = uv$ and assume that $v(x)$ is a solution of the linear equation

$$v'(x) = g(x)v + Af(x)$$

This means, see **2**, that

$$v(x) = e^\phi[B + A\int f(x)e^{-\phi}dx]; \quad \phi(x) = \int g(x)dx$$

where A, B are constants. If they can be determined so that $v(x) = (f/h)^{1/n}$, it follows that $u(x)$ is the solution of

$$\int \frac{du}{u^n - Au + 1} = \int \frac{f(x)}{v(x)}dx + C$$

c. $y' = f(x)y^m + g(x)y^n$. This equation, like that of **b**, is similar to, but not identical with, several previous types. If $m = 1$, it is a Bernoulli equation; see **5**. If $m \neq 1$, let $u(x) = y^{m-1}$ and get

$$u'(x) = (m-1)f(x)u^2 + (m-1)g(x)u^k$$

where $k(m-1) = (m+n-2)$. There are several cases.

    i. $k = 0$ or $k = 1$. It is a Riccati equation; see **3-1**.

    ii. $k = 2$. It is separable, type **1-2**.

    iii. $k = 3$. It is an Abel equation; see **4-1**.

    d. $xy' = yf(x^m y^n)$. Let $u(x) = x^m y^n$ and get a new equation

$$xu'(x) = nuf(u) + mu$$

It is separable, type **1-2**, with solution

$$\ln Cx = \int \frac{du}{u(m + nf)}$$

9-3. Two New Variables. If the new variables are defined by the relations

$$x = f(z, u); \quad y = g(z, u)$$

it follows that $y'(x) = g'(z)/f'(z)$. Thus, given $P(x, y)y' + Q(x, y) = 0$, suppose that it has been converted to $P_1(z, u)u'(z) + Q_1(z, u) = 0$. If this equation can be solved to get a general solution $F(z, u) = C$, then the general solution of the original equation in x, y is

$$F[f_1(x, y), g_1(x, y)] = C$$

where $z = f_1(x, y)$ and $u = g_1(x, y)$.

An especially useful case is that of polar coordinates with

$$x = r\cos\theta, \quad y = r\sin\theta$$

and

$$y'(x)[r'(\theta) - r\tan\theta] = \tan\theta[r'(\theta) + r\cot\theta]$$

The transformation is often more easily made with the following relations

$$xdx + ydy = rdr; \quad xdy - ydx = r^2 d\theta$$

$$dx = \cos\theta dr - r\sin\theta d\theta; \quad dy = \sin\theta dr + r\cos\theta d\theta$$

It may be desirable to leave the solution in terms of r, θ and not convert it back to the original variables x and y.

Conspicuous combinations of x, y in the differential equation may suggest other transformations to try.

9-3-1. The Legendre Transformation.

Given the differential equation, where $p = dy/dx$,

$$f(x, y, p) = 0 \tag{1}$$

take p as a new independent variable, calling it X for symmetry. Also take a new dependent variable, $Y = xp - y$. A dual relationship exists between the two sets of variables, provided that $dp/dx \neq 0$,

$$\begin{aligned} x &= P(X), \quad y = XP - Y \\ X &= p, \qquad Y = xp - y \end{aligned} \tag{2}$$

In the new variables, (1) becomes

$$f(P, XP - Y, X) = 0 \tag{3}$$

A solution of (1) will give a solution of (3) by algebraic processes alone, and the reverse. Thus, suppose that (3) is the easier one of these equations to solve and that its solution is

$$F(X, Y) = 0 \tag{4}$$

Then, by differentiation

$$F_X + F_Y P = 0 \tag{5}$$

Use x and y, as defined by (2), together with (4) and (5) to eliminate X, Y, P with the result $g(x, y) = 0$, which is the general solution of (1).

The method of this section is often applicable to equations of degree two or higher; see **A2**.

10. The General Equation of First Order and First Degree

The equation has the form

$$y' = f(x, y) \tag{1}$$

If this section has been reached without finding some method for solving the equation, no simple solution of it is likely. It is possible to state necessary restrictions on the form of $f(x, y)$ so that the equations could be solved by elementary methods alone. The solutions would then all be simple combinations of algebraic or elementary transcendental functions; see **3**. Mathematicians, however, have preferred another procedure and have sought algebraic differential equations which define new transcendental functions through their solutions. In doing so, they have studied certain classes of differential equations which will be presented in the appropriate places later in this book.

Given an equation like (1) to solve, there are three common procedures, if the elementary methods have all failed.

a. Solutions as an infinite series; see **11**.

b. Solution as an integral; see **12**.

c. Solution by an approximate method; see **13**.

In the usual case, **a** will be preferred. The remaining parts of this section summarize some general properties of (1). They are inserted here for convenience of reference and can be consulted as needed.

10-1. Analytic Functions. According to existence theorems, see Introduction-**3**, the differential equation (1) will have a unique solution $y = y(x)$ provided that $f(x, y)$ is analytic near the point (x_0, y_0). The solution will satisfy the condition $y = y_0$ when $x = x_0$; thus y_0 is the constant of integration, since both x_0 and y_0 can be chosen arbitrarily, within certain limits. It is the purpose of this section to consider some properties of analytic functions as used in the study of differential equations. For further details and proofs of the statements which follow, see appropriate references in the Bibliography, for example, Ince-1, Codding-ton and Levinson.

There is no loss in generality if the point (x_0, y_0) is taken as the origin, for two new variables $u = y - y_0$ and $x = x - x_0$ could be used to shift any given point (x_0, y_0) to the origin. Similarly, if $x_0 = \infty$ is of interest, take $x_0 = 1/z_0$ and investigate the behavior at $z_0 = 0$. With these restrictions, a function $f(x, y)$ is said to be analytic near the origin if it can be expanded as a Taylor series, or more correctly as a Maclaurin series,

$$
\begin{aligned}
f(x, y) &= A_{00} + (A_{10}x + A_{01}y) + (A_{20}x^2 + A_{21}xy + A_{02}y^2) \\
&\quad + \ldots + (A_{n0}x^n + \ldots + A_{0n}y^n) + \ldots
\end{aligned}
\tag{2}
$$

There are two constants such that $|x| < a$, $|y| < b$ and the coefficients in (2) are determined from

$$
A_{n-k,k} = \frac{1}{k!(n-k)!} \frac{\partial^n f(x, y)}{\partial x^{n-k} \partial y^k} \bigg|_{x = 0, \, y = 0}
\tag{3}
$$

Convergence and other properties of such series are well-known; for the details, see references in the Bibliography.

If a given function $f(x, y)$ cannot be expanded to get a series like (2), the function is not analytic at the origin. The test for analyticity can be be made simply, for it is only necessary, according to (3), that the function and its derivatives exist at the point in question.

Any point (x_0, y_0) for which $f(x, y)$ is analytic is an *ordinary point*; any other point is a *singular point*. According to Liouville's theorem, every function except a constant possesses at least one singular point. Thus, $y = 1/x$ has a singular point at $x = 0$ and $y = x$ has a singular point at $x = \infty$. There are several kinds of singular points.

a. Poles. Suppose that $y = f(x)$ is singular at $x = x_0$ but that $(x - x_0)^n f(x)$ is analytic, where n is a positive integer, $n \geqslant 1$. Such a singularity is called a *pole* of order n or a nonessential singular point. The misbehavior of the function is effectively avoided by use of the multiplicative term. A typical example is the function $y = 1/x(x - a)^2(x - b)^3$, which has a simple pole at $x = 0$, a double pole at $x = a$, and a triple pole at $x = b$.

If a circle can be drawn with center at the singular point so that no other singular point is enclosed, the singular point is an isolated one. An example is $y = \csc x$, which has an infinite number of isolated simple poles at $x = \pm n\pi$, with n an integer or zero. A nonisolated singular point occurs for $y = \sec 1/x$, whenever $1/x = (2n + 1)\pi/2$. Thus

$$x = 2/\pi(2n + 1)$$

and the most distant poles are at $n = 0$ or $n = -1$. Within a circle of radius less than $2/\pi$, there are an infinite number of poles.

b. Essential singular points. Consider $y = \sin 1/x$. Its series expansion about $x = 0$ is $y = 1/x - 1/3!x^3 + 1/5!x^4 - 1/7!x^4 \pm \ldots$ and no finite value of n in x^n will remove such a singular point. It is said to be an essential singular point.

c. Branch points. If $y = f(x)$ is not single-valued, a branch point can occur. Consider $y = x^2$, the plot of which is a parabola extending in the positive x-direction and with vertex at the origin. There are two branches of it, $y = \pm \sqrt{x}$ for a given nonzero value of x. At $x = 0$, there is a branch point. Note also that the derivative of the function, $y' = 1/2\sqrt{x}$ is ambiguous for $x \neq 0$ and infinite at $x = 0$. Whatever the order, some derivatives of finite order and all higher ones will be infinite at a branch point.

d. Fixed and movable singular points. Examination of the coefficients in a differential equation will reveal the nature of its singular points, which can be of the kinds described in **a**, **b**, **c**. These are the *fixed* or *intrinsic singular points* of the differential equation. It does not follow that solutions of the equation will also have singular points of the same kind. Thus, consider $xy' = ay$, which has a simple pole at $x = 0$. Its general solution is $y = Cx^a$. Only under special conditions is the origin a singular point of the solution. If a is any finite negative integer, it has a pole of finite order; if $a = 1/2$, it has a branch point; if a is a positive integer, the origin is an ordinary point and the only singular point for the solution is at $x = \infty$.

Now consider the equation $yy' + x = 0$, with the general solution $x^2 + y^2 = C$. If initial values are chosen as $y = y_0$ for $x = x_0$, then $y = \sqrt{x_0^2 - x^2 + y_0^2}$ and any point $x = x_k$ can be made a branch point of the solution with the choice of x_0, y_0 so that $x_k^2 = x_0^2 + y_0^2$. Such a singular point, which moves about as the initial values are varied, is a *movable* or *parametric singular point*.

Singular points for linear equations are always fixed. A nonlinear equation of first order and of first degree can have movable poles and movable branch points but no movable essential singularities. Nonlinear equations of second or higher order can have movable singular points of all kinds. Movable branch points and essential singularities, excluding poles of finite order, are often called *critical points* of the differential equation.

11. Series Solution

The equation is

$$y' = f(x, y) \tag{1}$$

and a solution of it is wanted as an infinite series in powers of x. There are several cases, depending on the nature of $f(x, y)$. Proceed as follows.

a. $f(x, y)$ is an analytic function; see **11-1**.

b. $f(x, y)$ is not analytic; see **11-2**.

c. There are certain special forms for $f(x, y)$; see **11-3**.

11-1. $f(x,y)$ *is Analytic at* (x_0, y_0). It is convenient to take $x_0 = 0$, see **10-1**, but for symmetry write $y_0 = A_0$. Since the latter constant is arbitrary it will be the constant of integration. Assume as the general solution of the differential equation

$$y = A_0 + A_1 x + A_2 x^2 + \ldots + A_n x^n + \ldots \tag{2}$$

There are several methods for finding the coefficients in the series; see **a, b, c**. For some comments on convergence, see **d**.

a. The method of undetermined coefficients. If $f(x, y)$ is a polynomial or an infinite series in x, y, substitute (2) for y. If it is some more complicated function of the variables, expand it about $x = 0$ by Maclaurin's theorem, see **10-1**, and then use (2). Replace the left-hand side of the differential equation by the derivative of (2). The result, which no longer contains y, is an identity in x. Equate coefficients of equal powers of x in this equation and obtain relations with which $A_1, A_2, \ldots$ can be calculated as functions of A_0. There are three possibilities.

i. All coefficients after A_k are zero so that (2) is a polynomial of degree k. The method of this section was not needed for (1) could have been solved by one or more of the methods in earlier sections. The present procedure can, of course, be used in such cases, if desired.

ii. A general law results for the coefficients in terms of A_0. In this case, there is a relation connecting A_k and A_{k-1} and by successive use of this relation it becomes possible to define A_k in terms of A_0. Such a relation is called a *two-term recursion formula* or a *first-order difference equation;* see also **B1-8-1-1**.

iii. There is no general law for the coefficients so that three-term formulas or even more complicated ones occur. This means that A_k will usually depend on A_{k-1}, A_{k-2}, etc. In fact, it may depend in some rather involved way on all of the coefficients which precede it and no explicit solution can be found for A_k as a function of A_0. It will become more and more laborious to calculate successive coefficients but, nevertheless, such calculations may be continued as long as desired. Many-term recursion formulas are linear finite-difference equations. It is often convenient to study them by such methods; see, for example, Jordan, Milne-1, Milne-Thompson.

Frequently, one wishes a series solution so that y can be determined within some specified limits of error. This will fix the number of coefficients which must be calculated; see also **d**. It should be noted that the existence theorems guarantee that the solution is valid but it is not possible to make tests for convergence, as in **ii**, since the general term is unknown.

b. Expansion in a Taylor series. The method is equivalent to that of **a**, which in the usual case will be easier to apply. Calculate successively

$$y'' = f_x + f_y y'$$
$$y''' = f_{xx} + 2f_{xy}y' + f_{yy}y'^2 + f_y y'' \tag{3}$$
$$y^{\text{iv}} = f_{xxx} + 3f_{xxy}y' + 3f_{xyy}y'^2 + f_{yyy}y'^3 + 3f_{xy}y'' + 3f_{yy}y'y'' + f_y y'''$$

$$\cdots \quad \cdots \quad \cdots \quad \cdots \quad \cdots \quad \cdots \quad \cdots \quad \cdots \quad \cdots$$

Here, subscripts indicate partial derivatives; thus, $f_{xxy} = \partial^3 f / \partial^2 x \partial y$.

It has been required that $y = A_0$ when $x = 0$; hence $y' = f(0, A_0)$ when $x = 0$. Use this result, together with f_x and f_y, to calculate y'' in (3). Continue in this way to find the third derivative and as many more terms as may be wanted. The general solution of (1) will be

$$y = A_0 + y_0'x + \frac{y_0''}{2!}x^2 + \ldots + \frac{y_0^{(n)}}{n!}x^n + \ldots$$

where $y_0^{(n)}$ means the value of the nth derivative at $x = 0$. It will usually be easier to differentiate $f(x, y)$, successively and to substitute $x = 0$, $y = A_0$, rather than to use the general relations (3).

Either of the three cases in **a** may arise. Evaluation of the successive derivatives can become quite complicated, if it is necessary to use more than a few terms in the series; see also **d**.

c. The coefficients by integration. For an alternative way of determining the coefficients in the series (2), repeated integrations may be used rather than differentiations. For the details, see **12**.

d. Convergence of the series solution. If the conditions required by the existence theorem hold, it is certain that (2) is the general solution of (1). A more exact statement of these conditions may be useful. If further details and proofs are wanted, other sources must be consulted. Some suitable references are Coddington and Levinson, Goursat, Ince-1.

Suppose that $f(x, y)$ is analytic for $|x| < a$, $|y| < b$; see **10-1**. Select appropriate numerical values for these constants and calculate

$$c_{00} + c_{10}a + c_{01}b + c_{20}a^2 + c_{11}ab + c_{02}b^2 + \ldots + c_{n0}a^n + \ldots + c_{0n}b^n + \ldots$$

where c_{ij} is the absolute value of the coefficient A_{ij} in (2). Take M equal to or greater than this sum, so that

$$|f(x, y)| \leqslant M; \quad |x| \leqslant a, \ |y| \leqslant b$$

The solution then holds for any $|x| < r$, where

$$r = a(1 - e^{-1/s}); \quad s = 2Ma/b$$

It may converge for larger values of $|x|$ but if $|x| < a$, $|y| < b$, it will still satisfy the differential equation. In general, $f(x, y)$ will be meaningless for $|x| > a$, $|y| > b$.

To determine how rapidly the series converges, consider the remainder after n terms

$$R_n = y(x) - y_n(x)$$

where $y_n(x)$ is the series (2) ending with the nth term. Then,

$$|R_n| \leqslant F(t) \frac{|x|^{n+1}}{t^n(t - |x|)}; \quad |x| < t < r \tag{4}$$

where

$$F(t) = b[2 + s\{|\ln(1 - t/a)|\}^{1/2}]$$

If a solution of (1) is wanted with a predetermined error less than some value δ, use (4) to calculate the number of terms required in (2). If t is fixed, the right-hand side of (4) will decrease as $|x|$ decreases. Thus, with a selected value of $|x|$ and $|R_n| \leqslant \delta$, the same inequality will hold for all smaller $|x|$.

11-2. $f(x, y)$ Not Analytic at (x_0, y_0). The quantity $f(x, y)$ and each coefficient in the power series solution would become infinite at (x_0, y_0).

Thus, (x_0, y_0) is a singular point, see **10-1**, and the methods of **11-1** will not apply.

It is still possible, in this case, to solve the differential equation. Consider $g(x, y) = 1/f(x, y)$ and write it as

$$g(x, y) = X_0(x) + X_1(x)y + X_2(x)y^2 + \ldots$$

Choose both $x_0 = 0$ and $y_0 = 0$, a restriction with no loss of generality, for only a simple variable transformation is involved for other initial values; see **10-1**. Since $f(x, y)$ became infinite at the singular point, it follows that $g(x, y)$ vanishes and it is necessary that $X_0(0) = 0$. There are two cases.

a. $X_1(0) = X_2(0) = \ldots = X_n(0) = \ldots = 0$. All coefficients vanish at $x = 0$, which means that each term in the right-hand member of the differential equation contains x as a factor. It is then possible to take the equation as

$$xy' = F(x, y)$$

In this case, refer to **11-3**.

b. $X_1(0) = X_2(0) = \ldots = X_{m-1}(0) = 0$; $X_m(0) \neq 0$, $m \geqslant 1$. Interchange the variables and get

$$\frac{dx}{dy} = g(x, y) = y^m[X_m(x) + X_{m+1}(x)y + \ldots]$$

The method of **11-1** now applies to give a solution

$$x = y^{m+1}(A_0 + A_1 y + A_2 y^2 + \ldots); \quad A_0 \neq 0$$

When this series is inverted,

$$y = x^{1/(m+1)}[a_0 + a_1 x^{1/(m+1)} + \ldots]; \quad a_0 \neq 0$$

There are thus $(m+1)$ solutions satisfying the given conditions that $x_0 = y_0 = 0$ and the origin is a branch point; see **10-1**.

11-3. The Equation of Briot and Bouquet. This is case **a** of **11-2**. For a generalization of it, see **11-4**. Let the equation be

$$xy' = a_{00} + a_{10}x + a_{01}y + a_{20}x^2 + a_{11}xy + a_{02}y^2$$
$$+ \ldots + a_{n0}x^n + \ldots + a_{0n}y^n + \ldots \tag{5}$$

If $a_{00} = 0$, and $x = y = 0$, the indeterminate form $0/0$ results for y'. Nevertheless, assume a solution

$$y = A_1 x + A_2 x^2 + \ldots + A_n x^n + \ldots \tag{6}$$

For convenience, take $a_{01} = k$ and use the method of **11-1**. The coefficients in (6) are found to be

$$(1-k)A_1 = a_{10}$$
$$(2-k)A_2 = a_{20} + a_{11}A_1 + a_{02}A_1^2$$

$$\dots \quad \dots \quad \dots \quad \dots \quad \dots$$

$$(n-k)A_n = p_n(a_{n0}, \dots, a_{0n}; \quad A_1, A_2, \dots, A_{n-1})$$

(7)

where p_n is a polynomial in its arguments, with positive integers for its coefficients. There are three possible situations.

a. k is not a positive integer. Successive values of the A_i are obtained from (7). The series converges and it is the unique analytic solution of (5), satisfying the initial conditions $x = y = 0$. Nonanalytic solutions may also exist; see **c**. If k is zero or a real negative integer, the analytic solution is the only one with $x = y = 0$.

b. k is a positive integer. There are two cases.

i. There are relations between k and the coefficients a_{ij} so that (7) can be used to calculate the coefficients A_i. The requirements are

$$k = 1, \quad a_{10} = 0$$
$$k = 2, \quad a_{20} - a_{11}a_{10} + a_{02}a_{10}^2 = 0$$

(8)

$$\dots \quad \dots \quad \dots \quad \dots \quad \dots \quad \dots$$

For $k = n$, the sum involves every a_{ij}, $(i + j) = n$. Since the coefficient A_n is arbitrary, the series solution is the general solution of (5).

The preceding result can be obtained in another way. Use (5), let $y = ux$, and get

$$xu' = a_{10} + (a_{01} - 1)u + x(a_{20} + a_{11}u + a_{02}u^2) + \dots$$

(9)

Then, if $a_{01} = k = 1$ and $a_{10} = 0$, according to (8), the result is

$$u'(x) = a_{20} + a_{11}u + a_{02}u^2 + \dots$$

(10)

which is analytic at the origin and its general solution can be obtained according to **11-1**.

Now suppose that $a_{01} = k$, a positive integer greater than unity. Let $y = x(A + u)$; $A = a_{10}/(1 - k)$ and (5) becomes

$$xu' = b_{10}x + (k - 1)u + \phi(x, u)$$

where $b_{10} = a_{20} + a_{11}A + a_{02}A^2$. The function $\phi(x, u)$ is a double series, beginning with terms of the second degree. The last differential equation is similar to (5) but the coefficient of u has been reduced by unity. A finite number of such transformations will eventually produce the case

$k = 1$ and one more change of variable will give an equation like (9) or (10), which has an analytic solution.

ii. The relations of **i** do not hold; for example, $k = 1$, $a_{10} \neq 0$. There are no solutions analytic at the origin but there is a general solution containing an arbitrary constant. It is a series in x and $x \ln x$; it approaches zero as x approaches zero along a properly chosen path. For references and further details, see Ince-1.

c. Nonanalytic solutions. Suppose that k is not a positive integer, that the analytic solution of (5), according to **a**, is

$$u(x) = A_1 x + A_2 x^2 + \ldots + A_n x^n + \ldots$$

and that a nonanalytic solution $v(x)$ also exists. The general solution of (5) must be $y = u + v$, with

$$xv'(x) = v(k + b_{10}x + b_{01}v + \ldots)$$

Its coefficients b_{ij} are polynomials in a_{ij} and A_i. Transform again with $v = x^k w(x)$ to get

$$xw'(x) = w(b_{10}x + b_{01}x^k w + \ldots)$$

and assume a solution

$$w = \sum_{i,j=0} c_{ij} x^{i+jk}$$

Its coefficients can be calculated successively with the relation

$$(i+jk)c_{ij} = p_{ij}(b_{rs}, c_{mn})$$

where p_{ij} is a polynomial in its arguments and $(m+n) < (i+j) > 0$. The first coefficient c_{00} is arbitrary. The series approaches zero as x approaches zero along a properly chosen path. More complete details are given by Goursat, Ince-1, Valiron.

11-4. The Generalized Equation of Briot and Bouquet.

In a case more complicated than that of **11-3**, let the differential equation be

$$Q(x, y)y' = P(x, y) \tag{11}$$

Solutions are wanted with $y = 0$ when $x = 0$. This means that if $P(0, 0) = Q(0, 0) = 0$, then y' has the indeterminate form $0/0$. It is assumed that both P and Q are convergent double series in x and y, similar to the right-hand member of (5). However, P and Q are not divisible by any power of x or y. Thus, it is possible to take, as a simple case,

$$P(x, y) = a_1 x + b_1 y + f_1(x, y)$$
$$Q(x, y) = a_2 x + b_2 y + f_2(x, y) \tag{12}$$

where the $f_i(x, y)$ are series beginning with terms of the second degree. When $P(x, y)$ and $Q(x, y)$ have more general forms, the following method is also applicable but the steps are more complicated. They are described, for example, by Ince 1.

To solve (12), let $y = ux$ and get

$$xq(x, u)u' = p(x, u) \tag{13}$$

where

$$\begin{aligned} p(x, u) &= (u - u_0)F'(u_0) + xF_1(x, u) \\ q(x, u) &= c_0 + c_1(u - u_0) + xF_2(x, u) \end{aligned} \tag{14}$$

In these equations,

$$F(u) = u(a_2 + b_2 u) - (a_1 + b_1 u)$$

and u_0 is a root of $F(u) = 0$. The derivative $F'(u_0)$ is to be evaluated at $u = u_0$. Higher-order terms are indicated by $F_i(x, y)$. There are three possible cases.

a. u_0 is a simple root. Take $v = (u - u_0)$, so that (13) becomes

$$xv'(x) = ax + kv + \dots \tag{15}$$

where a, k are constants. The equation is now of type **11-3** and can be handled further as described there.

b. u_0 is a double root. In this case, (14) becomes

$$p_1(x, u) = xF_1(x, u)$$

and (15) becomes

$$xv'(x) = ax + \dots$$

This differential equation is now that of case **a**, with $k = 0$.

c. u_0 is a common root of $F(u) = 0$ and $q(x, u) = 0$. In this case, (15) becomes

$$xq_1(x, v)v' = p_1(x, v)$$

where the coefficients are similar to those in (12)

$$\begin{aligned} p_1(x, v) &= A_1 x + B_1 v + \dots \\ q_1(x, v) &= A_2 x + B_2 v + \dots \end{aligned}$$

Provided that $B_1 \neq 0$, let

$$v = x(v_1 - A_1/B_1) \tag{16}$$

and get

$$x^2 Q_1(x, v_1)v_1' = P_1(x, v_1) \tag{17}$$

where

$$\begin{aligned} P_1(x, v_1) &= B_1^2 v_1 + \dots \\ Q_1(x, v_1) &= A_0 + B_1 B_2 v_1 + \dots \end{aligned}$$

and $A_0 = A_2B_1 - A_1B_2$. There are two cases. If $A_0 \neq 0$, (17) can be written as

$$x^2v_1' = ax + kv_1 + \dots \tag{18}$$

If $A_0 = 0$, (18) is indeterminate at the origin but a finite number of reductions similar to (16) will finally convert it to

$$x^{m+1}v_m' = ax + kv_m + \dots \tag{19}$$

In either case, there is a differential equation like (18) or (19) with $m \geqslant 1$, a positive integer. There are two conclusions, both for $k \neq 0$.

    i. $m = 1$ and (19) is formally satisfied by a series which diverges for all $x > 0$.

    ii. $m > 1$ and there is no solution in ascending powers of x. The origin is an essential singular point; see **10-1**.

There are two special cases of interest, which in terms of the original variables, are as follows.

$$x^{m+1}y' = ax + by$$

This is a linear equation, type **2**. The second equation is of Riccati type; see **3-1**.

$$x^2y' = ax^3 + by^2$$

12. Solution as an Integral Equation

    Given

$$y' = f(x, y) \tag{1}$$

it follows that a solution is

$$y = \smallint f(x, y)dx + C \tag{2}$$

This symbolic solution, however, is not immediately helpful since the unknown function $y(x)$ occurs under an integral sign. Thus (2) is an *integral equation* which should be solved. It is convenient to require that $y = y_0$ when $x = x_0$, so that (2) becomes

$$y = y_0 + \int_{x_0}^{x} f(x, y)dx \tag{3}$$

This is the general solution of (1), since the arbitrary quantity y_0 can be regarded as the constant of integration.

    In order to solve (3), let $y = y_0$ under the integral sign and let ^1y be a first approximation to the general solution of (1), where

$$^1y = y_0 + \int_{x_0}^{x} f(x, y_0)dx$$

The integral can be evaluated, at least in principle, since it involves only a single variable x and a constant y_0. Continue in this way and calculate

$$^2y = y_0 + \int_{x_0}^{x} f(x, {}^1y)dx$$

$$\cdots \quad \cdots \quad \cdots \quad \cdots \quad \cdots$$

$$^ny = y_0 + \int_{x_0}^{x} f(x, {}^{n-1}y)dx$$

The work is stopped with a solution ^ky, which is a sufficiently close approximation to the exact solution. The procedure may become quite tedious, since the integrations are usually more and more difficult to perform. With appropriate restrictions, existence theorems show that the successive integrals converge and that the solution is unique. Suitable references are Coddington and Levinson, Ince-1, Whittaker and Watson.

13. Approximate Methods

Given the differential equation

$$y' = f(x, y)$$

suppose that all previous methods have failed, or have been unsatisfactory, for one reason or another. It may then be possible to find an approximate solution by one of the following means:

a. graphical integration
b. mechanical integration
c. numerical integration

There is an extensive literature of each, there are many variations of them, and the details are lengthy. For these reasons, we limit the description of them here. Some suitable references are Levy and Baggott, Milne-1, Milne-2, Scarborough, Collatz, and other books cited in the Bibliography.

a. Graphical methods. Considered geometrically, the differential equation assigns a slope to every point (x, y) in the x, y-plane. Any point for which $f(x, y)$ becomes infinite, of course, must be excluded. Draw short, straight-line segments with slope $f(x_i, y_i)$ through a number of points (x_i, y_i). Each will determine a small portion of an integral curve. The general shape of that curve will become apparent as the plotting is continued. A smooth curve with the line segments as tangents will be the integral curve sought. The final result is a family of curves $\phi(x, y, C)$, each member of which has a slope given by the differential equation.

In some cases, the given problem might require only a special solution, satisfying the condition that $x = x_0$ when $y = y_0$. This situation is equivalent to the general solution if x_0 is a constant and y_0 is a variable parameter or the constant of integration.

Following these general principles, many ingenious variations have been devised. As one possibility, *isoclines* are first drawn. These are the loci along which the slope required by the differential equation has a constant value. When a number of isoclines have been drawn, the integral curves can then be sketched on the same plot.

As another possibility, a first approximation to an integral curve could be drawn and this could be improved by redrawing, until two successive curves coincide. To compute corrections to the first curve, the Taylor series method, see **11-1b**, or the integral equation method, see **12**, could be used. In other cases, a nomograph might be constructed for calculating the corrections.

No high order of precision can be expected by graphical means but the results may be acceptable for special problems, especially if the graphs are carefully constructed and of sufficiently large size. Lacking some particular reason for using this method, one of those in **c** would usually be preferred. For more details about the graphical methods, the book of Levy and Baggott is recommended.

b. Mechanical methods. Devices for mechanical integration have a long history. Two such instruments are the integraph and the polar planimeter. The former, described by Abdank-Abakanowicz in 1889, contains a tracing point, which moves along a graph of the integrand. An attached pen draws the integral curve. The polar planimeter, one model of which was invented by Amsler in 1854, also has a point, which moves along the integrand curve. A connected scale and vernier indicates the number of complete or fractional revolutions made in tracing out the perimeter of the integrand curve. A simple calibration and calculation give the area under this curve, which, of course, equals the value of the definite integral. Either of these devices could be used to solve a simple differential equation in several ways. For example, the integral equation method, see **12**, would give successive approximations to the solution, when the various integrals had been evaluated mechanically.

A wide variety of more sophisticated instruments has been described in the literature and many of them actually constructed. In some cases, the machine has been invented to solve a particular type of equation, such as that of Riccati, see **3**, or of Abel, see **4**. In other cases, the machine may be more versatile but none of them are simple and all are expensive to build. For many references and further description of such instruments, see Kamke.

Of great importance in the development of modern computing methods was the Bush differential analyzer. It was based on addition and integration. The former was achieved by gear boxes and the latter, by a wheel and disk mechanism, similar to that of the polar planimeter. Originally, a curve was followed manually by the user of the machine. Later, photoelectric curve tracers were added and, eventually, the moving parts were replaced by electronic components. These developments were a logical outcome of the Mallock electronic machine, which had been invented for solving simultaneous equations. The modern versions of these machines are called analogue computers. For more details, see Johnson, Soroka.

c. Numerical methods. The methods of **a** and **b** are based on measurement and on the properties of smooth curves. The somewhat inexact title of this section suggests that number is now of major importance. Thus, all operations in these methods are essentially addition or subtraction. They can be carried out by any of the commercially available desk calculating machines or by those high-speed devices known as *digital computers*.

In general, numerical methods are based on *step-by-step integration*. Thus, suppose that $y' = f(x, y)$ is given for solution with specified initial values (x_0, y_0). Graphically, as explained in **a**, one could draw a short segment through (x_0, y_0) with slope $f(x_0, y_0)$; proceed to a neighboring point (x_1, y_1) with $x_1 > x_0$ and calculate $f(x_1, y_1)$, drawing a segment of that slope; continue to the next point (x_2, y_2) and so on. The broken-line curve resulting would be a rough approximation to the integral curve desired. Obviously, the same procedure could be followed with numbers as it is certainly not necessary to draw the curves.

Similarly, if successive derivatives of $f(x, y)$ can be found analytically they could also be calculated numerically. The solution of the differential equation would follow from the Taylor series method of **11-1b**. When the derivatives are not easy to obtain, the method could be modified by using interpolation formulas for them. Alternatively, the integral equations of **12** could be used. First evaluate the integrals, if this is possible, and then calculate them numerically. If the integration is difficult, use numerical integration.

A slightly different method is that of Runge and Kutta. It is based on the Gauss method of numerical integration and it reduces to Simpson's rule for integration if $y' = f(x)$, where $f(x)$ is independent of y. In the usual case, it may be the most suitable procedure if a desk machine must be used.

One of these numerical methods may be preferred, even though a complete solution of the differential equation can be found by another method. Suppose $\phi(x, y, C) = 0$ is the general solution of the differential equation and that it is a relatively complicated transcendental function of x and y.

Especially in some physical problems, solutions may be wanted for particular values of x. It may then be easier to solve the differential equation numerically than to solve the transcendental equation.

Numerical methods are not limited to equations of first order but may be extended to equations of order two or more and to systems of simultaneous equations. For some references where more details can be found, see Milne-2, Scarborough. If a digital computer is available for solving the equation, see Wilkes, Wheeler, and Gill.

A2. THE EQUATION IS OF FIRST ORDER AND OF SECOND OR HIGHER DEGREE

It is convenient to use the symbol p, in place of dy/dx or y'. The general equation is

$$f(x, y, p, p^2, \dots , p^m) = 0$$

where the integer m is the highest nonvanishing power of p which occurs and the *degree* of the equation. If $m = 1$, return to **A1**; if m is greater than unity, proceed with the various cases of this part, until an appropriate method can be found. If m is a fraction, it will be necessary to rationalize the differential equation and clear it of fractions in order to determine the degree. However, some of the following methods will apply, even if m is fractional. When transcendental functions of p occur, like $\ln p$ or $\cos p$; see **11**.

The General Solution of the Equation. Provided that the differential equation has a solution, it will be some function $F(x, y, C) = 0$, where C is an arbitrary constant. Because of algebraic difficulties, it may not always be possible to solve this relation to get an explicit solution $y = \phi(x, C)$. Thus, alternative forms of the general solution may be required. They are described in **a**, **b**, **c** and will be called solutions of types I, II, III, respectively, in the following sections.

In addition to the general solution, a *singular solution* may also exist. It will satisfy the differential equation but it will not be a special case of the general solution. When it alone is of interest, go directly to **10**, for it may often be obtained without solving the differential equation. Alternatively, a singular solution may also appear in the methods which follow, when the general solution of the equation is sought. However, the singular solution will usually be lost if common factors are eliminated from both sides of an equation or if they are canceled out in a numerator and a denominator.

When a series solution of the differential equation is desired, or when the behavior of such a solution is to be investigated in the neighborhood of a *singular point*, see **A1-10-1**, proceed at once to **7**.

a. Solutions of Type I. Suppose that the given differential equation is of degree $m > 1$; then there will be m solutions $f_i(x, y, C) = 0$, $i = 1, 2, \ldots, m$ and the general solution of the equation is

$$f(x, y, C) = f_1(x, y, C)f_2(x, y, C) \ldots f_m(x, y, C) = 0 \qquad (1)$$

There is only one arbitrary constant C, since the equation is of first order, but if it occurs algebraically in the solution its degree will be m. It does not need to occur algebraically, however, and in that case, the only requirement is that C be arbitrary.

b. Solutions of Type II. The general solution in the form (1) might be a complicated algebraic or transcendental function. In such cases, it may be more convenient to present the general solution of the equation as

$$f_1(x, y, C) = 0; \quad f_2(x, y, C) = 0; \quad \ldots ; \quad f_m(x, y, C) = 0$$

c. Solutions of Type III. When the given differential equation can be written as $x = F_1(y, p)$ or $y = F_2(x, p)$, the methods of the following sections yield relations like $y = \phi_1(x, p, C)$ or $x = \phi_2(y, p, C)$. If the algebra is not too complicated, p could be eliminated between the two simultaneous equations in F_i and ϕ_i and the general solution presented as in **a** or **b**. However, in many cases, such algebraic elimination can be formidable. It is then much simpler, and just as satisfactory, to regard p as a parameter. To emphasize this meaning for p, it will be replaced by the symbol t. Thus, the general solution of the differential equation will be given as either of the simultaneous parametric solutions $x = F_1(y, t)$, $y = \phi_1(x, t, C)$; or, $x = \phi_2(y, t, C)$, $y = F_2(x, t)$. A more symmetrical solution can often be taken as $x = F(y, t, C)$, $y = G(x, t, C)$.

1. Missing Variables

If x, y, or both are missing, there are several procedures. Sometimes, one is easier than the others. For an equation of this type, look at all of the subcases before making a choice of the method to be used.

1-1. Dependent Variable Missing.

The general equation is

$$f(x, p) = 0$$

Whichever is easier, solve for p or x, and proceed as indicated. If a new variable is suggested, see **1-1-3**. Conversion of the equation into type **1-2** is sometimes helpful; see **1-1-4**.

1-1-1. Solve for p.

Since the equation is of degree $m > 1$, there will be m different first-order equations

$$p_i = F_i(x) \qquad (1)$$

Each is separable, type **A1-1-1**, and there are m solutions

$$y_i = \int F_i(x)dx + C \tag{2}$$

Present the general solution of the equation as type I or type II, whichever is more convenient.

1-1-2. Solve for x. Then, differentiate with respect to y and get

$$x = F(p) \tag{3}$$

and $dx/dy = 1/p = F'(p)dp/dy$. The last equation is separable, type **A1-1-1**, and integration yields

$$y = \int pF'(p)dp + C \tag{4}$$

An equivalent form is $y = xp - \int F(p)dp + C$. There are two possibilities.

a. Eliminate p between (3) and (4) to get $\phi(x, y, C) = 0$ as the general solution.

b. Replace p by t and take (3), (4) as a parametric solution of type III.

1-1-3. Use a New Variable. The form of the given equation suggests taking $p = G(u)$. The parametric solution is

$$x = F(u); \quad y = \int F'(u)G(u)du + C$$

1-1-4. Exchange Variables. The new dependent variable will be x and $1/p = dx/dy$. It is of type **1-2**, since the differential equation has become $F(x, 1/p) = 0$.

1-2. Independent Variable Missing. The general equation is

$$f(y, p) = 0$$

Whichever is easier: solve for p, see **1-2-1**; solve for y, see **1-2-2**; introduce a new variable, see **1-2-3**.

1-2-1. Solve for p. There are m different first-order differential equations

$$p_i = F_i(y)$$

but each is separable, type **A1-1-3**. The result of integration is

$$x = \int \frac{dy}{F_i(y)} + C$$

The general solution of the equation is

$$x = \phi_1(y, C); \quad x = \phi_2(y, C); \quad \dots; \quad x = \phi_m(y, C)$$

which is of type II. It can also be given as $g(x, y, C) = 0$, which is type I.

1-2-2. Solve for y. Then, differentiate with respect to x and get

$$y = F(p) \tag{5}$$

$dy/dx = p = F'(p)dp/dx$. The last equation is separable, type **A1-1-3**, and its solution is

$$x = \int \frac{F'(p)dp}{p} + C \tag{6}$$

An equivalent form is

$$x = y/p + \int \frac{F(p)}{p^2} dp + C$$

There are two cases.

   a. Eliminate p between (5) and (6) to get $\phi(x, y, C) = 0$.
   b. Replace p by t; use (5) and (6) as a parametric solution of type III.

1-2-3. Use a New Variable. If the form of the equation suggests $p = G(u)$, the parametric solution is

$$y = F(u); \quad x = \int \frac{F'(u)}{G(u)} du + C$$

1-3. Both Variables Missing. The form of the equation is $f(p) = 0$. Factor it, if possible, to get

$$(p - r_1)(p - r_2) \dots (p - r_m) = 0$$

where r_i is a root of the polynomial in p. The individual factors can be integrated since the variables are separated in each. The result will be $y = r_i x + C$, and the general solution of the equation will be

$$(y - r_1 x + C)(y - r_2 x + C) \dots (y - r_m x + C) = 0$$

It may be desirable to give the solution as type II.

2. No Missing Variables

The general form of the equation is

$$f(x, y, p) = 0$$

If it can be solved readily for p, x, or y, refer to **2-1, 2-2, 2-3**, respectively. Occasionally, the method of **2-4** might be useful. Consult **3, 4, 5, 6** also, for these methods may be appropriate in certain cases. Sometimes, the Legendre transformation, see **A1-9-3-1**, will be helpful.

2-1. Solve for p. The result is

$$(p - F_1)(p - F_2) \dots (p - F_m) = 0$$

where $F_i = F_i(x, y)$. Since each factor is of first degree, the methods of **A1** can be used. Suppose that $g_i(x, y, C) = 0$ is a solution of $p = F_i(x, y)$; then the general solution of the differential equation is

$$g_1(x, y, C)g_2(x, y, C) \dots g_m(x, y, C) = 0$$

A solution of type II may be preferred. Some further information on equations of this case will be found in **8**.

2-2. Solve for x. The result,

$$x = F(y, p) \tag{1}$$

can be treated in either of the following ways.

a. Differentiate with respect to y. A first-order equation in y and p is obtained but x is missing. Solve it by a method of **A1** and get

$$G(y, p, C) = 0 \tag{2}$$

Then, whichever is easier:

i. Eliminate p between (1) and (2) to get an explicit solution, $y = \phi(x) + C$.

ii. Retain both (1) and (2) as a parametric solution in terms of the parameter t, which has replaced p. Thus, the solution is type III.

b. Regard y as a function of p. Calculate

$$\frac{dy}{dp} = \frac{pF_p}{1 - pF_y}$$

Here, the subscripts designate partial derivatives: $F_p = \partial F/\partial p$, etc. Solve the first-order equation by a method of **A1**. The result is

$$y = Y(p) \tag{3}$$

Then, whichever is easier:

i. Eliminate p between (1) and (3) to get $y = \phi(x) + C$.

ii. Keep (1) and (3) as a parametric solution of type III, replacing p by the parameter t.

2-3. Solve for y. Treat the result

$$y = F(x, p) \tag{4}$$

according to either **a** or **b**, but see also **c**.

a. Differentiate with respect to x. The dependent variable is eliminated and the result is

$$g(x, p, p') = 0$$

Solve this first-order equation by a method of **A1**, if possible. Suppose that its solution is

$$G(x, p, C) = 0 \tag{5}$$

Choose the easier one of the following:

i. Eliminate p between (4) and (5) to get an explicit solution, $y = \phi(x) + C$.

ii. Call p a variable parameter, rename it t, and give the solution as type III, with both (4) and (5).

b. Calculate

$$\frac{dx}{dp} = \frac{F_p}{p - F_x}$$

where the subscripts mean partial derivatives; see **2-2b**. Solve it, if possible, by a method of **A1** to get

$$x = X(p) \tag{6}$$

There are two possibilities.

i. Eliminate p between (4) and (6) to get an explicit solution, $y = \phi(x) + C$.

ii. Use both (4) and (6) as a parametric solution of type III, with p replaced by t.

c. Special cases.

i. If the given differential equation is linear in y, with a constant for its coefficient, the differentiation in **a** or **b** can be carried out at once; it is not necessary to solve for y.

ii. Refer to **4**. Equations of the special type described there can be solved very easily.

3. Homogeneous Equations and Related Types

For the meaning of the word homogeneous, as used here, see **A1-8**. There are several different kinds of equations.

3-1. $x^n f(y/x, p) = 0$. Let $y = ux$, so that the equation becomes $f(u, p) = 0$, after the factor x^n has been removed. Proceed in one of the following ways, whichever seems the easiest.

3-1-1. Solve for p. The result, $p = F(u)$ is homogeneous and of first order; see **A1-8-1**. Its solution is

$$\ln x = \int \frac{du}{F(u) - u} + C$$

Sometimes, polar coordinates are useful; see **A1-8-1**.

3-1-2. Solve for y. The method of **2-3** is applicable, for $y = xg(p)$ and the solution is

$$\ln x = \int \frac{g'(p)}{p - g(p)} dp + C$$

If p can be eliminated without difficulty, the solution is $\phi(x, y, C) = 0$. Otherwise, let p be a parameter, renamed t, and give a solution of type III.

3-1-3. Solve for x. Use **2-2.** The equation has become $x = yG(p)$ and its solution is

$$\ln y = \int \frac{p\,G'(p)}{1 - pG}dp + C$$

When the integration has been completed, the final result is $\phi(x, y, C)$, provided that p can be eliminated. As another possibility, replace p by t and give a parametric solution of type III.

3-1-4. Introduce a New Variable. The form of the equation may suggest the appropriate transformation. There are two cases.

a. Let $y/x = F(v)$, $p = G(v)$. Then, whichever seems easier:

  i. Solve for x and proceed according to **b.**

  ii. Solve for y. The result, $y = xF(v)$ can be further treated according to **2-3.** That method yields

$$\ln x = \int \frac{F'(v)}{G(v) - F(v)}dv + C$$

When the quadrature has been completed, it may be possible to restore the original variables so that the final solution is $\phi(x, y, C) = 0$. If algebraic difficulties are severe, replace v by the parameter t and give a solution of type III.

b. Take $x = yF_1(v)$, $p = G_1(v)$. The method of **2-2** is applicable so that

$$\ln y = \int \frac{G_1(v)F_1'(v)}{1 - G_1F_1}dv + C$$

Restore the original variables or give a parametric solution as in **a.**

3-2. The Isobaric Equation. The form of the equation is

$$f(y, xp) = 0$$

It has been called *homogeneous, one-dimensional* and, in German, *gleich-gradig*; see **A1-8-2.** Take 1, n, $(n-1)$ for the dimensions of x, y, p, respectively. A general term in the equation is $x^a y^b p^c$ and its weight is $w = a + bn + c(n-1)$. If n is the same for each term in the differential equation, let $y = x^n u(z)$; $z = \ln x$. Then, $p = e^{(n-1)z}[u'(z) + nu]$ and the new equation in $u(z)$ does not contain z. It is type **1-2** and its solution can be found by a method of that section.

3-3. The Equation has the Form $yf(x, p/y) = 0$. Let $y = e^\phi$, $\phi = \int u(x)dx$, and get $e^\phi f(x, u) = 0$. Delete the exponential factor, solve $f(x, u) = 0$ for u, and integrate to get $\phi(x)$.

4. Clairaut's Equation and Related Types

There are three different equations, each quite similar in form.

4-1. Clairaut's Equation. Given $f(x, y, p) = 0$, it is of this type if it becomes, when solved for y,

$$y = xp + f(p) \tag{1}$$

It is now **2-3** and if the procedure of **2-3a** is used, the result is

$$p = p + [x + f'(p)]\frac{dp}{dx} \tag{2}$$

which may be satisfied in two ways. Note that Clairaut's equation may often be recognized without actually solving for y; see **4-2**.

a. Let $dp/dx = 0$. Then $p = C$ and the general solution of the equation is

$$y = Cx + f(C) \tag{3}$$

b. Take

$$x + f'(p) = 0 \tag{4}$$

Eliminate p between (1) and (4) to get $\phi(x, y) = 0$. It contains no arbitrary constant; it is not a special case of the general solution (1); it satisfies the differential equation. Alternatively, (1) and (4) may be used as a parametric solution of type III. In either case, the result is a *singular solution*; see **10** for further details.

4-2. $f(y - xp, p) = 0$. When solved for y, the result is Clairaut's equation, type **4-1**. The general solution is

$$f(y - Cx, C) = 0$$

A singular solution may also exist; see **10**.

4-3. d'Alembert's Equation (also called Lagrange's Equation). Its form is

$$y = xf(p) + g(p) \tag{5}$$

There are several possibilities.

a. Special cases. When $f(p) = p$, it is Clairaut's equation; see **4-1**. If $g(p) = 0$, the equation is homogeneous; see **3-1**.

b. Differentiate with respect to x. Make x the dependent variable and p the independent variable. The result is

$$\frac{dx}{dp} = \frac{g'(p)}{p - f(p)} + \frac{f'(p)x}{p - f(p)} \tag{6}$$

If the denominators on the right do not vanish, the equation is linear, type **A1-2**, and the solution of (6) is

$$x = CF(p) + G(p) \qquad (7)$$

Eliminate p between (5) and (7) to get an explicit solution, $y = \phi(x) + C$. Alternatively, retain (5) and (7) as a solution of type III, replacing p by a parameter t. A singular solution may also exist; see **10**.

c. The Legendre transformation. With $x = P(X)$, $y = XP - Y(X)$, $P = dY/dX$, the result is linear; see **A1-2** and **A1-9-3-1**.

$$[X - f(X)]P = g(X) + Y(X)$$

5. The Method of Lagrange

Suppose that the given equation

$$F(x, y, p) = 0 \qquad (1)$$

can be written as $F(f, g)$, where $f(x, y, p) = 0$, $g(x, y, p) = 0$ are two first-order equations, derivable from a common primitive

$$\phi(x, y, C_1, C_2) = 0 \qquad (2)$$

Here, C_1 and C_2 are two arbitrary constants. The solution of (1) is also given by (2), but the constants are related by

$$F(C_1, C_2) = 0 \qquad (3)$$

The method will apply provided that

$$f_p(g_x + pg_y) = g_p(f_x + pf_y)$$

where the subscripts indicate partial derivatives.

Alternatively, differentiate (1) with respect to x, solve the resulting second-order equation, see **B**, to get (2) and use (3) to eliminate one constant.

6. Change of Variable

Try to convert the differential equation into one of the preceding types by a new dependent variable, a new independent variable, or two new variables. Specific directions are not readily given but a number of suggestions may result from **A1-9**. See also **A1-9-3-1**. Modifications needed for equations of second or higher degree are usually obvious. Since an equation of Clairaut type, see **4-1**, is quite simple to solve, seek a transformed equation of that kind, as one possibility. A few special cases of variable transformation are listed in the next section. Many further examples will be found in Part II.

6-1. Polar Coordinates. Let $r^2 = x^2 + y^2$ and use new variables r, θ, defined by $x = r\cos\theta$, $y = r\sin\theta$. If the differential equation contains a term $\phi(x, y, r)$, examine one of the following types; see also **A1-9-3**.

a. $f(r^2)(1+p^2) = (y-xp)^2$. In the new variables, the equation is type **1-1**,

$$r^2(r^2 - f)\theta'^2(r) = f(r^2)$$

Its solution is

$$\theta = \pm \int \left(\frac{f}{r^2 - f}\right)^{1/2} \frac{dr}{r} + C$$

It may be easier to keep r, θ as variables in the final solution, for an explicit solution in terms of x and y may be complicated.

b. $r^2 f(x/r)(1+p^2) = (y-xp)^2$. The new equation is of type **1-2**,

$$r^2[1 - f(\cos\theta)]\theta'^2(r) = f(\cos\theta)$$

The solution is

$$\ln r = \pm \int \left(\frac{1-f}{f}\right)^{1/2} d\theta + C$$

c. $r^2 f(y/r)(1+p^2) = (y-xp)^2$. With the new variables, an equation of type **1-2** results

$$r^2[1 - f(\sin\theta)]\theta'^2(r) = f(\sin\theta)$$

Its solution is

$$\ln r = \pm \int \left(\frac{1-f}{f}\right)^{1/2} d\theta + C$$

7. The General Equation

Given the general equation of first order and mth degree ($m > 1$)

$$f(x, y, p) = 0$$

if no method has yet been found for solving it, no solution is likely in finite form. In that case, it may be possible to use:

a. An infinite series; see **A1-11**.
b. A definite integral; see **A1-12**.
c. An approximate method; see **A1-13**.

The references apply to an equation of the first degree but they may be modified for equations of higher degree. Since problems of this sort are not common, no further details will be given here.

As stated in **A1-10**, mathematicians have been interested in finding certain special classes of differential equations which define new transcendental functions. The class concerned here is that with no movable singular points; see **A1-10-1**. The necessary conditions for equations of degree two or greater are stated in **8** and its subsections. With still further restrictions, the special cases of **9** result.

8. $X_0(x, y)p^m + X_1(x, y)p^{m-1} + \ldots + X_m(x, y) = 0.$

This special case of **7** is restricted as follows: the coefficients $X_i(x, y)$ are polynomials in y; the coefficients of y and its powers are analytic functions of x, see **A1-10-1**; the equation is *irreducible*. The last property means that the differential equation cannot be written identically as

$$f(x, y, p) = F_i(x, y, p)F_j(x, y, p) = 0$$

where F_i, F_j are polynomials in p of degrees i, j, respectively, with $(i+j) = m$. If this were so, there would be two separate equations $F_i = 0$, $F_j = 0$, and each could be treated according to the procedures following, or in some simpler way.

For the general differential equation of this section, use the abbreviated symbol

$$f(x, y, p) = 0 \tag{1}$$

Differentiate it partially with respect to p and call this result

$$f_p(x, y, p) = 0 \tag{2}$$

Finally, eliminate p between (1) and (2) to get the *p-discriminant relation*; see **10-1**,

$$\Delta_p(x, y) = 0 \tag{3}$$

It is analytic in x and a polynomial in y. Note that the subscript in (3) does not mean a partial derivative, as it does in (2).

Examine the coefficients $X_i(x, y)$ for *fixed singular points*; see **A1-10-1**. There are four cases.

a. Δ_p vanishes independently of y.
b. X_0 vanishes independently of y.
c. There are singular points of X_i for general values of y.
d. There are singular points for y_i, a root of (3).

Values of x so determined are fixed singular points, depending only on the coefficients x_i. Exclude each of them from subsequent consideration, for we are interested here only in the *movable singular points*.

Let (x_0, y_0) be some point other than those which have been excluded. It may, or may not, be a movable singular point. Series solutions of (1) are wanted in the neighborhood of (x_0, y_0). Provided that the origin is not a fixed singular point, a suitable choice is often $x_0 = y_0 = 0$. There are four special cases. A study of them will reveal the conditions for a solution with no movable singular points. If that case along is of interest, go to **9.1**, at once.

8-1. $X_0(x_0, y_0) \neq 0$, $\Delta_p(x_0, y_0) \neq 0$. These two conditions guarantee that (1), a polynomial in p, will have m different finite roots in the neighborhood of (x_0, y_0). Each is an analytic function there. Select one of them, say p_1, and develop it as a double series

$$p_1 = \sum_{i,j} a_{ij}(x - x_0)^i (y - y_0)^j$$

Solve this first-order equation according to **A1-11**. Call its solution $y_1 = F_1(x, x_0, y_0)$ and it will equal y_0, when $x = x_0$. Treat each of the other roots in the same way. The general solution of (1) will be, see **2-1**.

$$y = F_1(x, x_0, y_0) F_2(x, x_0, y_0) \dots F_m(x, x_0, y_0)$$

It has one arbitrary constant y_0. There are no solutions of any other type.

8-2. $X_0(x_0, y_0) = 0$, $\Delta_p(x_0, y_0) \neq 0$. With these conditions there are m different roots of (1), but *one* of them becomes infinite at (x_0, y_0). If there were two infinite roots, the further condition $X_1(x_0, y_0) = 0$ would be required, and so on, for a greater number of infinite roots.

Use **8-1** to find $(m-1)$ solutions for the finite roots. The method of **A1-11-2b** is applicable for the single infinite root and the result is, with $a_0 \neq 0$, $k \geqslant 1$

$$y = y_0 + (x - x_0)^{1/(k+1)}[a_0 + a_1(x - x_0)^{1/(k+1)} + \dots]$$

This case *always* has a movable branch point at $x = x_0$. There can be no general solution in this case entirely free from such a point.

8-3. $X_0(x_0, y_0) \neq 0$, $\Delta_p(x_0, y_0) = 0$. Since (3) is a polynomial in y, it will have some solution $y = \phi(x)$. Ignoring the singular points of $\Delta_p = 0$, see **8d**, this solution will be an analytic function of x. For general values of y there will be m different roots of p; see **8-1**. Call them $p_1, p_2, \dots, p_m$ but when $y = \phi(x)$, there is at least one multiple root, q. Suppose that the roots equal to q are $p_1, p_2, \dots, p_r$; $r > 1$.

Keep x fixed and let y make a small circuit around the point so determined, $y = \phi(x)$. Then, one of the equal roots, p_1 for example, will either return to its initial value or become equal to one of its partners p_2, $p_3, \dots, p_r$. Eventually, after $\alpha \leqslant r$ complete circuits it will return to p_1. Thus, p_1, as a function of y, has a branch point of order $(\alpha - 1)$ at $y = \phi(x)$. Let $Y(x) = y - \phi(x)$, and use Maclaurin's theorem to get

$$p_1 = q + Y^{k/\alpha}(g_k + g_{k+1}Y^{1/\alpha} + \dots) \tag{4}$$

The coefficients in this first-order differential equation are functions of x and the first nonvanishing one is g_k. There are several special cases.

a. $\alpha = 1$. The differential equation is analytic in x and Y. Its solution is an analytic function; see **A1-11**.

b. $\alpha > 1$. The right-hand side of (4) shows that p_1 is branched. There are two cases.

i. $q \neq d\phi/dx$. The solution of (1) is

$$y = \phi(x) + (x - x_0)[a_0 + a_1(x - x_0)^{1/\alpha} + a_2(x - x_0)^{2/\alpha} + \ \ldots \ ]$$

It has a movable branch point.

ii. $q = d\phi/dx$. Three possibilities arise in this case.
One solution is $y = \phi(x)$. It is a singular solution; see **10**.

$(\alpha - 1) > k$. Let $s \geqslant 1$, so that $\alpha = k + s + 1$. The solution of the differential equation is

$$y = \phi(x) + P_\alpha[(x - x_0)^{1/(s+\alpha)}]$$

where P_α designates a polynomial in its argument, with a leading term of degree α. This solution has a movable branch point.

$(\alpha - 1) \leqslant k$. Let $\alpha = k - s + 1$ and there are two subcases.

$s > 0$. The only solution of (1) is the singular solution, $y = \phi(x)$. This is the same situation as that in the first case of **ii**.

$s = 0$. The solution of (1) is

$$y = \phi(x) + P_\alpha[(x - x_0)]$$

There is no branch point at $x = x_0$.

8-4. $X_0(x_0, y_0)' = 0$, $\Delta_p(x_0, y_0) = 0$. The function $y = \phi(x)$ satisfies both $X_0 = 0$ and $\Delta_p = 0$, for general values of x and y. The conclusions are similar to those in **8-3**, except that the multiple root is at infinity. The differential equation corresponding to (4) is

$$p_1 = Y^{-k/\alpha}(g_0 + g_1 Y^{1/\alpha} + \ \ldots)$$

and the solution of (1) is

$$y = \phi(x) + P_\alpha[(x - x_0)^{1/(k+\alpha)}]$$

Since $k > 0$, there is a movable branch point, even though $\alpha = 1$.

9. $p^m + f_1(x, y)p^{m-1} + \ \ldots \ + f_{m-1}(x, y)p + f_m(x, y) = 0.$

This is a special case of **8**, where restrictions are imposed so that the solution has no movable branch points, see **A1-10-1**. The coefficients $f_i(x, y)$ are analytic in x and polynomials in y. Other special cases of **8** are presented in **9-1ff**.

Designate the general equation of this section by

$$f(x, y, p) = 0 \tag{1}$$

and let its p-discriminant relation be $\Delta_p(x, y) = 0$; see **10-1**. For further details about the equation, see the following parts of this section.

a. Movable branch points. They always occur when $X_0(x, y) = 0$, according to **8-2** and **8-4**. To avoid them, require that X_0 be a function of x alone. Thus, with this restriction, use the general equation of **8**, divide each of its coefficients by $X_0(x)$, and get (1).

b. A singular solution. Suppose that $y = \phi(x)$ is a root of $\Delta_p(x, y) = 0$ and that $p = q(x)$ is a multiple root of $f(x, \phi, p) = 0$; see **8-3**. At the same time, let the corresponding root of $f(x, y, p) = 0$, as a function of $Y(x) = y - \phi(x)$, be branched. Then, $q = d\phi/dx$ and $y = \phi(x)$ is a singular solution but there may be others.

c. A restriction on α. If the order of any branch is α, the equation has the form, see **8-3**,

$$Y'(x) = g_k[Y(x)]^{k/\alpha}$$

To prevent a movable branch point, it is necessary that $(\alpha - 1) \leqslant k$.

d. Further restrictions. If y becomes infinite at a branch point, let $y = 1/u$, so that $u = 0$ at $x = x_0$, $y = \infty$. Also let $P = du/dx = -p/u^2$ and (1) becomes

$$P^m - f_1(x, y)u^2 P^{m-1} + \ldots + (-1)^m f_m(x, y)u^{2m} = 0 \qquad (2$$

It is necessary that the coefficients of P^i be rational in u; thus $f_i(x, y)$ must be of degree $2i$ in y, or less. If $i = 1$, and all of the other conditions are met, the result is a Riccati equation; see **A1-3**.

e. u is a factor of $\Delta_p(x, u)$. Suppose also that P is a many valued function of u. It is required that u be a factor of both f_m and f_{m-1}.

f. A branch of order α. It is necessary, according to **c**, that $(\alpha - 1) \leqslant k$. The differential equation becomes

$$P(x) = du/dx = B_k u^{k/\alpha} + \ldots$$

g. No movable essential singular points. This is true for (1), independent of the presence or absence of movable branch points.

9-1. $p^m + Y_1(y)p^{m-1} + \ldots + Y_m(y) = 0$. The coefficients $Y_i(y)$ are polynomials in y, of degree no greater than $2i$. There can be no fixed singular points, except possibly one at infinity, since the coefficients do not depend on x. If all conditions of **9** are met, there can be no movable branch points. Furthermore, there are no essential singularities for finite x. The point at infinity can be an essential singular point, but not a branch point.

9-2. $p^m + X(x, y) = 0$. This is a special case of the general equation in **9**. It is assumed to be irreducible, see **8**, and to satisfy all further requirements of **9**. Its solutions, therefore, have no movable branch points, but the latter condition means that the equation must take the restricted form

$$p^m + F(x)G(y) = 0 \qquad (3)$$

However, there are still further limitations for only certain values of the constant m are permitted. If uninterested in the details, go to **9-3**, where these permitted cases are listed. If the arguments for (3) are wanted, see the following.

a. The degree of $X(x, y)$ can be no greater than $2m$, see **9d**. If the degree is less than $2m$, there are two possibilities, but both can be reduced to the case where the degree is $2m$. For convenience, the degree of $X(x, y)$ will be taken as exactly $2m$.

i. The degree of $X(x, y)$ is less than $2m$, but it does not contain y as a factor. Let $y = 1/u$, as in **9d**, so that the equation is transformed into

$$P^m + (-1)^m X(x, y)u^{2m} = 0$$

where $P = du/dx$. It has become of degree $2m$ in the variables u and x.

ii. The degree of $X(x, y)$ is less than $2m$, but it contains y as a factor. If it does not contain $(y - a)$ as a factor, let $(y - a) = 1/u$ and the equation is transformed into that of case **i**.

b. There are equal roots. This means that $\Delta_p(x, y) = 0$; see **8-3** and **8-4**. It also means that $\Delta_p = X(x, y)$. Suppose that $Y(x) = y - \phi(x)$ is a factor of $X(x, y)$, so that $p = 0$ is a root of $p^m + X(x, \phi) = 0$. It follows that the roots of the equation may be branched or may not be branched when $y = \phi(x)$.

i. A root is branched when $y = \phi(x)$. From **9b**, it follows that $d\phi/dx = 0$; hence $\phi(x)$ is a constant.

ii. A root is not branched when $y = \phi(x)$. In this case, $X(x, y)$ must contain $Y^m(x)$ or $Y^{2m}(x)$ as a factor; see **9b**.

In the first case, suppose that $Y^m(x) = [y - \phi(x)]^m$ is a factor of $X(x, y)$. The remaining factor will have the form $g(x)[y - \phi_1(x)]^m$ and the differential equation is irreducible, see **8**, contrary to assumption. The second factor of $X(x, y)$ will be of degree less than m and the corresponding value of p will be branched. It follows that $\phi_1(x)$ is a constant; see **i**.

In the second case, $Y^{2m}(x, y)$ may be a factor of $X(x, y)$. Then, the differential equation becomes $p^m + F(x)Y^{2m}(x) = 0$, which is reducible, see **8**, contrary to the original assumption about the differential equation.

9-3. $p^m + F(x)G(y) = 0$. When the differential equation of **9-2** is restricted so that there are no movable branch points, the equation of this section results. From **9-2b**, there are two possibilities for

$$X(x, y) = F(x)G(y)$$

a. $Y^m(x) = [y - \phi(x)]^m$ is not a factor of $X(x, y)$. Then, (3) must contain a factor

$$G(y) = (y - a_1)^{m_1}(y - a_2)^{m_2} \ldots (y - a_n)^{m_n}$$

where the a_i are constants and $(m_1 + m_2 + \ldots + m_n) = 2m$. A power series expansion, in terms of any a_i and m_i, will give

$$p = A(x)(y - a_i)^{m_i/m} + \ldots$$

Reduce m_i/m to its lowest terms and suppose that the result is k_i/α_i. It follows from **9c** that $(\alpha_i - 1) \leqslant k_i$ and, as a consequence of this inequality, that $k_i/\alpha_i \geqslant 1/2$, $\alpha_i \geqslant 2$, $m_i \geqslant m/2$. The possible equations are those satisfying the conditions $m_i/m \geqslant 1/2$, $(m_1 + m_2 + \ldots + m_n) = 2m$, where each m_i is an integer. The results are listed in **9-4a**.

b. $Y^m(x) = [y - \phi(x)]^m$ is a factor of $X(x, y)$. In this case, the differential equation must contain a factor $Y^m(x)G(y)$ and the condition $m_i \geqslant m/2$ must hold as in **a**. However, $m_i < m$, $(m_1 + m_2 + \ldots + m_n) = m$. There is only one possible differential equation; see **9-4b**.

9-4. The Binomial Equations. If all conditions in **9-3** are met, the resulting equations are called *binomial*. There are three cases: the first two correspond to **a** and **b** of **9-3**; the third includes some degenerate forms. For a method of solving each differential equation, see Part II.

The general equation is

$$p^m + F(x)G(y) = 0 \tag{3}$$

where

$$G(y) = (y - a_1)^{m_1}(y - a_2)^{m_2}(y - a_3)^{m_3}(y - a_4)^{m_4}$$

The quantities a_i are constants; m and each m_i is a positive integer; $(m_1 + m_2 + m_3 + m_4) = 2m$. The case $m = 1$ is excluded since it would be of first degree; see **A1**. There could be further special types such as $p^m + H(y) = 0$. These were first studied by Briot and Bouquet and they are listed in **d**.

a. The cases of **9-3a**. There are six possible types; see Table 1.

TABLE 1. CONSTANTS IN THE BINOMIAL EQUATIONS
$$p^m + F(x)G(y) = 0$$

Type	m	m_1	m_2	m_3	m_4
I	m	$m+1$	$m-1$	0	0
II	2	2	1	1	0
III	2	1	1	1	1
IV	3	2	2	2	0
V	4	3	3	2	0
VI	6	5	4	3	0

b. The case of **9-3b**. Refer to type II in Table 1, replace $(y - a_1)$ by $Y(x) = y - \phi(x)$ and call this type IIa. It becomes type II, if $\phi(x)$ is a constant, not equal to a_2 or a_3.

c. Degenerate cases. Substitute $(y - a_i) = 1/u$ into the six types of **a**. Each will give one or more degenerate cases of degree lower than $2m$. If the dependent variable is again called y, the results are of the same form as (3), but $G(y)$ is a product of three terms, rather than four terms. The possible cases are listed in Table 2.

TABLE 2.   CONSTANTS IN THE DEGENERATE
CASES OF THE BINOMIAL EQUATIONS

$$p^m + F(x)G(y) = 0$$

Type	m_1	m_2	m_3
I–1	m 1	0	0
I–2	$m+1$	0	0
II–1	2	1	0
II–2	1	1	0
III–1	1	1	1
IV–1	2	2	0
V–1	3	3	0
V–2	3	2	0
VI–1	5	4	0
VI–2	5	3	0
VI–3	4	3	0

d. The transformed equation $p^m + H(y) = 0$. In (3), let $y(x) = u(z)$; $z = \int F^{1/m}(x)dx$. The result is $u'(z) = G^{1/m}(u)$, a first-order equation of separable type, **A1-1-3**. Each binomial equation of this section could thus be written in the simpler form $p^m + H(y) = 0$.

10. Singular Solutions

Given an equation of degree $m \geqslant 2$

$$f(x, y, p) = 0 \tag{1}$$

it is often possible to find a function $E(x, y) = 0$, with the following properties:

a. It satisfies the differential equation.

b. It contains no arbitrary constant.

c. It cannot be obtained by assigning a particular value to the integration constant in the general solution of (1).

Such a function is a *singular solution*. Its properties are frequently of interest and, in some problems, it is wanted rather than the general solution of the differential equation.

There are two possibilities.

i. The equation is reducible. This means that (1) can be written as the product of two or more rational functions; see **2-1** and **8**. There will be no singular solution. A check on this situation can be made, for the p-discriminant, see **10-1**, will vanish identically.

ii. The equation is irreducible. A singular solution *may* exist. In such a case either **10-1** or **10-2** could be used. The former may be simpler, since the general solution of the differential equation need not be known. However, it would be preferable to complete the work of both **10-1** and **10-2**, in that order. Then, refer to **10-3** for a more complete treatment of the problem.

10-1. The p-discriminant. Calculate the partial derivative of (1) with respect to p

$$f_p(x, y, p) = 0 \tag{2}$$

Eliminate p between this equation and (1). The result, $\Delta_p(x, y) = 0$, called the *p-discriminant relation*, will contain the singular solution, if one exists. Note that the subscript in this relation does not mean a partial derivative.

Clear the p-discriminant relation of fractions and radicals, discard any constant factors, but do not reject any functions of the variables. The equation will then usually be a product of two or more functions of x and y. Test each to see if it satisfies the differential equation. If it does, it is either a singular solution or a special case of the general solution. Any factor which does not satisfy the differential equation describes a curve related to the general solution of (1). If such a function is of interest, see **10-3**.

There are two modifications of the general procedure which may be helpful.

a. Suppose that (1) has the form, see **8**

$$X_0(x, y)p^m + X_1(x, y)p^{m-1} + \ldots + X_m(x, y) = 0$$

The p-discriminant relation is equivalent to the algebraic problem of a polynomial with equal roots. Thus, for $m = 2, 3$, differentiation and elimination of p can be avoided with the explicit relations

$$m = 2, \quad \Delta_p = 4X_0X_2 - X_1^2$$

$$m = 3, \quad \Delta_p = 18X_0X_1X_2X_3 + X_1^2X_2^2 - 27X_0^2X_3^2 - 4X_1^3X_3 - 4X_0X_2^3$$

When $m > 3$, similar but more complicated relations can be found but it may be simpler in such cases, or even if $m < 3$, to determine the discriminant by differentiation and elimination of p.

b. Calculate

$$f_x + pf_y = 0 \tag{3}$$

where the subscripts mean partial derivatives. Provided that $f_y \neq 0$, a factor of $\Delta_p = 0$ is a singular solution, if it simultaneously satisfies (1), (2), and (3).

10-2. The C-discriminant. The procedure of this section can be used as an alternative or a supplement to that of **10-1**. In either case, the general solution of (1) is first required. Suppose that some of the methods of preceding sections have been used to get a general solution of (1)

$$F(x, y, C) = 0 \tag{4}$$

Differentiate it partially with respect to C; that is, assume C to be a variable parameter rather than a constant. Write the result as

$$F_C(x, y, C) = 0 \tag{5}$$

and eliminate C between (4) and (5). The *C-discriminant relation* is obtained, $\Delta_C = 0$. Note, that C here does not mean a partial derivative. The C-discriminant relation will usually be a product of two or more factors. Test each to see if it satisfies the differential equation. If it does, it is either a singular solution or a special case of the general solution. If this section has been preceded by the work of **10-1**, the singular solution found there will again appear in Δ_C. The present section thus furnishes a check on the earlier calculations.

If a factor in Δ_C fails to satisfy the differential equation, it may or may not duplicate a similar function found by **10-1**. For further information about such functions, see **10-3**.

It is often convenient to calculate Δ_C as follows. Write (4), if possible, in the form

$$A_0(x, y)C^m + A_1(x, y)C^{m-1} + \ldots + A_m(x, y) = 0$$

Then, for $m = 2$ or $m = 3$, use the equations of **10-1a**, replacing X_i by A_i. There is no equation analogous to (3) for the C-discriminant.

10-3. Singular Solutions and Associated Curves. There is no generally accepted definition of a singular solution and at least three have been used by different writers:

i. A function which satisfies the differential equation but which cannot be obtained by assigning a special value to the arbitrary constant in the general solution.

ii. An envelope to the family of curves given by the general solution of the differential equation.

iii. A solution of the equation which occurs in Δ_p. In this book, definition **i** is used. If conclusions followed are compared with those in other books, discrepancies may occur unless the same definition has been used in each case.

Two discriminant relations will result, if the work of both **10-1** and **10-2** has been completed. Each will generally be a product of two or more functions. Its factors may describe curves of three different kinds: a singular solution, a particular solution, a function which does not satisfy the differential equation. These three cases are conveniently discussed in geometric terms. If uninterested in the details, skip the rest of this section and go to **10-3-1**.

Let the given differential equation be (1) and let its general solution be (4). If (1) is of first order and first degree, its solution describes a family of plane curves. A single curve of this family is completely identified when a definite value is assigned to the constant C. The differential equation itself, when solved for $p = dy/dx$, fixes the slope of the tangent to any curve of the family at a chosen point. Singular points, where the slope becomes indeterminate, require special treatment; see **A1-11-2**. Otherwise, only one curve of the family will pass through any chosen point and there will be a unique slope at that point.

On the other hand, when (1) is still of first order, but of degree $m \geqslant 2$, there will be m slopes at a given point and m curves, as specified by (4), may intersect at that point. In algebraic terms, both (1) and (4) are polynomials of degree m, the first in the variable p and the second in C. Each of these polynomials must have m roots but there need not be m *different* roots in either case, so there may be less than m curves or slopes at a selected point. An indeterminate slope at a particular point is temporarily excluded; see **d** and **e** for such cases. Equality of roots is recognized in algebra by the vanishing of the discriminant. The appropriate equations for $m = 2, 3$ have been given in **10-1** and **10-2**. An alternative method, based on calculus, has also been given in **10-1b**.

The existence of singular solutions and the other functions that might have arisen by the methods of **10-1** and **10-2** depends on the unusual behavior when there are two or more equal roots for p and C. This is the reason for calculating both discriminants. The possible consequences are described in the following sections.

a. The envelope. If a curve is tangent to some member of the family (4) at every point, it is the *envelope* of the family. The slope of the envelope is the same as the slope of the integral curves at the points of common intersection. This situation should thus be revealed by examination of both Δ_p and Δ_C. In some cases, a special solution of the differential equation will also be an envelope. According to our definition, such an envelope would not be called a singular solution.

b. A particular solution. Occasionally, a particular solution of the differential equation will appear in both discriminants. As C in (4) varies, it may reach a certain value at which the integral curves approach a limiting slope, different in value from others in the family. At the same time, a special curve may intersect all other members of the family at the same point, so that an infinite number of curves meet there. A smaller number of curves than usual will pass through any other point on the particular curve. The equation for this special curve will thus appear in both Δ_p and Δ_C and, in fact, three times in the former but only once in the latter. Such properties often make it possible to identify the situation from the two discriminants; see also **10-3-1**. Confirmation of the conclusion, of course, comes from the fact that the particular solution is fixed by some special value of C in the general solution. As explained in **a**, a particular solution which is also an envelope is not regarded here as a singular solution.

c. Tac locus. Suppose that two curves of a family are tangent to each other at some point. This means that there will be two equal values of p, a fact which will be revealed if Δ_p is examined. On the other hand, Δ_C will show nothing about this behavior since the proper number of curves pass through the point of intersection. Such a point is called a *tac point*; the locus of these points is a *tac locus*. It should be noted that there may be three types of tac points: the two touching curves can have the same curvature; they can have opposite curvatures; a point of inflection can occur for one curve at the tac point. The nature of the tac locus can be investigated by a study of the equation

$$p^2 F_{yy} + 2p F_{xy} + F_{xx} = 0$$

where p is the direction of the tangent at the tac point and the subscripts indicate partial derivatives of the general solution (4).

As in other cases, the tac locus can play more than one role. Thus, it could also be an envelope but, in that case, we would not consider it to be a singular solution. If the same integral curve is determined by two different values of C, the equation of this curve will also be a tac locus. Moreover, a nodal locus, see **d**, of the slopes will generally be a tac locus of the integral curves.

d. Nodal locus. In some cases, a singular point may occur on each of the integral curves. There, the slope takes the indeterminate form $0/0$, but the methods of calculus can be used to evaluate the tangents to the curve. If there are k tangents to the curve at some point, it is a *multiple point* of order k. The simplest case is that with $k = 2$ and there are three possibilities. The singular point itself can be found from the conditions $F(x, y, C) = 0$; $F_x = 0$; $F_y = 0$. Calculate also $\phi(x, y) = F^2_{xy} - F_{xx} F_{yy}$. If $\phi > 0$, the point is a *node*, also called a *crunode*; if $\phi = 0$, it is a *cusp*, see **e**; if $\phi < 0$, the tangents are imaginary and the point is called *conjugate*. The last case, and those with $k > 2$, will not be discussed here.

When $\phi(x, y) > 0$ at a singular point, there are two real and unequal tangents, so two branches of the curve cross at that point. In such a case, two consecutive curves of the integral family will intersect at three different points. In the limit when consecutive curves approach coincidence, two points of intersection approach the crossing point of the curves and a *nodal locus* results. The third point of intersection becomes the envelope of the family.

The nodal locus will appear twice in Δ_C, corresponding to the two branches of the curve. The tangents of each are different, so the nodal locus will not occur in Δ_p. In unusual cases, it is also possible for the nodal locus to be an envelope, thus also a singular solution. As explained in **c**, a tac locus commonly exists when the integral curves contain nodes.

e. Cuspidal locus. Suppose that the three points of intersection in **d** coincide. The node has become a *cusp*, also called a spinode, keratoid cusp, or cusp of the first kind. The position of the singular point is determined as in **d**, but with $\phi(x, y) = 0$. There are two real, equal values of the slope and the curve recedes from the point of tangency in one direction. The two branches of it, however, are on opposite side of the common tangent. The cuspidal locus will appear three times in Δ_C, since three loci coincide there. It will normally appear only once in Δ_p, because there are two equal values of the slope. Sometimes, but not in the usual case, the cuspidal locus may also be an envelope, thus a singular solution.

There are other kinds of cusps but they can occur only with multiple points of order greater than two; see **d**.

10-3-1. Summary on Singular Solutions. It is assumed that the calculations of both **10-1** and **10-2** have been performed. Two discriminant relations will thus be available. Each will usually be a product of two or more functions. Compare Δ_p with Δ_C and it will often be true that both contain one or more factors in common but they are not always raised to the same power in the two discriminants. Use symbols, as follows, to designate the possible functions: a singular solution or envelope, E; a particular solution, P; a tac locus, T; a nodal locus, N; a cuspidal locus, K. The two discriminant relations will then have the following forms

$$\Delta_p(x, y) = EP^3T^2K = 0$$

$$\Delta_C(x, y) = EPN^2K^3 = 0$$

These equations may often serve to determine the meaning of each factor. If a function belongs to more than one category, it will be repeated the proper number of times. Thus, an envelope which is also a cuspidal locus will occur twice in Δ_p and four times in Δ_C.

The correct interpretation of the discriminant relations is not always easy and incorrect conclusions are often reached. The following comments may be helpful.

a. Do not cancel out any functions of the variables in calculating the discriminants. Constant factors, however, may be discarded.

b. A singular solution is an unusual case, rather than the general case. Solve $f(x, y, p) = 0$ and $f_p = 0$ to get the functions $y = f_1(x)$, $p = f_2(x)$. In order for $f_1(x)$ to be a solution of the differential equation, hence a singular solution, it is necessary that $f_2(x) = df_1/dx$. Such a relation cannot be expected to hold in general.

c. No cuspidal or nodal loci can occur for a differential equation which has families of straight lines or conic sections for a general solution.

d. The general solution of a differential equation can often be given in several different equivalent forms. It sometimes happens that the C-discriminant will give the singular solution with one form, but not with another. This difficulty would be avoided if both discriminants were studied.

e. The two equations of this section are said to give correct results always if the degree of the differential equation is two or three. A number of examples, where they appear to give incorrect conclusions, are discussed by Piaggio. Some of his examples have degree greater than three; some have degree of three or less. Note, however, that he regards *any* envelope as a singular solution, which is equivalent to the definition here in **10-3ii**.

f. Some equations of the preceding sections are completely general; others apply only if the two discriminants are polynomials. If the degree of the differential equation is finite, Δ_p will be a polynomial in p. On the other hand, the coefficients of p and its powers are unrestricted so Δ_C need not be a polynomial. If either Δ_p or Δ_C contain transcendental functions, see **11**, the singular solutions may be much more complicated than those which have been discussed here. Such cases have been treated by Hill.

11. The Equation Is Transcendental in dy/dx

The general equation is $f(x, y, P) = 0$, where P is some transcendental function of $p = dy/dx$. Typical cases are $\ln p$, e^p, $\cos p$, $\sin p$, etc. The differential equation is of infinite degree since the expansion of P would yield an infinite series in p.

Such equations are not common and they seldom arise in problems of applied mathematics. Some of the preceding methods are directly applicable to equations of this type. As another possibility, seek a change of variable to convert P into p and then use one of the methods of this part. Some examples of such differential equations will be found in Part II.

B. THE DIFFERENTIAL EQUATION IS OF SECOND ORDER

<hr>

The general equation is $F(x, y, y', y'') = 0$. If the second derivative is missing, return to **A**; if derivatives occur of order higher than two, refer to **C**.

Writing the equation as $y'' = f(x, y, y')$, it is often useful to replace the second-order equation by a system of two first-order equations $y' = z$; $y'' = dz/dx = f(x, y, z)$. Suppose that the system can be solved to get $y = g(x); z = h(x)$; it then follows that

$$g'(x) = h(x); \quad h'(x) = f[x, g(x), h(x)]$$

$$g''(x) = f[x, g(x), g'(x)]$$

and $y = g(x)$ is the solution of the given second-order equation. It should be noted that the decomposition of a single equation into a system of equations is not unique.

This book does not contain methods for solving systems of equations. They are frequently convenient when matrix algebra is to be used, for numerical solutions of equations, and for the study of properties of differential equations. Suitable references are Frazer, Duncan, and Collar; Ince-1; Kaplan-1 and Kaplan-2.

There are two types of second-order equations. Classify the given equation and proceed as directed.

a. The linear equation. It is of the first degree in the dependent variable and both derivatives

$$A_0(x)y'' + A_1(x)y' + A_2(x)y = f(x)$$

One or all of the coefficients $A_i(x)$ and $f(x)$ may be constants; any of them may vanish except A_0. Consult **B1**.

b. The nonlinear equation. This is the general equation of order two but not of type **a**; see **B2**.

B1. THE LINEAR EQUATION OF SECOND ORDER

The general equation is

$$A_0(x)y'' + A_1(x)y' + A_2(x)y = f(x) \tag{1}$$

For some properties of it and of its solutions, see **c**. There are two main cases; see **a** and **b**.

a. The homogeneous equation. In this case, $f(x) = 0$. The word *homogeneous* is used with a different meaning from that of **A1-8**. There, it refers to the homogeneous form of the coefficients; see also **B2-3**. Here, it suggests the similarity to a set of simultaneous homogeneous linear algebraic equations. The equation is also said to be reduced or without second member. Refer to **1** and following sections until a suitable method is found.

b. The nonhomogeneous equation. In this case $f(x) \neq 0$. The equation is complete, nonhomogeneous, inhomogeneous, not reduced, or with a second member. If the corresponding homogeneous equation can be solved, it is possible, at least in principle, to solve the nonhomogeneous equation. Assume temporarily that $f(x) = 0$, solve the resulting homogeneous equation by one of the following methods, and then refer to **12**. The general solution of the related homogeneous equation is the *complementary function* of the nonhomogeneous equation.

c. General properties of the linear equation. With appropriate restrictions on the coefficients in (1), there are existence theorems, see Introduction-3, guaranteeing that the differential equation has a unique solution in the neighborhood of some point (x_0, y_0). The solution also satisfies the conditions $y(x_0) = y_0$, $y'(x_0) = y_0'$. Since, within wide limits, the point (x_0, y_0) is arbitrary, the two constants y_0 and y_0' can be taken as the two integration constants in the general solution of the differential equation.

Some further properties of the equation and its solutions follow. For more details and proofs of them, as well as more exact statements about the existence theorems, see appropriate references in the Bibliography. Especially recommended are Coddington and Levinson, Ince-1.

i. The general solution of the homogeneous equation. Let y_1, y_2 be linearly independent solutions of the homogeneous equation

$$A_0(x)y'' + A_1(x)y' + A_2(x)y = 0 \tag{2}$$

Its general solution is

$$y = C_1 y_1 + C_2 y_2 \tag{3}$$

where C_1, C_2 are arbitrary constants. Every solution of (2) is contained in (3).

ii. The solution of the nonhomogeneous equation. Let $F(x)$ be any special solution of (1) and let $Y(x) = C_1 y_1 + C_2 y_2$ be the general solution of (2). Then, the general solution of (1) is $y = Y(x) + F(x)$. The solution $Y(x)$ is the *complementary function* of (1).

iii. Linear independence. Suppose that y_1 and y_2 are two special solutions of (2). They may, or may not, be linearly independent. To test this property, calculate the *Wronskian*, a determinant of second order,

$$W(y_1, y_2) = \begin{vmatrix} y_1 & y_2 \\ y_1' & y_2' \end{vmatrix}$$

There are two possibilities.

$W(y_1, y_2) \neq 0$. The two functions are linearly independent, see **i**, hence the general solution of (2) is given by (3).

$W(y_1, y_2) = 0$. The two functions are not linearly independent and there is a relation $C_1 y_1 + C_2 y_2 = 0$. One function is thus a multiple of the other and the general solution of (2) has not yet been obtained. For one method of finding a second linearly independent solution, see **4-1-1**.

iv. Fundamental basis or set of solutions. The two linearly independent solutions of (2) are said to form a *fundamental set* of solutions or a *basis*. When either is multiplied by an arbitrary constant, a fundamental set again results; hence there is an infinite number of such sets. One is of special interest. It is that with $y_1(x_0) = 1$, $y_1'(x_0) = 0$; $y_2(x_0) = 0$, $y_2'(x_0) = 1$; $W(y_1, y_2) = 1$. In such a case, the first solution has zero slope and unit value at $x = x_0$, with x_0 frequently taken as the origin of a coordinate system. The second solution has zero value and unit slope at x_0.

v. Constants of integration. Given $y = f(x, C_1, C_2)$ as the solution of a second-order equation, the constants are independent if

$$\begin{vmatrix} \dfrac{\partial f}{\partial C_1} & \dfrac{\partial f}{\partial C_2} \\ \dfrac{\partial^2 f}{\partial C_1 \partial x} & \dfrac{\partial^2 f}{\partial C_2 \partial x} \end{vmatrix} \neq 0$$

1. The Linear Homogeneous Equation with Constant Coefficients

The general equation is

$$y'' + a_1 y' + a_2 y = 0 \tag{1}$$

where a_1, a_2 are constants. Either or both may be zero and, in that case, the equation is also of type **B2-2**. However, the methods of this section are probably simpler. If the coefficient of y'' is a constant other than unity, divide the other coefficients by that number so that the standard form results.

If the right-hand side of (1) is a constant not equal to zero, or even a function of x, disregard this fact, solve the resulting homogeneous equation, and then refer to **12**.

Equations like (1) are often presented in symbolic form as

$$(D^2 + a_1 D + a_2)y = 0 \tag{2}$$

where $D = d/dx$ is a differential operator; see also **5-2** and **6**.

To solve (1), determine the roots of the quadratic equation

$$r^2 + a_1 r + a_2 = 0 \tag{3}$$

This is the *auxiliary* or *characteristic equation*. The roots of (3), r_1 and r_2, are the *characteristic roots* of the differential equation and $(r_1 + r_2) = -a_1$; $r_1 r_2 = a_2$. There are three possibilities.

a. $r_1 \neq r_2$ and both are real. The discriminant, $\Delta = (a_1{}^2 - 4a_2) > 0$. The general solution of (1) is

$$y = C_1 e^{r_1 x} + C_2 e^{r_2 x} \tag{4}$$

In some physical problems, it is desirable to use hyperbolic functions. There are several equivalent forms.

i. Suppose, as a special case, that $r_1 = -r_2 = r$. The general solution of (1) is

$$y = A \cosh rx + B \sinh rx \tag{5}$$

$$A = C_1 + C_2; \quad B = C_1 - C_2 \tag{6}$$

For alternative forms, see **ii** and **iii**; if $r_1 \neq -r_2$, see **iv**.

ii. A solution equivalent to (5) is

$$y = A_1 \cosh (rx + B_1)$$

where $A_1{}^2 = A^2 - B^2$. $\tanh B_1 = B/A$.

iii. Another form of the solution is

$$y = A_2 \sinh(rx + B_2)$$

where $A_2{}^2 = B^2 - A^2$, $\tanh B_2 = -B/A$.

iv. If $r_1 \neq -r_2$, as was assumed in **i**, **ii**, and **iii**, let $r_1 = a+b$ $r_2 = a-b$, where a, b are two real numbers. The general solution of the equation is then

$$y = e^{ax}(A \cosh bx + B \sinh bx)$$

with A, B as given in (6).

b. $r_1 = r_2 = r$; $\Delta = (a_1{}^2 - 4a_2) = 0$. The general solution is

$$y = e^{rx}(C_1 + C_2 x)$$

c. $r_1 \neq r_2$ and both are complex numbers; $\Delta = (a_1{}^2 - 4a_2) < 0$. Take $r_1 = a+ib$, $r_2 = a-ib$, where a, b are real numbers. The general solution is

$$y = e^{ax}(A \cos bx + B \sin bx)$$

The integration constants are related to those of **a**, for $A = C_1 + C_2$, $B = i(C_1 - C_2)$. As in that case, alternative solutions are often desired.

i. $y = A_1 e^{ax} \cos (bx + B_1)$; $A_1{}^2 = A^2 + B^2$, $A_1 \cos B_1 = A$, $A_1 \sin B_1 = -B$, $\tan B_1 = B/A$.

ii. $y = A_2 e^{ax} \sin (bx + B_2)$; $A_2{}^2 = A^2 + B^2$, $A_2 \sin B_2 = A$, $A_2 \cos B_2 = B$, $\tan B_2 = A/B$.

2. The Linear Homogeneous Equation with Variable Coefficients

The general equation is

$$A_0(x)y'' + A_1(x)y' + A_2(x)y = 0$$

or, alternatively,

$$y'' + P(x)y' + Q(x)y = 0$$

Read the following for suggestions about procedures.

a. A term $f(x)$ or $R(x)$ occurs in the preceding equations. Ignore it, solve the related homogeneous equation as directed in this section, and then refer to **12**.

b. All of the coefficients are constants, return to **1**. The constant zero is permitted for every term except A_0.

c. Proceed with this section if $A_1(x)$ or $P(x)$ equals zero but $A_2(x)$ or $Q(x)$ is a function of x.

d. If $A_2(x)$ or $Q(x)$ vanish, consult **B2-1-2**.

e. See **3**; the equation may be reducible to case **b**.

f. None of the preceding cases occur. It is likely that several methods could be used, possible that one is much easier than the others for a given equation, and probable that no simple solution exists. Consider each of the following before deciding which to try.

i. See **B2-3** for different types of homogeneity. The word now refers to the definition of **A1-8**, not that of **1**.

ii. Seek one or more variable transformations so that the equation can be solved; see **4**.

iii. Test the equation for exactness or look for an integrating factor; see **5**.

iv. See **6** for a symbolic method which may apply in certain cases.

v. Refer to **7**. A solution in some infinite form is probably required if all of the preceding methods have failed or have seemed unsatisfactory.

3. Equations Reducible to Type 1

If the special cases **a**, **b**, **c**, **d** of **2** do not apply, compare the given equation with the two types of this section. If they are inapplicable, return to **2f**.

3-1. The Euler Equation.   Its form is

$$x^2 y'' + a_1 x y' + a_2 y = 0 \tag{1}$$

where a_1, a_2 are constants. It is also called the *Cauchy linear equation*, the *linear equidimensional equation*, or the *general homogeneous linear equation*, where the word homogeneous refers to the meaning of **A1-8**; see also **B2-3**.

Let $y(x) = u(z)$, $z = \ln x$ and (1) becomes

$$u''(z) + (a_1 - 1)u' + a_2 u = 0$$

which is type **1**. If r_1 and r_2 are the roots of the auxiliary or characteristic equation

$$r^2 + (a_1 - 1)r + a_2 = 0$$

there are three cases, as in **1**. Alternative solutions, as shown there and omitted here, may be found. For another procedure, not necessarily to be preferred, see **B2-3-2, 3-5**.

a. $r_1 \neq r_2$; $y = C_1 x^{r_1} + C_2 x^{r_2}$

b. $r_1 = r_2 = r$; $y = x^r(C_1 + C_2 \ln x)$

c. $r_1 \neq r_2$, $r_1 = a + ib$, $r_2 = a - ib$, where a, b are real numbers; $y = x^a[C_1 \cos (b \ln x) + C_2 \sin (b \ln x)]$.

Operator methods are often useful in this case, especially for the non-homogeneous equation; see **12-2**. With $z = \ln x$, let $D = d/dz$, $xy' = u'(z) = Du$, $x^2 y'' = D(D-1)u$, and (1) becomes

$$[D^2 + (a_1 - 1)D + a_2]u = (D - r_1)(D - r_2)u = 0$$

Alternatively, define the operator $x\,d/dx = \theta$, $x^2 d^2/dx^2 = \theta(\theta - 1)$, and get

$$[\theta^2 + (a_1 - 1)\theta + a_2]y = (\theta - r_1)(\theta - r_2)y = 0$$

3.2. The Legendre Linear Equation. This case is

$$(a+bx)^2y'' + a_1(a+bx)y' + a_2y = 0 \tag{2}$$

If $a = 0$, $b = 1$, it becomes type **3-1**. There are two procedures.

a. Let $y(x) = u(z)$, $z = a + bx$ and the result is

$$z^2u''(z) + b_1zu' + b_2u = 0$$

It has become type **3-1**, with $b_1 = a_1/b$, $b_2 = a_2/b^2$.

b. Let $y(x) = u(z)$, $z = \ln(a + bx)$. The new equation is

$$u''(z) + b_1u' + b_2u = 0$$

It is type **1**, with $b_1 = (a_1 - b)/b$, $b_2 = a_2/b^2$.

4. Transformations of the Linear Equation

The given equation is not one of the types in **3**, which were reduced to a simpler case. Attempt to transform the general linear equation so that it can be treated in a similar way. For most practical purposes, the new equation should be one of the following types:

    i. An equation with constant coefficients; see **1**.

    ii. The Euler equation or the Legendre equation; see **3**.

    iii. An equation with dependent variable missing; see **B2-1**.

Consult the various parts of this section for detailed procedures.

If appropriate transformations are not found after some study, refer in turn to **5** and **6**, for these methods may apply in some cases. When they, too, are discouraging, reconsider the use of a new variable but look for it according to the more formal methods of **9**.

4-1. A New Dependent Variable. Take the standard form of the equation as

$$y'' + P(x)y' + Q(x)y = 0 \tag{1}$$

For an alternative form, see **4-1-3**. When $P(x)$ and $Q(x)$ are given in explicit form, a new trial variable may be suggested. In the more general case, try each of the following.

a. Let $y' = y(x)\,u(x)$, so that (1) becomes

$$u'(x) + u^2 + Pu + Q = 0$$

This is a Riccati equation; see **A1-3**. Little has been gained by the transformation for the new equation may be as difficult to solve as the old one, unless it is an integrable case of the Riccati equation.

b. Assume $y(x) = u(x)v(x)$. Then, $y' = uv' + u'v$, $y'' = uv'' + 2u'v' + u''v$, and (1) becomes

$$u'' + p(x)u' + q(x)u = 0 \tag{2}$$

where $vp(x) = 2v' + Pv$, $vq(x) = v'' + Pv' + Qv$. The general form of the new equation is the same as that of (1) but the coefficients are different. Consult the following sections, to see if (2) can be solved.

4-1-1. One or More Particular Integrals Known. If a particular integral of (1) can be found by inspection or otherwise, see **a**. If two linearly independent solutions are known, the general solution follows immediately; see **B1ci**. Suggestions for finding particular integrals are given in **b**.

a. Suppose that $v(x) = y_1$ is a particular integral of (1). Then, (2) becomes

$$y_1 u'' + (2y_1' + Py_1)u' = 0$$

This is a first-order equation of separable type, see **A1-1-2**, if the variables are taken as $u'(x)$ and x. The general solution of (1), after two quadratures, is

$$y = y_1[C_1 + C_2 \int X(x)dx]$$
$$X(x) = e^{-\phi}/y_1^2; \quad \phi(x) = \int P(x)dx$$

b. It may not be easy to find a particular integral of (1). The following simple cases and suggestions may be helpful.

  i. If $P(x) + xQ(x) = 0$, $y_1 = x$.

  ii. Seek a number k, such that $k^2 + kP + Q = 0$. If it exists, $y_1 = e^{kx}$.

  iii. Set $x = 0$ in (1) and solve the resulting equation if possible, for $y = y_1$.

  iv. Set $x = \infty$ in (1). If the result can be solved, its solution is $y = y_1$.

  v. Assume a polynomial solution, $y_1 = a_0 + a_1 x + \ldots + a_n x^n$. Sometimes, there are enough relations to determine the a_i, if there is a particular solution of this kind.

  vi. See **4-1-3** for further suggestions.

4-1-2. The Normal Form of the Equation. Choose $v(x)$ in **4-1b** so that (2) lacks a term in u'. This is the *normal* or *canonical* form of the differential equation

$$u''(x) + I(x)u(x) = 0 \tag{3}$$

The quantity $I(x)$ is the *invariant* of (1). It follows that

$$v(x) = \exp[-\tfrac{1}{2}\int P(x)dx] \tag{4}$$
$$I(x) = Q - \tfrac{1}{2}P' - \tfrac{1}{4}P^2 \tag{5}$$

It is usually easier to find a special solution of (3) by inspection, or otherwise, than it is to find a special solution of (1). The normal form can also be obtained with a new independent variable; see **4-2-1b**.

When (3) has been solved, the general solution of (1) is known as soon as $v(x)$ is determined from (4). If $I(x)$ is a constant, (3) has become type

1; if $I(x)$ equals a constant divided by x^2, (3) has become type **3-1**.

The following properties of the normal form are often useful.

i. Let the given equation be

$$Y'' + p(x)Y' + q(x)Y = 0 \tag{6}$$

with an invariant $I_1(x)$. Further, suppose that $I_1(x) = I(x)$, where $I(x)$ is the corresponding invariant of (1). It follows that (1) can be transformed into (6) by the relations $y = Yw(x)$, $w(x) = \exp\left[\frac{1}{2}\int(p-P)dx\right]$. The coefficients in the two equations are also related by the equations $p = 2w'/w + P$, $q = w''/w + Pw'/w + Q$.

ii. Suppose that $I(x)$ and $I_1(x)$ are polynomials, both of the same degree in x, but with different numerical coefficients. Equate coefficients of equal powers of x and, if a solution of (6) is known, that of (1) is obtained at once, or the reverse.

iii. Let $u_1(x)$ and $u_2(x)$ be two linearly independent solutions of (3), so that two solutions of (3) are

$$y_i(x) = u_i(x) \exp\left[\tfrac{1}{2}\int P(x)dx\right]$$

where $i = 1, 2$. It follows that $u_1/u_2 = y_1/y_2 = s(x)$. The differential equation satisfied by $s(x)$ is nonlinear and of third order

$$\frac{s'''}{s'} - \frac{3}{2}\left(\frac{s''}{s'}\right)^2 = 2I(x)$$

The left-hand side of this equation, commonly denoted by the symbol $\{s, x\}$ is called the *Schwartzian derivative*. It will usually be difficult to solve but suppose that some particular integral can be found. Then, $u_2'/u_2 = -s''/2s'$. Here, the variables are separable, so that $u_2\sqrt{s'} = C$. A second solution is $u_1 = u_2 s = Cs/\sqrt{s'}$. Two linearly independent solutions of (3) are now known and the general solution of (1) follows.

4-1-3. Special Cases of Dependent Variable Transformations
Some specific forms for the new variable $v(x)$ are given in this section. They may be most useful for purposes of reference, but see **d**. The necessary algebraic manipulations are usually easier if the standard form of the equation is taken as

$$A_0(x)y'' + A_1(x)y' + A_2(x)y = 0 \tag{7}$$

With $y(x) = u(x)v(x)$, it becomes

$$B_0(x)u'' + B_1(x)u' + B_2(x)u = 0 \tag{8}$$

The new coefficients are

$$B_0 = A_0 v; \quad B_1 = 2A_0 v' + A_1 v; \quad B_2 = A_0 v'' + A_1 v' + A_2 v$$

If (1) is preferred as the standard form, see **4-1b**.

Examine the following cases to see if (8) is easier to solve than (7). Reread **4**, if necessary for further advice.

a.
$$v = ax^k$$
$$xv' = kv, \quad x^2v'' = k(k-1)v$$
$$B_0 = x^2A_0, \quad B_1 = x(2kA_0 + xA_1), \quad B_2 = k(k-1)A_0 + kxA_1 + x^2A_2$$

b.
$$v = \exp[k\phi(x)]$$
$$v' = k\phi'v, \quad v'' = k(\phi'' + k\phi'^2)v$$
$$B_0 = A_0, \quad B_1 = 2k\phi'A_0 + A_1, \quad B_2 = k(\phi'' + k\phi'^2)A_0 + k\phi'A_1 + A_2$$

c.
$$v = e^{kx}$$
$$v' = kv, \quad v'' = k^2v$$
$$B_0 = A_0, \quad B_1 = 2kA_0 + A_1, \quad B_2 = k^2A_0 + kA_1 + A_2$$

This is the special case of **b**, where $\phi(x) = x$.

d. If the forms of A_i are such that B_2 can be made to vanish in any of the preceding cases, the equation has become

$$B_0(x)u'' + B_1(x)u' = 0$$

which is case **B2-1-2**. Its solution will be similar to that in **4-1-1a**, since $v(x) = y_1$ is a particular integral of (1) or (8).

4-2. A New Independent Variable. Take the original equation in the standard form (1), let $y(x) = u(z)$ with some relation $f(x, z) = 0$ defining a new independent variable, and get the transformed equation

$$u'' + p(z)u' + q(z)u = 0 \tag{9}$$

Relations between $P(x)$, $p(z)$ and $Q(x)$, $q(z)$ are given in **4-2-2**, for the general case and for certain special cases.

Any desired value could be assigned to $p(z)$ and the new variable determined by the relation between $p(z)$ and $P(x)$. Similarly, $q(z)$ could be chosen and the new variable determined. For practical purposes, the transformed equation should be one of the types listed in **4**. Such cases are considered in **4-2-1**; see also **4-2-2**.

4-2-1. Special Cases of Independent Variable Transformation. Try **a** and **b**. If neither is helpful, proceed to **4-2-2**.

a. Calculate the quantity $[2PQ + Q']/Q^{3/2}$. If it equals a constant, including zero, see **i** or **ii**; if it is a function of x, go to **b**.

i. The new variable $z = k \int \sqrt{Q(x)}dx$ will convert (1) into a linear equation in $u(z)$ and z, with constant coefficients, type **1**. The constant k is arbitrary; it can be taken as unity or any other nonzero value as convenient.

ii. The new variable $\ln z = k \int \sqrt{Q(x)}dx$ will convert (1) into an Euler equation, type **3-1**. There seems to be no advantage in this case over **i**, which would usually be chosen.

b. Let $z = \int e^{-\phi}dx$, $\phi(x) = \int P(x)dx$. The transformed equation is the normal form, $u''(z) + q(z)u = 0$. It may be integrable; see **4-1-2**.

4-2-2. General Relations for Independent Variable Transforformation.

If the special cases of **4-2-1** were unsuccessful, it is likely that a suitable new variable will be found only by the more elaborate methods of **9**. This section is included primarily for reference. Glance through it to see if some transformation of variable is suggested. If not, go to **4-3**.

Choose the standard form as (7); let $y(x) = u(z)$, with $f(x, z) = 0$. The new equation is

$$B_0(z)u'' + B_1(z)u' + B_2(z)u = 0$$

It is sometimes easier to solve $f(x, z) = 0$ and get $z = f_1(x)$; at other times, $x = f_2(z)$ is easier. Let $z_x = df_1/dx$, $z_{xx} = d^2f_1/dx^2$; $x_z = df_2/dz$, $x_{zz} = d^2f_2/dz^2$. For the general case, use either **a** or **b**, whichever seems simpler. For some special cases, see **c**.

a.

$$y' = z_x u', \quad y'' = z_x^2 u'' + z_{xx}u'$$
$$B_0 = z_x^2 A_0, \quad B_1 = z_{xx}A_0 + z_x A_1, \quad B_2 = A_2$$

b.

$$x_z y' = u', \quad x_z^3 y'' = x_z u'' - x_{zz}u'$$
$$B_0 = x_z A_0, \quad B_1 = x_z^2 A_1 - x_{zz}A_0, \quad B_2 = x_z^3 A_2$$

c. A few special cases, which are frequently useful, are the following.

i.

$$z = ax^k, \quad z_x = kz/x, \quad z_{xx} = k(k-1)z/x^2$$
$$B_0 = k^2 z^2 A_0(z)/x^2, \quad B_1 = kz[(k-1)A_0/x^2 + A_1/x], \quad B_2 = A_2$$

ii.

$$z = 1/x, \quad z_x = -z^2, \quad z_{xx} = 2z^3$$
$$B_0 = z^4 A_0(z), \quad B_1 = z^2(2zA_0 - A_1), \quad B_2 = A_2$$

iii.

$$x = z^2$$
$$B_0 = zA_0(z), \quad B_1 = 2z^2 A_1 - A_0, \quad B_2 = 4z^3 A_2$$

This is a special case of **i**, known as the quadratic transformation; see also **9-5-1**.

4-3.   Two New Variables.   Let the new variables be defined with the equations $x = f(z, u)$, $y = g(z, u)$ and it follows that $y' = g'(z)/f'(z)$; $y''(x) = [f'(z)g''(z) - f''(z)g'(z)]/[f'(z)]^3$. An especially simple case is that where the dependent and independent variables are exchanged. The appropriate equations are $y'(x) = 1/x'(y)$; $y''(x) = -x''(y)/x'^3(y)$.

New variables are often suggested by some prominent combination of x and y in the given equation. Polar coordinates are often suitable. In that case,

$$x = r \cos \theta, \quad y = r \sin \theta, \quad y'(x) = R \tan \theta(r' + r \cot \theta)$$

$$y'' = R^3 \sec^3\theta(r^2 + 2r'^2 - rr'')$$

where

$$r' = dr/d\theta, \quad r'' = d^2r/d\theta^2, \quad R = (r' - r \tan \theta)^{-1}$$

A more formal method of finding the new variable is possible in principle, but it may not be easy to apply. Given an equation like (1), suppose that a solution of (9) is known. Let the respective invariants of these equations, see **4-1-2**, be $I(x)$ and $J(z)$. There are two relations between them

$$I(x) - \tfrac{1}{2}\{z, x\} = J\left(\frac{dz}{dx}\right)^2; \quad ye^{\phi_1}\sqrt{z_x} = ue^{\phi_2}$$

where $\phi_1 = \tfrac{1}{2} \int P dx$, $\phi_2 = \tfrac{1}{2} \int p dz$ and $\{z, x\}$ is the Schwartzian derivative; see **4-1-2**. The first equation fixes the independent variable; the second one, the dependent variable. Unfortunately, the first equation is non-linear and of third order. It may be difficult to solve. A suitable choice of $J(z)$ might help; the simplest one is probably $J(z) = 0$. Unless there are special reasons to use this procedure, it may be wiser to try **5** or some later method.

5. The Exact Equation

The standard form of the equation can be taken as

$$A_0(x)y'' + A_1(x)y' + A_2(x)y = 0 \tag{1}$$

Test it for exactness; see **5-1**. If the test fails, seek an integrating factor according to **5-2**.

5-1.   Test for Exactness.   The linear equation (1) is exact if

$$A_0'' - A_1' + A_2 = 0$$

If this relation does not hold, go to **5-2**; if it does hold, a first integral of
(1) is
$$B_0 y' + B_1 y = C_1$$
where $B_0 = A_0$, $B_1 = A_1 - A_0'$. Since this first integral is a differential
equation of first order, use a method of **A1** to get the general solution of
(1); see also **4-1-1a**.

If $(B_1 - B_0') = (A_1 - 2A_0') = 0$, the first integral is also exact and, in
that case, see **A1-7**.

When the given differential equation is nonhomogeneous, see **12**, so
that (1) contains a term $f(x)$ on the right-hand side, add a term $\int f(x)dx$
to the right-hand side of the first integral.

5-2. The Integrating Factor. The test for exactness, see **5-1**, has
failed and an integrating factor is to be sought. Every first-order differential equation can be made exact with an integrating factor, if it has a
unique solution; see **A1-7-2**. Such a factor may, or may not, exist for an
equation of order higher than the first. It can sometimes be determined
by inspection. In the general case describe (1) in terms of a *linear differential operator*
$$L = A_0 D^2 + A_1 D + A_2$$
where $D = d/dx$. Then, (1) becomes $L(y) = 0$ or, alternatively, $L(D)y
= 0$, $L_x(y) = 0$, etc. If $u(x)$ is an integrating factor for (1), it follows that
$uL(y)dx$ is a perfect differential. The integrating factor is determined by
the *adjoint equation* to $L(y) = 0$,
$$\bar{L}(u) = (A_0 u)'' - (A_1 u)' + A_2 u = 0$$
which can also be written as
$$A_0 u'' + (2A_0' - A_1)u' + (A_0'' - A_1' + A_2)u = 0$$
The original differential equation and its adjoint are related by the
Lagrange identity
$$uL(y) - y\bar{L}(u) = \frac{d}{dx}[P(y, u)]$$
where the term on the right-hand side, called the *bilinear concomitant*, is
$$P(y, u) = A_0(y'u - yu') + (A_1 - A_0')yu$$

Since the adjoint equation is also of second order, it may be as difficult
to solve as the original equation. Suppose, however, that a solution of
$\bar{L}(u) = 0$ can be found; then the solution of $L(y) = 0$ is given by the
first-order equation $P(y, u) = C$, where C is an arbitrary constant. The
general solution of (1) can thus be found by a method of **A1**.

If two linearly independent solutions, u_1 and u_2, can be found for $\bar{L}(u) = 0$, there will be two first-order equations $P(y, u_1) = C_1$, $P(y, u_2) = C_2$. Elimination of y' between these two equations, by algebraic processes, will give the general solution of (1) as $y(x) = f(u_1, u_2, C_1, C_2)$.

If any special solution y_1 of (1) is known, an integrating factor is

$$u(x) = y_1(x)e^\phi/A_0(x); \quad \phi(x) = \int \frac{A_1(x)}{A_0(x)}dx$$

The general solution of (1) is then, see **4-1-1**,

$$y(x) = y_1(x)[C_1\int X(x)dx + C_2]$$

where $X(x) = e^{-\phi}/y_1^2$.

5-3. Properties of the Adjoint Equation.   The following properties may not be particularly helpful in solving (1). They are, however, of importance in the general study of the linear equation. Many other properties are known; see, for example, Ince-1.

a. The operators L and $\bar{L}$ enjoy a reciprocal relationship. If $\bar{L}$ is the adjoint of L, then L is the adjoint of $\bar{L}$. The corresponding differential equations $L(y) = 0$ and $\bar{L}(u) = 0$ have similar properties.

b. If $L = \bar{L}$, the operators are *self-adjoint*. It is only necessary that $A_1 = A_0'$. If this is true, $(A_0y')' + A_2y = 0$ and the Lagrange identity becomes

$$uL(y) - y\bar{L}(u) = \frac{d}{dx}[A_0(y'u - yu')]$$

c. The equation $L(y) = 0$ can be made self-adjoint, if it is not already so, in three different ways.

   i. Multiply it by $w(x) = e^\phi$, where

$$\phi(x) = \int \frac{(A_1 - A_0')}{A_0}dx$$

   ii. Introduce a new independent variable, $z = \int e^{-\phi}dx$.
   iii. Introduce a new dependent variable, $v(x) = y(x)e^\phi$.

6. Resolution of Operators

Use the differential operator $D = d/dx$, see **5-2**, and take the equation in the form

$$[D^2 + P(x)D + Q(x)]y = 0 \tag{1}$$

Attempt to factor it, so that $(D+u)(D+v)y = 0$. The last form can also be taken as

$$(D+u)\phi = 0; \quad (D+v)y = \phi \tag{2}$$

The first of these equations is $\phi'(x) + u(x)\phi(x) = 0$, which is separable and of first order; see **A1-1-2**. Its solution is

$$\phi(x) = C_1 e^{-\int u(x)dx}$$

The second equation in (2) is linear and of first order, see **A1-2**, $y' + vy = \phi(x)$. Its solution will be the general solution of (1).

This method is simple, when it can be used. In general, the factorization is impracticable. In attempting it, proceed as follows.

a. Seek the two factors by inspection.

b. Assume $u(x)$ and $v(x)$ to be polynomials. When coefficients are equated, it will be found that $(u + v) = P(x)$; $(v' + uv) = Q(x)$. These identities will furnish the coefficients in the assumed polynomials. However, it may be simpler to seek a series solution of the differential equation, see **8**.

c. In the general case, elimination of $u(x)$ in **b** will give a Riccati equation

$$v'(x) + vP(x) - v^2 = Q(x)$$

Since such an equation is seldom easy to solve, see **A1-3**, the method of this section will be successful only in certain special cases.

7. Solution of the Equation in Infinite Form

If this section has been reached, elementary methods have failed and it is unlikely that the equation can be solved in terms of simple functions. Thus, the equation and its solution serve to define new transcendental functions, characterized by various kinds of singular points. Since the differential equation itself is linear there can be fixed singular points but no movable ones; see **A1-10-1**.

There are several possibilities. The one chosen will depend on the purpose for which the solution is wanted, personal preferences, and perhaps other reasons.

a. Series solution, see **8**. The method is reasonably simple; it is given in most elementary texts on differential equations; it may be used with a negligible knowledge of advanced mathematics, such as complex variable theory. Moreover, the solutions frequently involve known series for which numerical tabulations, as well as other properties, are available. Lacking some reason to select another method, this one should normally be chosen.

b. Integral solution; see **10**. Instead of an infinite series, the solution of a differential equation can generally be represented by an integral. There are certain advantages, especially in many branches of applied mathematics, but some knowledge of complex variable theory is usually needed. Often, the point at infinity is a singular point. In such cases, the series solution will probably diverge. The convergence, asymptotic behavior, and other properties of the solution can then frequently be best studied with an integral, rather than a series.

c. Continued fraction solution; see **11**. The method is direct but has not been extended to equations of third or higher order. It requires some knowledge of the properties of infinite continued fractions and this may be an objection.

d. Approximate solution; see **A1-13**. If all other methods fail, this one may be required. In many cases, it may be preferred. Graphical, mechanical, or numerical procedures are possible.

8. Series Solution

The equation is taken in the standard form

$$y'' + P(x)y' + Q(x)y = 0 \tag{1}$$

It is desired to find a solution as an infinite series in powers of x or of $(a-x)$, where a is a constant. Any $x = a$ can be either an ordinary point or a singular point; see **A1-10-1**. In the latter case, there are two possibilities. If the singular point for $P(x)$ is a pole of order one or less and that for $Q(x)$ is a pole of order no greater than two, the singularity is called *regular*. Any other kind of singular point is *irregular*.

These properties of the differential equation can be determined by inspection when the point of interest is at $x = a < \infty$. To study the behavior at $x = \infty$, use new variables $y(x) = u(z)$, $z = 1/x$, so that (1) becomes

$$u''(z) + p(z)u' + q(z)u = 0$$

where

$$p(z) = 2/z - P(z)/z^2; \quad q(z) = Q(z)/z^4$$

Test this transformed equation at $z = 0$. If it is an ordinary point, regular singular point, irregular singular point, respectively, then $x = \infty$ has the same property.

It is sometimes simpler to use the symbol $O(x^{-m})$. Consider some function $f(x)$ such that $|x^m f(x)| < C$ as $x \to 0$ or $x \to \infty$, where C is a positive constant or zero. Then, $f(x)$ is said to be of the order of x^{-m}, or $f(x) = O(x^{-m})$. Furthermore, there is a pole of order m at $x = \infty$. Following these conventions, there are three possibilities for the coefficients in (1).

i. An ordinary point at $x = \infty$.

$$p(z) = O(1); \quad q(z) = O(1); \quad z \to 0$$

$$P(x) = \frac{2}{x} + O(1/x^2); \quad Q(x) = O(1/x^4); \quad x \to \infty$$

ii. A regular singular point at $x = \infty$.

$$p(z) = O(1/z); \quad q(z) = O(1/z^2); \quad z \to 0$$
$$P(x) = O(1/x); \quad Q(x) = O(1/x^2); \quad x \to \infty$$

iii. An irregular singular point at $x = \infty$. The preceding conditions do not hold.

Given an equation to be solved with a series solution there are two procedures.

a. Find all singular points of the equation and classify them; see **A1-10-1**. If a solution has been determined which is valid in the neighborhood of $x = a$, either an ordinary point or a singular point, it will probably fail at $x = b$, the nearest singular point to $x = a$. However, the process of *analytic continuation* can often be used to find a series for a wider range of the independent variable. Other sources must be consulted for the details; suitable references are Coddington and Levinson, Whittaker and Watson. Here, we note only that the equation can have two linearly independent solutions, if the existence theorems permit them; see Introduction-**3**. Convergence of the series can be tested by appropriate means; see **8-1-1**. To proceed further, refer to one of the following sections

    i. Solution near an ordinary point, **8-1**.

    ii. Solution near a regular singular point; **8-2**.

    iii. Solution near an irregular singular point; **8-3**.

b. As an alternative method, suppose that a number of standard differential equations have been selected and that their general solutions have been obtained by the procedures of **8-1**, **8-2**, or **8-3**. Then, as will be shown, any given equation which is to be solved is either the standard equation or an equation convertible to a standard type by variable transformations. If this method is to be used, go at once to **9**. The advantage of this procedure arises from the fact that the standard equations will usually have series solutions, previously studied; thus they can be regarded as known functions. Some special cases of these equations are of interest. They are the equations of classical mathematical physics, see **9-6**; equations in which the coefficients have certain special properties, see **9-7**.

8-1. Series Solution Near an Ordinary Point.

If the ordinary point is at $x = a$, where a is finite, introduce two new variables $y(x) = u(z)$, $z = (a-x)$. Complete the work of this section, replacing x, y everywhere by z, u and then return to the original variables. If the ordinary point is at $x = \infty$, use the new variable $z = 1/x$. See **4-2-2** for some useful formulas and also **9-5** for further information about an ordinary point. In any of these cases, it is thus possible to take the ordinary point at the origin, $x = 0$. There are two possible procedures; that of **a** will generally be preferred.

a. Assume a solution

$$y = A_0 + A_1x + A_2x^2 + \dots + A_kx^k + \dots \tag{2}$$

where the A_i are constants to be determined. In case the ordinary point is at $x = \infty$, it may be easier to assume a solution

$$y = A_0 + A_1/x + A_2/x^2 + \dots ,$$

rather than to use a new independent variable, as previously suggested.

There are two ways in which the coefficients can be evaluated. They are equivalent but differ somewhat in details. It is unlikely that **i** has any particular advantage over **ii**, in the usual case. Either would fail if $x = 0$ were not an ordinary point, because each coefficient in (2) would then become infinite. However, $x = 0$ would be a singular point and **8-2** or **8-3** should have been used.

i. When $x = 0$, call the corresponding values of $P(x)$, $Q(x)$, y, and its derivatives, P_0, Q_0, y_0, y_0', y_0'', etc. There are two arbitrary constants in (2); take them as y_0 and y_0'. Use (1) to calculate $y_0'' = -(y_0'P_0 + y_0Q_0)$. Differentiate (1) to get $y''' = -[Py'' + (P' + Q)y' + Q'y]$ and find y_0''' from it. Continue the differentiation to get y^{iv}, y^{v}, etc., and calculate y_0^{iv}, y_0^{v}, etc., by setting $x = 0$ in each. Finally, take the coefficients in (2) as

$$A_0 = y_0 = C_1, \quad A_1 = y_0' = C_2, \quad A_2 = y_0''/2!$$
$$A_3 = y_0'''/3!, \quad \dots, \quad A_k = y_0^{(k)}/k!, \quad \dots$$

The solution can also be written as

$$y = C_1y_1 + C_2y_2 \tag{3}$$

where

$$y_1 = 1 + a_2x^2 + a_3x^3 + \dots$$
$$y_2 = x(1 + b_1x + b_2x^2 + \dots) \tag{4}$$

A few of the constants a_i, b_i are given explicitly in **ii**. They, as well as the A_i, may become increasingly more laborious to calculate for the higher powers of x; see **8-1-1**.

It is useful to note that y_1 is the special solution of (1) with unit value and zero slope at $x = 0$, while y_2 has zero value and unit slope there; see **B1-c**.

ii. Since $x = 0$ is an ordinary point for (1), both $P(x)$ and $Q(x)$ are analytic functions there and they may be expanded as

$$P(x) = p_0 + p_1x + p_2x^2 + \dots$$
$$Q(x) = q_0 + q_1x + q_2x^2 + \dots \tag{5}$$

Here, p_i and q_i are constants but they may be complex numbers. When $P(x)$, $Q(x)$ are polynomials, as is often the case, they already appear in the form of (5). In other cases, they may be converted to that form in several ways.

1. Suppose that $P(x)$ is a rational function, so that its form is $P(x) = P_1(x)/P_2(x)$, where P_1, P_2 are polynomials. The result (5) follows by division, using detached coefficients if so desired. The procedure for $Q(x)$ is similar.

2. Use the method of undetermined coefficients.

3. Expand $P(x)$, $Q(x)$ by Maclaurin's theorem. The coefficients in (5) will be given by $p_k = P_0^{(k)}/k!$, $q_k = Q_0^{(k)}/k!$, where the subscript designates that the kth derivative is to be evaluated at $x = 0$.

Substitute (2) and (5) into (1). Equate coefficients of equal powers of x to zero; that is, use the method of undetermined coefficients to find the A_k. A typical term will contain A_0, A_1, A_2, ... , A_k; p_0, p_1, ... , p_{k-2}; q_0, q_1, ... , q_{k-2}. The general equation, called a recursion relation, see **8-1-1**, is

$$k(k-1)A_k + \sum_{m=1}^{k-1} mA_m p_{k-m-1} + \sum_{m=0}^{k-2} A_m q_{k-m-2} = 0 \tag{6}$$

It can be used to get the a_i of (4) with $A_0 = 1$, $A_1 = 0$. Similarly, let $A_0 = 0$, $A_1 = 1$ and get the b_i of (4). A few of these coefficients follow.

$$a_2 = -q_0/2$$
$$a_3 = (p_0 q_0 - q_1)/3!$$
$$a_4 = (q_0^2 - p_0^2 q_0 + p_0 q_1 + 2p_1 q_0 - 2q_2)/4!$$
$$\ldots \quad \ldots \quad \ldots \quad \ldots \quad \ldots \quad \ldots \quad \ldots \quad \ldots \tag{7}$$
$$b_1 = -p_0/2$$
$$b_2 = (p_0^2 - q_0 - p_1)/3!$$
$$b_3 = (2p_0 q_0 - p_0^3 + 3p_0 p_1 - 2q_1 - 2p_2)/4!$$
$$\ldots \quad \ldots \quad \ldots \quad \ldots \quad \ldots \quad \ldots \quad \ldots \quad \ldots$$

b. Write (1) in the normal form, see **4-1-2**,

$$u'' + I(x)u = 0$$

Its solution is

$$u = F_0 + F_1 + F_2 + \ldots F_k + \ldots$$

where $F_0(x) = C_1 + C_2 x$ and, for $k \geqslant 1$,

$$F_k(x) = \int_0^x (t - x)I(t)F_{k-1}(t)\,dt$$

Successive terms become increasingly difficult to evaluate. If $I(x)$ is a simple polynomial of low degree, the work is easier but a might still be preferred. The method will fail if $x = 0$ is a singular point, because then each integral becomes infinite. In that case, 8-2 or 8-3 should have been used.

8-1-1. Recursion Relations. In practice, it may be simpler to avoid the use of (6). Clear (1) of fractions, if necessary, so that it becomes

$$X_0(x)y'' + X(x)y' + X_2(x)y = 0 \qquad (8)$$

Substitute the assumed solution (2) into (8) and use the method of undetermined coefficients to find the A_k.

As seen from (6), a recursion relation, also called a recurrence relation, is an equation defining a coefficient A_k in terms of two or more coefficients with smaller subscripts. Most examples in elementary texts—see Kaplan-1, for example—are carefully chosen so that this relation connects only two coefficients. In such cases, many of the p_k, q_k in (7) will be zero, and the calculations will be relatively easy. Moreover, a general rule for the coefficients can be found and the solution can be presented in compact form.

When three-term or many-term recursion relations occur, it becomes increasingly laborious to calculate the coefficients and to test the series for convergence or asymptotic behavior, but see also 11. Two examples in a may help to clarify the situation. Additional comments will be found in b.

a. Consider two differential equations, both of which have $x = 0$ for an ordinary point and no singular point in the finite plane.

i. $y'' + xy = 0$. The recursion relation is found to be

$$k(k-1)A_k + A_{k-3} = 0$$

Take $A_0 = 1$, $A_1 = 0$ for y_1 and $A_0 = 0$, $A_1 = 1$ for y_2. The coefficients in (4) are

$$a_{3k} = \frac{(-1)^k 1 \cdot 4 \cdot 7 \ldots (3k-2)}{(3k)!}; \quad b_{3k+1} = \frac{(-1)^k 2 \cdot 5 \cdot 8 \ldots (3k-1)}{(3k+1)!}$$

The solution of the differential equation is completely determined, the ratio test can be used to test the series for convergence, and the 89th term in the series could be calculated without a great amount of labor, if that were wanted.

ii. $y'' + (1+x)y = 0$. The recursion relation has three terms:

$$k(k-1)A_k + A_{k-2} + A_{k-3} = 0$$

Take A_0 and A_1 as before but there is no general law for the coefficients. A few of them are: $a_2 = -1/2$, $a_3 = -1/3!$, $a_4 = 1/4!$, $a_5 = 4/5!$, $a_6 = 3/6!$, ...; $b_1 = 0$, $b_2 = -1/3!$, $b_3 = -2/4!$, $b_4 = 1/5!$, $b_5 = 1/5!$, etc. The coefficient of x^7 could not be predicted, as in **i**, and the 89th term would require an extraordinary amount of labor to compute. The ratio test cannot be used to study the convergence of the series, but, of course, the existence theorems guarantee that the series does actually converge. In **i**, the solution is a completely defined function; here, it is known only as far as the number of terms calculated.

b. The form of the differential equation does not always indicate the nature of the recursion relation that will result. The following general conclusions can be stated. For a simple relation both $P(x)$ and $Q(x)$ must be rational functions of x. Otherwise, seek a variable transformation so that the new coefficients are rational functions. There can be no more than three regular singular points for a two-term formula. Even with three regular singular points, the relation may contain more than three terms. As before, a new dependent variable may simplify the recursion formula. When more than one singular point is irregular, the simplest possibility is a three-term relation and it may contain more than three terms.

The methods of **9** are especially useful in the study of equations with many term recursion relations. They will convert the equation into one which has been investigated; hence the properties of the solutions can be related to known functions. It should be noted that a recursion formula is also a *finite difference equation*. Properties of such equations are of considerable interest, especially in connection with partial differential equations. For some references, see **A1-11-1a**.

8-2. Series Solution Near a Regular Singular Point. Let $x = 0$ be the regular singular point; see **8** and **9-5**. If the singular point is at $x = a$ or $x = \infty$, use a new independent variable, as explained in **8-1**. The coefficients in (1) will have the forms

$$P(x) = p(x)/x; \quad Q(x) = q(x)/x^2 \tag{9}$$

where

$$p(x) = p_0 + p_1 x + p_2 x^2 + \ldots + p_k x^k + \ldots$$
$$q(x) = q_0 + q_1 x + q_2 x^2 + \ldots + q_k x^k + \ldots \tag{10}$$

The quantities p_k, q_k are constants but they may be complex numbers; p_0, q_0, q_1 cannot all be zero. Note that p_k, q_k differ from the constants in (5). However, if $p_0 = q_0 = q_1 = 0$, (5) and (9) are identical; hence $x = 0$ is an ordinary point. If necessary, use the methods of **8-1a** to find the coefficients in (10).

With the abbreviation $L(y) = 0$ for (1), assume a solution

$$y = x^s(A_0 + A_1x + A_2x^2 + ...)$$

where s and the coefficients A_k are to be determined. It is assumed that $A_0 \neq 0$, but there is no loss in generality with $A_0 = 1$, because any other value of it desired could be absorbed into the integration constant required for the general solution. Substitute the assumed solution into the differential equation and use the properties (9) and (10). The result can be written as

$$L(y) = x^s(\beta_0 + \beta_1x + \beta_2x^2 + ...) = 0$$

This is an identity; hence each coefficient β_k must vanish. The following relations are obtained

$$\beta_0 = s^2 + (p_0 - 1)s + q_0 = 0$$
$$\beta_1 = A_1[(s+1)^2 + (s+1)(p_0-1) + q_0] + sp_1 + q_1 = 0$$
$$\beta_2 = A_2[(s+2)^2 + (s+2)(p_0-1) + q_0] + A_1[(s+1)p_1 + q_1] + sp_2 + q_2 = 0 \tag{11}$$
$$\cdots \quad \cdots \quad \cdots \quad \cdots \quad \cdots \quad \cdots \quad \cdots$$
$$\beta_k = A_k[(s+k)^2 + (s+k)(p_0-1) + q_0] +$$
$$+ \sum_{m=1}^{k-1} A_{k-m}[(s+k-m)p_m + q_m] + sp_k + q_k = 0$$

The first equation, conveniently designated as $F(s) = 0$, serves to determine the constants s. It is the *indicial equation* and its two roots, s_1 and s_2, which may be complex, are the *exponents* of (1) at the regular singular point, $x = 0$. Select their subscripts so that $\mathrm{Re}(s_1) \geqslant \mathrm{Re}(s_2)$, where $\mathrm{Re}(s)$ means the real part of $s = \alpha + i\beta$; α, β are real numbers, and $\mathrm{Re}(s) \geqslant 0$. Then, define $\Delta = s_1 - s_2$, hence $\mathrm{Re}(\Delta) \geqslant 0$. It follows that

$$F(s) = (s - s_1)(s - s_2) = 0$$

and that $F(k + s_1) = k(k + \Delta)$. When a value of s has been calculated from (11), the coefficients A_k can be found successively from the equations for β_k provided that $F(k + s) \neq 0$. There are three cases.

    a. $\Delta \neq n$; an integer; see **8-2-1**, case 1.
    b. $\Delta = 0$; see **8-2-2**, case 2.
    c. $\Delta = n$; an integer but not zero; see **8-2-3**, case 3.
    If an exponent is complex, the solution of the differential equation will contain the factor $x^s = \exp[(\alpha + i\beta)\ln x] = x^\alpha[\cos \beta \ln x + i \sin \beta \ln x]$. Such a factor will have a complicated behavior at $x = 0$; hence equations of this kind will seldom arise in a physical problem.

In the following cases, fractional exponents may occur, and this means that the solution will have a branch point at $x = 0$. A negative exponent means that there is a pole in the solution. In cases **8-2-2** and **8-2-3**, the general solution may also contain powers of $\ln x$. When such exponents occur, the point $x = 0$ is called a *real singularity* and the corresponding solutions are *regular solutions*. However, in spite of the fact that $x = 0$, or more generally that $x = a$, is a singular point for the differential equation, it may happen that every solution of the equation is analytic near the singular point, which is then said to be an *apparent singular point*.

The following tests can be made to show that $x = 0$ is an apparent singularity. First, calculate $p(0)$; see (9). It must be a negative integer, numerically greater than zero. Then, examine the two exponents and the quantity $\Delta = s_1 - s_2$. Case 3 must occur; see **8-2-3**. Finally, the non-logarithmic subcase **a** of **8-2-3** must result. If any of these requirements fail, the singularity is real not apparent.

8-2-1. Case 1; $\Delta \neq$ n, an integer. The solution of (1) is given by (3), where

$$y_i = x^{s_i}(A_0 + A_1 x + A_2 x^2 + ...)$$

The successive coefficients are found from the recursion relation

$$k(k \pm \Delta)A_k + \sum_{m=0}^{k-1} A_m[(m+s_i)p_{k-m} + q_{k-m}] = 0$$

Take $A_0 = 1$, the plus sign, and s_1 for y_1; $A_0 = 1$, the minus sign, and s_2 for y_2.

8-2-2. Case 2; $\Delta = 0$. In this case, as well as in case 3, where $\Delta = n$, an integer not equal to zero, only one solution would result by the procedure of **8-2-1**. A general method, applicable to either case 2 or **3**, is described in **a**. Two modifications of it, for case 2 alone, are given in **b** and **c**; for case 3, see **8-2-3**.

a. Assume that s_1 has been used to get a solution by the method of **8-2-1**

$$y_1 = x^{s_1}(1 + A_1 x + A_2 x^2 + ...) = x^{s_1} Y_1(x) \tag{12}$$

It follows from **4-1-1a** that the general solution of the equation is

$$y(x) = y_1(x)u(x)$$

where $u(x)$ is to be determined by solving the first-order equation

$$u'(x) = X(x) = e^{-\phi}/y_1^2; \quad \phi(x) = \int P(x)dx \tag{13}$$

From the properties of (11), it is seen that

$$(s_1 + s_2) = (1 - p_0); \quad (s_1 - s_2) = \Delta$$

hence $(2s_1 + p_0) = (\Delta + 1) = m$, an integer in cases 2 and 3. If $\phi(x)$ is now evaluated, the result is $X(x) = C_2 x^{-m} g(x)$, where

$$g(x) = Y_1^{-2} \exp(-p_1 x - p_2 x^2/2 - \ldots)$$

and C_2 is the integration constant from the quadrature. Examination of $g(x)$ shows it to be analytic at $x = 0$; hence it can be expanded in a Maclaurin series

$$g(x) = 1 + c_1 x + c_2 x^2 + \ldots$$

The first-order equation (13) can now be integrated, since it has separable variables; see **A1-1-1**. The result is

$$u(x) = C_2[c_{m-1} \ln x + v(x)] + C_1$$

where

$$v(x) = -[x^{1-m}/(m-1) + c_1 x^{2-m}/(m-2) + \ldots + c_{m-2}/x] + c_m x + c_{m+1} x^2/2 + \ldots$$

The general solution of (1) is seen to consist of three parts:

    i. $y_1 C_2 c_{m-1} \ln x$.
    ii. $y_1 C_2 v(x)$.
    iii. $C_1 y_1$.

Consider **ii** further. Multiplication of the two series y_1 and $v(x)$ will give $x^{1-m+s_1}(B_0 + B_1 x + \ldots)$, where the constants B_i are some combinations of the constants c_i, A_i, and m. However, we note that $(1 - m + s_1) = s_2$; hence the general solution of (1) can be written as

$$y = C_1 y_1 + C_2 (y_1 c_{m-1} \ln x + x^{s_2} \Sigma B_k x^k) \tag{14}$$

If $s_1 = s_2$, as it is in case 2, then $m = 1$, $c_{m-1} = 1$, and a logarithmic term always occurs. For conclusions about (14) in case 3, see **8-2-3**.

    b. For case 2 alone, where $s_1 = s_2 = s$, another procedure is the following. Find y_1 by **8-2-1**. The second solution, according to (14), will have the form

$$y_2 = y_1 \ln x + x^s \Sigma B_k x^k \tag{15}$$

Put it into (1) and determine the B_k by the method of undetermined coefficients.

    c. The method of Frobenius. It seems likely that in the usual case, this method would be preferred to that of either **a** or **b**. Assume a solution of the form

$$Y_s = x^s (A_0 + A_1 x + A_2 x^2 + \ldots + A_k x^k + \ldots)$$

ignoring the fact that the indicial equation has equal roots. Use the recursion relation

$$[(k+s)(k+s-1)+(k+s)p_0+q_0]A_k+ \sum_{m=0}^{k-1} A_m[(m+s)p_{k-m}+q_{k-m}] = 0$$

to determine the coefficients, but keep s as a parameter. Then, calculate

$$y_1(x) = (Y_s)_{s=s_1}; \quad A_0 = 1$$

$$y_2(x) = \left(\frac{\partial Y_s}{\partial s}\right)_{s=s_1}$$

The second solution will be identical with (15), and $B_k = [\partial A_k(s)/\partial s]_{s=s_1}$. Since Y_s is a rational function of s, logarithmic differentiation is convenient in calculating $\partial Y/\partial s$. Thus, suppose that $Y_s = Y_1 Y_2 Y_3 ... Y_n$, where each Y_i is a function of the parameter s. Now

$$\ln Y_s = \ln Y_1 + \ln Y_2 + ... + \ln Y_n$$

and, if a prime means a partial derivative with respect to s,

$$Y_s' = Y_s\left[\frac{Y_1'}{Y_1}+\frac{Y_2'}{Y_2}+...+\frac{Y_n'}{Y_n}\right] \tag{16}$$

8-2-3. Case 3; $\Delta = n$, an Integer Not Equal to Zero. There are two types. In case **a**, there is no logarithmic term, since $c_{m-1} = 0$. In case **b**, a logarithmic term results, since $c_{m-1} \neq 0$. In either case, one solution may be obtained with **8-2-1** and the exponent s_1. Find the second solution with (15) of **8-2-2a**, using the method of undetermined coefficients. Omit the logarithmic term in case **a**. The method of Frobenius will probably be preferred.

  a. The method of Frobenius. Assume a solution of the form

$$Y(x) = x^{s_2}(A_0+A_1x+A_2x^2+...) \tag{17}$$

and use the recursion formula of **8-2-1**. If both A_0 and A_Δ are arbitrary constants, the general solution of (1) is of the form (3), where both y_1 and y_2 are found from (17). For y_1, take $A_0 = 1$, $A_\Delta = 0$; for y_2, $A_0 = 0$, $A_\Delta = 1$. If only one arbitrary constant results, the equation is type **b**. Use of s_1 in (17) would have given only one solution y_2.

  b. When only one arbitrary constant results from the method of **a**, a logarithmic term will occur in the second solution. Proceed as in **8-2-2c**, with a parameter s, but use s_2 instead of s_1, and let $A_0 = s$, before the limiting step, $s \to s_2$. This choice of A_0 will avoid indeterminate expressions for some A_k, which would otherwise have zero in the denominator. The series in the second solution may not start with B_0, for several B_k may vanish, $k \geq 0$.

8-3. Series Solution Near An Irregular Singular Point. With (1) as the standard form of the equation, suppose that the coefficients are

$$P(x) = p(x)/x^m; \quad Q(x) = q(x)/x^n$$

where $p(x)$, $q(x)$ have the form of (10). Then, if $m > 1$, $n > 2$, or both, the poles of $P(x)$ and $Q(x)$ are of orders m, n, respectively. The point $x = 0$ is therefore an irregular singular point; see **9-5c**. If the irregular singular point occurs at $x = a$, shift it to $x = 0$, as directed in **8-1**. An irregular singular point may be classified in two different ways and each suggests a method for solving the differential equation.

a. When the irregular singular point has resulted from the coalescence of $(p+2)$ elementary singular points, see **9-5**, the methods of **9** can be used. Find the original equation with $(p+2)$ elementary singular points and solve it by the methods of either **8** or **9**. Apply a suitable limiting process to its solution so that the elementary singular points coalesce to form the irregular singular point. The result will be the solution of the given equation. The method is simple when it can be used but it may not be easy to find the original equation. See **9** for some typical examples.

b. The equations of **8-2** have always had at least one integral, which was a convergent power series in x. The second integral was either of the same kind or of this kind, with a logarithmic multiplier. Such solutions are called *regular integrals*. The equations of this section may have one regular integral or none.

To investigate the situation, let $h_0 = 2$, $h_1 = m+1$, $h_2 = n$, remembering that m, n are the orders of the poles in $P(x)$, $Q(x)$, respectively. Select the largest of these three integers and call it h_r. Its subscript, the integer r, is the *class* or *characteristic index* of the irregular singular point. If two h_i are equal and larger than the third one, choose r as the one with the smaller subscript. Equality of all three h_i means that

$$h_0 = h_1 = h_2 = 2$$

Thus, the rule gives $r = 0$, but then $m = 1$, $n = 2$ and the singular point was not irregular but regular; return to **8-2**.

Calculate $d = 2-r$. It is the degree of the indicial equation, see **8-2**, and also the possible number of regular solutions. There are three cases.

i. $d = 0$. There is no regular integral but there *may* be one or two integrals of a more complicated type, known as *normal* or *subnormal integrals*. Methods of seeking them are given in **c**. In general, normal and subnormal solutions are *divergent* power series, although purely formally they do satisfy the differential equation. Actually, they are *asymptotic* expansions of the solution to (1) and they are of considerable importance, in spite of their divergent character.

ii. $d = 1$. The indicial equation is of first degree in s, there is only one exponent, and the single regular solution can be found by the methods of **8-2**. The exponent is determined by one of the following relations

$$n+i = m \geqslant 2; \quad i = 0, 1, 2, \ldots; \quad n \neq 0; \quad s = 0$$

$$n-i = m \geqslant 2; \quad s = -q_0/p_0$$

The second integral can be found by **4-1-1a**.

iii. $d = 2$. There are two regular integrals, since $r = 0$; return to **8-2**.

c. There are no regular integrals, since $d = 0$. Assume a solution

$$y = e^{\phi(x)}u(x) \tag{18}$$

The differential equation (1) becomes

$$u''(x) + P_1 u' + Q_1 u = 0 \tag{19}$$

where

$$P_1 = P + 2\phi'; \quad Q_1 = Q + P\phi' + \phi'' + \phi'^2 \tag{20}$$

If $\phi(x)$ can be determined so that (19) has regular integrals, the solution (18) is a *normal integral*. The function $\phi(x)$ must be a polynomial in $1/x$; hence $\exp[\phi(x)]$ cannot be expanded as a power series in x. In other words, there is an essential singular point at $x = 0$ in e^ϕ. The difficulty in this case arises from the fact that the poles of $P(x)$, $Q(x)$ are of orders greater than 1, 2, respectively. If $\phi(x)$ can be chosen so that the unwanted terms in $P(x)$, $Q(x)$ can be removed, a solution will result and $u(x)$ will be a power series in x or in reciprocal powers of x. There are two possibilities; choose either, as convenient.

i. If $P(x)$ contains terms $f(x) = a_2/x^2 + a_3/x^3 + \ldots$, let $2\phi' + f(x) = 0$. The result is $P_1 = a_1/x + b_0 + b_1 x + \ldots$. If, at the same time, the coefficient of u in (19) becomes

$$Q_1 = c_m/x^m + c_{m-1}/x^{m-1} + \ldots + c_1/x + e_0 + e_1 x + \ldots,$$

there are two cases.

1. $m > 2$. There is no regular integral for u and therefore no normal integral for y, the solution of (1).

2. $m \leqslant 2$. There are two regular integrals for u of (19). They may be found by the methods of **8-2**, or otherwise. It follows that there are two normal integrals for y, the solution of (1).

ii. Choose $\phi'(x)$ so that terms in $Q(x)$ of the type $1/x^3$, $1/x^4$, etc., are removed. Normal integrals of (1) will exist, provided that $P_1(x)$ and $Q_1(x)$, as defined by (20), have poles of orders 1, 2, respectively. This means that (19) has regular integrals which can be found by **8-2**.

In the special case that $P(x)$ is a constant or if there is a pole of order one in $P(x)$, this method must be used, rather than that of **i**.

It may happen that fractional powers of $1/x$ occur in $\phi'(x)$. The resulting integrals are then called *subnormal*. The procedure for finding them is the same as that for normal integrals.

For a more elaborate treatment of series solutions near an irregular singular point, it is convenient to choose that point at $x = \infty$, rather than at $x = 0$ or $x = a$, where a is finite. Helpful references are Ince-1, Erdélyi-2. The latter may also be consulted for a discussion of asymptotic series.

9. Equations of Standard Type

A differential equation with a finite number of regular singularities, see **9-5**, is said to be of *Fuchsian type*, after Lazarus Fuchs (1833–1902). Many linear second-order differential equations are of this type or they are degenerate cases of it. Most of the ordinary differential equations of classical mathematical physics are also of this kind; see **9-6**.

In the method now to be described we first select a finite number of standard differential equations, which could be called $I_1, I_2, \ldots, I_k$. Suppose that one of them, say I_r, has r singularities. It will be characterized by the location of the r singularities and the two exponents at each, a total of $3r$ parameters. However, there is no essential loss in generality if the singular points are taken as elementary ones, meaning that their exponent differences are $1/2$; see **9-5**. Furthermore, investigation of the situation shows that there are additional relations so that an equation with r elementary singularities contains only $(2r - 6)$ arbitrary parameters. A general solution of such an equation can then be found by the methods of **8**, or otherwise.

Now, let the differential equation X be given for solution. Suppose that it also has r elementary singular points. It can differ from I_r in one or more of the following ways:

   i. It is equal to I_r, except for the arbitrary parameters.

   ii. It differs only in the location of one or more singular points.

   iii. It differs only in the exponents.

In either of these cases, suitable transformation of variable will change X into I_r. It is assumed that the solution of the standard equation I_r is available, hence the solution of X follows.

Suppose, however, that X has no elementary singular points but that it has either regular or irregular singular points. In either case X can be obtained by requiring that several elementary singular points occur at the same value of x. This process is known as the *coalescence* of singular points and the resulting differential equation is a degenerate case of I_r.

Thus, a Fuchsian equation X, with $s \leqslant r$ singularities of any kind, is a special case of the standard equation I_r.

To use the proposed method, first find all singular points of the given differential equation, not forgetting to examine the point $x = \infty$. Then, classify them as elementary, regular, irregular and use the symbols k_1, k_2, k_3 for the number of singular points of each type, respectively. More exactly, use k_{3_p} to mean that the irregular singular point is of *species* p, referring to **9-5** for a definition of the species.

Let $k = k_1 + k_2 + k_3$ and see **9-1**, **9-2**, **9-3**, **9-4**, respectively, for the possible equations with $k = 1$, 2, 3, 4. The equations themselves are designated with the corresponding symbol $[k_1, k_2, k_3]$. If an equation is given for solution and it is not found, a shift of the singular points, the exponents, or both will produce the standard equation as previously explained; for the details, see **9-5**. Equations with $k_1 > 4$ or $k > 4$ are not listed since they are seldom needed. They could be found from **9-5**, where the general case is discussed. When $k \leqslant 3$, some of the cases can be solved by elementary means but they are also included for completeness. Further information for each equation in the following sections will also be found in Part II.

9-1. Equations With One Singular Point, $k = 1$. The types $[1, 0, 0]$ and $[0, 0, 1]$ cannot occur.

$[0, 1, 0]$. The singular point can be taken at $x = \infty$. The equation results by coalescence from $[2, 0, 0]$

$$y''(x) = 0$$

Its solution by **1**, **B2-1-1**, or **B2-2-1**, for $x < \infty$, is $y = C_1 + C_2 x$. To find the equation with a regular singular point at $x = a < \infty$, let $y(x) = u(z)$, $x = 1/(a - z)$ and get

$$(a - z)u'' - 2u' = 0$$

Its solution, from **B2-1-2** is $(a - z)(u + C_1) = C_2$. If the coefficient of u' were anything other than -2, the singular point at $z = a$ would be accompanied by another at $z = \infty$. For that case, see **9-2**.

$[0, 0, 1_2]$. The standard form, with a single irregular singular point of the second species at $x = \infty$, is

$$y'' - y = 0$$

Its solution, for $x < \infty$, from **1** or **B2-2-1**, is

$$y = C_1 e^x + C_2 e^{-x}$$

The equation can be obtained as a limiting case of $[1, 0, 1]$, $[0, 2, 0]$, or $[4, 0, 0]$. There are two generalizations in this case.

a. If the singular point is wanted at $a < \infty$, let $y(x) = u(z)$, $x = 1/(a-z)$, and get

$$(a-z)^4 u'' - 2(a-z)^3 u' - u = 0$$

Its solution is

$$u = C_1 e^{1/(a-z)} + C_2 e^{-1/(a-z)}$$

b. A more general case of this type is the equation with constant coefficients, see **1**,

$$y''(x) + a_1 y' + a_2 y = 0$$

It can be solved directly. Alternatively, reduce it to normal form, see **4-1-2**,

$$u''(x) - k^2 u = 0$$

where $y(x) = u(x)v(x)$, $v = \exp(-a_1 x/2)$, $k^2 = a_1^2/4 - a_2$. The constant can be eliminated with one more transformation, $u(x) = w(z)$, $x = kz$, and the standard equation can be taken as

$$w''(z) - w = 0$$

$[0, 0, 1_3]$. If the five singular points in $[5, 0, 0]$ are made to coalesce at $x = \infty$, the result is

$$y'' + (A + Bx)y = 0$$

Every $x < \infty$ is an ordinary point. Both constants in the equation can be removed with $y(x) = u(z)$, $B^{2/3}z = A + Bx$, and the result taken as the standard form of this type

$$u''(z) + zu = 0$$

A series solution of it has been given in **8-1-1a**. Another variable transformation will convert it to a special case of Bessel's equation, which is type $[0, 1, 1_2]$. Thus, the series solution can also be presented in terms of Bessel functions.

$[0, 0, 1_4]$. Coalescence of six elementary singular points in $[6, 0, 0]$ at $x = \infty$ gives

$$y'' + (A + Bx + Cx^2)y = 0$$

One of its constants can be removed with a new independent variable $y(x) = u(z)$, $2C(z - x) = B$, and the result is

$$u''(z) + (a + bz^2)u = 0$$

where $a = A - B^2/4C$, $b = C$. To fix a second constant, let $u(z) = w(t)$, $cz^2 = t^2$, and get

$$w''(t) + \left(k + \frac{1}{2} - \frac{t^2}{4}\right)w = 0$$

with $a/c = (2k+1)/2$, $b/c^2 + 1/4 = 0$. This is Weber's equation and its solutions are parabolic cylinder or Weber-Hermite functions. They can be found by the methods of **8**, or the equation can be transformed into a special case of the Whittaker equation or the Kummer equation; see **9-2**. The general solution in this case can thus be given in terms of parabolic cylinder, Whittaker, or Kummer functions.

[0, 0, 1_r]. The general case, where r elementary singularities coalesce at $x = \infty$, is

$$y'' + (A_0 + A_1 x + A_2 x^2 + \ldots + A_{r-2} x^{r-2})y = 0$$

It contains $(r-1)$ constants, but two of them can be fixed as for [0, 0, 1_4]. A convenient procedure is the following. First, let $y(x) = u(z)$, $z = a + x$, choosing a so that the new equation lacks a term in z,

$$u''(z) + (B_0 + B_2 z^2 + B_3 z^3 + \ldots + B_{r-2} z^{r-2})u = 0$$

Then, transform again, with $u(z) = w(t)$, $cz = t$, and get

$$w''(t) + (b_0 + b_2 t^2 + b_3 t^3 + \ldots - k^2 t^{r-2})w = 0$$

The relations between the various coefficients are rather complicated and will not be given here. Note, however, that the general equation of this type can be reduced to one with only $(r-3)$ constants.

To study this type further, consider the more general case [1, 0, 1_r] with r an odd integer and x as the independent variable. Use the quadratic transformation, $x = z^2$, see **9-5**, and get the type [0, 0, 1_{2r}] in the variable z. Similarly, an equation of type [0, 1, 1_r] can be converted into [0, 1, 1_{2r}] so that the standard equation of [0, 0, 1_r] can always be taken of even species and, in the form,

$$y''(x) + (A_0 + A_2 x^2 + A_3 x^3 + \ldots + A_{2r-3} x^{2r-3} - k^2 x^{2r-2})y = 0$$

Since $x = 0$ is an ordinary point, the methods of **8-1** can be used to find series solutions, convergent for all $x < \infty$. However, many-term recursion relations will result, see **8-1-1**, and calculation of the coefficients in the series will be laborious.

If a solution of the equation is wanted at the irregular singular point $x = \infty$, see **8-3**. A normal integral, if one exists, is said to be of *rank* r and the determining factor is

$$\phi(x) = \left(\pm \frac{kx^r}{r} + \frac{a_1 x^{r-1}}{r-1} + \ldots + a_{r-1} x \right)$$

where the a_i are constants. The coefficient k^2 in the previous equations was selected to simplify this relation. These results hold, even if there are other singularities, elementary or regular, in addition to the irregular singularity at $x = \infty$.

9-2. Equations With Two Singular Points, $k = 2$.

[2, 0, 0]. This is a trivial case of [0, 2, 0]. The two singular points are at $x = 0$, ∞ and the differential equation is

$$2xy'' + y' = 0$$

Its solution, by **B2-1-2**, is $y = C_1 + C_2\sqrt{x}$, valid for $x < \infty$. The exponents at $x = 0$ are 0; $1/2$; at $x = \infty$, they are 0, $-1/2$.

[0, 2, 0]. Take the singular points at $x = 0$, ∞. If the exponents at $x = 0$ are α, β, they must be $-\alpha$, $-\beta$ at $x = \infty$ and the differential equation is

$$x^2 y'' + (1 - \alpha - \beta)xy' + \alpha\beta y = 0$$

This is an Euler equation; see **3-1**. Its solution is $y = C_1 x^\alpha + C_2 x^\beta$, if $\alpha \neq \beta$; if $\alpha = \beta$, the solution is $y = x^\alpha(A + B \ln x)$. When α, β are complex numbers, refer to **3-1**. There are some more general cases.

a. To find the equation with singular points at $x = a$, b let $y(x) = u(z)$, $(b - z)x = (a - z)$. The result is

$$(a - z)^2(b - z)^2 u'' + (a - z)(b - z)[b(\alpha + \beta - 1) - a(\alpha + \beta + 1) + 2z]u' +$$
$$+ \alpha\beta(a - b)^2 u = 0$$

Its solution is $u(z) = C_1 U^\alpha + C_2 U^\beta$, $U = (a - z)/(b - z)$, if $\alpha \neq \beta$. If $\alpha = \beta$, $u = U^\alpha(A + B \ln U)$.

b. When [4, 0, 0] is used and the singular points allowed to coalesce so that $a_1 = a_2 = 0$, $a_3 = a_4 = \infty$, the result is

$$x^2 y'' + xy' - k^2 y = 0$$

It is a special case of the standard equation, with exponents $\pm k$ at both singular points. To convert it to the standard equation, let $y = x^h u(x)$, which shifts the exponents and produces

$$x^2 u'' + (2h + 1)xu' + (h^2 - k^2)u = 0$$

It is identical with the standard equation if $(k - h) = \alpha$, $(k + h) = -\beta$.

c. Another special case of this type is

$$xy'' + (1 + c)y' = 0$$

Its exponents are 0, $-c$ and its solution is $y = C_1 + C_2 x^{-c}$, $c \neq 0$; $y = A + B \ln x$, $c = 0$.

[1, 0, 1]. Use [4, 0, 0] and take its singular points as $a_1 = 0$, $a_2 = a_3 = \infty$. The result is

$$2xy'' + y' - 2k^2 y = 0$$

The constant can be removed with $z = k^2 x$, so that

$$2zu''(z) + u' - 2u = 0$$

The quadratic transformation $z = t^2$ converts the equation into

$$w''(t) - 4w = 0$$

which is type $[0, 0, 1_2]$, with an ordinary point at $t = 0$ and the irregular singular point at $t = \infty$. In terms of the original variables, its general solution by **1** or **B2-2-1** is

$$y = C_1 e^{2k\sqrt{x}} + C_2 e^{-2\sqrt{x}}$$

$[0, 1, 1]$. The regular singular point is at $x = 0$ and the irregular one at $x = \infty$. The equation is

$$x^2 y'' + xy' + (A_0 + A_1 x)y = 0$$

The exponents at $x = 0$ are the roots of $s^2 + A_0 = 0$. Since the constant is arbitrary, it may be chosen as $A_0 = -k^2$ so that the exponents are $\pm k$. Shift them to new values with $y(x) = x^h u(x)$ and get

$$x^2 u''(x) + (1 - \alpha - \beta)xu' + (\alpha\beta + A_1 x)u = 0$$

where $\alpha = (k - h)$, $\beta = -(k + h)$. In the special case with $\beta = 0$, $A_1 = 1$, $\alpha + p = 0$, the result is a Bessel-Clifford differential equation

$$xu'' + (1 + p)u' + u = 0$$

The quadratic transformation, $x = z^2$, will produce a special case of $[0, 1, 1_2]$

$$z^1 u''(z) + (1 - 2\alpha - 2\beta)zu' + 4(\alpha\beta + A_1 z^2)u = 0$$

Convert A_1 to unity, with the variable change $u(z) = w(t)$, $t^2 = bz^2$, $b = 4A_1$, so that

$$t^2 w''(t) + (1 - 2\alpha - 2\beta)tw' + (4\alpha\beta + t^2)w = 0$$

This can be converted into Bessel's equation of order p, if $h = (\alpha + \beta)$, $y(x) = x^h u(x)$, $p^2 = 2(\alpha^2 + \beta^2)$, and successive transformations, beginning with the standard equation. The result is finally

$$t^2 w''(t) + tw' - (p^2 - t^2)w = 0$$

$[1, 0, 1_2]$. This case can be obtained from $[5, 0, 0]$ with one singular point at $x = 0$ and coalescence of the others at $x = \infty$. The standard form is

$$2xy'' + y' + (A + Bx)y = 0$$

Since there are only two singular points, see $[1, 0, 1]$, one constant can be fixed and the result is

$$4xy'' + 2y' + \left(k + \frac{1}{2} - \frac{x}{4}\right)y = 0$$

The quadratic transformation, $x = z^2$, produces type $[0, 0, 1_4]$, which is Weber's equation, see **9-1**,

$$u''(z) + \left(k + \frac{1}{2} - \frac{z^2}{4}\right)u = 0$$

$[0, 1, 1_2]$. The general equation is

$$x^2 y'' + xy' + (B_0 + B_1 x + B_2 x^2)y = 0$$

The exponents at $x = 0$ are the roots of $s^2 + B_0 = 0$. They can be shifted to s_1, s_2 if $y = x^k u(x)$, $k^2 + B_0 = s_1 s_2$, $2k = -(s_1 + s_2)$. The result is

$$x^2 u'' + (1 - s_1 - s_2)xu' + (s_1 s_2 + B_1 x + B_2 x^2)u = 0$$

Further simplification can be secured with $u = x^{s_1} w(x)$, which changes the exponents to 0, $(s_2 - s_1)$, and gives

$$xw'' + (1 + s_1 - s_2)w' + (B_1 + B_2 x)w = 0$$

A similar result would have been obtained with $u = x^{s_2} w_1(x)$.

Now let $w = e^{hx} F(x)$, which will insure one normal integral at $x = \infty$. Choose h as a root of $h^2 + B_2 = 0$. The constant B_2 is arbitrary; a convenient value is $B_2 = -b^2$, so that $h = -b$. The differential equation is

$$xF'' - (2bx - 1 - s_1 + s_2)F' + [B_1 - b(1 + s_1 - s_2)]F = 0$$

Since there are only two singular points, see $[1, 0, 1]$, a new independent variable will fix one constant. A suitable relation is $z = 2bx$, and if $F(x) = f(z)$, the result is

$$zf'' + (1 + s_1 - s_2 - z)f' - \frac{1}{2b}[b(1 + s_1 - s_2) - B_1]f = 0$$

This is a confluent form of the Gauss hypergeometric equation, known as the confluent hypergeometric equation or the Kummer equation, see $[0, 3, 0]$. The standard form of it is usually taken as

$$zf''(z) + (\gamma - z)f' - \alpha f = 0$$

with $\gamma = (1 + s_1 - s_2)$, $2\alpha = (1 + s_1 - s_2) - B_1/b$.

The Kummer equation can also be obtained directly from the Gauss hypergeometric equation; see $[0, 3, 0]$. Let the latter be

$$x(1 - x)y'' + [\gamma - (1 + \alpha + \beta)x]y' - \alpha\beta y = 0$$

Replace x by x/β and permit β to approach infinity. The result is the Kummer equation

$$xy'' + (\gamma - x)y' - \alpha y = 0$$

Its normal form, see **4-1-2**, is known as Whittaker's equation. Let $y = x^{-\gamma/2}e^{x/2}W(x)$ and get

$$W''(x) + \left[\frac{1/4 - b^2}{x^2} + \frac{k}{x} - \frac{1}{4}\right]W = 0$$

where $k = \gamma/2 - \alpha$, $b = (1 - \gamma)/2$.

Whittaker's equation can also be obtained directly from $[6, 0, 0]$ with $a_1 = a_2 = 0$; $a_3 = a_4 = a_5 = \infty$.

Two other equations with one regular and one irregular singular point are generalizations of this type. They are

$$x^2 y'' + (a_1 + b_1 x)xy' + (a_2 + b_2 x + c_2 x^2)y = 0$$

and

$$(a_0 + b_0 x)y'' + (a_1 + b_1 x)y' + (a_2 + b_2 x)y = 0$$

Either of them can be solved in terms of the confluent hypergeometric equation or of the Bessel equation, after suitable transformation of variables.

$[1, 0, 1_3]$. Use $[6, 0, 0]$, take one singular point at $x = 0$ and let the others coalesce at $x = \infty$. The result is

$$4xy'' + 2y' + (A_0 + A_1 x + A_2 x^2)y = 0$$

One constant can be removed with $z = bx$, choosing b as convenient. With $b^3 = A_2$, the latter constant is replaced by unity, and if $y(x) = u(z)$, the result is

$$4zu''(z) + 2u' + (B_0 + B_1 z + z^2)u = 0$$

where $B_1 = A_1/b^2$, $B_0 = A_0/b$.

The quadratic transformation yields a special case of $[0, 0, 1_6]$, see **9-1**, $u(z) = w(t)$, $z = t^2$,

$$w''(t) + (B_0 + B_1 t^2 + t^4)w = 0$$

$[0, 1, 1_r]$. The general case is

$$x^2 y'' + xy' + \tfrac{1}{4}(B_r x^r + B_{r-1}x^{r-1} + ... + B_1 x - k^2)y = 0$$

There are r constants. The transformation $x = z^2$ gives a special case of $[0, 1, 1_{2r}]$

$$z^2 u''(z) + zu' + (B_r z^{2r} + B_{r-1}z^{2r-2} + ... + B_1 z^2 - k^2)u = 0$$

The exponents at $x = 0$ are the roots of $4s^2 = k^2$. The coefficient $1/4$ thus simplifies the calculations when either form of the equation is used.

$[0, 0, 2]$. This equation comes from $[6, 0, 0]$. Let three of its elementary singular points coalesce at zero and the other three at infinity. The result is

$$x^3 y'' + x^2 y' + (A_0 + A_1 x + A_2 x^2)y = 0$$

One constant can be removed. Let $y(x) = u(z)$, $z = kx$, $k^2 = A_2/A_0$, and get

$$z^3u''(z) + z^2u' + [A(1+z^2) + A_1z]u = 0$$

where $A^2 = A_0A_2$.

The transcendental transformation $u(z) = w(t)$, $\ln z = 2it$, produces Mathieu's equation

$$w''(t) + (a + b\cos 2t)w = 0$$

where $a = -4A_1$, $b = -8A$.

[0, 0, 2₂]. Apply the quadratic transformation to [0, 0, 2] and get

$$x^4y'' + x^3y' + (A_0 + A_1x^2 + A_2x^4)y = 0$$

As in the preceding case, there are only two constants. Use the successive transformations, $z = kx$, $k^4 = A_2/A_0$, $\ln z = it$, $A^2 = A_0A_2$, $y(x) = u(z) = w(t)$. The result is again Mathieu's equation

$$w''(t) + (a + b\cos 2t)w = 0$$

where $A_1 + a = 0$, $2A + b = 0$.

9-3. Equations With Three Singular Points, $k = 3$.

[3, 0, 0]. This is a special case of [0, 3, 0], obtained by assigning exponents $0, 1/2$; $0, 1/2$; $1/4, -1/4$, respectively, to the singular points at $x = 0, 1, \infty$. The equation is

$$16x(1-x)y'' - 8(1-2x)y' + y = 0$$

Its solution can be given in terms of the Gauss hypergeometric functions, see [0, 3, 0].

[2, 1, 0]. Use [4, 0, 0] and let $a_3 = \infty$. It is convenient to select $x = \pm 1$ as the two elementary singular points, rather than 0, ∞, as is usually done. The result, with one arbitrary constant, is

$$2(1-x^2)y'' - xy' + 2k^2y = 0$$

It is a special case of the Gegenbauer equation.

[2, 0, 1]. The equation comes from [5, 0, 0] with $a_1 = 0$, $a_2 = 1$, $a_3 = a_4 = \infty$. The result, with two arbitrary constants, is

$$4x(1-x)y'' + 2(1-2x)y' + (A + Bx)y = 0$$

It is the Lindemann-Stieljes equation, often called the algebraic form of the Mathieu equation; see [0, 0, 2], [0, 0, 2₂]. The presence of the irregular singular point at $x = \infty$ causes trouble; see 8-1-1. Let $y(x) = u(z)$, $x = \sin^2 z$, and get the Mathieu equation

$$u''(z) + (a + b\cos 2z)u = 0$$

where $2A + B = 2a$, $B + 2b = 0$.

The general equation of this type can also be converted into a special case of $[2, 0, 1_2]$. Let $y(x) = w(t)$, $x = t^2$, and get

$$(1 - t^2)w'' - tw' + (A + Bt^2)w = 0$$

Here, $t = 0$ is an ordinary point; the two elementary singular points at $t = \pm 1$ have equal exponents. The irregular singular point at infinity is of species two. A solution at $t = 0$ in the form of an infinite series involves a three-term recursion formula; either of the series at $t = \pm 1$, a four-term formula. It is usually simpler to study this equation in the variables u and z.

$[2, 0, 1_2]$. Coalescence of singularities in $[6, 0, 0]$ gives

$$4x(1 - x)y'' + 2(1 - 2x)y' + (A_0 + A_1 x + A_2 x^2)y = 0$$

It has three constants; its singular points are at $0, 1, \infty$. The transcendental variable change $y(x) = u(z)$, $x = \cos^2 z$, gives

$$u''(z) + (a + b \cos 2z + k \cos 4z)u = 0$$

For a generalization of this case, see $[2, 0, 1_r]$.

$[2, 0, 1_r]$. This is a generalization of the two preceding types. It has $(r + 1)$ arbitrary constants

$$4x(1 - x)y'' + 2(1 - 2x)y' + (A_0 + A_1 x + ... + A_r x^r)y = 0$$

Let $y(x) = u(z)$, $x = \cos^2 z$, and get

$$u''(z) + (A_0 + A_1 \cos^2 z + ... + A_r \cos^{2r} z)u = 0$$

Use the relation

$$2^{n-1} \cos^n z = \cos nz + n \cos(n - 2)z + \frac{n(n - 1)}{2!} \cos(n - 4)z + ...$$

$$+ \frac{n(n - 1)...(n/2 + 1)}{2(n/2)!}$$

to obtain an alternate form,

$$u'' + (B_0 + B_1 \cos 2z + ... + B_r \cos 2rz)u = 0$$

Note that $\cos z$ appears only to even powers; hence even multiples of z occur in the second form. The relation between the A_i and the B_i is rather complicated.

Sometimes, the equation occurs with the elementary singular points at ± 1. Let $u(z) = w(t)$, $t = \cos z$, and the result is

$$(1 - t^2)w''(t) - tw' + (A_0 + A_1 t^2 + ... + A_r t^{2r})w = 0$$

If the two elementary singular points coalesce at $x = 0$, the result is $0, 1, 1_r]$.

[1, 2, 0]. When [5, 0, 0] is used with $a_1 = 0$, $a_2 = a_3 = 1$, $a_4 = \infty$, the result is

$$4x(1-x)^2 y'' + 2(1-x)(1-3x)y' + (A+Bx)y = 0$$

Use the quadratic transformation, $y(x) = u(z)$, $x = z^2$, and get

$$(1-z^2)^2 u'' - 2z(1-z^2)u' + (A+Bz^2)u = 0$$

The point $x = 0$ has become an ordinary point; $x = \infty$ remains a singular point; $x = 1$ has been shifted to $z = \pm 1$, both of which are regular singular points. The new equation is a special case of [0, 3, 0] with only two constants, rather than the full number of three, since the exponents at $z = \pm 1$ are identical. The equation in z is that of the associated Legendre functions.

[1, 1, 1]. The general equation of this type, with three arbitrary constants, is

$$4x(1-x)y'' + 2[1-(3-2b)x]y' + (a+k^2 x)y = 0$$

It comes from [6, 0, 0] with an elementary singular point at $x = 0$; a regular singular point at $x = 1$, with $a_2 = a_3 = 1$ and exponents 0, b; an irregular singular point at $x = \infty$, since $a_4 = a_5 = a_6 = \infty$.

The quadratic transformation $y(x) = u(z)$, $x = z^2$, will shift the finite singular points to $z = \pm 1$ and give a special case of [0, 2, 1_2]

$$(1-z^2)u'' - 2(1-b)zu' + (a+k^2 z^2)u = 0$$

The exponents at the two finite singular points are 0, b. A trigonometric transformation gives the associated Mathieu equation, see also [0, 2, 1_r], $y(x) = Y(X)$, $x = \cos^2 X$.

$$Y''(X) + (1-2b)Y' \cot X + (a+k^2 \cos^2 X)Y = 0$$

Rewrite this equation in terms of x, y as variables and reduce it to the normal form; see **4-1-2**. The result is

$$u''(x) + (\alpha_0 + \alpha_1 \cos^2 x + \alpha_2 \csc^2 x)u = 0$$

where $y(x) = u(x)v(x)$, $v = \sin^\beta x$, $2\beta = (2b-1)$, $4\alpha_0 = (1-2b)^2 + 4a$, $\alpha_1 = k^2$, $4\alpha_2 = 1-4b^2$. A further transformation yields the trigonometric form of the equation for spheroidal wave functions; see [0, 2, 1_r]. Let $u(x) = tw$, $t^2 = \sin x$, and the result is

$$w''(x) + w' \cot x + (A_0 + A_1 \sin^2 x + A_2 \csc^2 x)w = 0$$

with $A_0 = \alpha_0 + \alpha_1 - 1/4$, $A_1 = -\alpha_1$, $A_2 = \alpha_2 + 1/4$.

[0, 3, 0]. The general case is the Riemann-Papperitz equation with three regular singular points at $x = a$, b, c and corresponding exponents α_1, β_1; α_2, β_2; α_3, β_3. Writing it as

$$y'' + P(x)y' + Q(x)y = 0$$

the coefficients are

$$P(x) = \frac{1-\alpha_1-\beta_1}{x-a} + \frac{1-\alpha_2-\beta_2}{x-b} + \frac{1-\alpha_3-\beta_3}{x-c}$$

$$Q(x) = \frac{1}{(x-a)(x-b)(x-c)}$$
$$\times \left[\frac{\alpha_1\beta_1(a-b)(a-c)}{x-a} + \frac{\alpha_2\beta_2(b-a)(b-c)}{x-b} + \frac{\alpha_3\beta_3(c-a)(c-b)}{x-c}\right]$$

The standard form of this equation is the *Gauss hypergeometric equation*

$$x(1-x)y'' + [\gamma - (1+\alpha+\beta)x]y' - \alpha\beta y = 0$$

with regular singular points at $x = 0, 1, \infty$ and exponents of $0, 1-\gamma$; $0, \gamma-\alpha-\beta$; α, β, respectively. Suitable variable transformations, see **9-5** and **9-5-1**, convert the Riemann-Papperitz equation into the standard form. More directly, substitute the new singular points and exponents, using a limiting process for the point at infinity. The Gauss equation can also be found from [6, 0, 0] by confluence if $a_1 = a_2 = 0$, $a_3 = a_4 = 1$, $a_5 = a_6 = \infty$.

[0, 2, 1_r]. The equation is

$$x^2(1-x)^2y'' + x(1-x)(1-2x)y' + (A_0 + A_1 x + ... + A_r x^r)y = 0$$

The two regular singular points are at $x = 0, 1$ and the exponents are the roots of $s^2 + A_0 = 0$; $s^2 + A_0 + A_1 + ... + A_r = 0$, respectively. The solutions of such an equation are complicated functions. Special cases of it are of more interest. They occur in a number of physical problems, usually with the regular singular points at ± 1 and with $r \leqslant 4$.

Let $y(x) = u(z)$, $2x = 1-z$, and get

$$(1-z^2)^2u'' - 2z(1-z^2)u' + (B_0 + B_1 z + ... + B_r z^r)u = 0$$

where

$$B_0 = 4(A_0 + A_1/2 + A_2/4 + ... + A_r/2^r)$$
$$B_1 = -4(A_1/2 + A_2/2 + ... + rA_r/2^r)$$
$$B_2 = A_2 + 3A_3/2 + ... + r(r-1)A_r/2^{r-1}; ...$$
$$B_r = (-1)^r A_r/2^{r-2}$$

The singular points have been shifted to $z = \pm 1$ but the exponents remain unchanged.

A special case, with $r = 4$, is the equation of spheroidal wave functions; see **9-6** and [1, 1, 1]. Choose $B_1 = B_3 = 0$; $B_0 = a + 4b - k^2$; $B_2 + a + 8b = 0$; $B_4 = 4b$. The result can be written as

$$(1-z^2)^2u'' - 2z(1-z^2)u' - [k^2 - a(1-z^2) - 4b(1-z^2)^2]u = 0$$

It has exponents of $\pm k/2$ at the regular singular points $z = \pm 1$. The equation can be simplified with $u = (1-z^2)^{\pm k/2}w(z)$. The result is

$$(1-z^2)w'' - 2z(1 \pm k)w' + (\alpha + \beta z^2)w = 0$$

where $\alpha = a + 4b \mp k(1 \pm k)$, $\beta + 4b = 0$. Now, the exponents at $z = \pm 1$ are 0, $\pm k$. With further relations between the constants, the last differential equation is that of prolate, oblate, or elliptic cylinder functions; see **9-6**. However, series solutions about the ordinary point $z = 0$ give three-term recursion formulas; see **8-1-1**. Four-term formulas occur for the regular singular points at $z = \pm 1$. A trigonometric form for the equation in $u(z)$ is usually more convenient. Let $u(z) = w(\phi)$, $z = \cos\phi$ and the result is

$$w'' + w' \cot\phi + (a + 4b \sin^2\phi - k^2 \csc^2\phi)w = 0$$

It can be converted into the associated Mathieu equation; see [1, 1, 1].

9-4. Equations With Four Singular Points, $k = 4$

[4, 0, 0]. Take three finite elementary singular points at $x = a_1, a_2, a_3$ and the fourth one at infinity. The equation is

$$2(a_1 - x)(a_2 - x)(a_3 - x)y''$$
$$- [a_1 a_2 + a_1 a_3 + a_2 a_3 - 2(a_1 + a_2 + a_3)x + 3x^2]y' + Ay = 0$$

Two of the finite singular points can be fixed and a convenient choice would be $x = 0, 1$. Two arbitrary constants remain and the position of the third finite singular point is also arbitrary. This is a special case of the *Lamé equation*; see [3, 1, 0].

[3, 1, 0]. Use the equation of [5, 0, 0], retaining three finite elementary singular points and taking the regular singular point at infinity. The equation is

$$4(a_1 - x)(a_2 - x)(a_3 - x)y''$$
$$- 2[a_1 a_2 + a_1 a_3 + a_2 a_3 - 2(a_1 + a_2 + a_3)x + 3x^2]y' + (A + Bx)y = 0$$

It has three disposable constants, A, B, and the position of one singular point. It is the algebraic form of the *Lamé equation*.

A standard form can be defined with $a_1 = 0$, $a_2 = 1$, $a_3 = 1/k^2$ and exponents of $(n+1)/2$, $-n/2$ at $x = \infty$. The result, now with three constants h, k, and n, is

$$4x(1-x)(1-k^2 x)y'' + 2[1 - 2(1+k^2)x + 3k^2 x^2]y' + [h - n(n+1)k^2 x^2]y = 0$$

The Lamé equation has been studied extensively; see Whittaker and Watson for further details. It is often convenient to convert the last equation into other forms.

a. Let $y(x) = u(z)$, $x = \mathrm{sn}^2 z$; see Erdélyi-1, Vol. 2. The result is the Jacobian form of the Lamé equation

$$u''(z) + [h - n(n+1)Z^2]u = 0; \quad Z = k\,\mathrm{sn}(z, k)$$

Numerical computations are generally easier with this equation than with some of the alternate forms. In many physical problems k lies between 0 and 1; it is not necessary that n be an integer; h is often restricted by physical boundary conditions.

b. The Weierstrassian form of the equation comes from the Jacobian form with

$$u(z) = w(t); \quad (e_1 - e_3)k^2 = e_2 - e_3; \quad z = iK' + t\sqrt{e_1 - e_3}$$

$$(e_1 - e_3)h + n(n+1)e_3 = H; \quad \mathrm{sn}(z,k) = \sqrt{e_1 - e_3}/[\mathscr{P}(t) - e_3]^{1/2}$$

see Erdélyi-1, Vol. 2, for definitions of the quantities used here and further details. The real (imaginary) quarter-periods of the Jacobian functions are K, K' and the differential equation becomes

$$w''(t) + [H - n(n+1)\mathscr{P}(t)]w = 0$$

With new variables, $w(t) = v(p)$, $p = \mathscr{P}(t)$, the result is

$$4(e_1 - p)(e_2 - p)(e_3 - p)v''(p)$$
$$- 2[e_1e_2 + e_1e_3 + e_2e_3 - 2(e_1 + e_2 + e_3)p + 3p^2]v'$$
$$- [H - n(n+1)p]v = 0$$

The three finite singular points are at e_1, e_2, e_3; the infinite regular singular point has exponents of $(n+1)/2$, $-n/2$ as before.

c. The Jacobian form of the equation, see **a**, can be converted to a trigonometric form. Let $u(z) = w(\phi)$, $\mathrm{sn}\, z = \cos\phi$, $\phi = \pi/2 - \mathrm{am}\, z$, and get

$$(1 - k^2 \cos^2\phi)w'' + k^2 \cos\phi \sin\phi w' + [h - n(n+1)k^2 \cos^2\phi]w = 0$$

[2, 2, 0]. This is a special case of the preceding type. It comes from [6, 0, 0] with $a_1 = 0$, $a_2 = a_3 = a$, $a_4 = 1$ and it has no particular interest.

[0, 4, 0]. Take the four regular singular points at $x = 0, 1, a, \infty$, with corresponding exponents 0, $1 - \gamma$; 0, $1 - \delta$; 0, $1 - \epsilon$; α, β. It is necessary that $(1 + \alpha + \beta - \gamma - \delta - \epsilon) = 0$. The result, known as *Heun's equation*, is a generalization of the Gauss hypergeometric equation, see [0, 3, 0].

$$x(1-x)(a-x)y'' + [\gamma - (\gamma + \alpha\gamma - \alpha\delta - \epsilon)x + (\gamma + \delta + \epsilon)x^2]y' - (k - \alpha\beta x)y = 0$$

There are six arbitrary constants: four exponents; the position a of one singular point; and the constant k, called the accessory parameter.

9-5. Equations With r Singular Points; $k_1 = r$ or $k_2 = r$. The general case of the Fuchsian equation, see **9**, is presented in this section. The preceding sections have listed a number of special or degenerate cases. Take the equation as

$$y'' + P(x)y' + Q(x)y = 0 \tag{1}$$

There are to be r *regular* singularities; see **8**. The coefficients $P(x)$ and $Q(x)$ are to be analytic functions of x throughout the entire plane except at the singular points. The integrals of (1) will be regular in the vicinity of these points.

If $x = \infty$ is to be an ordinary point, see **a**; if it is to be a singular point, see **b**. Degenerate cases, resulting from coalescence of singular points, are discussed in **c**.

a. The singular points are to be located at $x_i = a_i$, $i = 1, 2, \ldots, r$ and the two exponents at $x = a_i$ are α_i and β_i. There is to be an ordinary point at $x = \infty$; if a regular singular point is wanted there, see **b**; if there is to be an irregular singular point anywhere, including infinity, see **c**.

It is necessary, first of all, that the coefficients in (1) have the forms

$$P(x) = \frac{p_{r-1}(x)}{(a_1 - x)(a_2 - x)\ldots(a_r - x)}$$

$$Q(x) = \frac{q_{2r-4}(x)}{(a_1 - x)^2(a_2 - x)^2\ldots(a_r - x)^2}$$

where $p_{r-1}(x)$, $q_{2r-4}(x)$ are polynomials of degrees $(r-1)$, $(2r-4)$, or less, respectively. Moreover, to prevent a singular point at $x = \infty$, the coefficient of x^{r-1} in $p_{r-1}(x)$ must equal 2, provided it is not zero.

If the exponents are selected beforehand, as has been assumed, there are further restrictions on the coefficients. Each may be written, by the method of partial fractions, as follows:

$$P(x) = \sum_{i=1}^{r} \frac{(\alpha_i + \beta_i - 1)}{a_i - x} \tag{2}$$

$$Q(x) = \sum_{i=1}^{r} \left[\frac{\alpha_i \beta_i}{(a_i - x)^2} - \frac{B_i}{(a_i - x)} \right] \tag{3}$$

There are also relations between the constants, the first equation being known as the Fuchsian invariant.

$$\sum_{i=1}^{r} (\alpha_i + \beta_i) = r - 2 \tag{4}$$

$$\sum_{i=1}^{r} B_i = 0 \tag{5}$$

$$\sum_{i=1}^{r} (a_i B_i + \alpha_i \beta_i) = 0 \tag{6}$$

$$\sum_{i=1}^{r} (a_i^2 B_i + 2a_i \alpha_i \beta_i) = 0 \tag{7}$$

The complete set of solutions to such a Fuchsian equation is conveniently indicated by the Riemann P-symbol, the meaning of which should be self-explanatory.

$$y = P \begin{bmatrix} a_1 & a_2 & \ldots & a_r & \\ \alpha_1 & \alpha_2 & \ldots & \alpha_r & ; & x \\ \beta_1 & \beta_2 & \ldots & \beta_r & \end{bmatrix}$$

Examination of it, and of the equations for $P(x)$ and $Q(x)$, shows that the differential equation contains three categories of constants.

i. The singular points, r in number. Consider the introduction of a new independent variable by means of the *general bilinear* or *linear fractional transformation* (also called a *homographic substitution*)

$$z = \frac{Ax + B}{Cx + D}; \quad AD - BC \neq 0$$

Since there are essentially three independent constants in this equation, it follows that three (but only three) singular points, say $x = a_1, a_2, a_3$ can be transformed into three new singular points at $z = z_1, z_2, z_3$. Their location is arbitrary but if three of them are so fixed, there will remain $(r-3)$ arbitrary constants in this category. See **9-5-1** for further details about such variable transformations.

ii. The exponents, $2r$ in number, since there are two at each of the r singular points. A suitable choice is $\beta_i = \alpha_i + 1/2$, which fixes r of the exponents. When chosen in this way, they are called *elementary singular points*.

Consider now the transformation

$$y(x) = (x - a_i)^{\alpha_i} u(x)$$

The new differential equation in $u(x)$ will have the same singular points as the original one in $y(x)$, but the exponents at a_i have become 0, 1/2 instead of α_i, β_i. Successive applications of such transformations will fix $2(r-1)$ of the exponents at 0, 1/2. Remembering that (4) must hold and, provided that each singular point is required to be elementary, the last pair of exponents is fixed by the relations

$$\alpha_r - \beta_r = 1/2$$

$$\alpha_r + \beta_r = (r-2) - \sum_{i=1}^{r-1} (\alpha_i + \beta_i)$$

There remain no arbitrary constants in this category.

iii. The constants B_i in the coefficient $Q(x)$; see (3). There are r of these but there are three relations connecting them; see (5), (6), (7). The arbitrary constants in this category number $(r-3)$.

iv. Using the results of **i**, **ii**, and **iii**, it is seen that the arbitrary constants in all three categories are $K_1 = (r-3)$, $K_2 = 0$, $K_3 = (r-3)$. The differential equation (1) is thus completely fixed except for $K = 2r-6$ parameters or arbitrary constants, which are completely free. It should be noted that if $r \leqslant 3$, the differential equation and its solutions are determined unambiguously by the Riemann P-symbol. If $r > 3$, there will be one or more parameters unspecified by that symbol.

b. The differential equation is to have r singular points but they are to be chosen as $x = a_1, a_2, \dots, a_{r-1}, \infty$. The required form of the coefficients is

$$P(x) = \frac{p_{r-2}(x)}{(a_1 - x)(a_2 - x)\dots(a_{r-1} - x)}$$

$$Q(x) = \frac{q_{2r-4}(x)}{(a_1 - x)^2(a_2 - x)^2\dots(a_{r-1} - x)^2}$$

where $p_{r-2}(x)$, $q_{2r-4}(x)$ are polynomials in x of degrees no greater than $(r-2)$, $(2r-4)$, respectively. There is no restriction on the highest power of $p_{r-2}(x)$, as in **a**. Alternative forms of the coefficients can also be given, corresponding to (2) and (3).

$$P(x) = \sum_{i=1}^{r-1} \frac{(4\alpha_i - 1)}{2(a_i - x)}$$

$$Q(x) = \sum_{i=1}^{r-1} \frac{\alpha_i(1 + 2\alpha_i)}{2(a_i - x)^2} + \frac{A_0 + A_1 x + \dots + A_{r-3} x^{r-3}}{(a_1 - x)(a_2 - x)\dots(a_{r-1} - x)}$$

The constants $A_0, A_1, \dots, A_{r-4}$ are arbitrary; the last constant is fixed

$$A_{r-3} = \left[\sum_{i=1}^{r-1} \alpha_i \right]^2 - \sum_{i=1}^{r-1} \alpha_i^2 - \frac{(r-2)}{2} \sum_{i=1}^{r-1} \alpha_i + \frac{(r-2)(r-4)}{16}$$

Some further simplifications are possible, since the singular points may be taken as elementary ones; see **aii**; that is, $\alpha_i = 0$, $\beta_i = 1/2$, $i = 1, 2, \dots$, $(r-1)$. The coefficients then become

$$P(x) = -\sum_{i=1}^{r-1} \frac{1}{2(a_i - x_i)}$$

$$Q(x) = \frac{A_0 + A_1 x + \dots + A_{r-3} x^{r-3}}{(a_1 - x)(a_2 - x)\dots(a_{r-1} - x)}$$

but the last constant must take the value

$$A_{r-3} = \frac{(r-2)(r-4)}{16}$$

It is sometimes convenient to take the exponents at the finite singular points as $1/4$, $3/4$, instead of 0, $1/2$. They are still elementary but the differential equation assumes the normal form, see **4-1-2**, with $P(x) = 0$. The other coefficient is

$$Q(x) = \frac{3}{16} \sum_{i=1}^{r-1} \frac{1}{(a_i - x)^2} + \frac{A_0 + A_1 x + \dots + A_{r-3} x^{r-3}}{(a_1 - x)(a_2 - x) \dots (a_{r-1} - x)}$$

and $A_{r-3} = 3(2-r)/16$.

c. Degenerate forms of (1) can result when two or more singular points are allowed to coalesce. This means that the equation is first written with the singular points at the points $x = a_1$, a_2, etc., and then two or more a_i are set equal to each other. The resulting equation is called a *confluent form*. Assume, originally, that the singular points are $x = a_1$, $a_2, \dots, a_{r-1}$, ∞, with all $a_i < \infty$, $i \leqslant (r-1)$. There are several possibilities.

i. Let a_1 coalesce with a_2, both originally elementary. The resulting singular point is no longer elementary but it is regular. The exponents at this point are now given by the two numbers α, β rather than α_1, β_1; α_2, β_2, as was true before the coalescence, and

$$\alpha + \beta = 2(\alpha_1 + \alpha_2)$$
$$\alpha\beta = \alpha_1(\alpha_1 + 1/2) + \alpha_2(\alpha_2 + 1/2) + A$$

remembering that $\beta_i = \alpha_i + 1/2$.

The exponent difference, no longer $1/2$ since the singular point is regular and not elementary, is determined by

$$A = \frac{A_0 + A_1 a_1 + \dots + A_{r-3} a_1^{r-3}}{(a_1 - a_3)(a_1 - a_4) \dots (a_1 - a_{r-1})}$$

The exponent difference is fixed, if $r \leqslant 3$; it is arbitrary, if $r \geqslant 4$.

ii. Let a_{r-1} coalesce with $a_r = \infty$. In the limiting process, as a_r approaches infinity, take

$$\lim \frac{A_i}{a_{r-1}} = -B_i; \quad i = 0, 1, \dots, (r-3)$$

$$\lim \frac{A_{r-3}}{a_{r-1}} = 0$$

The sums and products in b have $(r-2)$ as their last terms, rather than $(r-1)$; the last term in $A(x)$ is $A_{r-4}x^{r-4}$.

iii. Let $p > 2$ elementary singular points coalesce. The singular point has become irregular. If $p = 3$, it is of the first species; if $p = n+2$, it is of the nth species. A differential equation with k_1 elementary singular points, k_2 regular singular points, and k_3 irregular singular points has been designated by the symbol $[k_1, k_2, k_3]$ in **9**. If there are several irregular singular points, one may write $[k_1, k_2, k_{31}, k_{32}, \dots, k_{3s}, \dots]$, where the second subscript indicates the species of the irregular singular points.

iv. Given an equation of type $[k_1, 0, 0]$, the possible number of equations with regular singular points that can be obtained from it is $k_1/2$ if k_1 is even, and $(k_1 - 1)/2$ if k_1 is odd. In either case, the confluent equation is of type $[k_1 - 2k_2, k_2, 0]$.

If there is one irregular singular point of species unity, the number of types is $k_1/2 - 1$ for k_1 even, or $(k_1 - 1)/2$, for k_1 odd. The total number of types with one irregular singular point of any species is $k_1(k_1 - 2)/4$ or $(k_1 - 1)^2$ for k_1 even, odd, respectively.

The total number of equations of all types obtainable from $[k_1, 0, 0]$ by coalescence is the same as the number of partitions of k_1 into any number of integral parts, each less than k_1. The results for all $k_1 \leqslant 7$, are given in Table 1.

9-5-1. Transformations of the Independent Variable.

It is often convenient to introduce a new independent variable in the study of a differential equation. Two transformations of particular importance are the following.

a. The general bilinear transformation. Let x be the original independent variable and z be the new variable with a relation

$$z = \frac{Ax+B}{Cx+D}; \quad AD - BC \neq 0$$

TABLE 1. CONFLUENT TYPES OF DIFFERENTIAL EQUATIONS
OBTAINABLE FROM THE EQUATION WITH r ELEMENTARY
SINGULAR POINTS

r	k_1	k_2	k_3
2	0	1	0
3	1	2	0
	0	0	1
4	2	1	0
	0	0	1
	0	2	0
	0	0	1_2
5	3	1	0
	2	0	1
	1	2	0
	1	0	1_2
	0	1	1
	0	0	1_3
6	4	1	0
	3	0	1
	2	2	0
	2	0	1_2
	1	1	1
	1	0	1_3
	0	3	0
	0	1	1_2
	0	0	2
	0	0	1_4
7	5	1	0
	4	0	1
	3	2	0
	3	0	1_2
	2	1	1
	2	0	1_3
	1	3	0
	1	1	1_2
	1	0	2
	1	0	1_4
	0	2	1
	0	1	1_3
	0	0	$1, 1_2$
	0	0	1_5

Other names for this transformation are linear fractional or Möbius transformation and homographic substitution. Its properties include the following.

i. If $(AD - BC) = 0$, z is a constant and the right-hand side of the equation is meaningless.

ii. Although there are four constants in the equation defining z as a function of x, only three of them can be assigned arbitrarily. Take $x = a_1, b_1, c_1$ and $z = a, b, c$. The resulting equation is

$$[(a-b)(a_1-c_1)(x-b_1)+(a-c)(b_1-a_1)(x-c_1)](z-a)$$
$$= (a-b)(a-c)(c_1-b_1)(x-a_1)$$

iii. A simple choice for $z = a, b, c$ is $z = 0, 1, \infty$. The equation connecting new and old variables is

$$(x-a_3)(a_2-a_1)z = (x-a_1)(a_2-a_3)$$

It follows that $x(a_1) = z(0)$, $x(a_2) = z(1)$, $x(a_3) = z(\infty)$. Alternatively, it may be useful to take $z = \pm 1, \infty$. The relation between x and z could be found from **ii**.

b. The quadratic transformation. Let the old and new variables be x, z, respectively, and let them be related by the equation $x = z^2$. An elementary singular point at $x = 0$, ∞ becomes an ordinary point; a regular singular point at either of these locations remains regular; an irregular singular point of species p becomes of species $2p$. A singularity at any other point, say $x = a$, gives two singularities of the same type at $z = \pm \sqrt{a}$.

9-6. The Equations of Mathematical Physics. Many ordinary differential equations in mathematical physics arise in solving a partial differential equation

$$\nabla^2 U + k^2 U = 0 \tag{1}$$

In this equation, ∇^2 is the Laplacian operator in three independent variables; q_1, q_2, q_3; U is the single dependent variable; k is an arbitrary constant. When $k = 0$, the result is Laplace's equation which describes gravitational, electrostatic, magnetic, or electric potentials; temperature distributions in equilibrium systems; velocity potentials in hydrodynamics. The wave equation for sinusoidal time dependence or the diffusion equation for exponential time dependence are examples when k is a real constant. The Schrödinger wave equation of quantum mechanics occurs for a particle with constant energy when k is a function of the coordinates.

In each of these cases, and in many others, a solution of the partial differential equation is often wanted in the form

$$U(q_1, q_2, q_3) = u(q_1)v(q_2)w(q_3) \tag{2}$$

where u, v, w are the general solutions of three second-order ordinary linear differential equations. The latter equations are all special cases of those given in the preceding sections, **9-1** to **9-5**. Solutions of the partial differential equations, like (2), however, can be obtained only in certain special coordinate systems, eleven in number. Some additional coordinate systems can be used for Laplace's equation.

The systems of interest are orthogonal curvilinear coordinates. In rectangular Cartesian coordinates, the position of a point $P(x, y, z)$ is determined by the intersection of three mutually perpendicular planes, $x =$ const., $y =$ const., $z =$ const. When x, y, z are related to three new quantities q_1, q_2, q_3 the position of a point can also be specified by the intersection of three surfaces $q_1 =$ const., $q_2 =$ const., $q_3 =$ const. It is the purpose of this section to summarize the properties of these systems and to list the ordinary differential equations which result when a solution of (1) is obtained in the form (2). In the more complicated cases, the ordinary differential equations will involve not only the constant k but two other separation constants as well. They will be designated as α, β, respectively. Boundary conditions or other requirements in many physical problems often force them to be integers or to be otherwise restricted. It is usually convenient to take the constants as k^2, α^2, β^2, which will avoid square root signs in the solutions.

When the separated ordinary differential equations contain two or all three of the constants, they become more difficult to solve than the simpler cases, where only one constant occurs. In the remainder of this section, the various systems are listed in the order of increasing complexity. For methods of solving each equation, see Part II.

An especially useful reference for further details of separable coordinate systems is that of Morse and Feshbach. They discuss, with many examples, the very important matter of suitable boundary conditions for physical problems, a subject which is entirely lacking in this book. An authoritative reference for many properties of the solutions to the equations is that of Erdélyi-1. Unfortunately, notation and definitions of the functions involved differ in the works of various authors. As far as practical here we have followed the usage of Erdélyi-1.

For the Schrödinger wave equation of a particle with constant energy E, the constant k^2 is proportional to the difference between E and the potential energy V of the particle. For separability, the potential energy is restricted in form and this result is also given for each coordinate system in the following sections.

I. Rectangular Cartesian Coordinates. The coordinate surfaces are the families of planes perpendicular to the x, y, z-axes, respectively. The coordinates are $x = q_1$, $y = q_2$, $z = q_3$. The differential equations are

$$u''(x) + (k^2 - \alpha^2 - \beta^2)u = 0$$

$$v''(y) + \alpha^2 v = 0$$

$$w''(z) + \beta^2 w = 0$$

There is an irregular singular point at infinity in each case. For the Schrödinger equation, $V = f_1(x) + f_2(y) + f_3(z)$.

II. **Circular Cylinder Coordinates.** The coordinate surfaces are families of cylinders forming concentric circles about the origin in the xy-plane, half-planes from the z-axis, planes parallel to the xy-plane. The coordinates are $x = r \cos \phi$, $y = r \sin \phi$; $q_1 = r$, $q_2 = \cos \phi$, $q_3 = z$. The differential equations are

$$q_1{}^2 u'' + q_1 u' - [\alpha^2 + (\beta^2 - k^2) q_1{}^2] u = 0$$

$$(1 - q_2{}^2) v'' - q_2 v' + \alpha^2 v = 0$$

$$w''(q_3) + \beta^2 w = 0$$

There are regular singular points at $q_1 = 0$, $q_2 = \pm 1$, ∞ and irregular ones at $q_1 = \infty$, $q_3 = \infty$. The second equation can also be written in trigonometric form

$$v''(\phi) + \alpha^2 v = 0$$

For the Schrödinger equation, $r^2 V = r^2[f_1(r) + f_3(z)] + f_2(\phi)$.

III. **Spherical Polar Coordinates.** The coordinate surfaces are families of concentric spheres about the origin, right circular cones with apex at the origin and axis along z, half-planes from the z-axis. The coordinates are $x = r \sin \theta \cos \phi$, $y = r \sin \theta \sin \phi$, $z = r \cos \theta$; $q_1 = r$, $q_2 = \cos \theta$, $q_3 = \cos \phi$. The differential equations are

$$q_1{}^2 u'' + 2 q_1 u' + (\alpha^2 + k^2 q_1{}^2) u = 0$$

$$(1 - q_2{}^2)^2 v'' - 2 q_2 (1 - q_2{}^2) v' + [\beta^2 - \alpha^2 (1 - q_2{}^2)] v = 0$$

$$(1 - q_3{}^2)^2 w'' - q_3 w' - \beta^2 w = 0$$

There are regular singular points at $q_1 = 0$, $q_2 = \pm 1$, ∞, $q_3 = \pm 1$, ∞; an irregular singular point at $q_1 = \infty$.

Trigonometric forms of the equations are

$$v''(\theta) + v' \cot \theta - [\alpha^2 - \beta^2 \csc^2 \theta] v = 0$$

$$w''(\phi) - \beta^2 w = 0$$

Separation of the Schrödinger equation is possible, if

$$r^2 V = r^2 f_1(r) + f_2(\theta) + \csc^2 \theta f_2(\phi).$$

IV. **Parabolic Cylinder Coordinates.** There are two families of parabolic cylinders, opening in both directions along the x-axis, and a family of planes perpendicular to the z-axis. The coordinates are $2x = q_1{}^2 - q_2{}^2$, $y = q_1 q_2$, $z = q_3$. Each differential equation has an irregular singular point at $q_i = \infty$.

$$u''(q_1) - (\beta^2 - \alpha^2 q_1{}^2)u = 0$$
$$v''(q_2) + (\beta^2 + \alpha^2 q_2{}^2)v = 0$$
$$w''(q_3) + (k^2 - \alpha^2)w = 0$$

The potential energy in the Schrödinger equation must have the form $rV = f_1(q_1) + f_2(q_2) + rf_3(z)$, where $r^2 = x^2 + y^2$.

V. **Elliptic Cylinder Coordinates.** The coordinate surfaces are families of elliptic cylinders, hyperbolic cylinders, and planes parallel to the xy-plane. The coordinates are $x = q_1 q_2 = a \cosh t \cos \phi$, $y = a \sinh t \sin \phi$, $z = q_3$; $q_1 = a \cosh t$, $q_2 = \cos \phi$, where the confocal ellipses and hyperbolas have foci at $x = \pm a$, $y = 0$. The differential equations are

$$(a^2 - q_1{}^2)u'' - q_1 u' + [\alpha^2 + (k^2 - \beta^2)(a^2 - q_1{}^2)]u = 0$$
$$(1 - q_2{}^2)v'' - q_2 v' + [\alpha^2 + a^2(k^2 - \beta^2)(1 - q_2{}^2)]v = 0$$
$$w''(q_3) + \beta^2 w = 0$$

There are regular singular points at $q_1 = \pm a$, $q_2 = \pm 1$ and irregular singular points at $q_1 = \infty$, $q_2 = \infty$, $q_3 = \infty$. Trigonometric forms of the equations are

$$u''(t) - [\alpha^2 - a^2(k^2 - \beta^2) \sinh^2 t]u = 0$$
$$v''(\phi) + [\alpha^2 + a^2(k^2 - \beta^2) \sin^2 \phi]v = 0$$

Let r_1, r_2 be the distances from the point (x, y) to the two foci of this coordinate system. It is found that $2q_1 = r_1 + r_2$; $2aq_2 = r_1 - r_2$. In terms of these parameters, the potential function in the Schrödinger equation has the form

$$r_1 r_2 V = f_1(r_1 + r_2) + f_2(r_1 - r_2) - r_1 r_2 f_3(z)$$

VI. **Parabolic Coordinates.** The coordinate surfaces are two paraboloids of revolution extending in both directions along the z-axis and a family of planes through the z-axis. The coordinates are $x = q_1 q_2 \cos \phi$, $y = q_1 q_2 \sin \phi$, $2z = q_1{}^2 - q_2{}^2$; $q_1{}^2 = r - z$, $q_2{}^2 = r + z$, $q_3 = \cos \phi$; $r^2 = x^2 + y^2 + z^2$. The differential equations are

$$q_1{}^2 u'' + q_1 u' + [\beta^2 + (\alpha^2 + k^2 q_1{}^2)q_1{}^2]u = 0$$
$$q_2{}^2 v'' + q_2 v' + [\beta^2 - (\alpha^2 - k^2 q_2{}^2)q_2{}^2]v = 0$$
$$(1 - q_3{}^2)w'' - q_3 w' - \beta^2 w = 0$$

For Laplace's equation $k = 0$ and the equations in q_1, q_2 can be solved in terms of Bessel functions.

The last equation is simpler in the variable ϕ

$$w''(\phi) - \beta^2 w = 0$$

There are regular singular points at $q_1 = 0$, $q_2 = 0$, $q_3 = \pm 1$, ∞; irregular singular points at $q_1 = \infty$, $q_2 = \infty$. The potential energy in the Schrödinger equation must have the form

$$V = [f_1(q_1) + f_2(q_2)]/r + f_3(q_3)/(x^2 + y^2).$$

VII. Prolate Spheroidal Coordinates. The coordinate surfaces are families of prolate spheroids, two-sheeted hyperboloids of revolution, and planes through the z-axis. The coordinates are $x = a \sinh t \sin \theta \cos \phi$, $y = a \sinh t \sin \theta \sin \phi$, $z = a \cosh t \cos \theta$; $q_1 = a \cosh t$, $q_2 = \cos \theta$, $q_3 = \cos \phi$. If r_1 and r_2 are the distances from the two common foci of the system to a point where two surfaces of the families intersect, $r_1 + r_2 = 2a \cosh t$, $r_1 - r_2 = 2a \cos \theta$. The differential equations are

$$(a^2 - q_1{}^2)u'' - 2q_1(a^2 - q_1{}^2)u' + [a^2\beta^2 - \alpha^2(a^2 - q_1)^2 + k^2(a^2 - q_1{}^2)^2]\,u = 0$$
$$(1 - q_2{}^2)v'' - 2q_2(1 - q_2{}^2)v' + [\beta^2 - \alpha^2(1 - q_2{}^2) + k^2a^2(1 - q_2{}^2)^2]\,v = 0$$
$$(1 - q_3{}^2)w'' - q_3w' - \beta^2 w = 0$$

In trigonometric form, the equations become

$$u''(t) + u'\coth t + [\alpha^2 + \beta^2 \operatorname{csch}^2 t + k^2a^2 \sinh^2 t]u = 0$$
$$v''(\theta) + v'\cot\theta - [\alpha^2 - \beta^2 \csc^2\theta - k^2a^2 \sin^2\theta]v = 0$$
$$w''(\phi) - \beta^2 w = 0$$

The equations are simpler if $k = 0$, which is then Laplace's equation.

There are regular singular points at $q_1 = \pm a$, $q_2 = \pm 1$, $q_3 = \pm 1$; an irregular singular point in each case at infinity. For separability of the Schrödinger wave equation it is required that

$$V = \frac{f_1(r_1 + r_2) + f_2(r_1 - r_2)}{r_1 r_2} + f_3(\phi)\operatorname{csch} t \csc \theta$$

VIII. Oblate Spheroidal Coordinates. The coordinate surfaces are confocal families of oblate spheroids, one-sheeted hyperboloids, and planes through the z-axis. The coordinates are $x = a \cosh t \sin \theta \cos \phi$, $y = a \cosh t \sin \theta \sin \phi$, $z = a \sinh t \cos \theta$; $q_1 = a \sinh t$, $q_2 = \cos \theta$, $q_3 = \cos \phi$. The focal circle for the surfaces is $x^2 + y^2 = a^2$, $z = 0$. The differential equations are

$$(a^2 + q_1{}^2)^2u'' + 2q_1(a^2 + q_1{}^2)u' - [a^2\beta^2 - \alpha^2(a^2 + q_1{}^2) - k^2(a^2 + q_1{}^2)^2]u = 0$$
$$(1 - q_2{}^2)^2v'' - 2q_2(1 - q_2{}^2)v' + [\beta^2 - \alpha^2(1 - q_2{}^2) - k^2a^2(1 - q_2{}^2)^2]v = 0$$
$$(1 - q_3{}^2)w'' - q_3w' - \beta^2 w = 0$$

There are regular singular points at $q_1 = \pm ia$, $q_2 = \pm 1$, $q_3 = \pm 1$. Each equation has an irregular singular point at ∞. Trigonometric forms of the equations are

$$u''(t) + u' \tanh t + (\alpha^2 - \beta^2 \operatorname{sech}^2 t + k^2 a^2 \cosh^2 t)u = 0$$
$$v''(\theta) + v' \cot t - (\alpha^2 - \beta^2 \csc^2 \theta + a^2 \sin^2 \theta)v = 0$$
$$w''(\phi) + \beta^2 w = 0$$

If the Schrödinger equation is separable, the potential energy must have the form

$$V = \frac{f_1(q_1) + f_2(q_2)}{q_1{}^2 + a^2 q_2{}^2} + \frac{f_3(q_3)}{(a^2 + q_1{}^2)(1 - q_2{}^2)}$$

IX. Conical Coordinates. The coordinate surfaces are spheres and two families of cones with elliptical cross-section. The coordinates are

$$a^2 x^2 = q_1{}^2(a^2 - q_2{}^2)(a^2 + q_3{}^2)$$
$$b^2 y^2 = q_1{}^2(b^2 + q_2{}^2)(b^2 - q_3{}^2)$$
$$ab z = q_1 q_2 q_3$$

If r is the radius of the spheres, $q_1{}^2 = r^2 = x^2 + y^2 + z^2$. The two other coordinates are conveniently given in terms of Jacobian elliptic functions $q_2 = a \operatorname{cn} u_1$, $q_3 = b \operatorname{cn} u_2$, with modulus of a, b, respectively, and $a^2 + b^2 = 1$. It follows that $x = r \operatorname{sn} u_1 \operatorname{dn} u_2$, $y = r \operatorname{dn} u_1 \operatorname{sn} u_2$, $z = r \operatorname{cn} u_1 \operatorname{cn} u_2$; see also XI. The differential equations are

$$q_1{}^2 u'' + 2q_1 u' + (\alpha^2 + \beta^2 + k^2 q_1{}^2)u = 0$$
$$(a^2 - q_2{}^2)(b^2 + q_2{}^2)v'' + q_2[(a^2 - b^2) - 2q_2{}^2]v' + [(a^2 - q_2{}^2)\beta^2 - (b^2 + q_2{}^2)\alpha^2]v = 0$$
$$(a^2 + q_3{}^2)(b^2 - q_3{}^2)w'' - q_3(a^2 - b^2 + 2q_3{}^2)w' + [(b^2 - q_3{}^2)\alpha^2 - (a^2 + q_3{}^2)\beta^2]w = 0$$

There are regular singular points at $q_1 = 0$; $q_2 = \pm a$, $\pm ib$, ∞; $q_3 = \pm ia$, $\pm b$, ∞. At $q_1 = \infty$, there is an irregular singular point.

Alternative forms of the equations are special cases of the Lamé equation

$$v''(u_1) + [\alpha^2 + a^2(\beta^2 - \alpha^2) \operatorname{sn}^2 u_1]v = 0$$
$$w''(u_2) - [\beta^2 - b^2(\alpha^2 + \beta^2) \operatorname{sn}^2 u_2]w = 0$$

For the Schrödinger equation to separate, the potential energy must have the form

$$V = f_1(r) + \frac{f_2(q_2) + f_3(q_3)}{q_2{}^2 + q_3{}^2}$$

X. Paraboloidal Coordinates. The coordinate surfaces are families of elliptic paraboloids, with parabolic traces on the x, z- and y, z-planes but elliptic traces on the xy-plane; hyperbolic paraboloids with parabolic and hyperbolic traces; elliptic paraboloids as before but pointing in the opposite direction on the z-axis. The coordinates are

$$(b^2 - a^2)x^2 = (a^2 - q_1{}^2)(a^2 - q_2{}^2)(a^2 - q_3{}^2)$$
$$(a^2 - b^2)y^2 = (b^2 - q_1{}^2)(b^2 - q_2{}^2)(b^2 - q_3{}^2)$$
$$2z = (q_1{}^2 + q_2{}^2 + q_3{}^2 - a^2 - b^2)$$

The inverse relations are conveniently given in terms of Jacobian elliptic functions; see XI; $q_1 = a \operatorname{dc} u_1$, $q_2 = a \operatorname{dn} u_2$, $q_3 = a \operatorname{nc} u_3 \sqrt{\operatorname{cn}^2 u_3 - m'^2}$, where the modulus of u_1, u_3 is m and that of u_2 is m'; $b = ma$, $a^2 - b^2 = c = m'^2 a^2$, $m^2 + m'^2 = 1$. It follows that

$$x = c \operatorname{sc} u_1 \operatorname{sn} u_2 \operatorname{nc} u_3, \quad y = c \operatorname{nc} u_1 \operatorname{cn} u_2 \operatorname{sc} u_3$$
$$2z = c(\operatorname{sc}^2 u_1 - \operatorname{dn}^2 u_2/m'^2 - \operatorname{sc}^2 u_3)$$

The differential equation for u and q_1 is

$$cq_1(a^2 - q_1{}^2)(b^2 - q_1{}^2)u'' - c(a^2b^2 - q_1{}^4)u'$$
$$- q_1{}^3[c(b^2 - q_1)^2\alpha^2 + \beta^2(a^2 - q_1{}^2) - ck^2(a^2 - q_1{}^2)(b^2 - q_1{}^2)]u = 0$$

The other two equations are similar, with q_1 replaced by q_2, q_3 and u by v, w. There are regular singular points in each case at 0, $\pm a$, $\pm b$. The potential energy in the Schrödinger equation must have the form

$$(q_1{}^2 - q_2{}^2)(q_1{}^2 - q_3{}^2)(q_2{}^2 - q_3{}^2)V$$
$$= f_1(q_1)(q_2{}^2 - q_3{}^2) + f_2(q_2)(q_1{}^2 - q_3{}^2) + f_3(q_3)(q_1{}^2 - q_2{}^2)$$

XI. **Ellipsoidal Coordinates.** This is the general coordinate system for separation of the partial differential equation. Each of the preceding systems is a degenerate case of the ellipsoidal system. Consider the equation

$$\frac{x^2}{q^2 - a^2} + \frac{y^2}{q^2 - b^2} + \frac{z^2}{q^2 - c^2} = 1; \quad a \geqslant b \geqslant c \geqslant 0$$

If $q > a$, it represents a family of confocal ellipsoids; if $a > q > b$, a family of confocal one-sheeted hyperboloids; if $b > q > c$, hyperboloids of two sheets. The traces of these surfaces on the various planes are ellipses and hyperbolas. The constants a, b, c determine the foci of the conic sections. There is no loss of generality with $c = 0$. The three mutually orthogonal coordinate surfaces are families of ellipsoids, two-sheeted hyperboloids, and one-sheeted hyperboloids. The coordinates are

$$a^2(b^2 - a^2)x^2 = (a^2 - q_1{}^2)(a^2 - q_2{}^2)(a^2 - q_3{}^2)$$
$$b^2(a^2 - b^2)y^2 = (b^2 - q_1{}^2)(b^2 - q_2{}^2)(b^2 - q_3{}^2)$$
$$abz = q_1 q_2 q_3.$$

These equations do not determine the position of a point in the coordinate system uniquely since $\pm x$, $\pm y$, $\pm z$ are identical. The difficulty can be avoided by the use of elliptic functions. In terms of Jacobian functions, let $q_1 = a \, dc \, u_1$, $q_2 = a \, dn \, u_2$, $q_3 = b \, sn \, u_3$, where $b = ma$, $a^2 - b^2 = m'^2 a^2 = c^2$. The modulus of u_1, u_3 is m and that of u_2 is m', $m^2 + m'^2 = 1$. In these variables $x = c \, sc \, u_1 \, sn \, u_2 \, dn \, u_3$, $y = c \, nc \, u_1 \, cn \, u_2 \, cn \, u_3$, $z = a \, dc \, u_1 \, dn \, u_2 \, sn \, u_3$. The three differential equations are alike. Replace q_1 by q_2, q_3 and u by v, w to get the other two.

$$c^2(a^2 - q_1^2)(b^2 - q_1^2)u'' - c^2 q_1 (a^2 + b^2 - 2q_1^2)u'$$
$$- [(a^2 - q_1^2)\beta^2 + c^2(b^2 - q_1^2)\alpha^2 - c^2 k^2(a^2 - q_1^2)(b^2 - q_1^2)]u = 0$$

There are regular singular points, in each case, at $\pm a$, $\pm b$, ∞. For separation, the potential energy in the Schrödinger equation must have the form

$$(q_1^2 - q_2^2)(q_1^2 - q_3^2)(q_2^2 - q_3^2) V$$
$$= f_1(q_1)(q_2^2 - q_3^2) + f_2(q_2)(q_1^2 - q_3^2) + f_3(q_3)(q_1^2 - q_2^2)$$

XII. Toroidal Coordinates. The system of this and the following section can be used to separate Laplace's equation $\nabla^2 U = 0$. Neither will apply for the more general equation $\nabla^2 U + k^2 U = 0$, $k > 0$.

For toroidal coordinates, the orthogonal surfaces are anchor rings or tores, with axial circles of radius $a \coth t$ and circular cross sections of radius $a \operatorname{csch} t$; spheres with centers $\pm a \cot \theta$ from the origin and radius of $a \csc \theta$; planes through the z-axis. The coordinates are

$$(\cosh t - \cos \theta)x = a \sinh t \cos \phi$$
$$(\cosh t - \cos \theta)y = a \sinh t \sin \phi, \ (\cosh t - \cos \theta)z = a \sin \theta$$
$$q_1 = \cosh t, \ q_2 = \cos \theta, \ q_3 = \cos \phi$$
$$0 \leqslant t \leqslant \infty, \ 0 \leqslant \theta \leqslant 2\pi, \ 0 \leqslant \phi \leqslant 2\pi$$

The separated differential equations are

$$(1 - q_1^2)^2 u'' - 2q_1(1 - q_1^2)u'' - [\beta^2 - (\alpha^2 - 1/4)(1 - q_1^2)]u = 0$$
$$(1 - q_2^2)v'' - q_2 v' + \alpha^2 v = 0$$
$$(1 - q_3^2)w'' - q_3 w' + \beta^2 w = 0$$

In trigonometric form, the equations are

$$u''(t) + u' \coth t - [(\alpha^2 - 1/4) + \beta^2 \operatorname{csch}^2 t]u = 0$$
$$v''(\theta) + \alpha^2 v = 0$$
$$w''(\phi) + \beta^2 w = 0$$

XIII. **Bispherical Coordinates.** This system can be used for Laplace's equation only; see XII. The orthogonal surfaces are spheres of radius $a \operatorname{csch} t$ with centers on the z-axis at $z = a \coth t$; a fourth-order surface obtained by rotation of circles about the z-axis; planes through the z-axis. The circles have radius of $a \csc \theta$ and a center at $x = a \cot \theta$, $z = 0$. The coordinates are

$$(\cosh t - \cos \theta)x = a \sin \theta \cos \phi, \quad (\cosh t - \cos \theta)y = a \sin \theta \sin \phi$$

$$(\cosh t - \cos \theta)z = a \sinh t$$

$$q_1 = \cosh t, \quad q_2 = \cos \theta, \quad q_3 = \cos \phi$$

$$-\infty \leqslant t \leqslant \infty, \ 0 \leqslant \theta \leqslant \pi, \ 0 \leqslant \phi \leqslant 2\pi$$

The differential equations are

$$(1 - q_1{}^2)u'' - q_1 u' - (\alpha^2 + 1/4)u = 0$$

$$(1 - q_2{}^2)^2 v'' - 2q_2(1 - q_2{}^2)v' + [\beta^2 - \alpha^2(1 - q_2{}^2)]v = 0$$

$$(1 - q_3{}^2)w'' - q_3 w' - \beta^2 w = 0$$

The equations are somewhat simpler in terms of the variables t, θ, ϕ:

$$u''(t) + (\alpha^2 + 1/4)u = 0$$

$$v''(\theta) + v' \cot \theta - (\alpha^2 - \beta^2 \csc^2 \theta)v = 0$$

$$w''(\phi) - \beta^2 w = 0$$

A simpler case of this system is that of bipolar coordinates. It is often limited to two dimensions, rather than three. A more general case is that of confocal cyclides of revolution. For details, see Erdélyi-1 or Morse and Feshbach.

9-7. Some Other Special Equations. Linear equations of Fuchsian type, see 9, were studied extensively by nineteenth-century mathematicians. Besides finding their general solution, it was of interest to study conditions under which the solution would be a polynomial or other simple function. Further investigations were concerned with linear equations having periodic coefficients or algebraic coefficients. Boole developed symbolic methods for the study of equations having solutions in finite form. Since no new methods of solution are involved, we discuss a few of these special equations briefly and refer the reader to Ince-1, Kamke-1, Boole, or Forsyth-2 for more details.

a. The Halphen equation. The type is

$$X_0(x)y'' + X_1(x)y' + X_2(x)y = 0$$

where the $X_i(x)$ are polynomials in x; the degree of $X_0(x)$ is not less than that of $X_1(x)$ or $X_2(x)$. The finite singular points are all regular but $x = \infty$

may be a regular or an irregular singular point. Finally, the general solution of the equation is to be free from logarithms and the exponents at every finite singular point are to be integers. When all of these conditions are satisfied, the general solution of the differential equation is

$$y = C_1 e^{r_1 x} F_1(x) + C_2 e^{r_2 x} F_2(x)$$

where r_1, r_2 are constants, not necessarily unequal, and $F_1(x)$, $F_2(x)$ are rational functions.

b. The Hamburger equation. The general case is

$$x^2 y'' + x p_1(x) y' + p_2(x) y = 0$$

where $x = 0$ is a regular singular point and $x = \infty$ is an essential singular point for every solution. It is convenient to take the equation in its normal form; see **4-1-2**. Again using x, y as the variables, the result can be written as

$$y'' - \left(a + 2\frac{b}{x} + \frac{c}{x^2} \right) y = 0$$

Assume that a normal solution of it exists; see **8-3**. The following relations arise

$$y = e^{\phi(x)} u(x); \quad \phi(x) = b_0 x^r / r + \ldots + b_{r-1} x$$

Furthermore,

$$u''(x) + P_1 u' + Q_1 u = 0$$
$$P_1 = 2\phi'; \quad Q_1 = \phi'' + \phi'^2 - a - 2b/x - c/x^2$$
$$u(x) = x^s (1 + c_1/x + c_2/x^2 + \ldots)$$

When these relations are put into the original equation, it is found that

$$r = 1, \quad b_0^2 = a, \quad b_0 s = b, \quad 2b_0 c_1 = s(s-1) - c,$$
$$2k b_0 c_k = [(s-k+1)(s-k) - c] c_{k-1}; \quad k = 2, 3, 4, \ldots .$$

The series for $u(x)$ is divergent for all z. To avoid this difficulty, require it to be a finite series with $c_m x^{-m}$ as its last term. Then, $(s-m)(s-m-1) = c$. Therefore, if $(m - b/b_0)(m + 1 - b/b_0) = c$ has a root which is zero or a positive integer for $b_0 = \pm \sqrt{a}$, the assumed normal solution exists.

The condition for two normal solutions can also be investigated. Suppose that the indicial equation at $x = 0$ is $\beta(\beta - 1) = c$, with exponents β_1, β_2. Let the exponents at $x = \infty$ be s_1, s_2 with $s_{1,2} = \pm b/\sqrt{a}$, not zero. It follows that $s_1 = m_1 + \beta_1$, $s_2 = m_2 + \beta_2$, and $s_1 + s_2 = 1 + m_1 + m_2$, which is not possible since m_1, m_2 have been shown to be positive integers or zero.

As a second possibility, suppose that $s_1 = s_2 = 0$, $b = 0$, and that

$m(m+1) = c$ has a positive integral root. There are two normal solutions

$$y_1 = e^{x\sqrt{a}}(1 + c_1/x + \dots + c_m/x^m)$$
$$y_2 = e^{-x\sqrt{a}}(1 - c_1/x + \dots \pm c_m/x^m)$$

There is still a third case. Let $s_1 \neq s_2$; $s_1 = m_1 + \beta_1$, $s_2 = m_2 + \beta_1$; $s_1 - s_2 = m_1 - m_2$, $s_1 + s_2 = 0$. It follows that $2s_1$ and $2s_2$ are integers, $2b/\sqrt{a}$ is an integer, $m_1 + m_2 + 2\beta_1 = 0$, $2\beta_1$ is a negative integer, not zero. Finally, $4c+1 = 4\beta_1(\beta_1 - 1) + 1 = (2\beta_1 - 1)^2$. Thus, $4c+1$ is the square of an integer, not zero, and under these conditions there are two normal solutions.

c. Equations with periodic coefficients. If the coefficients of a differential equation are single-valued, continuous, and periodic it does not follow that the general solution of the equation will also be periodic. A carefully investigated case is that of Mathieu's equation, see **9-2** and Part II. It can be taken as

$$y'' + (a + b\cos 2x)y = 0$$

More general cases, with doubly-periodic coefficients, have also been studied.

Picard's equation is of a related type. Its coefficients are elliptic functions with identical periods. If its general integral is analytic except for poles, that general solution can be given in terms of standard elliptic functions.

10. Integral Solution

Take the differential equation as

$$A_2(x)y'' + A_1(x)y' + A_0(x)y = 0 \tag{1}$$

Note that the subscripts are different (2 and 0 have been interchanged) from those in the standard form previously used. The change will simplify some equations here. The coefficients in (1) are continuous functions of x, frequently polynomials. Use the symbolic operators $D = d/dx$ and $L_x = A_2 D^2 + A_1 D + A_0$, see **5-2**, so that (1) becomes

$$L_x(y) = 0 \tag{2}$$

Alternative forms often seen are $L(y)$, $L(D)y$, etc. It is desired to find a solution of (2) as a definite integral

$$y(x) = \int_a^b K(x, t)u(t)dt \tag{3}$$

The simplest case is that indicated with real variables, functions, and integration limits. There are advantages when complex variables are used, see **7b**, and then the definite integral is replaced by a contour integral. Only the real case will be discussed here. For treatments involving the complex variable and contour integrals, see Ince-1 or Kamke-1. Illustration of the methods with many physical problems has been made by Morse and Feshbach.

A solution in the form of (3) is especially suitable if it becomes necessary to evaluate the integral by approximate methods; see **A1-13**. However, much information can be obtained even from the unintegrated form of the solution.

There are three different kinds of quantities in (3). Each must be properly determined so that the integral satisfies the differential equation; see **a**, **b**, **c**. For a general summary of the method, see **d**.

a. The kernel or nucleus, $K(x, t)$. Let M_t be a linear differential operator in t, which produces the second-order equation

$$M_t(v) = B_2(t)v'' + B_1(t)v' + B_0(t)v = 0 \tag{4}$$

Choose the kernel, which depends on both x and t, to satisfy the partial differential equation

$$L_x(K) = M_t(K) \tag{5}$$

In many cases, (5) can be replaced by $L_x(K) = M_t(K_1)$, where K, K_1 are two different kernels. If L_x can be applied to (3), the result is

$$L_x(y) = \int_a^b L_x(K)u(t)dt = \int_a^b M_t(K)u(t)dt \tag{6}$$

b. The modulation factor, $u(t)$. When a kernel has been determined, so that (5) is satisfied, it follows that $M_t(K) = 0$, and its adjoint equation, see **5-2**, is

$$\overline{M}_t(u) = (B_2u)'' - (B_1u)' + B_0u = 0 \tag{7}$$

Use the Lagrange identity, see **5-2**,

$$u(t)M_t[K(x, t)] = K(x, t)\overline{M}_t[u(t)] = \frac{\partial}{\partial t}P(K, u) \tag{8}$$

and calculate the bilinear concomitant, which contains x as a parameter,

$$P(K, u) = B_2(uK' - Ku') + (B_1 - B_2')Ku \tag{9}$$

Here, the derivatives are with respect to t. Integrate both sides of (8) between the limits a and b, simplify the notation somewhat and the result is known as Green's formula

$$\int_a^b [uM_t(K) - K\overline{M}_t(u)]dt = P(K, u)\Big|_{t=a}^{t=b} \tag{10}$$

If the right-hand side of this equation can be made to vanish, see **c**, the solution of (2) is given by (3). The first term in (10) equals $L_x(y)$ according to (6), but $u(t)$ is a solution of (7); hence $\overline{M}_t(u) = 0$.

c. The integration limits, a and b. It is not necessary that M_t, $\overline{M}_t$ be second-order operators, as indicated in (4) and (7). For the more general case, see **10-1**. Suppose, however, that the general solution of (7) is $u(t) = C_1 u_1 + C_2 u_2$. Reference to (9) shows that $u(t)$ and $u'(t)$ must vanish at both limits. However, neither will vanish unless a, b are singular points of (7). If both are singular points, and if the solution $u(t)$ has exponents greater than unity, $P(K, u)$ will vanish as required. Therefore, choose a, b as two singular points of (7). Alternatively, any values of t common to both $u(t) = 0$ and $u'(t) = 0$ will make the bilinear concomitant vanish and can be taken as a, b. Each pair of such points will give a particular solution of (1). If enough different pairs exist, the general solution is obtained. If only one particular solution results, the general solution can be found by **4-1-1**.

d. Summary of the method. Given $L_x(y) = 0$ to solve, see (1) and (2), proceed as follows.

    i. Select an appropriate kernel. Some examples and suggestions are given in **10-1**.

    ii. Calculate the linear operator M_t from (5).

    iii. Calculate the adjoint equation (7) and solve it to get $u(t)$.

    iv. Calculate $P(K, u)$, the bilinear concomitant from (9).

    v. Determine two integration limits, a and b in (3), so that $P(K, u) = 0$ at both. For possible choices of the limits, see **c**.

    vi. The solution of (1) is given by (3).

10-1. Kernels for the Integral Solution. When a kernel can be found which satisfies (5), the solution of (1) may usually be obtained according to **10**. The following include some well-known examples.

a. The Laplace transform, $K(x, t) = e^{xt}$. Suppose that the coefficients in (1) are polynomials of degree m or less

$$A_r(x) = a_{r0} + a_{r1}x + a_{r2}x^2 + \ldots + a_{rm}x^m; \quad r = 0, 1, 2 \tag{11}$$

where the a_{rs} are constants. Then, if the coefficients in M_t are

$$B_s(t) = a_{0s} + a_{1s}t + a_{2s}t^2; \quad s = 1, 0, \ldots, m \tag{12}$$

the condition of (5) is satisfied with $K = e^{xt}$.

For simplicity in **10**, both (4) and (7) were assumed to be second-order equations. Here, both are of mth order, for

$$M_t(v) = B_m(t)v^{(m)} + B_{m-1}(t)v^{(m-1)} + \ldots + B_1(t)v' + B_0(t)v = 0$$

and its adjoint equation is

$$\overline{M}_t(u) = (-1)^m(B_m u)^{(m)} + (-1)^{m-1}(B_{m-1}u)^{(m-1)} + \ldots + B_0 u = 0 \quad (13)$$

The conclusions and directions in **10** still hold but if $m \geq 2$, it may be more difficult to solve (13) than to use another method for the given differential equation · see, however, **10-1d**. If $m = 1$, see **i**; for $m = 2$, some integrable cases are presented in **ii**. A generalization of the Laplace transform is given in **iii**. For its use in another way, see **12-1-4**.

   i. When $m = 1$, the $A_r(x)$ in (11) are linear in x, and the differential equation corresponding to (1) is Laplace's linear equation of second order. Then, (7) or (13) become $B_1 u'(t) - (B_0 - B_1')u = 0$, which can be written as

$$f(t)u' = g(t)u \quad (14)$$

where $f(t)$, $g(t)$ are quadratics in t. This equation is type **A1-1-2**, with separable variables. Use partial fractions and get

$$\frac{g(t)}{f(t)} = k + \frac{p}{t-a} + \frac{q}{t-b}$$

where k, p, q are constants and a, b are the zeros of $f(t)$, both real and assumed to be unequal. Integration of (14) then gives

$$u = e^{kt}(t-a)^p(t-b)^q$$

The bilinear concomitant is found to be $P(x, t) = f(t)u(t)e^{xt}$, or after elimination of constant factors, $[(t-a)^{p+1}(t-b)^{q+1}e^{(k+x)t}]$. If this expression can be made to vanish at two values of t, a solution of the differential equation is given by (3). It is seen that a, b are suitable values.

   ii. When $m = 2$, the adjoint equation (13) becomes

$$T_2(t)u'' + T_1(t)u' + T_0(t)u = 0 \quad (15)$$

where

$$T_2(t) = B_2(t); \quad T_1(t) = 2B_2' - B_1; \quad T_0(t) = B_2'' - B_1' + B_0$$

The coefficients $B_s(t)$ are quadratics in t, with constant coefficients a_{rs}, $r = 0, 1, 2; s = 0, 1, 2$, see (12). There are several readily integrable cases. Find $u(t)$ as a solution of (15) and determine the integration limits, so that (9) vanishes; see also **10c**.

   1. Suppose the a_{rs} are such that $T_0(t) = 0$ for all t. Then, (15) is of type **B2-1-2**, with solution

$$u = C \int B_2^{-2} e^{\phi} dt; \quad \phi(t) = \int \frac{B_1}{B_2} dt$$

2. The quantity $B_2(t)$ is an integrating factor for (15), provided that $B_2 B_2'' + B_1 B_2' + B_0 B_2 = 0$. If the constants a_{rs} make this equation an identity, a first integral of (15) is $u'(t) = f(t) + g(t)u$; $f(t) = C_1 B_2{}^2$, $g(t) = B_1/B_2$; see **5-1**. This first-order equation is linear, see **A1-2**, with solution

$$u = C_2 e^\phi + C_1 e^\phi \int B_2{}^{-2} e^{-\phi} \, dt$$

where $\phi(t)$ is the same function as that in the previous case. The general solution is not necessary; hence the constants C_1 and C_2 may be chosen in any convenient way.

3. Reduce (15) to normal form; see **4-1-2**. Let $u(t) = v(t)w(t)$ and get

$$w''(t) + I(t)w(t) = 0 \qquad (16)$$

where $v(t) = e^{\phi/2}/B_2$; $I(t) = B_0/B_2 - B_1{}^2/4 B_2{}^2 - (B_1/B_2)'/2$; and $\phi(t)$ is the same function as before. Cases where (16) can be readily solved include: $I(t)$ is zero or any constant and it is type **1**; $I(t) = 1/(a+bt)^2$ or $1/(a+bt)^4$, when it is type **3-2**. See also **4-1-2**, for other possibilities.

iii. Equations of the Laplace type, see **i**, can also be produced with a linear operator $L_x = xF(D) + G(D)$, where F, G are polynomials in $D = d/dx$ with constant coefficients; see also **b**. A suitable kernel in such cases is

$$K(x, t) = \exp[xt + \int G(t)u(t)dt]$$

where $u(t) = 1/F(t)$.

b. The Euler transform, $K(x, t) = K(x - t)$. Define the symbolic operators $D = d/dx$, $D_t = d/dt$, $D_z = d/dz$, $z = (x - t)$. Consider a linear operator $L_x = xF(D) + G(D)$, which will yield an equation of the Laplace type; see **a**. Choose a kernel $K(x, t) = K(x - t) = K(z)$. The partial differential equation corresponding to (5) requires that

$$M_t = tF(-D_t) + H(-D_t)$$

provided that $K(z)$ satisfies

$$[xF(D_z) + G(D_z) - H(D_z)]K(z) = 0$$

Finally, $u(t)$ is a solution of $F(D_t)tu + H(D_t)u = 0$, which is the adjoint of M_t. Continue as directed in **10d**.

The Euler transform is usually taken as $K(x, t) = (x - t)^p$. It is especially suitable for the Pochhammer differential equation which is of order n, with polynomials for coefficients. For the general case, see Ince-1 or Kamke-1. Here, we consider only the second-order equation. Its coefficients A_r are polynomials of degree r, which means that $A_2(x)$ in (1) is a quadratic. The two roots of this quadratic, as well as $x = \infty$, will be singular points for (1). Use Taylor's theorem, and expand about $x = t$ to get $L_x(K) = B_2(t)K'' + B_1(t)K' + B_0(t)K = 0$, where

$$B_2(t) = A_2(t)$$
$$B_1(t) = -[(p-1)A_2'(t) + A_1(t)] \qquad (17)$$
$$B_0(t) = \frac{1}{2}p(p-1)A_2''(t) + pA_1'(t) + A_0(t)$$

There are no higher terms in the $B_s(t)$, since the restriction imposed on $A_r(x)$ means that $A_2'''(t)$, $A_1''(t)$, $A_0'(t)$, etc., will vanish.

The condition (5) is satisfied with the chosen kernel and the adjoint equation is given by (7). However, the constant p is arbitrary; select it so that $B_0(t) = 0$. The third equation of (17) thus determines two values of p, either of which may be used in the integral solution.

Explicitly, the adjoint equation becomes

$$\overline{M}_t(u) = (B_2 u)'' + (B_1 u)' = 0$$

It is easily reduced to a first-order equation with $U(t) = B_2(t)u(t)$, for then

$$U''(t) + (B_1 u)' = 0; \quad U'(t) + B_1 U/B_2 = 0;$$

$$\ln U + \int \frac{B_1}{B_2} dt + C.$$

Restoration of the original variables and functions from (17) gives

$$u(t) = C_1 e^{-\phi}/A_2{}^p; \quad \phi(t) = \int \frac{A_1}{A_2} dt$$

From (9), the bilinear concomitant is

$$P(K, u) = -pA_2(t)u(t)(x-t)^{p-1}$$

Complete the solution as described in **10d**.

c. The Mellin transform, $K(x, t) = K(xt)$. As in **b**, let $D = d/dx$, $D_t = d/dt$, $D_z = d/dz$. The linear operator is to have the form

$$L_x = x^n F(xD) + G(xD).$$

The kernel is $K(x, t) = K(xt)$ and the partial differential equation (5) requires that $M_t = G(tD_t) + t^{-n}H(tD_t)$, where F, G, H are polynomials in their arguments. It is further required that $K(z)$ be any solution of

$$[z^n F(zD_z) - H(zD_z)]K(z) = 0$$

The rest of the work is that directed in **10d**.

A kernel of this type is $J_p(z)$, a Bessel function of order p; see **9-2**, type [0, 1, 1]. Let $w(z) = J_p(z)$ and its differential equation is

$$z^2 w''(z) + zw' + (z^2 - p^2)w = 0 \qquad (18)$$

Let the equation given for solution be

$$L_x(y) = x^2 y'' + x(1 + ax^2)y' + (aqx^2 - p^2)y = 0$$

where a, q are constants. With $K(xt) = J_p(xt)$, it is found that $L_x(K) = B_1(t)K' + B_0(t)K = 0$; $B_1 = at$, $B_0 = aq + ct^2$. However, from (18),

$$c = z^{-2}(z^2 w'' + zw' - p^2 w) = -w(z)$$

and, it follows that $M_t(K) = atK' + (aq - t^2)K = 0$. Its adjoint equation is $\overline{M}_t(u) = -(atu)' + (aq - t^2)u = 0$. The variables are separable in this first-order equation, see **A1-1-2**, and its solution is $u(t) = Ct^{q-1}e^{-t^2/2a}$. The bilinear concomitant is $P(J_p, u) = Cat^q e^{-t^2/2a} J_p(xt)$. Proceed further as in **10d**.

d. A kernel in three variables. In most cases, the adjoint equation is difficult to solve, when of higher than first order. The following procedure may be helpful. Choose a kernel in three variables $K(x; s, t)$ The equation corresponding to (5) is $L_x(K) = M_{s,t}(K)$, where

$$M_{s,t} = B_0(s, t)\partial^2/\partial s \partial t + B_1(s, t)\partial/\partial s + B_2(s, t)\partial/\partial t + B_3(s, t)$$

The adjoint operator is $\overline{M}_{s,t} = \partial^2 B_0/\partial s \partial t - \partial B_1/\partial s - \partial B_2/\partial t + B_3$. In the general case, $\overline{M}_{s,t}[u(s, t)] = 0$ is a partial differential equation which may not be easy to solve. In special cases, $u(s, t) = v(s)w(t)$, so the adjoint equation becomes a pair of first-order differential equations, $a_0(s)v'(s) + a_1(s) = 0$; $b_0(t)w'(t) + b_1(t) = 0$. The rest of the work is like **10d**, with

$$y = \iint K(x; s, t)u(s, t)ds\,dt$$

and suitable limits determined from the bilinear concomitant.

11. Continued Fraction Solution

The equation in its standard form is taken as

$$y'' + P(x)y' + Q(x)y = 0$$

Solve it for y and get $y = F_0(x)y' + G_1(x)y''$; $F_0 = -P/Q$; $G_1 = -1/Q$. One differentiation gives $y' = F_1(x)y'' + G_2(x)y'''$, where

$$F_1(x) = (F_0 + G_1')/(1 - F_0'); \quad G_2(x) = G_1/(1 - F_0')$$

After n differentiations, $y^{(n)} = F_n y^{(n+1)} + G_{n+1}y^{(n+2)}$, where

$$F_n = (F_{n-1} + G_n')/(1 - F_{n-1}'), \quad G_{n+1} = G_n/(1 - F_{n-1}')$$

From these equations, it follows that

$$\frac{y}{y'} = F_0 + G_1\frac{y''}{y'} = F_0 + G_1/(F_1 + G_2 y'''/y'') = \ldots$$
$$= F_0 + \frac{G_1}{F_1} + \frac{G_2}{F_2} + \ldots + \frac{G_n}{(F_n + R_n)}$$

The last term is $R_n = G_{n+1}y^{(n+2)}/y^{(n+1)}$. Invert the equation for y/y' and get

$$\frac{y'}{y} = \frac{d\ln y}{dx} = \frac{1}{G_0} + \frac{G_1}{F_1} + \frac{G_2}{F_2} + \ldots + \frac{G_n}{F_n} + \ldots$$

a. If n is finite, one integration of the last equation gives $\ln y$; hence the solution of the differential equation.

b. The continued fraction converges to y'/y if the following conditions are met; see also Erdélyi-1, Vol. 3,

    i. $y \neq 0$.

    ii. F_n, G_n approach limits F, G as n approaches infinity.

    iii. The roots s_1, s_2 of $s^2 - Fs + G = 0$ are of unequal moduli.

    iv. $|s_2| < |s_1|$, $\lim |y^{(n)}|^{1/n} < |s_2|^{-1}$, $|s_2| \neq 0$. If the limit is finite, $|s_2| = 0$.

c. Some further comments may be helpful.

    i. Convert the second-order differential equation into a first-order equation of Riccati type; see **A1-3-1-1**. The latter will show the conditions for a solution as a finite continued fraction.

    ii. The procedure of this section could be modified by using integration instead of differentiation.

    iii. The method cannot be extended, in any obvious way, to equations of order higher than two.

    iv. When the series solution of a differential equation produces a many-term recursion relation, see **8-1-1**, a continued-fraction solution may be preferred. An example of interest in some physical problems is Mathieu's equation; see **9-2**, type [0, 0, 2] or, for more details about the equation and its solution, Erdélyi-1. In this case, it is simpler to find the three-term recursion formula by the methods of **8** and then to convert that result into the form of a continued fraction.

12. The Linear Nonhomogeneous Equation

The general equation is

$$y'' + P(x)y' + Q(x)y = R(x)$$

If the coefficient of y'' is not unity, convert the equation to the standard form. It is assumed that the general solution of the corresponding homogeneous equation, see **B1**, is known. This means that the equation has been solved, by some of the preceding methods, for the case $R(x) = 0$. Let this solution, called the *complementary function*, be $Y(x) = C_1y_1 + C_2y_2$. Then, if $F(x)$ is any *special* solution, a particular integral of the nonhomogeneous equation, the general solution of the latter is

$$y = C_1y_1 + C_2y_2 + F(x) = Y(x) + F(x)$$

The problem of this section is thus a search for a particular integral of the nonhomogeneous equation and the simplest possible form is acceptable.

There are three cases, depending on the coefficients $P(x)$ and $Q(x)$. It does not matter whether $R(x)$ is a constant or a function of x; if it is a function of x and y, the equation is no longer linear and, in that case, refer to **B2**.

a. The coefficients $P(x)$ and $Q(x)$ are both constants; see **12-1**.

b. The coefficients $P(x)$, $Q(x)$ are functions of x, one or both of them, but the equation is reducible to **a**; see **12-2**.

c. The general case, where one or both of the coefficients depend on x but **b** does not apply; see **12-3**.

12-1. The Nonhomogeneous Equation with Constant Coefficients. The standard form is

$$y'' + a_1y' + a_2y = R(x) \tag{1}$$

where a_1, a_2 are constants, and $R(x)$ may be a constant or a function of x. The equivalent operator form, see **1**, is often useful

$$(D - r_1)(D - r_2)y = R(x)$$

where $D = d/dx$ and r_1, r_2 are the characteristic roots of the auxiliary equation. It is desired to find a particular integral, $F(x)$. If more than one can be found, select the simplest. Since such an integral is a special solution of the differential equation, it will contain no arbitrary constant. If the following methods yield an integration constant, set it equal to zero, unity, or any other convenient value.

a. When $R(x) = R_0$, a constant, the particular integral is:

   i. $F(x) = R_0/a_2$; $a_2 \neq 0$.

   ii. $F(x) = R_0x/a_1$; $a_1 \neq 0, a_2 = 0$.

   iii. $F(x) = R_0x^2/2$; $a_1 = a_2 = 0$.

b. A particular integral by inspection. Sometimes, such an integral is obvious; in other cases, it is found only after a number of trials or with some lucky guesses. Do not overlook this possibility as the more formal procedures may be lengthy.

There are a number of methods for seeking a particular integral of the nonhomogeneous equation. However, one may be more suitable than the others in a given case. Look at all of the following methods before a final choice is made. Similarly, consult **12-3**, methods for the equation with variable coefficients, for they also apply to the equation with constant coefficients.

12-1-1. The Method of Undetermined Coefficients. This method, when it can be used, is probably preferable to all others. It depends only on differentiation and the solution of simultaneous linear algebraic equations. Integration is not required, nor is it necessary to know the general solution of the homogeneous equation beforehand, as is true for most of the other methods. For the method to apply, the function $R(x)$ must contain only terms which have a finite number of linearly independent derivatives. A fairly general situation is that where

$$R(x) = R_1(x) + R_2(x) + \ldots + R_m(x)$$

and a typical term is

$$R_i(x) = e^{ax}[\cos bx(\alpha_0 + \alpha_1 x + \ldots + \alpha_n x^n) + \sin bx(\beta_0 + \beta_1 x + \ldots + \beta_n x^n)]$$

Here, a, b, n, α_i, β_i are constants and some of them may be zero. Write $R_1(x)$ in this form, temporarily ignore $R_2, R_3, \ldots$, and assume a trial particular integral

$F_1(x)$

$$= x^r e^{ax}[\cos bx(A_{01} + A_{11}x + \ldots + A_{n1}x^n) + \sin bx(B_{01} + B_{11}x + \ldots + B_{n1}x^n)]$$

where the A_{i1}, B_{i1} are constants to be determined. If $(a \pm ib)$ is not a root of the characteristic equation, see **1**, take $r = 0$; otherwise r is the multiplicity of the root, which can be no greater than two, since the differential equation is assumed to be of the second order.

Repeat the procedure with $R_2, R_3, \ldots$, to get further functions F_2, $F_3, \ldots$, but take different constants for each, A_{i2}, B_{i2}, A_{i3}, B_{i3}, etc. The complete trial integral is the sum of these $F_i(x)$. Substitute it into the left-hand side of the differential equation and equate the result to the sum of the $R_i(x)$, so that

$$F''(x) + a_1 F'(x) + a_2 F(x) = R(x)$$

Collect coefficients of like terms on both sides of the identity. Since each sum must vanish, a set of simultaneous equations will result. Solve them for the A_{ij}, B_{ij} which will then determine the required particular integral, $F(x) = F_1(x) + F_2(x) + \ldots + F_m(x)$.

12-1-2. Reduction of Order. Use the factored form

$$(D - r_1)(D - r_2)y = R(x)$$

where $D = d/dx$ and r_1, r_2 are the roots of the auxiliary equation; see **1**. Let $(D - r_2)y = u(x)$, so that $(D - r_1)y = R(x)$, which is a linear equation of the first order. When its solution is found by the method of **A1-2**, the second-order equation can be reduced to one of first order, which is also linear. The final result is

$$y = e^{r_2 x} \int e^{(r_1 - r_2)x}\phi(x)dx + C_1 e^{r_1 x} + C_2 e^{r_2 x} \tag{2}$$

where

$$\phi(x) = \int^x e^{-r_1 t}R(t)dt$$

The lower limit in the last integral is arbitrary; zero is often a convenient value but, in other cases, a different constant may give a simpler answer. Since the order of the terms in (2) is unimportant, it sometimes helps in evaluating integrals if the subscripts 1, 2 are properly assigned to the characteristic roots.

It should be noted that the first term on the right of (2) is a particular integral of the nonhomogeneous equation while the other terms are the complementary function. It may be convenient to determine the latter in some other way. In that case, this method could be used to find the particular integral only. If the characteristic roots are equal, the correct particular integral will still be obtained but only one term in the complementary function.

Another form of the particular integral may be useful. It results by partial integration of the preceding result.

$$(r_1 - r_2)F(x) = \int^x e^{r_1(x-t)}R(t)dt - \int^x e^{r_2(x-t)}R(t)dt$$

As before, the lower limits are arbitrary; choose them as convenient. This equation will obviously not hold if the characteristic roots are equal.

Evaluation of the integrals in this method may not be easy. The operator methods of **12-1-3** are often simpler.

12-1-3. Operator Methods. Quite different from **12-1-1** and **12-1-2**, the methods now to be described are applicable to the same kinds of equations, but they may produce an integral with less labor. Considerable space is usually devoted to them in elementary courses on differential equations.

Define the linear operator, see **5-2**,

$$L(D) = D^2 + a_1 D + a_2 = (D - r_1)(D - r_2)$$

where $D = d/dx$, $(r_1 + r_2) = -a_1$, $r_1 r_2 = a_2$. The differential equation becomes $L(D)y = R(x)$ and a particular integral of it can be written symbolically as $F(x) = L^{-1}(D)R(x)$. There are two ways in which the right-hand side of this equation can be evaluated. They are described in **a** and **b**, when $R(x)$ is of general form. Shorter methods, when $R(x)$ has certain special forms are given in **c**.

a. In factored form, $F(x) = L^{-1}(D)R(x) = [(D-r_1)(D-r_2)]^{-1}R(x)$. However, $(D-r_2)^{-1}R(x)$ is a particular integral of the linear first-order equation, $y' - r_2y = R(x)$. It can be solved by **A1-2**. Application of the second operator $(D-r_1)^{-1}$ to this result gives an equation which is equivalent to the first solution in **12-1-2**.

This method is particularly useful for an equation of the form

$$(D-r)^2y = e^{rx}R(x),$$

where $R(x)$ can be integrated easily twice in succession.

b. Resolve the operator into partial fractions,

$$F(x) = L^{-1}(D)R(x) = \frac{1}{r_1 - r_2}\left[\frac{1}{D - r_1} + \frac{1}{D - r_2}\right]R(x)$$

Evaluation of the right-hand side of this equation by means similar to that of **a** gives a particular integral, as shown in the second solution of **12-1-2**. The integrations may be easier than in **a**.

If $R(x)$ is a sum of terms, the two operators are applied successively to each term in the sum. The particular integral is the sum of these results.

c. The following special forms of $R(x)$ frequently occur. In such cases, the general methods of **a** or **b** lead to relatively simple operations.

i. $R(x) = R_0$, a constant; see **12-1**.

ii. $R(x) = c_0 + c_1x + c_2x^2 + \ldots + c_nx^n$. Expand $L^{-1}(D)$ as a series in D but stop with the term in D^n, so that

$$L^{-1}(D) = A_0 + A_1D + A_2D^2 + \ldots + A_nD^n$$

Let each term in this polynomial operate on each term in $R(x)$. The sum of the results is the particular integral. A term such as A_mD^m, $m > n$, is omitted from the expansion, since such derivatives of $R(x)$ would vanish.

iii. $R(x) = Ae^{kx}$; $F(x) = AL^{-1}(k)e^{kx}$, provided that $L(k) \neq 0$. In the exceptional case, there are two possibilities. If $L(D) = (D-k)^2$, then $F(x) = x^2e^{kx}/2$; if $L(D) = (D-k)(D-b)$, then $F(x) = xe^{kx}/(k-b)$.

iv. $R(x) = A \cos(ax+b)$. A particular integral is the real part of $F(x) = AL^{-1}(ia)e^{i(ax+b)}$; $L(ia) \neq 0$, remembering that $e^{iz} = \cos z + i \sin z$. In the exceptional case, define $L'(ia) = (dL/dD)_{D=ia}$ and select the real part of $F(x) = AL'^{-1}xe^{i(ax+b)}$.

v. In **iv**, if $R(x) = A \cos ax$ and

$$L(D) = D^2 + r^2, \quad F(x) = A \cos ax/(r^2 - a^2), \quad r \neq a$$

If $r = a$,

$$F(x) = \frac{Ax}{2a} \sin ax$$

More generally, when $R(x) = \cos bx$ and $L(D) = D^2 + a_1D + a_2$, the particular integral is

$$F(x) = \frac{(a_2 - b^2) \cos bx + a_1 b \sin bx}{(a_2 - b^2)^2 + a_1^2 b^2}$$

vi. $R(x) = A \sin (ax + b)$. Replace A by $-iA$ in case **iv**; interchange $\cos ax$ and $\sin ax$ in case **v**, taking a negative sign when $r = a$. Finally, if $R(x) = \sin bx$ and $L(D) = D^2 + a_1D + a_2$, use the last equation in case **v**, interchange $\cos bx$ and $\sin bx$, take the difference between the two terms in the numerator.

vii. $R(x) = A \cos (ax + b)X(x)$. The particular integral is the real part of $F(x) = Ae^{i(ax+b)}L^{-1}(D + ia)X(x)$.

viii. $R(x) = A \sin (ax + b)X(x)$. Replace A by $-iA$ in case **vii**.

ix. $R(x) = Ae^{kx}X(x)$; $F(x) = Ae^{kx}L^{-1}(D + k)X(x)$. This procedure, known as the *exponential shift*, is often useful because with it an exponential factor may be transferred from one side of a differential operator to the other side. When $X(x) = c_0 + c_1x + c_2x^2 + \ldots + c_nx^n$ and $L(D) = D^2 + a_1D + a_2$, the particular integral is

$$F(x) = Ae^{kx}\left[g(k)X(x) + g'(k)X'(x) + \ldots + \frac{g^{(n)}(k)}{n!}X^{(n)}(x)\right]$$

where $g(k) = L^{-1}(k)$.

x. $R(x) = Ae^{kx} \cos (ax + b)$. Take the real part of

$$F(x) = Ae^{i(ax+b)}L^{-1}(k + ia)e^{kx}$$

provided $L(k + ia)$ does not vanish. Otherwise, replace A by Ax and use $L'(k + ia)$; see case **iv**.

xi. $R(x) = Ae^{kx} \sin (ax + b)$. Replace A by $-iA$ in case **x**.

xii. Let $R(x)$ be a general function of x and $L(D) = (D - a)^2$. In this case,

$$F(x) = e^{ax} \int^x e^{-at}(x - t)R(t)dt$$

where the lower limit of the integral is arbitrary. Sometimes, it is useful to take $L(D) = (D - a)^2 + b^2$, and then

$$F(x) = \frac{e^{ax}}{b} \int^x e^{-at} \sin b(x - t)R(t)dt$$

12-1-4. The Laplace Transform.   While more generally useful for partial differential equations, the method of this section has advantages for ordinary differential equations, especially where preassigned conditions are given.   It is popular with many applied physical scientists and engineers.   The following preliminary material may be helpful.   For more details and proofs see, for example, Churchill.

The preliminary material is given in **a**.   The method is described in **b**. An example of the method is presented in **c**.

a. Let $f(x)$ be defined for $0 \leqslant x \leqslant \infty$ and consider the integral

$$L[f(x)] = F(p) = \int_0^\infty e^{-px} f(x)dx$$

where p is a number, usually complex, but with a real part positive and large enough to make the integral convergent.   This integral is the Laplace transform of $f(x)$ and a function of the complex variable p.   It transforms complex-valued functions of the real variable x into functions of a complex variable p.

Given $f(x)$ it is often possible to find $F(p)$ by simple integration.   In more complicated cases, an inversion theorem involving a contour integral is needed to evaluate $F(p)$.   Lengthy tables of $f(x)$ and $F(p)$ are available; see Erdélyi-3, Gardner and Barnes, Hodgman.   For a very brief one, see Table 1.   In the usual case, especially for an equation with constant coefficients, the Laplace transform method can be used by merely selecting the required answer from such tables.

The Laplace transform is a linear operator.   Thus, if c_1, c_2 are constants

$$L[c_1 f_1 + c_2 f_2] = c_1 L[f_1] + c_2 L[f_2]$$

Of especial importance for differential equations is the Laplace transform of derivatives

$$L[f'(x)] = pL[f] - f(0)$$

This result follows on integration by parts

$$\int_0^\infty e^{-px} f'(x)dx = p \int_0^\infty e^{-px} F(x)dx + e^{-px}f(x)\Big|_0^\infty$$

provided that $e^{-px}f(x) \to 0$ as $x \to \infty$.   The quantity $f(0)$ is thus the value of $f(x)$ at the lower limit of the integral.   In a similar way, it can be shown that

$$L[f''] = p^2 L[f] - pf(0) - f'(0)$$
$$L[f'''] = p^3 L[f] - p^2 f(0) - pf'(0) - f''(0)$$
$$\cdots \quad \cdots \quad \cdots \quad \cdots \quad \cdots \quad \cdots \quad \cdots \quad \cdots$$
$$L[f^{(n)}] = p^n L[f] - p^{n-1}f(0) - \cdots - pf^{(n-2)}(0) - f^{(n-1)}(0)$$

b. Details of the method. Given an equation to solve like (1), let $y(0) = C_1$, $y'(0) = C_2$, $L[y] = \bar{y}$, $L[R(x)] = \bar{R}$. Take the Laplace transform of the equation to get

$$(p^2 + a_1 p + a_2)\bar{y} = \bar{R} + C_1(a_1 + p) + C_2$$

Now, $L[R(x)] = \bar{R}(x)$ is some function of p; hence $\bar{y} = \bar{f}(p)$. By the method of partial fractions, it is usually possible to write

$$\bar{f}(p) = \bar{f}_1(p) + \bar{f}_2(p) + \cdots,$$

but reference to a table of transforms, at least in simple cases, will show that

$$\bar{f}_i(p) = L_i[f_i(x)] = f_i(x)$$

One may thus write

$$\bar{y} = \bar{f}_1(p) + \bar{f}_2(p) + \cdots$$

The inverse transform then gives the general solution of the differential equation as

$$y(x) = f_1(x) + f_2(x) + \cdots$$

TABLE 1. LAPLACE TRANSFORMS

$F(p)$	$f(x)$	$F(p)$	$f(x)$
$\dfrac{1}{p}$	1	$\dfrac{a}{p^2 - a^2}$	$\sinh ax$
$\dfrac{1}{p-a}$	e^{ax}	$\dfrac{n!}{p^{n+1}}$	x^n
$\dfrac{p}{p^2 + a^2}$	$\cos ax$	$\dfrac{n!}{(p-a)^{n+1}}$	$x^n e^{ax}$
$\dfrac{a}{p^2 + a^2}$	$\sin ax$	$\dfrac{(p-a)}{[(p-a)^2 + b^2]}$	$e^{ax} \cos bx$
$\dfrac{p}{p^2 - a^2}$	$\cosh ax$	$\dfrac{b}{[(p-a)^2 + b^2]}$	$e^{ax} \sin bx$

c. Illustration of the method. Since the procedure has been described briefly, a simple example may help to show how it is used. Let the given equation be

$$y'' + a^2 y = e^{bx}$$

Taking the transforms of both sides, the result is

$$(p^2 + a^2)\bar{y} = \frac{1}{p-b} + C_1 p + C_2$$

Write this equation in the form

$$\bar{y} = \frac{A_1}{p-b} + \frac{A_2 + C_2 + (A_3 + C_1)p}{p^2 + a^2}$$

where $A_1 = -A_3 = 1/(a^2 + b^2)$; $A_2 = -b/(a^2 + b^2)$.   From   Table   1,
$$\bar{f}_1 = A_1/(p-b), f_1 = A_1 e^{bx}$$

$$\bar{f}_2 = \frac{A_2 + C_2}{p^2 + a^2}, \quad f_2 = \frac{A_2 + C_2}{a} \sin ax$$

$$\bar{f}_3 = \frac{(A_3 + C_1)p}{p^2 + a^2}, \quad f_3 = (A_3 + C_1)\cos ax$$

The general solution of the equation is thus

$$y = A_1 e^{bx} + \frac{(A_2 + C_2)}{a} \sin ax + (A_3 + C_1)\cos ax$$

12-2. The Equation Reducible to Type 12-1.   If the homogeneous equation can be reduced to an equation with constant coefficients, see **1**, any of the methods of **12-1** will then apply to the nonhomogeneous equation. The simplest cases are the Euler equation, see **3-1**, and the Legendre linear equation, see **3-2**. In the latter case, transform to type **12-1** and proceed as directed there or transform to the nonhomogeneous equation of type **3-1** and use the methods of this section.

In the particular case of the Euler nonhomogeneous equation, see **3-1**, the operator methods of **12-1-3** have some advantages but changes occur in notation and details.

Alternatively, the methods of **12-3** may be useful, especially **12-3b**.

Let the given equation be

$$x^2 y'' + a_1 x y' + a_2 y = R(x)$$

where a_1, a_2 are constants. Define a linear operator, see **3-1**.

$$L(\theta) = \theta^2 + A_1 \theta + A_2 = (\theta - r_1)(\theta - r_2)$$

where
$$\theta = xD = xd/dx; \quad \theta(\theta - 1) = x^2 D^2; \quad A_1 = a_1 - 1; \quad A_2 = a_2;$$

r_1, r_2 are the characteristic roots of the auxiliary equation. The differential equation becomes $L(\theta)y = R(x)$ and a particular integral of it is $F(x)$ $= L^{-1}(\theta)R(x)$

There are two general ways of finding $F(x)$; see **a** and **b**. When $R(x)$ has certain special forms, the procedure can often be simplified; see **c**.

a. The factored form. When the operator has been factored,

$$F(x) = [(\theta - r_1)(\theta - r_2)]^{-1}R(x)$$

$$= x^{r_1} \int^x x^{r_2 - r_1 - 1} \phi(x)dx; \quad \phi(x) = \int^x t^{-r_2 - 1} R(t)dt$$

The lower limit in the integrals is arbitrary and can be chosen to make the integration easy.

b. Partial fractions. When the operator is resolved into partial fractions, the result is

$$F(x) = L^{-1}(\theta)R(x) = \frac{1}{r_1 - r_2}\left[x^{r_1} \int^x t^{-r_1 - 1}R(t)dt - x^{r_2} \int^x t^{-r_2 - 1}R(t)dt \right]$$

As in **a**, the lower limit of the integrals is arbitrary. Note that this equation fails if $r_1 = r_2$, but see also **c**.

c. Special forms for $R(x)$.

i. $R(x) = Ax^n$; $F(x) = Ax^n/L(n)$; $L(n) \neq 0$. If n is a single root of $L(\theta)$, the denominator vanishes but $L(\theta) = (\theta - n)(\theta - m) = (\theta - n)M(\theta)$ and $F(x) = Ax^n \ln x/M(n)$; $M(n) \neq 0$. Finally, if $L(\theta) = (\theta - n)^2$, $F(x) = A x^n(\ln x)^2/2$.

ii. $R(x) = Ax^nX(x)$; $F(x) = Ax^nL^{-1}(\theta + n)X(x)$. Evaluate the operation on $X(x)$ by **a** or **b**, but see also **iii**.

iii. $R(x)$ is a rational integral function of $\ln x$. Expand $L^{-1}(\theta + n)$ in ascending powers of θ and operate on $X(x)$ with each term of this series. Stop at θ^k, where k is the highest power of $\ln x$ in $X(x)$, since $\theta \ln x = 1$.

12-3. The Nonhomogeneous Equation with Variable Coefficients. The standard form is

$$y'' + P(x)y' + Q(x)y = R(x)$$

It is desired to find a particular integral $F(x)$, for it is assumed that the general solution of the associated homogeneous equation has been found by some preceding method. Most of the procedures here are also applicable to the case where $P(x)$ and $Q(x)$ are constants· see **12-1**. Try each of the following until a suitable method is found. More than one may apply so it would be well to consider each before making a choice. If none seem satisfactory, a series solution may be necessary; see **12-3-1**.

a. Reduction of order. Select a special solution of the homogeneous equation and call it $u(x)$. Let it be as simple as possible, with arbitrary constants removed or fixed at some suitable values. Then, make the change of variable $y(x) = u(x)v(x)$ to get

$$uv'' + (2u' + Pu)v' + (u'' + Pu' + Qu)v = R(x)$$

The third term on the left of this equation vanishes, since $u(x)$ satisfies the equation in the last parenthesis. The remainder $uv'' + (2u' + Pu)v' = R(x)$ can be solved by **B2-1**.

b. The method of Lagrange or variation of parameter. Find the complementary function, see **2**, but take it as $Y_0(x) = A_1y_1 + A_2y_2$, assuming the A_i to be functions of x rather than arbitrary constants. When they are determined so that $Y_0(x)$ satisfies the nonhomogeneous equation $Y_0(x)$ becomes $y(x) = Y(x) + F(x)$, with $Y(x) = C_1y_1 + C_2y_2$.

The requirements are

$$y_1A_1' + y_2A_2' = 0$$

$$y_1'A_1' + y_2'A_2' = R(x)$$

The solution of these simultaneous equations is $A_1'(x) = -Ry_2/W$, $A_2'(x) = Ry_1/W$, where the Wronskian, $W(y_1, y_2) = y_1y_2' - y_1'y_2$, cannot vanish; see **B1c**. A quadrature for each $A_i'(x)$ gives $A_i(x)$ and the particular solution follows

$$F(x) = \int^x g(x, t)R(t)dt$$

where

$$g(x, t) = \frac{y_1(t)y_2(x) - y_2(t)y_1(x)}{W(t)}$$

The lower limit of the integral is arbitrary. The integration in this case may be easier than that in **a**.

c. The method of Cauchy. This is essentially the same as **b**, but the manipulations may be simpler in some cases. Let the complementary function be $Y(x) = C_1y_1 + C_2y_2$. Determine the two constants so that $Y(t) = 0$, $Y'(t) = R(t)$, when $x = t$. The particular integral, with arbitrary lower limit, is

$$f(x) = \int^x Y(x, t)dt$$

d. Solution by differentiation. Differentiate the given equation successively until it can be converted into a homogeneous equation of order $(k+2)$. If $R(x)$ vanishes after k differentiations, the method will apply. Alternatively, it is often possible to eliminate $R(x)$ and its derivatives after only a few differentiations. Solve the resulting homogeneous equation of order $(k+2)$, if possible, to get its general solution with $(k+2)$ arbitrary constants

$$y(x) = C_1y_1 + C_2y_2 + A_1f_1(x) + A_2f_2(x) + \dots + A_kf_k(x)$$

Substitute

$$F(x) = A_1f_1(x) + A_2f_2(x) + \dots + A_kf_k(x)$$

into the original nonhomogeneous second-order equation, determine the constants so that it is satisfied, and the result is the particular integral sought.

The method is relatively simple when the given differential equation has constant coefficients. In the more general case, the equation of order $(k+2)$ may be difficult to solve.

e. The exact nonhomogeneous equation. Take the equation as

$$A_0(x)y'' + A_1(x)y' + A_2(x)y = f(x)$$

The test for exactness is identical with that for the homogeneous case but ignoring the term $f(x)$; see **5-1**. A first integral is

$$B_0y' + B_1y = \int f(x)dx + C_1$$

where $B_0 = A_0$, $B_1 = A_1 - A_0'$. It, too, is exact if $B_1 = B_0'$. In that case, complete the integration by **A1-7**; otherwise, use **A1-2**.

Integrating factors, see **5-2**, can sometimes be found by inspection or after trying various functions. A simple case may occur if the $A_i(x)$ are polynomials in x. Assume an integrating factor of the form x^m, make the test for exactness, and see if it holds for some value of m.

12-3-1. Series Solution of the Nonhomogeneous Equation. When the homogeneous equation has been solved as an infinite series, see **8**, the nonhomogeneous equation may be reduced in order. Either method of **12-3** may be used. With suitable modifications, the method of undetermined coefficients might be preferred; see **12-1-1**.

Take the standard form of the equation as

$$x^2y'' + xp(x)y' + q(x)y = x^mr(x)$$

where

$$p(x) = p_0 + p_1x + p_2x^2 + \ldots; \quad q(x) = q_0 + q_1x + q_2x^2 + \ldots;$$

$$r(x) = r_0 + r_1x + r_2x^2 + \ldots$$

The coefficients are thus analytic at the origin, which could be an ordinary point or a regular singular point; see **8**. If an irregular singular point occurs, the equation will have a different form and, in that case, see **c**.

a. The origin is an ordinary point. This means that p_0, q_0, q_1 must vanish. Assume a particular integral

$$F(x) = x^m(B_0 + B_1x + B_2x^2 + \ldots)$$

and determine the coefficients so that the nonhomogeneous equation is satisfied.

b. The origin is a regular singular point. Calculate the exponents, s_1 and s_2 from the indicial equation; see **8-2**. There are several cases.

i. The quantity m is not equal to s_1, s_2, s_1+n, s_2+n, where n is an integer. Assume the same particular integral as that in **a**, proceeding as directed there.

ii. The quantity m equals s_1 or s_2 but $\Delta \neq n$, an integer, where $\Delta = s_1-s_2$; see **8-2-1**. Assume a particular solution

$$G(x) = Ay_i \ln x + F(x)$$

where y_i is that series solution of the homogeneous equation found according to **8-2-1** for $m = s_i$, and $F(x)$ is the function of **a**. Determine its coefficients B_i as directed there.

iii. The quantity m equals both s_1 and s_2. Assume a particular solution

$$H(x) = A\,(\ln x)^2\,y_1 + F(x)\ln x + x^m(c_0 + c_1x + c_2x^2 + \ ...)$$

and determine the coefficients as before. Here, $y_1(x)$ is the series solution found by **8-2-2** and $F(x)$ is the series in **a**.

iv. The quantity m satisfies none of the preceding requirements. It might, for example, equal an exponent where s_1 and s_2 differ by an integer or it might be unequal to an exponent but differ from one of them by an integer. Assume the particular integral of **iii** and determine the coefficients as before. Frequently, the final form of the particular integral will be simpler than the function $H(x)$ for one or both logarithmic terms may vanish.

c. The origin is an irregular singular point. Determine the complementary function according to **8-3**. Use either method of **12-3** to reduce the equation to one of first order and solve it according to **A1**.

B2. THE NONLINEAR EQUATION OF SECOND ORDER

The general equation is

$$f(x, y, y', y'') = 0$$

but terms like yy', yy'', y^2, xy^3, etc., will occur when it is given in explicit form. Nonlinear equations are usually more difficult to solve than linear ones. There are two important differences: the general solution is not a linear combination of two independent special solutions but it is a function of the two integration constants; singular solutions, not contained in the general solution, may also exist.

When the nonlinear equation has certain special forms, a solution may be easy to obtain. These cases, and the methods for solving them, are given in sections **1** to **5** following. The same procedures may often be used also for linear second-order equations, but usually a method of **B1** would be preferred. If none of them can be applied to a given nonlinear equation, see **6** for a certain class of equations. As a last resort, approximate methods may be tried; see **A1-13**. It should be noted that the general solution of a nonlinear second-order equation may be a complicated expression. Sometimes, a first integral is all that can be given in closed form.

1. The Dependent Variable Is Missing

The general equation is

$$f(x, y', y'') = 0 \tag{1}$$

and there are two cases, but see also **2-2**.

1-1. The First Derivative Is Missing. The equation becomes

$$f(x, y'') = 0$$

Solve it, if possible, and get $y'' = F(x)$. After two integrations, the result is

$$y = \int_{x_0}^{x} dx \int_{x_0}^{x} F(x)dx + C_1(x - x_0) + C_2$$

158

The lower limit of the integrals is chosen to make the integrations easy; frequently, 0 or 1 might be suitable.

An equivalent, and somewhat neater, form of the solution can be obtained by defining

$$Y(x) = \int_{x_0}^{x} (x-t)F(t)dt$$

for then, $Y''(x) = F(x)$. The solution of the equation is

$$y = \int_{x_0}^{x} (x-t)F(t)dt + C_1(x-x_0) + C_2$$

1-2. The General Case.   The first derivative is not missing so that the given equation has the form (1). Let $y'(x) = p(x)$, $y'' = p'$, and get an equation of first order

$$f(x, p, p') = 0 \tag{2}$$

Suppose that its solution, according to methods of **A1** or **A2**, is

$$F(x, p, C_1) = 0 \tag{3}$$

There are two possibilities, depending on whether it is easier to solve (3) for p or x.

a. Solve for p. The result, when (3) is solved for p, is separable and type **A1-1-1**. Let it be $p = g(x, C_1)$. The solution of it is

$$y = \int g(x, C_1)dx + C_2$$

b. Solve for x. If the solution of (3) is

$$x = G(p, C_1) \tag{4}$$

then, the solution of (1) is

$$y = \int p dx = \int p G'(p, C_1)dp + C_2 \tag{5}$$

An equivalent solution arises by partial integration of (5)

$$y = p G(p, C_1) - \int G(p, C_1)dp + C_2 \tag{6}$$

There are two possibilities for the final step.

   i. Regard p as a parameter and take (4), (5) or (4), (6) as a parametric solution of (1). It is often useful to replace p by another letter, t for example, in the final solution, emphasizing the fact that t is a parameter.

   ii. Eliminate p between either pair of functions given in **i**, to get an explicit solution $y = \phi(x, C_1, C_2)$.

2. The Independent Variable Is Missing

The general equation is

$$f(y, y', y'') = 0 \tag{1}$$

and there are three cases.

2-1. The First Derivative Is Missing. The equation becomes $y'' = F(y)$. Let $p = dy/dx$, $y'' = pdp/dy$, $pdp = F(y)dy$. One integration gives a first integral

$$p^2 = 2\int F(y)dy + C_1 = g(y) + C_1$$

With a second integration, using **A1-1-3**,

$$\int \frac{dy}{\sqrt{C_1 + g(y)}} = x + C_2$$

Alternatively, the first integral could have been obtained with the integrating factor $2p$; see **4**.

2-2. The Dependent Variable Is Missing. The equation has the form $y'' = F(y')$. There are two procedures.

a. Let $y' = p$, $y'' = dp/dx = F(p)$, Integrate once to get

$$x = \int \frac{dp}{F(p)} + C_1 = g(p) + C_1 \tag{2}$$

Solve this equation for p,

$$p = G(x, C_1) \tag{3}$$

Integrate once more and get the general solution of the equation

$$y = \int G(x, C_1)dx + C_2$$

b. An integration, from right to left, of

$$y = \int \frac{dp}{F(p)}\int \frac{p}{F(p)}dp$$

would give

$$H(y, p, C_1, C_2) = 0 \tag{4}$$

There are two possibilities.

i. Retain (3) and (4) as a parametric solution of the equation, with p replaced by the parameter t.

ii. Eliminate p between (3) and (4) to get an explicit relation between x and y.

2-3. The General Case. No variable is missing except x. The form of the equation is thus

$$f(y, y', y'') = 0$$

Let $y' = p$, $y'' = pdp/dy$ so that the equation becomes of first order

$$f\left(y, p, p\frac{dp}{dy}\right) = 0$$

Use a method of **A1** or **A2** and get a first integral $F(y, p, C_1) = 0$. Then, whichever is easier, follow **a** or **b**.

a. Solve the first integral for p and get $p = g(y, C_1)$. The variables are separable, see **A1-1-3**, and

$$\int \frac{dy}{g(y, C_1)} = x + C_2$$

b. Solve the first integral for y and get the result

$$y = G(p, C_1) \tag{5}$$

Another integration gives

$$x = \frac{y}{p} + \int \frac{G(p, C_1)}{p^2} dp + C_2 \tag{6}$$

There are two possibilities.

i. A parametric solution is given by (5) and (6). It may be useful to relabel p, calling it t, a parameter.

ii. Eliminate p between (5) and (6) to obtain an explicit function of x and y.

3. Homogeneous Equations

The following methods often apply to linear equations but they may be used with the proper kinds of nonlinear equations. Their object is the reduction of a second-order equation to one of first order, by appropriate variable transformations. The first-order equation is then solved, if possible, by a method of **A1** or **A2**. It must be recognized, however, that the first-order equation may not be solvable in terms of known functions so that one must often be satisfied with a first integral or a solution involving functions behind an integral sign. Singular solutions frequently occur for these types. If they are of interest be careful not to discard common factors which appear on both sides of an equality.

The homogeneity in the equations is algebraic, as described in **A1-8**. In the various types, replace x, y, y', y'' by the quantity indicated, where t is a constant multiplier. Examine the result to see if the method is applicable.

3-1. Homogeneous in y and Its Derivatives. In this case,

$$f(x, ty', ty'', ty'') = t^k f(x, y, y', y'')$$

Divide the equation by y^k and get

$$F(x, y'/y, y''/y) = 0$$

Introduce a new dependent variable, $y = \exp \int u(x)dx$, so that $y'/y = u(x)$, $y''/y = u' + u^2$, and the equation becomes of first order $F(x, u, u^2 + u') = 0$. If its solution, by a method of **A1** or **A2**, is $u = \phi(x, C_1)$, another quadrature will give

$$\ln y = \int \phi(x, C_1)dx + C_2$$

The new equation in u may be more difficult to solve than the original equation. For example, the linear equation $y'' + P(x)y' + Q(x)y = 0$ becomes $u'(x) + Q(x) + P(x)u + u^2 = 0$, which is a Riccati equation; see **A1-3**. Unless it happens to be one of the integrable cases, nothing has been gained with the new variable. It would usually be easier to seek a series solution for the linear second-order equation; see **B1-8**.

3-2. Homogeneous in x and dx. The requirement is

$$f(tx, y, y'/t, y''/t^2) = t^k f(x, y, y', y'')$$

Divide the equation by x^k and get

$$F(y\ xy', x^2y'') = 0$$

Let $y(x) = u(z)$, $z = \ln x$, $xy' = u'(z)$, $x^2y'' = u'' - u'$ and the result is of type **2-3**, with independent variable missing,

$$F(u, u', u'' - u') = 0$$

Reduce it to an equation of first order with $u'(z) = p$, $u'' = pp'(u)$, so that its form is

$$F(u, p, pp' - p) = 0$$

Solve this for p, if possible; determine u by another quadrature; finally restore the original variables to get the general solution, $\phi(x, y, C_1, C_2) = 0$. The Euler equation, see **B1-3-1**, is of this type.

3-3. Homogeneous in x and y. In this case,

$$f(tx, ty, y', y''/t) = t^k f(x, y, y', y'')$$

When divided by x^k it becomes

$$F(y/x, y', xy'') = 0$$

There are two procedures, the first of which may be preferable.
  a. Go to **3-4** and use that method with $n = 1$.
  b. Let

$$y = xz, \quad u(z) = x\frac{dz}{dx}, \quad y' = u + z, \quad xy'' = u(1 + u')$$

and the equation becomes

$$F(z, u + z, u + uu') = 0$$

Since this is of first order in u and z, try a method of **A1** or **A2**. If it can be solved, another quadrature will give $y(x)$.

3-4. The Isobaric Equation. The type is

$$f(tx, t^n y, t^{n-1}y', t^{n-2}y'') = t^k f(x, y, y', y'')$$

with n not necessarily an integer. Assign weights 1, n $(n-1)$, $(n-2)$ to $x, y, y,' y''$, respectively. A typical term in the equation will be $x^a y^b y'^c y''^d$. If every term has the common weight

$$k = a + bn + c(n-1) + d(n-2)$$

for the same value of n, the differential equation is isobaric and of weight k; see **A1-8-2**, for the corresponding first-order case. Divide by x^k and get

$$F(y/x^n, y'/x^{n-1}, y''/x^{n-2}) = 0$$

When $n = 0$, this is case **3-2**; proceed as directed there. When $n = 1$, it is case **3-3**; use that method or continue with the following procedure, setting $n = 1$. For n other than zero, any finite positive or negative rational quantity, the equation can be converted to case **3-2** and hence reduced to a first-order equation.

Let $y = x^n u(z)$, $z = \ln x$, and the new equation is free from z but still of second order. Then, take $u'(z) = p$ and the original equation becomes

$$f(x, y, y', y'') = f[1, u, p+nu, pp'(u) + (2n-1)p + n(n-1)u]$$

Suppose that it can be solved by a method of **A1** or **A2** to get $p = \phi(u, C_1)$. Another quadrature, and restoration of the original independent variable gives

$$\ln x = \int \frac{du}{\phi(u, C_1)} + C_2$$

Replace u by y/x^n, when the integration has been completed.

It is of interest to note that type **3-1** is a limiting case of this type, for if n becomes very large, the weights of y, y', y'' will become equal.

3-5. Homogeneous in y, xy'', and $x^2 y''$. The equation has the form $f(xy'/y, x^2 y''/y) = 0$, which can also be written as

$$x^2 y'' = yF(xy'/y)$$

It is thus an example of types **3-1**, **3-2**, **3-3**, and **3-4**. Let $xy' = uy$, $xy'' = yu' + (u-1)y'$, $x^2 y'' = xyu' + u(u-1)y$. The equation is now of first order, with separable variables,

$$xu' + u(u+1) = F(u)$$

Its solution can be obtained in two ways.

a. The last equation is equivalent to the two following ones.

$$\frac{dx}{x} = \frac{du}{F(u) - u(u-1)}$$

$$\frac{dy}{y} = \frac{u\,du}{F(u) - u(u-1)}$$

They are both of first order with separated variables; see **A1-1-2**. The two integrals will give a parametric representation of x and y in terms of u. Elimination of u would yield an explicit relation between x and y.

b. Integrate the first equation in **a**, to get

$$x = g(u, C_1) = g(xy'/y, C_1)$$

Solve it for $u = xy'/y$, which is another first-order equation with separable variables. Integrate it to get the general solution of the original equation.

The Euler linear equation, see **B1-3-1**, is of this kind.

4. The Exact Nonlinear Equation

Suppose that the given equation

$$\phi(x, y, y', y'') = 0 \tag{1}$$

is exact. If follows that $\phi\,dx = 0$ is the exact differential of some function $F(x, y, y', C_1)$, which is a first integral of the exact nonlinear second-order equation. Using the abbreviations $p = dy/dx$ and $p' = d^2y/dx^2$, the necessary and sufficient conditions for exactness are

$$\frac{\partial\phi}{\partial y} - \frac{d}{dx}\left(\frac{\partial\phi}{\partial p}\right) + \frac{d^2}{dx^2}\left(\frac{\partial\phi}{\partial p'}\right) = 0$$

Note, in making this test, that partial derivatives are to be taken of y, p, and p' but that the derivative with respect to x is made with y, p, and p' regarded as functions of x. If the test holds, the differential equation is exact. If it does not hold, an integrating factor could be sought; see **4-1**.

It is sometimes convenient to use (1) in the form

$$f(x, y, y')y'' + g(x, y, y') = 0$$

In that case, where a subscript now means a partial derivative, the test for exactness is

$$f_{xx} + 2pf_{xy} + p^2 f_{yy} = g_{xp} + pg_{yp} - g_y$$

$$f_{xp} + pf_{yp} + 2f_y = g_{pp}$$

In terms of the first integral

$$dF = F_x\,dx + F_y\,dy + F_p\,dp = 0$$

where

$$F_x = g - p(g_p - f_x - pf_y); \quad F_y = g_p - f_x - pf_y; \quad F_p = f$$

If y'' in (1) appears to a degree higher than one, the equation cannot be exact. If its degree is one and the tests for exactness hold, proceed as follows.

a. Write (1) in the form

$$\phi dx = f_1(x, y, p)dp + f_2(x, y, p)dx = 0$$

Integrate the term $f_1(x, y, p)dp = 0$ as if p were the only variable and x, y constants. Call the result $F_1(x, y, p) = 0$. An integration constant is unnecessary.

b. Differentiate $F_1(x, y, p) = 0$ totally with respect to x and subtract the result, $F_1' = 0$ from $\phi = 0$. The remainder should be a differential equation of order no greater than one. If the order is greater than one, the original differential equation was not exact. If the order equals one or less, integrate $dF_2 = \phi - F_1' = 0$ and call the result $F_2(x, y, p, C_1) = 0$, where C_1 is the integration constant.

c. A first integral of (1) is

$$F(x, y, p) = F_1(x, y, p) + F_2(x, y, p)$$

This integral, which is now of first order, may also be exact. Treat it according to **A1-7** or otherwise to get the general solution of the equation.

4-1. Integrating Factors for the Nonlinear Equation. An inexact nonlinear equation may sometimes be made exact with an integrating factor, $I(x, y, p)$. As is true also for first-order equations, see **A1-7-2**, if one such factor can be found, an infinite number of them can be found. However, if two independent integrating factors can be found, I_1 and I_2, the general solution of the differential equation follows by elimination of p between the two factors.

An integrating factor for a few equations of somewhat general type will be found in Table 1.

TABLE 1. INTEGRATING FACTOR FOR $y'' + g(x, y, y') = 0$

$g(x, y, y')$	$I(x, y, y')$
$g(y)$	y'
$g(y')$	$y'/g(y')$
$P(x)y' + Q(y)y'^2$	$1/y'$
$P(x, y)y' + Q(x, y)y'^2$; if $Pdx + Qdy$ is exact	$1/y'$

5. Change of Variable

A clever variable transformation may sometimes make a nonlinear equation integrable. A new independent variable, a new dependent variable, or two new variables might be sought. Try the exchange of x and y; see **B1-4-3**. The possibility of polar coordinates or some other orthogonal coordinate system, see **B1-9-6**, might also be considered. Refer to **A1-9**, **A2-6**, **B1-4**, for further hints. A number of examples will be found in Part II. The following additional procedures might also apply.

a. Use complex variables. Given $f(x, y, y', y'') = 0$, introduce the new variables $u = x - iy$, $z = x + iy$, and get the equation $g(z, u, u', u'') = 0$. Suppose that a first integral of it can be found, $G(z, u, u', C) = 0$, where the constant C is regarded as complex, $C = C_1 + iC_2$. Restore x and y, separate the real and imaginary parts of the first integral, getting

$$G_1(x, y, y', C_1) = 0; \quad G_2(x, y, y', C_2) = 0$$

When y' is eliminated between these two equations, the general solution follows, without further quadrature, $F(x, y, C_1, C_2) = 0$.

b. Variation of parameter. Sometimes the equation $f(x, y, y', y'') = 0$ could be solved if one of its terms were missing. Ignore the difficult term temporarily, find a first integral of the resulting equation, and call this solution $F(x, y, y', C) = 0$. Put $F = 0$ into the original equation but now regard C as a parameter. There may be enough relations to fix C so that $F(x, y, y', C_1) = 0$ is a first integral of the given equation; see **B1-12-3b**.

6. The General Nonlinear Equation of Second Order

It is supposed that the given equation is not one of the special types in the preceding sections. It is then unlikely that a solution can be obtained in simple form. A large class of nonlinear equations with certain special properties has been extensively studied by French mathematicians and they are described in the remaining sections of this part. If the given equation is not one of these some approximate method is probably required. Sometimes, the solution of an equivalent linear equation is an approximate solution to a nonlinear equation and approximate analytical solutions can also be obtained in other ways. Such cases have been discussed by McLachlan. The general introduction to his book is an interesting account of nonlinear equations and their use in a number of physical problems. For other approximate methods, which might be graphical, mechanical, or numerical, see **A1-13**.

7. The Equation with Fixed Critical Points

Let the given equation be

$$y'' = f(x, y\ y')$$

and suppose it to be rational in y', algebraic in y, analytic in x. Algebraic operations are understood to mean addition, subtraction, multiplication, division, raising to an integral power, and extraction of a root. A function involving a variable, a finite number of real numbers, and a finite number of algebraic operations is an algebraic function. A more restrictive class is that of rational functions, which are ratios of polynomials.

If one or more of the properties listed in the preceding paragraph are lacking, the following sections will not apply; return to **6** for suggestions. If the equation has all of these properties, consult **7**. The cases discussed there belong to a class of differential equations studied by the French mathematicians E. Picard, P. Painlevé, B. Gambier, and their colleagues. For references to their original papers and for proofs, which are omitted here, see Ince-1.

The particular class of differential equations now to be considered are those with solutions having fixed critical points; see **A1-10-1d**. Fundamental existence theorems, see Introduction-**3**, show that second-order differential equations will have a unique solution in the neighborhood of (x_0, y_0, y_0') provided that x_0 is not a critical point. Since two integration constants are required, they may be taken as $y_0 = C_1$, $y_0' = C_2$ and the general solution of the differential equation is $y = F(x - x_0, C_1, C_2)$. There are three classes of solutions, depending on the way C_1, C_2 appear in it.

a. A general solution of class A. The solution is an algebraic or rational function of C_1 and C_2. This case always occurs with linear equations.

b. A general solution of class B. One integration constant, but not both, appears algebraically. For example, a first integral of a nonlinear equation can often be found where its single arbitrary constant takes a simple form. When the general solution of the equation is found, the second integration constant will usually appear in a more complicated way. It will be remembered that any function, not algebraic, is transcendental. The simplest case is the integral transcendental function, which has a single essential singular point at infinity, see **A1-10-1b**. Typical examples are e^x, $\sin x$, $\cosh x$, etc. Rational transcendental functions have poles only in the finite plane. Examples are $\tan x$ and elliptic functions. These two classes of functions are often called classical transcendental functions. When one integration constant of the general solution to a nonlinear second-order differential equation occurs algebraically and the second one is a classical transcendental function, the solution will be called a semitranscendental function of C_1 and C_2, or a solution of class B.

c. A general solution of class C. The integration constants do not occur as in **a** or **b**, thus neither appears algebraically. Such solutions define a new type of function, said to be essentially transcendental. A number of such cases arise in the differential equations described in the next section. They are often called Painlevé equations and their solutions are also called Painlevé transcendents; see also **9**.

8. The Equation with Fixed Critical Points, Rational in *y*

The form of the equation is $y'' = f(x, y, y')$, where f is a rational function of both y and y'; its coefficients are analytic in x. If, more generally, f is algebraic, rather than rational, see **10**.

Make each of the tests in **a**, **b**, **c** following. If any of them fail, the solution cannot have fixed critical points; return to **6**. To proceed further, certain variable transformations are made so that the equations are converted to a standard or canonical type; see **d**. There are eight of them; see **a**. Each of the eight general types will produce a number of transformed equations with the required property, fifty in all. They are presented in sections **8-1** to **8-8** and it can be shown that the list of fifty is complete; no others can exist. Each of these equations will be designated by a number in brackets, such as [7]. The numbering corresponds to that used by Ince-1 and Davis. In many cases, the only simple solution is a first integral; see Part II for information about the solution of the equations. It will be seen that many of them and their solutions are quite complicated. For further details, see Ince-1 or Gambier.

a. The form of the equation is

$$y'' = X_0(x, y,)p^2 + X_1(x, y)p + X_2(x, y)$$

where $p = dy/dx$ and $X_i(x, y)$ is a rational function of y, with coefficients analytic in x. There are two possibilities.

i. $X_0(x, y) = 0$. It is then necessary that $X_1(x, y)$ be linear in y and that $X_2(x, y)$ be a polynomial in y of degree three or less; see **c**. In this case, proceed at once to **8-1**.

ii. $X_0(x, y) \neq 0$. Go to **b**.

b. Decompose $X_0(x, y)$ into partial fractions so that it becomes

$$X_0(x, y) = \sum_{i=1}^{4} \frac{m_i}{y - a_i(x)}$$

where the a_i can be constants or functions of x, and the m_i can only have the values listed in Table 1. There are five possible cases, corresponding to those for the first-order equation of A2-9-4. However, type II has been omitted here since it is a degenerate case of type III.

In the papers of Painlevé and Gambier, a more general form was taken for $X_0(x, y)$. Thus, in case IV, they give

$$X_0(x, y) = \frac{2}{3}\left[\frac{a_0}{a_0 y + a_1} + \frac{a_2}{a_2 y + a_3} + \frac{a_4}{a_4 y + a_5}\right]$$

where the a_i are functions of x, which can be identically zero or reduce to constants. The subsequent transformation for reduction to canonical form, see Table 2, then becomes generalized

$$u = \frac{(a_0 a_5 - a_1 a_4)(a_2 y + a_3)}{(a_2 a_5 - a_3 a_4)(a_0 y + a_1)}$$

The forms used in Table 1, however, are equivalent to those of the French mathematicians and the equations which follow are somewhat simplified.

c. Write the coefficients specified in **b** as

$$X_0(x, y) = A_0(x, y)/D(x, y)$$

and note that the degree of $D(x, y)$ in y is $\delta_0 \leqslant 4$, whereas the degree of $A_0(x, y)$ is at least one unit less. Take the other two coefficients as

$$X_i(x, y) = A_i(x, y)/D(x, y); \quad i = 1, 2$$

It is required that the numerators be polynomials in y of degrees

$$\delta_1 \leqslant \delta_0 + 1, \quad \delta_2 \leqslant \delta_0 + 3$$

respectively. These conditions insure simple poles of $X_i(x, y)$, which are included in the poles of $X_0(x, y)$.

d. The equations meeting the requirements of **a**, **b**, **c** are to be simplified by reduction to canonical forms. This is done by shifting the poles of $X_0(x, y)$ from the arbitrary positions of Table 1 to certain standard positions. Let a new variable by u and determine it from **i** if the a_i in **b** are constants; see **ii**, if the a_i are functions of x.

TABLE 1. TYPES OF EQUATIONS WITH FIXED CRITICAL POINTS

$$m \geqslant 1, \ \Sigma m_i = 2$$

Type	m	m_1	m_2	m_3	m_4
I	m	$(m+1)/m$	$(m-1)/m$	0	0
III	2	1/2	1/2	1/2	1/2
IV	3	2/3	2/3	2/3	0
V	4	3/4	3/4	1/2	0
VI	6	5/6	2/3	1/2	0

TABLE 2. VARIABLE TRANSFORMATIONS FOR CANONICAL FORMS

Poles in $X_0(x, y)$	New Variable, $u(x)$	Type from Table 1
a_1	$\dfrac{1}{(y-a_1)}$	III
a_1, a_2	$\dfrac{(y-a_2)}{(y-a_1)}$	I, III
a_1, a_2, a_3, a_4	$\dfrac{(a_1-a_3)(y-a_2)}{(a_2-a_3)(y-a_1)}$	III, IV, VI
a_1, a_2, a_3, a_4	$\dfrac{(a_2-a_3)(y-a_1)}{(a_2-a_1)(y-a_3)}$	V

i. The poles in $X_0(x, y)$, see Table 1, are a_i = constant. Use a new variable as specified in Table 2. It will be noted that the transformations there shift the poles from a_1, a_2, a_3 to 0, 1, ∞, but not necessarily in that order; see **B1-9-5-1**.

The new differential equation is

$$u''(x) = Y_0(x, u)u'^2 + Y_1(x, u)u' + Y_2(x, u)$$

and there are eight cases, depending on the form of $Y_0(x, u)$. Each is listed in Table 3. There are many subcases to make the total of fifty standard equations; refer to **8-i** ($i = 1, 2, \ldots , 8$) for the details of each. It will be convenient to retain the symbols x, y, $X_i(x, y)$ as in **a**. It must be understood, however, that x, u, Y_i should be used if the equation has resulted from that of **a**, with the transformations of Table 2.

ii. The poles of $X_0(x, y)$, see Table 1, are a_i which are not constants but functions of x. Introduce new variables

$$u = \frac{Ay+B}{Cy+D}; \quad z = \phi(x)$$

where A, B, C, D, ϕ are analytic functions of x; see **B1-9-5-1**. The results will again become one of the eight types in Table 3. Proceed to the appropriate section **8-i** ($i = 1, 2, \ldots 8,$).

8-1. $X_0(x, y) = 0$. The form of the equation, according to **8ai**, is

$$y''(x) = (f_0y+f_1)y' + g_0y^3 + g_1y^2 + g_2y + g_3 \tag{1}$$

where each coefficient f_i and g_i, is a constant or a function of x alone. The simplest case is that with $f_i = g_i = 0$; hence the first equation in the canonical set of fifty is the trivial linear one

$$y''(x) = 0 \tag{1}$$

TABLE 3. COEFFICIENT OF TRANSFORMED EQUATION
WITH FIXED CRITICAL POINTS

Type	$X_0(x, y)$	From Types of Table 1
1	0	See **8a**
2	$\dfrac{1}{y}$	III
3	$\dfrac{(m-1)}{my}, \; m > 1$	I
4	$\dfrac{1}{2y} + \dfrac{1}{(y-1)}$	III
5	$\dfrac{2}{3}\left(\dfrac{1}{y} + \dfrac{1}{y-1}\right)$	IV
6	$\dfrac{3}{4}\left(\dfrac{1}{y} + \dfrac{1}{y-1}\right)$	V
7	$\dfrac{2}{3}y + \dfrac{1}{2(y-1)}$	VI
8*	$\dfrac{1}{2}\left(\dfrac{1}{y} + \dfrac{1}{y-1} + \dfrac{1}{y-X}\right)$	III

* In case 8, $X = (a_1 - a_3)(a_2 - a_4)/(a_2 - a_3)(a_1 - a_4)$. It is possible for X to be a constant; if not, use it as a new independent variable; see **8dii**.

If the general solution of (1) is to be free from movable critical points, f_0 and g_0 are restricted to the five pairs of constants shown in Table 4. It is often convenient to use a new equation

$$u''(z) = (F_0 u + F_1)u' + G_0 u^3 + G_1 u^2 + G_2 u + G_3 \tag{2}$$

with the transformations

$$y(x) = u(z)v(x) + w(x); \quad z = \phi(x) \tag{3}$$

The coefficients F_i and G_i are the following functions of z, where a prime means differentiation with respect to the original variable x.

$$F_0 = f_0 v/\phi'$$
$$F_1 = (f_0 w + f_1 - 2v'/v - \phi''/\phi')/\phi'$$
$$G_0 = g_0 v^2/\phi'^2$$

$$G_1 = (f_0v' + 3g_0vw + g_1v)/\phi'^2$$

$$G_2 = (f_0v'w/v + f_1v'/v + f_0w' + 3g_0w^2 + 2g_1w + g_2 - v''/v)/\phi'^2$$

$$G_3 = (f_0ww' + f_1w' + g_0w^3 + g_1w^2 + g_2w + g_3 - w'')/v\phi'^2$$

When (2) is used, rather than (1), the quantities v, w, ϕ are chosen to obtain a standard form of the differential equation. The five possible cases follow.

a. $f_0 = g_0 = 0$. There are two cases.
 i. $g_1 = 0$. The equation is

$$y''(x) = f_1y' + g_2y + g_3$$

which is linear and nonhomogeneous. It can be solved by the methods of **B1-12**.

TABLE 4. ALLOWED COEFFICIENTS
IN (1) TO PREVENT MOVABLE
CRITICAL POINTS

Case	f_0	g_0
a	0	0
b	-2	0
c	-3	-1
d	-1	1
e	0	2

ii. $g_1 \neq 0$. Use (2) and the relations

$$2\frac{v'}{v} + \frac{\phi''}{\phi'} = f_1$$

$$g_1v = c\phi'^2 \tag{4}$$

$$2g_1w = \frac{v''}{v} - f_1\frac{v'}{v} - g_2$$

where c is an arbitrary constant. The differential equation becomes

$$u''(z) = G_1u^2 + G_3$$

where $G_1 = g_1v/\phi'^2 = c$, $G_3 = (f_1w' + g_1w^2 + g_2w + g_3 - w'')/v\phi'^2$. Integration of (4) gives $v^2\phi' = \exp\int f_1 dx$; $g_1v^5 = c\exp(2\int f_1 dx)$; w is found from the last equation of (4). However, unless $G_3(z)$ is linear, the equation will have movable singular points in its solution. Reverting to the original variables, the standard equation can be taken as

$$y''(x) = a + bx + cy^2$$

where a, b, c are constants. If $c = 0$, the equation is linear and it can be solved by two quadratures; see **1-1**; otherwise, it is convenient to take $c = 6$, which simplifies subsequent evaluation of integrals. A variable transformation will fix two other constants. The three possible standard equations which result are

$$a = b = 0; \qquad y''(x) = 6y^2 \qquad\qquad [2]$$

$$a \neq 0, \quad b = 0; \quad y''(x) = 6y^2 + \frac{1}{2} \qquad\qquad [3]$$

$$a = 0, \quad b \neq 0; \quad y''(x) = x + 6y^2 \qquad\qquad [4]$$

Some writers take $-1/24$ instead of $1/2$ in the second equation but the latter choice is usually more convenient. For the third equation, see **9**.

b. $f_0 = -2$, $g_0 = 0$. The equation becomes

$$y'' = (f_1 - 2y)p + g_1 y^2 + g_2 y + g_3$$

The term in y can be removed with the transformation

$$y(x) = u(x) + w(x); \quad 2w' = 2g_1 w + g_2$$

and the result is

$$u'' = (F_1 - 2u)u' + G_1 u^2 + G_3$$

To prevent movable critical points, it is further necessary that $G_1 = F_1$, so that

$$u'' = (F_1 - 2u)u' + F_1 u^2 + G_3 \qquad\qquad (5)$$

The functions $F_1(x)$, $G_3(x)$ are analytic but otherwise arbitrary. A first integral is a Riccati equation, see **A1-3**,

$$u' + u^2 = X(x) \qquad\qquad (6)$$

where $X(x)$ is determined from a linear first-order equation, see **A1-2**, $X'(x) = F_1(x)X + G_3(x)$.

An equation equivalent to (5) is more useful for the standard form

$$U''(x) = (q - 2U)U' + q'U \qquad\qquad [5]$$

where $q(x)$ is unrestricted, except that it must be analytic in x. Its first integral is also the Riccati equation (6), with $U = u + q/2$, $X = q^2/4 - q'/2$.

c. $f_0 = -3$, $g_0 = -1$. The desired equation must also have

$$f_1 = g_1, \quad g_2 = g_3 = 0$$

hence its form is

$$y''(x) = (f_1 - 3y)y' - y^3 + f_1 y^2 \qquad\qquad [6]$$

Its solution is $yu(x) = u'$, where $u(x)$ is determined from a linear third-order equation, see **C1-2** or **C2-1-2**,

$$u'''(x) = f_1(x)u''$$

d. $f_0 = -1$, $g_0 = 1$. Use (1) and get

$$y''(x) = (3g_1 - y)y' + y^3 + g_1 y^2 + g_2 y + g_3$$

where it is also required that $f_1 = 3g_1$. There are five special cases, each of which can be converted to the standard form

$$u''(z) + uu' = u^3 - 12r(z)u + 12r' \qquad [10]$$

The coefficients in terms of both x and z, together with the relations between y and u are as follows.

  i. $y(x) = u(z)v(x)$; $v(x) = dz/dx$; $v' = g_1 v$; $g_2(x) = g_1' - 2g_1^2$; $g_3 = 0$; $r(z) = 0$.

  ii. As in **i**, but $12v^2 = q(z)$; $g_1(x) = q'/2q$; $g_2 = q''/2q - (q'/q)^2 - q$; $g_3 = 0$; $r(z)$ is a constant, conveniently taken as unity.

  iii. As in **i**, with $q(x)$ defined as a solution of $r''(z) = 6r^2$ and $z = \exp\int qdx$; $g_1(x) = q'/q + q$; $g_2 = g_1' - 2g_1^2 - 12q^2$; $g_3 = -24q^3$.

  iv. Take $y(x)q^{1/2}(x) = u(z)$; $q(x) = 4x^3 - mx - k$, where $m = 0$, $k = 1$ or $m = 1$ and k is arbitrary. The new variable is given by the Weierstrass elliptic function $z = \mathscr{P}(z; m, c)$ and $g_1 = -2q/q'$; $g_2 = -24x/q$; $g_3 = 12/q$. The quantity $r(z)$ is determined from $r'' = 6r^2 + m$, where $m = 0$, 1. For references to the properties of the Weierstrass function, see Erdélyi-1, vol. 2.

  v. In this case, $g_1 = 0$; $g_2 = -12q$; $g_3 = 12q'$; q is a solution of $q''(x) = 6q^2 + x$. The equation in $u(z)$ is identical with the latter, replacing q by r.

  e. $f_0 = 0$, $g_0 = 2$. There are two cases.

  i. $f_1 = g_1 = 0$. The differential equation is

$$y''(x) = 2y^3 + g_2 y + g_3$$

When $g_2 = \alpha$, $g_3 = \beta$, both constants, the equation is integrable in terms of elliptic functions

$$y''(x) = 2y^3 + \alpha y + \beta \qquad [8]$$

If g_2 is not a constant it must be linear in x, say $g_2 = \alpha + x$ but $g_3 = \beta$. Use a new independent variable, $z = x + \alpha$, and get

$$u''(z) = 2u^3 + zu + \beta \qquad [9]$$

This is the second Painlevé equation, see **9**, with solution of class C.

  ii. $f_1 \neq 0$. It is required that $g_1 = g_3 = 0$; $f_1 = -3q$; $g_2 = 2q^2 - q'$, where $q(x)$ is an arbitrary analytic function of x. The equation becomes

$$y''(x) + 3q(x)y' = 2y^3 - (2q^2 + q')y$$

Its standard form is

$$u''(z) = 2u^3 \qquad [7]$$

with $y(x) = u(z)v(x)$; $\ln v = -\int q\,dx$; $z = \int v\,dx$.

8-2. $X_0(x, y) = 1/y$.   The differential equation is

$$yy''(x) = p^2 + (f_0 y^2 + f_1 y + f_2)p + g_0 y^4 + g_1 y^3 + g_2 y^2 + g_3 y + g_4$$

where $p = dy/dx$. It is required either that f_0, g_0 or f_2, g_4 vanish. There are six special cases, the coefficients of which are given in Table 5. There, the c_i are constants and $q(x)$, $r(x)$ are arbitrary analytic functions. When $f_0 \neq 0$, $f_2 = 0$, use [15] and [16], replacing x by $1/x$. All solutions are of class B, except [13], which is of class C; see also **9**. For methods of solving each equation, refer to Part II.

TABLE 5. COEFFICIENTS IN THE STANDARD EQUATIONS OF **8-2**

$$yy''(x) = p^2 + (f_0 y^2 + f_1 y + f_2)p + g_0 y^4 + g_1 y^3 + g_2 y^2 + g_3 y + g_4$$

f_0	f_1	f_2	g_0	g_1	g_2	g_3	g_4	Eq. No.
0	0	0	0	0	0	0	0	[11]
0	0	0	c_0	c_1	0	c_3	c_4	[12]
0	$-\dfrac{1}{z}$	0	c_0	$\dfrac{c_1}{z}$	0	$\dfrac{c_3}{z}$	c_4	[13]
q	0	r	0	q'	0	$-r'$	0	[14]
0	0	1	0	q	$-\left(\dfrac{q'}{q}\right)'$	0	0	[15]
0	0	$-q'$	1	$-q$	0	q''	0	[16]

8-3. $X_0(x, y) = \dfrac{m-1}{my}$.   The general equation is like that in **8-2**, except that p^2 is to be multiplied by $M = (m-1)/m$. There are twenty special cases, thirteen of which are given in **a** and the remainder in **b**.

a. All $f_i(x)$ vanish. The remaining coefficients are shown in Table 6, where the c_i are constants and m is an arbitrary integer greater than unity, unless otherwise specified.

It will be noted that the independent variable is missing from each equation except [20], [31], and [34]. Therefore, the method of **2-3** could be used to get a first integral at least. For example, the first integral of [30] is

$$p^2 = y^4 + 4c_1 y^3 + 4c_2 y^2 + 4Cy + c_4$$

Similarly, a first integral of [33] is

$$p^2 = 4y^3 + 2c_2 y^2 + 4Cy + 1$$

Solutions for the remaining equations of this part will be found in Part II.

Some cases of this type are equivalent to others in the set of fifty. Make the variable change $y(x) = u^2(x)$. The results follow, with the number of the original equation as designated in Table 6, the transformed equation, and the number of its equivalent equation.

  i. [20]; $u''(x) = 2u^3 + xu$; [9]
 ii. [21]: $2uu'' = u'^2 + 3u^4$; [29]
iii. [22]; $2uu'' = u'^2 - 1$; [32]
 iv. [23]; $2uu'' = u'^2 + 3u^4 + c_2 u^2 + u_3$; [30]

TABLE 6. COEFFICIENTS IN THE STANDARD EQUATIONS OF **8-3a**
$$yy''(x) = Mp^2 + g_0 y^4 + g_1 y^3 + g_2 y^2 + g_3 y + g_4; \quad M = (m-1)/m$$

m	g_0	g_1	g_2	g_3	g_4	Eq. No.
m	0	0	0	0	0	[17]
2	0	4	0	0	0	[18]
2	0	4	2	0	0	[19]
2	0	4	$2x$	0	0	[20]
4	0	3	0	0	0	[21]
4	0	0	0	-1	0	[22]
4	0	3	c_2	c_3	0	[23]
2	$\dfrac{3}{2}$	0	0	0	0	[29]
2	$\dfrac{3}{2}$	$4c_1$	$2c_2$	0	$-\dfrac{c_4}{2}$	[30]
2	$\dfrac{3}{2}$	$4x$	$2(x_2{}^2 - c_2)$	0	$-\dfrac{c_2{}^2}{2}$	[31]
2	0	0	0	0	$-\dfrac{1}{2}$	[32]
2	0	4	c_2	0	$-\dfrac{1}{2}$	[33]
2	0	$4c_1$	$-x$	0	$-\dfrac{1}{2}$	[34]

b. When the $f_i(x)$ do not vanish, the coefficients of the differential equation will be found in Table 7. Further information is given in the accompanying notes. For the solution of the equations, see the notes to Table 7 or refer to Part II. It is to be remembered that the original equations, with coefficients listed in Table 3, have been transformed to get the standard types of this section. It has been convenient, however, to again use x, y for the variables in the transformed equations. Some relations between old and new variables are given in the notes to Table 7.

8-4. $X_0(x, y) = \dfrac{3y-1}{2y(y-1)}$.   There are only four equations of this type. Constants are indicated by c_i. Analytic functions of the independent variable, otherwise arbitrary, are q, r. Two additional functions are determined from the equations $s' = 2qs$; $t' + 2rt = 0$. Actually, the variables should be called u, z as in **8-1** but, after the transformations have been completed, they have again been called y, x.

    a.

$$y(y-1)y'' = \frac{1}{2}(3y-1)y'^2 \qquad [37]$$

For the solution, see Part II.

    b.

$$y(y-1)y'' = \frac{1}{2}(3y-1)y'^2 + y^2[c_0 + c_1(y-1) + c_2(y-1)^3] + c_3(y-1)^3 \quad [38]$$

A first integral is

$$p^2 = y(y-1)^2\left[C - \frac{c_0}{(y-1)^2} - \frac{2c_1}{y-1} - \frac{2c_3}{y} + 2c_2y \right]$$

    c.

$$x^2y(y-1)y'' = \frac{1}{2}x^2(3y-1)y'^2 - xy(y-1)y' + c_2xy^2(y-1)$$

$$+ c_3x^2y^2(y+1) + c_1(y-1)^3 + c_0y^2(y-1)^3 \quad [39]$$

See Part II for the solution.

    d.

$$y(y-1)y'' = \frac{1}{2}(3y-1)y'^2 + 2y(qy+r)y' + 2(q^2 - r^2 - q' - r')y^2(y-1)$$

$$[40]$$

$$- \frac{1}{2}s^2y^2(y-1)^3 - \frac{1}{2}t^2(y-1)^3$$

The solution is given in Part II.

TABLE 7. COEFFICIENTS IN THE STANDARD EQUATIONS OF **8-3b**

$$yy''(x) = Mp^2 + (f_0y^2 + f_1y + f_2)p + g_0y^4 + g_1y^3 + g_2y^2 + g_3y + g_4; \quad M = (m-1)/m$$

m	f_0	f_1	f_2	g_0	g_1	g_2	g_3	g_4	Eq. No.	Note
m	q	0	0	$\dfrac{-mq^2}{(m+2)^2}$	$\dfrac{mq'}{(m+2)}$	0	0	0	[24]	1
4	$-\dfrac{3}{2}$	$\dfrac{q'}{2q}$	0	$-\dfrac{1}{4}$	$\dfrac{q'}{2q}$	r	q	0	[25]	1
4	0	0	$6q'$	0	3	$12q$	$-12q''$	$-36q^2$	[26]	2
m	h_0	h_1	$\dfrac{2-m}{m}$	$\dfrac{-mh_0^2}{(m+2)^2}$	$\dfrac{m(h_0'-h_0h_1)}{(m+2)}$	h_2	$-h_1$	$-\dfrac{1}{m}$	[27]	3
2	-2	0	0	$-\dfrac{1}{2}$	0	h	0	$-\dfrac{1}{2}$	[27a]	3
2	-1	q	0	$\dfrac{1}{2}$	$-2q$	$3\left(q'+\dfrac{q^2}{2}\right)$	0	$-72r^2$	[28]	4
3	$-\dfrac{2}{3}$	$\dfrac{2}{3}q$	r	$\dfrac{2}{3}$	$-\dfrac{10}{3}q$	$4q'+r+\dfrac{8}{3}q^2$	$2qr-3r'$	$-3r^2$	[35]	5
5	$-\dfrac{2}{5}$	$-\dfrac{4}{5}q$	s	$\dfrac{4}{5}$	$\dfrac{14}{5}q$	$s-3q'+\dfrac{6}{5}q^2$	$-\dfrac{1}{3}(qs+5r')$	$-\dfrac{5}{9}s^2$	[36]	6

Notes for Table 7

1. In the original equation $(m+2)^2 g_0 + m f_0^2 = 0$.

2. Determine q from [2], [3], or [4] in **8-1a**, where q is the dependent variable, rather than y. Originally, $f_0 = g_0 = 0$ and $(m-2)^2 g_4 + m f_2^2 = 0$. A solution of the equation is $3y = 2W' + W^2 - 12q$, where $W = (Q'-q')/(Q-q)$ and $Q(x)$ is determined from [2], [3], or [4], provided that $Q \neq q$.

3. Use the equation for m in note 2. The quantities h_0, h_1, h_2, h are definite rational functions of two arbitrary analytic functions $q(x), r(x)$ and their derivatives. When $m = 2$, the equation is somewhat simplified; see [27a].

4. In the original equation $f_0 = 2g_0$, $f_2 = 0$. Find two solutions q_1 and q_2, as directed in note 2. Then, $q(x) = (q_2' - q_1')/2r$; $2r(x) = q_2 - q_1$. A solution of the equation is $y = 6(W-q_1)(W-q_2)/(W'-V_1-qV_2)$, where $V_1 = (q_1'+q_2')/2$; $V_2 = W - (q_1+q_2)/2$ and W is a solution of the same equations for which q_1 and q_2 are solutions.

5. It is required originally that $3f_0^2 = 2g_0$, $3f_2^2 + g_4 = 0$. Calculate $q(x)$ and $r(x)$ from $q''(x) = 2q^3 + Sq + T$, $3r + S + 2(q'+q^2) = 0$. Determine t from $\phi(t) = 2t^3 + St + T$ and use for (S, T) one of the pairs $(0, 0)$, (α, β), (x, α), where α, β are constants. A solution of the equation is $y = (W'-q'+W^2-q^2)/(W-q)$, where $W(x)$ is any solution of $W'' = 2W^3 + SW + T$.

6. In the original equation, $5f_0^2 = g_0$, $5f_2^2 + 9g_4 = 0$. Calculate q_1, q_2, r as in notes 2 and 4. Determine s from $5s(x) = 72q_1 + 36q_2 - 9q^2$. Let $W(x)$ be the general solution of [2], [3], or [4]. Then, the solution of [36] is

$$y = \frac{W'-q'}{W-q} - \tfrac{1}{2}(q+x)$$

8-5. $X_0(x, y) = \dfrac{2(2y-1)}{3y(y-1)}$. There are two equations and the genera form is

$$y(y-1)y'' = \frac{2}{3}(2y-1)y'^2 + F(x, y)$$

See **8-4** for comments about the variables.

a.
$$F(x, y) = 0 \qquad [41]$$

A first integral is $p^3 = 27C_1^3 y^2(y-1)^2$. The general solution is

$$2y = 1 + \mathscr{P}'(C_1 x + C_2; \ 0, -1)$$

where the Weierstrass elliptic function results from the solution of the third degree equation; see **A2-1-2**.

b.
$$F(x, y) = [A_0 y + A_1 y(y-1) + A_2 y^2(y-1) + A_3(y-1)]y'$$
$$+ B_0 y^2 + B_1 y(y-1)^2 + B_2 y^2(y-1)$$
$$+ B_3 y^2(y-1)^2 + B_4 y^3(y-1)^2 + B_5(y-1)^2 \qquad [42]$$

The coefficients are given by the following equations:

$$A_0 = -s(x); \quad A_1 = -\frac{1}{2}(q+r+s); \quad A_2 = q(x); \quad A_3 = r(x)$$

$$B_0 = -3s^2; \quad B_1 = 3\left[r'+\frac{r}{2}(q-r-s)\right]; \quad B_2 = 3\left[s'-\frac{s}{2}(q+r+s)\right]$$

$$B_3 = 3\left[q'-\frac{q}{2}(q-r-s)\right]; \quad B_4 = 3q^2; \quad B_5 = 3r^2$$

To determine q, r, and s consider the equation

$$2vv'' = v'^2 + 3v^4 + 8av^3 + 4bv^2 - c^2$$

Choose its parameters in one of three possible ways.

  i. $a = b = c$; see [29].
 ii. a, b, c are constants; see [30].
iii. $a = x$, $b = x^2 - \alpha$, $c = \beta$; see [31].

Then, use the relations

$$3q = v'/v - v - 2a + c/v; \quad 3r = v'/v + v + 2a + c/v; \quad 3s = 2v$$

where v is any solution of the second-order equation in v.

The solution of the equation is

$$y = 1 + \frac{2V(V-v)}{V'-v'-V^2+v^2-3(q+r+s)(V-v)/2}$$

where $V(x)$ is the general solution of the second-order equation in v.

8-6. $X_0(x, y) = \dfrac{3(2y-1)}{4y(y-1)}$. There are five special cases of the general equation

$$y(y-1)y'' = \frac{3}{4}(1-2y)y'^2 + F(x, y)$$

Refer to **8-4** for a statement about the variables and see Part II for the general solution of those equations for which the solution is not given in this section.

a.

$$F(x, y) = 0 \tag{43}$$

b.

$$F(x, y) = c_0 y(y-1)^2 + c_1 y^2(y-1) + 2c_2 y^2(y-1)^3 \tag{44}$$

The solution is $y = 1 + yW^2$, where $W(x)$ is determined from the first-order equation

$$W'^2 = W(1-W^2)\left(c_0 W - \frac{c_1}{W} - \frac{c_2}{W-1} + C\right)$$

c.

$$-F(x, y) = [c_0 y - c_1 y(y-1) - c_2(y-1)]y'$$
$$+ c_0^2 y^2 - c_4 y(y-1)^2 - c_5 y^2(y-1)$$
$$- c_2^2(y-1)^2 - 4c_3^2 y^2(2y-1)^2(y-1)^2 \qquad [45]$$

The parameters are fixed with the following relations:

$$(v_2 - v_1)c_1 = v_2' - v_1'; \quad 2(c_2 - c_0) + 3(v_1 + v_2) = 0$$
$$2(c_2 + c_0) + 3c_1 = 0; \quad 2c_3 = v_2 - v_1; \quad c_4 = 2c_2' + c_1 c_2$$
$$c_5 = 2c_0' + c_0 c_1$$

The quantities $v_1(x)$ and $v_2(x)$ are any solutions of [7], [8], or [9]; see **8-1e**.

If $v(x)$ is the general solution of the latter equations, then the solution of [45] is given by

$$2(2y-1)(v-v_1)(v-v_2) = 2v' - v_1' - v_2' - c_1(2v - v_1 - v_2)$$

d.

$$-F(x, y) = \frac{q'}{q} y\left(y + \frac{1}{2}\right)y' + \left(\frac{3q'}{2q}\right)^2 y^2 - qy(y-1)^2$$

$$- \left(\frac{3q''}{q} - \frac{9q'^2}{2q^2}\right)y^2(y-1) + \frac{4c_0^2}{q^2}y^2(y-1)^2(2y-1) \qquad [46]$$

Find v_1, any solution of $v''(x) = 2v^3 + c_1 v + c_0$; see [8] in **8-1e**. Then, determine $q(x) = 2(v_1' + v_1^2) + c_1$.

Let $v(x)$ be the general solution of the second-order equation and $W(x) = v + v_1 + (v - v_1')/(v - v_1)$. Then, the general solution of [46] is

$$y[2W' + 2W^2 - (4C_1 + 4C_2 + 3C_3)W + q] = 3W^2$$

e.

$$-F(x, y) = \frac{q'}{q} y\left(y + \frac{1}{2}\right)y' + \left(\frac{3q'}{2q}\right)^2 y^2 - qy(y-1)^2$$

$$- \left(\frac{3q''}{q} - \frac{9q'^2}{2q^2}\right)y^2(y-1) - \frac{(2c_0^2 + 1)^2}{q^2}y^2(y-1)^2(2y-1) \qquad [47]$$

If v_1 is any solution of $v''(x) = 2v^3 + xv + c_0$; see [9] in **8-1e**; then $q(x) = 2(v_1' + v_1^2) + x$. The general solution of the equation is found by a method similar to that used for [46].

8-7. $X_0(x, y) = \dfrac{7y - 4}{6y(y-1)}.$ There is only one equation of this type.

See **8-4** for comments about the variables.

$$y(y-1)y'' = X_0(x, y)y'^2 + [A_0y(y-1) + A_1y^2(y-1) + A_2(y-1)]y'$$
$$+ A_3y^2 + A_4y(y-1)^2 + \frac{1}{3}A_3y^2(y-1)$$
$$+ A_5y^2(y-1)^2 + \frac{3}{8}A_1^2y^3(y-1)^2 + 3A_2^2(y-1)^2 \quad [48]$$

The coefficients are given by the following relations:

$A_0 = (5s+2t)/9; \quad A_1 = -10(s+t)/9; \quad A_2 = 4(2t-s)/9$

$A_3 = -9v^2/2; \quad 2A_4 = 6(A_2' - A_0A_2) - 3A_2^2; \quad 4A_5 = 6(A_1' - A_1A_0) - 3A_1^2$

Let v_1, v_2, v_3 be any three particular solutions of [2], [3], or [4] in **8-1a.**
Then, calculate

$$V_1 = (v_2' - v_1')/(v_2 - v_1); \quad V_2 = (v_3' - v_1')/(v_3 - v_1)$$
$$2t = V_1 + V_2; \quad 2v = V_1 - V_2; \quad vs + v' = 0$$

For the solution of the differential equation, let $W(x)$ be a solution of
[10], then

$$y = 1 + \frac{3}{2}\frac{(W-t)^2 - v^2}{W' - t' + s(W-t) - (W-t)^2 + v^2}$$

8-8. $X_0(x, y) = \dfrac{3y^2 - 2(X+1)y + X}{y(y-1)(y-X)}$. There are two cases. See **8-4**
concerning the variables. Solutions of both equations are given in Part II.

a. $X = a$, constant.

$$y(y-1)(y-a)y'' = \frac{1}{2}[3y^2 - 2(y+1) + a]y'^2$$
$$+ c_0y^2(y-1)^2 + c_1y^2(y-a)^2 + c_2(y-1)^2(y-a)^2$$
$$+ c_3y^2(y-1)^2(y-a)^2 \quad [49]$$

b. X is a function of x; see **8d.** Let $X(x)$ be a new independent
variable and call it z, so that $y(x) = u(z)$. Then, replace the variables z, u
by x, y respectively and the equation becomes

$$y(y-1)(y-x)y'' = \frac{1}{2}[3y^2 - 2y(1+x) + x]y'^2$$

$$- \frac{y(y-1)}{x(x-1)}[(2x-1)y + x^2]y' + \frac{1}{x^2(x-1)^2}[c_0y^2(y-1)^2(y-x)^2$$
$$+ c_1x(y-1)^2(y-x)^2 + c_2y^2(x-1)(y-x)^2$$
$$+ c_3xy^2(x-1)(y-1)^2] \quad [50]$$

9. Painlevé Equations

The preceding sections, **8-1** to **8-8**, list the standard equations, fifty in number, which have fixed critical points. Forty-four of them have general solutions of class A or class B; see **7**. The remaining six have solutions of a more complicated kind, class C, and they are called Painlevé equations. For convenience, they are collected here from the preceding sections. The variables in each case are called x, y; constants are a_0, a_1, a_2, a_3. The first number given to the equation is that which has been used in sections **8-1** to **8-8**; the second number will be used for reference in this section.

$$y'' = x + 6y^2 \qquad\qquad [4;1]$$

$$y'' = a_0 + xy + 2y^3 \qquad\qquad [9;2]$$

$$xyy'' = xp^2 - yp + a_0y^3 + a_1y + a_2xy^4 + a_3x \qquad\qquad [13;3]$$

$$2yy'' = p^2 + 3y^4 + 8xy^3 + 4(x^2 - a_0)y^2 + 2a_1 \qquad\qquad [31;4]$$

$$2x^2y(y-1)y'' = x^2(3y-1)p^2 - 2xy(y-1)p + 2a_0y^2(y-1)^3$$
$$+ 2a_1(y-1)^3 + 2a_2xy^2(y-1) + 2a_3x^2y^2(y+1) \qquad [39;5]$$

$$2x^2y(x-1)^2(y-1)(y-x)y'' = x^2(x-1)^2[3y^2 - 2y(1+x) + x]p^2$$
$$- 2xy(x-1)(y-1)[(2x-1)y + x^2]p$$
$$+ 2[a_0y^2(y-1)^2(y-x)^2 + a_1x(y-1)^2(y-x)^2$$
$$+ a_2y^2(x-1)(y-x)^2 + a_3xy^2(x-1)(y-1)^2] \qquad [50;6]$$

The solutions of [1], [2] and [4] have no branch points and have no other singularities except for movable poles. They are therefore uniform functions of x. The general solutions of [3] and [5] have $x = 0$ and $x = \infty$ as transcendental critical points. With the new variable $\ln z = x$, the solutions are uniform transcendental functions of z. For [6], the three points $x = 0,\ 1,\ \infty$ are transcendental critical points of the general solution.

The Painlevé equations have not been studied extensively. For the solutions of [1] and [2], see **a**, **b**, respectively. It can be shown that the first five equations are special cases of [6]; see **c**.

a. Solution of [1]. Given the equation

$$y'' = kx + 6y^2 \qquad\qquad (1)$$

where k is a constant, let $y(x) = k^{2/5}u(z)$, $k^{1/5}x = z$, and get the standard form

$$u''(z) = z + 6u^2 \qquad\qquad [1]$$

In the special case that $k = 0$, (1) is identical with [2] in **8-1**, but the transformed equation in u, z cannot be obtained in this way. To solve the equation with $k \neq 0$, assume

$$y(x) = A_{-2}/t^2 + A_{-1}/t + A_0 + A_1 t + A_2 t^2 + \quad \ldots \tag{2}$$

where $t = (x - x_1)$ and $x = x_1$ is a movable pole. The first eight coefficients in the series are

$$A_{-2} = 1; \quad A_{-1} = A_0 = A_1 = 0; \quad A_2 = -kx_1/10; \quad A_3 = -k/6;$$
$$A_4 = C, \quad A_5 = 0$$

It is the general solution, since x_1 and C are arbitrary constants.

Alternatively, a solution can be given

$$y = y_0 + y_0'(x - x_0) + \frac{y_0''}{2}(x - x_0)^2 + \quad \ldots \quad \frac{y_0^{(n)}}{n!}(x - x_0)^n + \quad \ldots \tag{3}$$

where $x = x_0$ is an ordinary point. The two integration constants in this general solution are $y(x_0) = y_0$, $y'(x_0) = y_0'$; see **B1-8-1**. Some of the coefficients are

$$y''' = 12yy' + k; \quad y^{iv} = 12(6y^3 + kxy + y'^2); \quad y^v = (360y^2 y' + 12ky + 36kxy')$$

Further coefficients in (2), up to A_{16}, and in (3), up to y^{xv}, have been given by Davis. He has also computed y and y' numerically for $k = 0, 1, 2, 3, 4, 5$; initial values 'of $y = 1$, $y' = 0$, $x = 0$; the range $-1 \leqslant x \leqslant 1$; intervals of 0.01. The tabulated values of y are given to four significant figures; those for y' to three significant figures.

b. Solution of [2]. Results like those in **a** have been given by Davis for the second Painlevé equation. The first few coefficients in (2) are

$$A_{-2} = 0; \quad A_{-1} = 1; \quad A_0 = 0; \quad A_1 = -x_1/6; \quad A_2 = -(1 + a_0)/6; \quad A_3 = C;$$
$$A_4 = x_1(1 + 3a_0)/72; \quad A_5 = (27 + 108a_0 - 216Cx_1 + 81a_0^2 - 2x_1^3)/3024$$

Similarly, for (3),

$$y''' = 6y^2 y' + xy' + y; \quad y^{iv} = 12y^5 + 8xy^3 + 6a_0 y^2 + x^2 y + a_0 x + 12yy'^2 + 2y';$$
$$y^v = 12y'^3 + 36yy'y'' + 6y^2 y''' + xy''' + 3y''$$

For additional coefficients, up to A_{15} and y^x, see Davis. He has also given numerical values of y and y' for $-1 \leqslant x \leqslant 1$; at intervals of 0.01; $y = 1$, $y' = 0$, $x = 0$; $a_0 = 1, 2, 3, 4, 5$. Both y and y' were computed to four decimal places between $x = 0$ and $x = 0.5$; from there to $x = 0.8$, the values of y' only to four significant figures; beyond $x = 0.8$, four and three significant figures for y, y', respectively.

c. Some properties of [6]. Painlevé showed that [1] did indeed have the behavior claimed for it: freedom from movable branch points and movable essential singularities; its solution is of class C; see **7c**. The details have been summarized by Ince-1. Painlevé also showed that the first five equations in the set can all be found as limiting cases of [6] and it follows that each has the properties which he proved for [1]. Unfortunately, the original paper of Painlevé contains a number of typographical errors and these have been reproduced or new errors have appeared in the paper of Gambier and in the book of Ince-1. It is believed that the following results are correct.

   i. Use [6] and let $y(x) = u(z)$; $x = 1 + \epsilon z$; $a_2 = b_2/\epsilon - b_3/\epsilon^2$; $\epsilon^2 a_3 = b_3$. When $\epsilon \to 0$, the new equation is like [5], with a_2, a_3, x, y replaced by b_2, b_3, z, u, respectively.

   ii. Take [5] with $y(x) = \epsilon u(z)/\sqrt{2}$; $x = 1 + \epsilon z \sqrt{2}$; $2\epsilon^4 = a_0$; $\epsilon^4 a_2 + 1 = 0$; $1 + 2\epsilon^4 a_3 + 2\epsilon^2 b_3$. The result is [4], when $\epsilon \to 0$ with u, z, $4a_1$, $-b_3$ in place of y, x, a_1, a_0.

   iii. Use [5] again but with $y(x) = 1 + \epsilon z u(z)$; $x = z^2$; $\epsilon^2 a_0 = \epsilon b_0 + b_1$; $\epsilon^2 a_1 + b_1 = 0$; $a_2 = b_2 \epsilon$; $a_3 = b_3 \epsilon^2$. The transformed equation is [3], when $\epsilon \to 0$, replacing x, y, a_0, a_1, a_2, a_3 by z, u, $4b_0$, $4b_2$, $8b_1$, $8b_3$, respectively.

   iv. Transform [4] with $\epsilon^3 y(x) = 1 + 2r\epsilon^2 u(z)$; $\epsilon^3 x = r^2 \epsilon^4 z - 1$; $r^3 = 1/2$; $2\epsilon^6(a_0 + b_0) + 1 = 0$; $2\epsilon^{12} a_1 + 1 = 0$. When $\epsilon \to 0$, replace u, z, $b_0/2$ by y. x, a_0 and get [2].

   v. Use [3]. Let $y(x) = 1 + 2\epsilon u(z)$; $x = 1 + \epsilon^2 z$; $2\epsilon^6 a_0 + 1 = 0$; $2\epsilon^6 a_1 = 1 + 4b_1 \epsilon^3$; $4\epsilon^6 a_2 = 1$; $a_3 = -a_2$. In the limit, when $\epsilon \to 0$, the equation is like [2]. Replace u, z, b_1 by y, x, a_0, respectively.

   vi. Change [2] to [1] with $\epsilon^5 y(x) = 1 + \epsilon^6 u(z)$; $\epsilon^{10} x = \epsilon^{12} z - 6$; $\epsilon^{15} a_0 = 4$. Let $\epsilon \to 0$ and replace u, z by y, x.

10. The Equation with Fixed Critical Points, Algebraic in *y*

   The general nonlinear second-order equation in **7**

$$y'' = f(x, y, y') \tag{1}$$

was assumed to be rational in y', algebraic in y, analytic in x. A restricted class of such equations, rational in y, was treated in **8**, **8-1** to **8-8**, **9**. Here, the more general case is considered. Let the parameter t be defined by a relation which is analytic in x and a polynomial in y and t

$$\phi(x, y, t) = 0 \tag{2}$$

Then, (1) becomes

$$y'' = F(x, y, y', t) \tag{3}$$

which is now rational in y, y', t. The equation defining t also describes a curve. Its genus (or deficiency) is either 0 or 1. A suitable reference for definitions and further details is Ford.

If the genus of (2) is zero, the resulting differential equation is reducible to one of the fifty standard types listed in **8-1** to **8-8**. When its genus is unity, three new types of differential equations occur.

a. Let g_2, g_3 be the invariants in the differential equation satisfied by the Weierstrass $\mathscr{P}$-function; see Erdélyi-1, vol. 2. The differential equation with fixed critical points is

$$y'' = \frac{6y^2 - g_2/2}{4y^3 - g_2y - g_3}p^2 + f_1(x)p + f_2(x)(4y^3 - g_2y - g_3)^{1/2}$$

Its solution is of class B; see **7b**. With variable transformations, the equation can be written in standard form

$$(4u^3 - g_2u - g_3)u''(z) = 6u^3 - \frac{g_2}{2}u'^2(z)$$

Compare it with [49] in **8-8**.

b. The second equation of this type is

$$y''(x) = X_0 p^2 + X_1 p + X_2 \tag{1}$$

where

$$X_0 = \frac{1}{2}\left[\frac{1}{y} + \frac{1}{y-1} + \frac{1}{y-x}\right]; \quad X_1 = -\left[\frac{1}{x} + \frac{1}{x-1} + \frac{1}{y-x}\right]$$

$$X_2 = \frac{y(y-1)}{2x(x-1)(y-x)} + f(x)\sqrt{y(y-1)(y-x)}$$

Its general solution is of class C; see **7c**. It is related to the solution of [50]; see **8-8** and Part II.

c. The third equation is again like (1), with

$$X_0 = (6y^2 - g_2/2)/R + i\pi/\omega\sqrt{R}; \quad X_1 = f_1(x); \quad X_2 = f_2(x)\sqrt{R}$$

where $R(y) = 4y^3 - g_2y - g_3$ and 2ω is any period of $\mathscr{P}(t, g_2, g_3)$. Its standard form can be taken as $u''(z) = U_0(u)u'^2$, where $U_0(u) = X_0(y)$.

11. Singular Solutions

A singular solution of the general nonlinear second-order differential equation may exist; see also **A2-10**. Let the given equation be

$$f(x, y, y', y'') = 0 \tag{1}$$

There are two alternative procedures.

a. A first integral of the equation is known. Let it be given as

$$F(x, y, y', C) = 0 \tag{2}$$

Calculate

$$\partial F / \partial C = 0 \tag{3}$$

and eliminate C between (2) and (3). The result is the singular first integral of (1). Suppose its form to be

$$\phi(x, y, y') = 0 \tag{4}$$

Its general solution will be a singular solution of (1). If (4) also possesses a singular solution, it will not, in general, satisfy (1). If two first integrals of (1) are known, both will yield the same singular integral.

b. No solution of the differential equation is known. If a singular integral exists, it is generally true that

$$\frac{\partial f / \partial y'}{\partial f / \partial y''} = \infty$$

It is only necessary, however, to use the relation $\partial f / \partial y'' = 0$, which will usually appear as

$$g(x, y, y', y'') = 0 \tag{5}$$

Solve (5) for y'', substitute the result in (1), and remove common factors, if they occur. The result will be the singular first integral. Continue as in **a** to get the singular solution of (1).

C. THE DIFFERENTIAL EQUATION IS OF ORDER GREATER THAN TWO

The general equation is

$$f(x, y, y', y'', y''', \ldots, y^{(n)}) = 0$$

where

$$y' = dy/dx, \ y'' = d^2y/dx^2, \ y''' = d^3y/dx^3, \ \ldots, \ y^{(n)} = dy^n/dx^n$$

If $n \leqslant 2$, return to **A** or **B**. For derivatives of order higher than three, it is convenient to use Roman numerals. Thus, $y^{\mathrm{iv}} = d^4y/dx^4$, $y^{\mathrm{v}} = d^5y/dx^5$, etc. In dealing with derivatives of higher order, it is often useful to remember Leibnitz's rule

$$\frac{d^n(uv)}{dx^n} = uv^{(n)} + nu'v^{(n-1)} + \frac{n(n-1)}{2!}u''v^{(n-2)} + \ldots + u^{(n)}v$$

The equations of this part are generalizations of those in **B** and the methods are similar. They are not usually as important as those of second order. For these reasons, the following sections are not given with as much detail as those in **B**. The missing steps can probably be inferred by reference to the corresponding methods in **B**.

It is sometimes useful to convert the single equation of order n to a system of n first-order equations. Thus,

$$y^{(n)}(x) = F(x, y, y', \ldots, y^{(n-1)})$$

is equivalent to

$$y_1' = y_2, \ y_2' = y_3, \ \ldots, \ y_{n-1}' = y_n, \ y_n' = F(x, y_1, y_2, \ldots, y_n)$$

where

$$y_1 = y, \ y_2 = y', \ y_3 = y'', \ \ldots, \ y_n = y^{(n-1)}$$

For references, see **B**.

There are two principal types of equations to be considered. Determine which is applicable and proceed as directed.

a. The linear equation. The general type is

$$A_0(x)y^{(n)} + A_1(x)y^{(n-1)} + \ldots + A_n(x)y = f(x)$$

188

Any of the $A_i(x)$ and $f(x)$ may be constants; some of them may vanish, but not A_0 if $n = 3$, for in that case the equation is of second order. Go to **C1** for further directions. Note, however, that some methods of **C2** will also apply to certain linear equations. In many cases, the nonlinear methods will be simpler, especially if there are missing variables. It would be well to consult **C2** before making a final choice of a method for a linear equation.

b. The nonlinear equation. Any equation of order $n \geqslant 3$ is of this kind, if it does not meet the requirements of **a.** Go to **C2**.

C1. THE LINEAR EQUATION OF ORDER GREATER THAN TWO

The general equation is

$$A_0(x)y^{(n)} + A_1(x)y^{(n-1)} + \ldots + A_n(x)y = f(x) \qquad (1)$$

For some of its properties, see **c**. There are two main cases; see also **B1**.

a. The homogeneous equation. The right-hand member of (1) vanishes; $f(x) = 0$. Consult **1** and following sections until a suitable method is found.

b. The nonhomogeneous equation. In this case, $f(x) \neq 0$. Ignore that fact, temporarily; solve the corresponding homogeneous equation as directed in **a**; then, refer to **8**.

c. General properties of the linear equation.

i. Existence theorem. With suitable restrictions, it can be shown that the equation possesses a unique solution. See **B1c** and references cited there.

ii. The general solution of the homogeneous equation. Let y_1, $y_2, \ldots, y_n$ be n linearly independent solutions of

$$A_0(x)y^{(n)} + A_1(x)y^{(n-1)} + \ldots + A_n(x)y = 0 \qquad (2)$$

Its general solution is

$$y = C_1 y_1 + C_2 y_2 + \ldots + C_n y_n \qquad (3)$$

where the C_i are arbitrary constants.

iii. The general solution of the nonhomogeneous equation. Let $F(x)$ be any special solution of (1) and let

$$Y(x) = C_1 y_1 + C_2 y_2 + \ldots + C_n y_n$$

be the general solution of (2). The general solution of (1) is

$$y = Y(x) + F(x)$$

where $Y(x)$ is the *complementary function* of (1).

190

iv. Linear independence. Suppose that $y_1, y_2, \ldots, y_n$ are any solutions of (2). Calculate the *Wronskian*

$$W(y_1, y_2, \ldots, y_n) = \begin{vmatrix} y_1^{(n-1)} & y_2^{(n-1} & \ldots & y_n^{(n-1)} \\ \ldots & \ldots & \ldots & \ldots \\ y_1' & y_2' & \ldots & y_n' \\ y_1 & y_2 & \ldots & y_n \end{vmatrix}$$

There are two possibilities.

1. $W(y_1, y_2, \ldots, y_n) \neq 0$. The n functions are linearly independent and (3) is the general solution of (2); see **ii**.

2. $W = 0$. There is at least one relation between the y_i and there may be more. The general solution of the differential equation has not yet been found.

v. Fundamental sets of solutions. Since the C_i in (3) are arbitrary, the differential equation has an infinite number of solutions. Each is a *fundamental set* or *system*. One particular set is usually convenient. Choose $y_i(x)$ such that $y_1(x_0) = 1$, $y_1'(x_0) = y_1''(x_0) = \ldots = y_1^{(n-1)}(x_0) = 0$. Define the remaining $y_i(x)$, $i = 2, 3, \ldots, n$ as that particular solution such that

$$y(x_0) = y'(x_0) = \ldots = y^{(i-2)}(x_0); \quad y^{(i-1)}(x_0) = 1$$
$$y^{(i)}(x_0) = y^{(i+1)}(x_0) = \ldots = y^{(n-1)}(x_0) = 0$$

Under these conditions, the solution is unique and its Wronskian equals unity when $x = x_0$. Alternatively, require the initial conditions

$$y(x_0) = y_0, \, y'(x_0) = y_0', \ldots, y^{(n-1)}(x_0) = y_0^{(n-1)}$$

Then, the unique solution of (2) is (3), with $C_1 = y_0$, $C_2 = y_0'$, $\ldots$, $C_n = y_0^{(n-1)}$.

1. The Linear Homogeneous Equation with Constant Coefficients

The general equation is

$$y^{(n)} + a_1 y^{(n-1)} + \ldots + a_n y = 0 \tag{1}$$

where each a_i is a constant and some of them may be zero. If $a_n = 0$, the method of **C2-2** might also be used but the present procedure will usually be preferred. If the coefficient of $y^{(n)}$ is other than unity, reduce the equation to the standard form (1).

Equations like (1) are often given in symbolic form as

$$f(D)y = 0 \tag{2}$$

where $D = d/dx$, a differential operator, and $F(D) = D^n + a_1 D^{n-1} + ... + a_n$; see also **B1-1**.

To solve (1) determine the n roots of the *auxiliary* or *characteristic equation*

$$r^n + a_1 r^{n-1} + ... + a_n = 0$$

The general solution is determined by these characteristic roots but there are several possibilities.

a. The roots are all real and unequal. Let them be $r_1, r_2, ... , r_n$ and the general solution of (1) is

$$y = C_1 e^{r_1 x} + C_2 e^{r_2 x} + ... + C_n e^{r_n x} \tag{3}$$

It is sometimes useful to replace the exponentials by hyperbolic functions. See **B1-1**, for the case of two roots. The procedure is easily generalized for n roots.

b. There are $m \leqslant n$ equal real roots, $r_1 = r_2 = ... = r_m$. Replace the corresponding m terms in (3) by

$$y_1 = e^{r_m x}(C_1 + C_2 x + ... + C_m x^{m-1})$$

Provided that case **c** does not also occur, the general solution of (1) is

$$y = y_1 + C_{m+1} e^{r_{m+1} x} + ... + C_n e^{r_n x}$$

c. There are m equal pairs of complex roots, $r = a \pm ib$. Replace the appropriate terms in (3) by

$$y_2 = e^{ax}[(A_1 + A_2 x + ... + A_m x^{m-1}) \cos bx + (B_1 + B_2 x + ... + B_m x^{m-1}) \sin bx]$$

where the A_i, B_i are arbitrary constants. The general solution of (1), provided that case **b** does not also occur, is

$$y = y_2 + C_{2m+1} e^{r_{2m+1} x} + ... + C_n e^{r_n x}$$

d. There are m_1 pairs of real roots and m_2 pairs of complex roots, $(m_1 + m_2) \leqslant n$. Use y_1 from **b**, y_2 from **c**, and complete the solution with y_3, so that $y(x) = y_1 + y_2 + y_3$, where y_3 contains the unrepeated roots as in (3). Take care that no more than n arbitrary constants occur in the general solution.

2. The Linear Homogeneous Equation with Variable Coefficients

There are two possible forms of the general equation

$$A_0(x)y^{(n)} + A_1(x)y^{(n-1)} + ... + A_n(x)y = 0$$
$$y^{(n)} + P_1(x)y^{(n-1)} + ... + P_n(x)y = 0$$

Note the following for special cases and directions.

a. A term $f(x)$ or $R(x)$ occurs on the right-hand side. Ignore it, proceed as directed, and then consult **8**.

b. Every coefficient in the equation is a constant or zero (but A_0 cannot vanish if the equation is of order n); return to **1**.

c. If $A_n = 0$ or $P_n = 0$, a method of **C2-2** could be used.

d. See **3**. The equation may be transformable into type **1**.

e. Examine the various methods of **C2**. Some of them may apply.

f. Consult **4ff**. If none of these methods appear suitable, it is likely that no simple solution of the equation exists and an approximate or numerical solution may be required; see also **B1-7** for further comments which may be adapted to the equation of order greater than two.

3. Equations Reducible to Type 1

If neither of the following cases applies, continue with **4ff**.

3-1. The Euler Equation.
The general case can be taken as

$$x^n y^{(n)} + a_1 x^{n-1} y^{(n-1)} + \ldots + a_n y = 0 \tag{1}$$

where the a_i are constants, some of which may be zero. Refer to **B1-3-1** for some further comments. With new variables, $y(x) = u(z)$, $z = \ln x$, the equation is converted into type **1**. Compute the roots of the auxiliary or characteristic equation

$$r(r-1) \ldots (r-n+1) + a_1 r(r-1) \ldots (r-n+2) + \ldots + a_n = 0$$

There are several cases. When the original variables are recovered, the general solution of (1) is as follows.

a. Real and unequal roots; $r_1, r_2, \ldots, r_n$. The solution is

$$y = C_1 x^{r_1} + C_2 x^{r_2} + \ldots + C_n x^{r_n} \tag{2}$$

b. A real root, repeated $m \leqslant n$ times; $r_1 = r_2 = \ldots = r_m$. Replace the corresponding m terms in (2) by

$$y_1 = x^{r_1}[C_1 + C_2 \ln x + \ldots + C_m(\ln x)^{m-1}]$$

The general solution, assuming that **c** does not also occur, is

$$y = y_1 + C_{m+1} x^{r_{m+1}} + \ldots + C_n x^{r_n}$$

c. A pair of complex roots occurs; $r = a \pm ib$. Replace the corresponding terms in (2) by

$$y_2 = x^a[A \cos(b \ln x) + B \sin(b \ln x)] \tag{3}$$

where A, B are arbitrary constants. If several pairs of complex roots occur, use the necessary number of terms like (3) with different constants A_i, B_i. If case **b** also arises, see **d**.

d. Repeated roots and complex roots. Combine the results of **b** and **c** to get a solution with n arbitrary constants.

3-2. The Legendre Linear Equation. See **B1-3-2** for the second-order equation. If $n > 2$, the general case is

$$(a+bx)^n y^{(n)} + a_1(a+bx)^{n-1}y^{(n-1)} + \ldots + a_n y = 0 \qquad (2)$$

If $a = 0$, $b = 1$, return to **3-1**. Otherwise, there are two procedures.
  a. Take $y(x) = u(z)$, $z = a + bx$, and get

$$z^n u^{(n)} + A_1 z^{n-1} u^{(n-1)} + \ldots + A_n u = 0 \qquad (3)$$

where $A_i = a_i/b^i$. The method of **3-1** can now be used. If the solution of (3) is $u = f(z)$, that of (2) is $y = f(a+bx)$.
  b. Take $y(x) = u(z)$, $z = \ln(a+bx)$. The new equation in u, z is type **1** and can be solved as described there. Then, return to the variables y, x.

4. Transformations of the Equation

Refer to **B1-4** and generalize the methods there for the nth order equation. The necessary formulas rapidly become quite complicated as n increases but they can be found by the usual methods of calculus. See also **4-1** and **4-2**.

4-1. A New Dependent Variable. The simplest possibility is

$$y(x) = u(x)v(x)$$

If the original equation is taken as

$$y^{(n)} + P_1(x)y^{(n-1)} + \ldots + P_n(x)y = 0 \qquad (1)$$

the new equation is

$$u^{(n)} + p_1(x)u^{(n-1)} + \ldots + p_n(x)u = 0 \qquad (2)$$

The new coefficients will be complicated functions of the $P_i(x)$, $v(x)$, and derivatives of the latter. For example, if $n = 3$, $vp_1 = 3v' + P_1v_1$; $vp_2 = 3v'' + 2P_1v' + P_2v$; $vp_3 = v''' + P_1v'' + P_2v' + P_3v$. For equations of higher order, Leibnitz's rule, see **C**, can be used with advantage.

Since the choice of $v(x)$ is arbitrary, attempt to fix it so that (2) is easier to solve than (1). Two obvious trial choices are shown in **4-1-1** and **4-1-2**. It cannot be hoped that either will always be successful.

4-1-1. One or More Special Solutions Known. Suppose that $v(x) = y_1(x)$ is a special solution of (1). It can sometimes be found by a lucky guess. If not, assume something simple like a polynomial, $y_1 = e^{kx}$, $y_1 = \ln x$, or some trigonometric function of x. See also **B1-4-1-1** for further suggestions which can be generalized in the case of an nth order equation.

Suppose, then, that such a special solution has been found by some means. The last term in (2) vanishes, since $p_n(x) = 0$, and the result is an equation of order $(n-1)$ in the variable $w(x) = u'$

$$u^{(n)} + p_1(x)u^{(n-1)} + \ldots + p_{n-1}(x)u' = 0$$

It is still linear; it may be easier to solve than the original equation or **C2-1** might be tried.

If $(n-1) \geqslant 2$, the same procedure might be repeated with successive reductions in order. Finally, if $(n-1)$ solutions of (1) can be found in this way, the general solution can be given in the following form

$$y = C_1 y_1 + C_2 y_2 + \ldots + C_{n-1} y_{n-1} + C_n(Y_1 + Y_2 + \ldots + Y_{n-1})$$

where

$$Y_k = y_k \int \frac{\Delta_k}{\Delta^2} X(x) dx$$

and $X(x) = \exp\left[-\int P_1(x)dx\right]$. The determinant Δ is obtained by deleting the first row and last column of the Wronskian; see **C1-c**.

$$\Delta = \begin{vmatrix} y_1^{(n-2)} & y_2^{(n-2)} & \ldots & y_{n-1}^{(n-2)} \\ \ldots & \ldots & \ldots & \ldots \\ y_1' & y_2' & \ldots & y_{n-1}' \\ y_1 & y_2 & \ldots & y_{n-1} \end{vmatrix}$$

The quantity Δ_k is the first minor of $y_k^{(n-1)}$ in Δ.

4-1-2. The Normal Form of the Equation. As a second possibility in the choice of a new dependent variable, reduce the equation to its normal form. For a second-order equation, see **B1-4-1-2**, the normal form is that containing no term in y'. For the nth order equation, the normal form can be taken as that in which the next highest derivative, $y^{(n-1)}$, has been removed. It may be no easier to solve than the original equation, but the procedure is worth trying. Let $y = u(x)v(x)$; $v(x) = \exp[-(1/n)\int P_1(x)dx]$ and the result is

$$u^{(n)} + p_2(x)u^{(n-2)} + \ldots + p_n(x)u = 0$$

The coefficients can be calculated as indicated in **4-1**. For $n = 3$, they are

$$p_2 = P_2 - P_1^2/3 - P_1'; \quad p_3 = P_3 - P_1 P_2/3 + 2P_1^3/27 - P_1''/3$$

4-2. Other Variable Transformations. Refer to **B1-4**, hoping that those methods might be generalized for an equation of order $n > 2$. The resulting relations will not be simple.

As a simple possibility, exchange the variables x and y; see also **B1-4-3**. The necessary equations, for $n = 3$, are

$$y'(x) = 1/x'(y); \quad y'' = -x''(y)/x'^3(y)$$
$$y'''(x) = (3x''^2 - x'''x')/x'^5$$

More generally, suppose that a new independent variable is chosen, so that $y(x) = u(z)$, with z defined by an equation $f(x, z) = 0$. It is sometimes easier to solve and get $z = f_1(x)$; otherwise, solve for $x = f_2(z)$. Let $z_x = df_1/dx$, $z_{xx} = d^2f_1/dx^2$, $z_{xxx} = d^3f_1/dx^3$; $x_z = df_2/dz$, etc. For $n = 3$, use **a** or **b**, whichever seems easier. For $n > 3$, the equations become quite complicated, but see **b**.

a. The derivatives with respect to the new independent variable are given by the relations

$$x_z y'(x) = u'(z); \quad x_z^3 y'' = x_z u'' - x_{zz} u'$$
$$x_z^5 y''' = x_z^2 u''' - 3x_z x_{zz} u'' + 3x_{zz}^2 u' - x_z x_{zzz} u'$$

b. If it is easier to solve $f(x, z) = 0$ for z, the new derivatives are

$$y'(x) = z_x u'(z); \quad y'' = z_x^2 u'' + z_{xx} u'$$
$$y''' = z_x^3 u''' + 3z_x z_{xx} u'' + z_{xxx} u'$$

The appropriate equations for $n > 3$ have been given by Sansone. He also gives further relations between the coefficients of the original equation in x, y and the transformed equation in z, u.

5. The Exact Equation

Take the standard form as

$$A_0(x)y^{(n)} + A_1(x)y^{(n-1)} + \ldots + A_n(x)y = 0 \tag{1}$$

It is exact, see also **B1-5**, if

$$A_n(x) - A_{n-1}'(x) + A_{n-2}''(x) \mp \ldots + (-1)^n A_0^{(n)} = 0 \tag{2}$$

If (2) holds, a first integral of (1) is

$$B_0(x)y^{(n-1)} + B_1(x)y^{(n-2)} + \ldots + B_{n-1}(x)y = C \tag{3}$$

where

$$B_0 = A_0; \quad B_1 = A_1 - A_0'; \quad B_2 = A_2 - A_1' + A_0''; \quad \ldots$$
$$B_{n-1} = A_{n-1} - A'_{n-1} + A''_{n-3} \mp \ldots + (-1)^{n-1} A_0(n-1)$$

If this first integral also satisfies the requirement for exactness, the process may be repeated. Continue as long as successive integrals are exact. If the test for exactness fails at any step, complete the solution of the differential equation by some other method.

Note that the test for a nonhomogeneous equation, see **8**, is identical with (2). When $f(x)$ occurs on the right-hand side of (1), add a term $\int f(x)dx$ to the right-hand side of (3).

Sometimes an integrating factor can be found for the inexact equation; see **5-1**.

5-1. The Integrating Factor and the Adjoint Equation.

Let the standard form (1) be abbreviated as $L(y) = 0$; see **B1-5-2**. An integrating factor $u(x)$ is to be sought so that $uL(y)dx$ is a perfect differential.

Apply the general formula for integration by parts to each derivative in $uL(y)$. A typical term is

$$(A_{n-k}u)y^{(k)} = \frac{d}{dx}[(A_{n-k}u)y^{(k-1)} - (A_{n-k}u)'y^{(k-2)} \pm \ldots$$
$$+ (-1)^{k-1}(A_{n-k}u)^{(k-1)}y] + (-1)^k(A_{n-k}u)^{(k)}y$$

When all such terms are collected, the result is

$$uL(y) = \frac{d}{dx}[X_0(y, u) + X_1(y, u) + \ldots + X_{n-1}(y, u)] + y\bar{L}(u) \qquad (4)$$

where

$$X_0(y, u) = (A_0u)y^{(n-1)} - (A_0u)'y^{(n-2)} \pm \ldots + (-1)^{n-1}(A_0u)^{(n-1)}y$$
$$X_1(y, u) = (A_1u)y^{(n-2)} - (A_1u)'y^{(n-3)} \pm \ldots + (-1)^{n-2}(A_0u)^{(n-2)}y$$
$$\ldots \quad \ldots \quad \ldots \quad \ldots \quad \ldots \quad \ldots \quad \ldots \quad \ldots \quad \ldots$$
$$X_{n-1}(y, u) = (A_{n-1}u)y$$

The last term in (4) contains the equation adjoint to $L(y)$

$$\bar{L}(u) = (-1)^n(A_0u)^{(n)} + (-1)^{n-1}(A_1u)^{(n-1)} \mp \ldots - (A_{n-1}u)' + A_n \qquad (5)$$

It may also be written as

$$\bar{L}(u) = B_0u^{(n)} + B_1u^{(n-1)} + \ldots + B_nu$$

where

$$B_0 = A_0$$
$$B_1 = A_1 - \binom{n}{1}A_0'$$
$$B_2 = A_2 - \binom{n-1}{1}A_1' + \binom{n}{2}A_0''$$
$$\ldots \quad \ldots \quad \ldots \quad \ldots \quad \ldots \quad \ldots$$

$$B_k = A_k - \binom{n-k+1}{1}A_{k-1}' + \binom{n-k+2}{2}A_{k-2}'' \mp \dots$$

$$\dots \quad \dots \quad \dots \quad \dots \quad \dots \quad \dots \quad \dots \quad \dots \quad \dots$$

$$B_n = A_n - A_{n-1}' + A_{n-2}'' \mp \dots$$

From (4), it follows that

$$uL(y) - y\bar{L}(u) = \frac{d}{dx}[P(y, u)]$$

where $P(y, u)$, the bilinear concomitant, is a differential equation of order $(n-1)$. Collecting coefficients from (4), it is found that

$$P(y, u) = Q_0 y^{(n-1)} + Q_1 y^{(n-2)} + \dots + Q_{n-1} y \qquad (6)$$

and its coefficients are

$$Q_0 = A_0 u$$
$$Q_1 = A_1 u - (A_0 u)'$$
$$\dots \quad \dots \quad \dots \quad \dots$$
$$Q_{n-1} = A_{n-1} u - (A_{n-2} u)' \pm \dots + (-1)^{n-1}(A_0 u)^{(n-1)}$$

The proposed method is the following. Determine the integrating factor $u(x)$ from (5), the adjoint equation of order n. It may be no easier to solve than (1), the original equation. However, any special solution of it would give (6), a differential equation of order $(n-1)$ and $P(y, u) = C$ is thus a first integral of (1).

If k independent solutions of $\bar{L}(u) = 0$ can be found, then there will be k different equations $P(y, u_1) = C_1, P(y, u_2) = C, \dots, P(y, u_k) = C_k$, each of order $(n-1)$ and each a first integral of (1). Use them to eliminate the $(k-1)$ quantities $y^{(n-1)}, y^{(n-2)}, \dots, y^{(n-k+1)}$ and get a linear differential equation of order $(n-k)$ with k arbitrary constants $C_1, C_2, \dots, C_k$. Finally, if $k = n$, all derivatives of y can be eliminated and the result is the general solution of (1).

Alternatively, it may be possible to find an integrating factor for $P(y, u) = C$, the equation of order $(n-1)$, and thus reduce the order of it to $(n-2)$. The procedure could be repeated until an equation of order two or one is produced. Its solution by a method of **B1** or **A1** would then give the general solution of $L(y) = 0$.

Sometimes, it may be possible to avoid the rather complicated operations of this section by assuming an integrating factor of some simple form. Suppose, for example, that the coefficients in (1) are all polynomials. Take $u(x) = x^m$ and test $x^m L(y) = 0$, to see if m can be determined so that this equation is exact; see **5**. This process will not always work but it may be worth trying.

It is of interest, and frequently of practical importance, to consider the case where $L(y) = (-1)^n(\bar{L}y)$. The two equations are then said to be self-adjoint. More precisely, some authors use self-adjointness to apply only with the positive sign, thus only for equations of even order. With the minus sign, thus for equations of odd order, they are said to be anti-self-adjoint.

If $n = 2m$, comparison of (1) with (5) shows that the required condition is

$$L(y) = \bar{L}(y) = (f_0 y^{(m)})^{(m)} + (f_1 y^{(m-1)})^{(m-1)} + \dots + f_m y \tag{7}$$

For the special case of $m = 2$, $n = 4$, see **b.**

For equations of odd order, let $n = 2m + 1$, and there are two possible forms of the equation

$$L(y) = -\bar{L}(y) = (f_0 y)^{(2m+1)} + f_0 y^{(2m+1)} + \dots + (f_m y)' + f_m y' \tag{8}$$

$$L(y) = -\bar{L}(y) = (f_0 y^{(m)})^{(m+1)} + (f_0 y^{(m+1)})^{(m)} + \dots + (f_m y)' + f_m y' \tag{9}$$

For the special case of $m = 1$, $n = 3$, see **a.**

a. The differential equation of third order. Let the standard form be

$$y''' + P_1(x)y'' + P_2(x)y' + P_3(x)y = 0 \tag{10}$$

An alternative equation, often useful, can be obtained as follows. Multiply (10) by $f^2(x)$, where

$$f(x) = \exp\left[\tfrac{1}{3} \int P_1(x)dx\right]$$

The result is

$$[f(fy')']' + gy' + hy = 0 \tag{11}$$

where

$$g(x) = f^2 P_2(x) - ff'' - f'^2; \quad h(x) = f^2 P_3(x)$$

There are three convenient forms of the anti-self-adjoint equation.

    i. Use (8) and get

$$L(y) = (f_0 y)''' + f_0 y''' + (f_1 y)' + f_1 y'$$
$$= 2f_0 y''' + 3f_0' y'' + (3f_0'' + 2f_1)y' + (f_0''' + f_1')y = 0$$

    ii. With (9), the result is

$$L(y) = (f_0 y')'' + (f_0 y'')' + (f_1 y)' + f_1 y'$$
$$= 2f_0 y''' + 3f_0' y'' + (f_0'' + 2f_1)y' + f_1' y = 0$$

    iii. In the special case of (11), where $g(x) = 2f_1(x)$, $h(x) = f_1'$, $f(x) = f_0(x)$, the anti-self-adjoint equation is

$$L(y) = [f_0(f_0 y')']' + 2f_1 y' + f_1' y$$
$$= f_0^2 y''' + 3f_0 f_0' y'' + (f_0'^2 + f_0 f_0'' + 2f_1)y' + f_1' y = 0 \tag{12}$$

If y_1, y_2 are two linearly independent solutions of the self-adjoint second-order equation, see **B1-5-3**,

$$2f_0(f_0y')' + f_1y = 0$$

then the general solution of (12) is $y = C_1y_1^2 + C_2y_1y_2 + C_3y_2^2$.

b. The differential equation of fourth order. According to (7), the self-adjoint fourth-order equation will have the form

$$(f_0y'')'' + (f_1y')' + f_2y = 0 \tag{13}$$

The derivative of third order can be eliminated; see **4-1-2**. Let

$$u(x) = f_0^{1/8}(x)y(x); \quad z = \int f_0^{-1/4}dx$$

The new equation is

$$u^{\mathrm{iv}} + [F(z)u']' + G(z)u = 0$$

where

$$F(z) = \frac{f_1}{r^4} - 6r^3r'' - 16r^2r'^2;$$

$$G(z) = f_2 - \frac{f_1}{r^2}\left(\frac{r^2}{2}\right)'' - \left(\frac{A_1}{r^3}\right)'r^2r' - r^7r^{\mathrm{iv}} - 8r^6r'r'''$$

$$+ 20r^5r'^2r'' - 2r^6r''^2 + 40r^4r'^4; \quad r^8(x) = f_0(x)$$

Another form of (13) can be obtained with $y(x) = U(x)Z(z)$; $z(x) = \int dx/f_0U^2$. The result is

$$Z^{\mathrm{iv}}(z) = \phi(z)Z$$

where $U(x)$ is a solution of

$$30\frac{U''}{U} - 20\left(\frac{U'}{U}\right)^2 + 10\frac{f_0'U'}{fU} + \left(\frac{f_0'}{f_0}\right)^2 - 3\frac{f_0''}{f_0} + 9\frac{f_1}{f_0} = 0$$

The last equation can be converted into one of Riccati type, see **A1-3-1**, with $Y(x) = U'U$. The result is

$$30Y' + 10Y^2 + 10\left(\frac{f_0'}{f_0}\right)Y + \left(\frac{f_0'}{f_0}\right)^2 - 3\frac{f_0''}{f_0} + 9\frac{f_1}{f_0} = 0$$

6. Series Solution

Read **B1-7**, where solution of the second-order linear equation is discussed. The suggestions there apply equally well to the nth order equation. If a series solution is desired, continue with this section and see **7** for some special cases. For definite integral solutions, go to **8**.

The standard form of the equation is

$$y^{(n)} + P_1(x)y^{(n-1)} + \ldots + P_n(x)y = 0 \tag{1}$$

Find all singular points of the equation and classify each; see also **B1-8**. If the point of interest is at $x = a$, use new variables $y(x) = u(z)$, $z = (a-x)$; if $x = \infty$, use $z = 1/x$. In either case, the point is shifted to $z = 0$. Continue with this section, replacing x, y by z, u and then return to the original variables. There are three cases.

   a. An ordinary point at $x = 0$; see **6-1**.
   b. A regular singular point at $x = 0$; see **6-2**.
   c. An irregular singular point at $x = 0$; see **6-3**.

6-1. Series Solution Near an Ordinary Point.

Let $x = 0$ be an ordinary point for (1); see also **B1-8-1**. Assume solutions

$$y_{k+1}(x) = x^k(1 + A_{k1}x + A_{k2}x^2 + \ldots); \quad k = 0, 1, \ldots, (n-1)$$

where the A_{ki} are constants to be determined. Substitute the series in (1), arrange the result in ascending powers of x, and equate coefficients of equal powers of x to zero. There will be a set of linear recursion relations, see **B1-8-1-1**, between the A_{ki}. When these coefficients are determined, the general solution of (1) is

$$y = C_1 y_1 + C_2 y_2 + \ldots + C_n y_n$$

Variations of this method can be made by generalizing the procedures in **B1-8-1**.

6-2. Series Solution Near a Regular Singular Point.

Let $x = 0$ be a regular singular point; see **B1-8-2**. The differential equation must hen have the form, see also **7**,

$$x^n y^{(n)} + x^{n-1} p_1(x) y^{(n-1)} + \ldots + x p_{n-1}(x) y' + p_n(x) y = 0 \qquad (2)$$

where $p_k(x) = p_{0k} + p_{1k}x + p_{2k}x^2 + \ldots$, and the p_{mk} are constants, possibly complex numbers. It is convenient to designate (2) by the abbreviation $L(y) = 0$.

   Assume a solution

$$Y(x) = x^s(A_0 + A_1 x + A_2 x^2 + \ldots); \quad A_0 = 1 \qquad (3)$$

in which s and the A_k are constants to be determined. Proceed as in **6-1**, by substituting (3) into (2) and arranging the result according to ascending powers of x. It is found that

$$L(Y) = f(s)x^s + [f(s+1)A_1 - B_1]x^{s+1} + \ldots + [f(s+k)A_k - B_k]x^{s+k} + \ldots$$

where the B_k are linear in $A_1, A_2, \ldots, A_{k-1}$, with polynomials in s as coefficients. If $Y(x)$ is to be a solution of (2), it is necessary that the coefficients of each power of x vanish. For the lowest power,

$$f(s) = [s]_n + [s]_{n-1}p_1(0) + \ldots + s p_{n-1}(0) + p_n(0) = 0$$

where $[s]_n = s(s-1) \ldots (s-n+1)$. This is the indicial equation and its roots determine the exponents of the differential equation.

For the coefficients of higher powers of x in (3), it is seen that

$$f(s+k)A_k = B_k; \quad k = 1, 2, 3, \ldots \tag{4}$$

This is a set of recursion formulas, see **B1-8-1-1**, from which the A_k can be calculated successively. There are two possibilities.

a. The indicial equation is independent of s or it is a polynomial in s of degree less than n. The singularity was irregular, the differential equation did not have the assumed form (2); see **6-3** for the procedure.

b. The indicial equation is a polynomial of degree n in s. Let its roots be $s_1, s_2, s_3, \ldots, s_n$. There are two cases.

i. All roots are different and no pair of them differs by an integer; $\Delta s = s_i - s_j \neq m$, where $m = 0$ or an integer. See **6-2-1**.

ii. Two or more roots are equal or the difference between two or more equals an integer; $\Delta s = s_i - s_j = m$. See **6-2-2**.

6-2-1. All Exponents are Different. Included in this case is the situation where $\Delta s = s_i - s_j \neq m$, with $m = 0$ or an integer. If there are $r < n$ nonintegral differences between the exponents and $(n-r)$ integral differences continue with this section. The procedure to be described will produce r solutions of the differential equation. Its order can thus be reduced from n to $(n-r)$ and the reduced equation might be solved by series or otherwise to find the general solution of (2); see **4-1-1**. It will usually be simpler to find the remaining $(n-r)$ solutions according to **6-2-2**.

Use the notation

$$f(x, s+k) = [s+k]_n + [s+k]_{n-1}p_1(x) + \ldots + [s+k]_1 p_{n-1}(x) + p_n(x)$$

where $[s+k]_n$ is defined as in **6-2**. It also follows that this function can be developed in a power series

$$f(x, s+k) = f_0(s+k) + f_1(s+k)x + \ldots + f_k(s+k)x^k + \ldots$$

where k indicates the power of x in the parentheses of (3). The resulting recursion formulas, corresponding to (4) are

$$A_0 f_0(s) = 0$$

$$A_1 f_0(s+1) + A_0 f_1(s) = 0$$

$$\ldots \quad \ldots \quad \ldots \quad \ldots$$

$$A_k f_0(s+k) + A_{k-1} f_1(s+k-1) + \ldots + A_0 f_k(s) = 0$$

The first equation of this set is the indicial equation; see **6-2**. Since it has been assumed that $A_0 = 1 \neq 0$, it will yield the n exponents. If one of them is chosen so that $f_0(s+k) \neq 0$ for any integral value of k, the remaining constants are determined uniquely from

$$f_0(s+1)f_0(s+2)\dots f_0(s+k)A_k = (-1)^k F_k(s)$$

where

$$F_k(s) = \begin{vmatrix} f_1(s+k-1) & f_2(s+k-2) & \dots & f_{k-1}(s+1) & f_k(s) \\ f_0(s+k-1) & f_1(s+k-2) & \dots & f_{k-2}(s+1) & f_{k-1}(s) \\ 0 & f_0(s+k-2) & \dots & f_{k-3}(s+1) & f_{k-2}(s) \\ \dots & \dots & \dots & \dots & \dots \\ 0 & 0 & \dots & f_0(s+1) & f_1(s) \end{vmatrix}$$

To each value of s, there will be a definite sequence of coefficients A_k and thus there will be n solutions, provided that $\Delta s = s_i - s_j \neq m$, for all i, j. For the exceptional case, see **6-2-2**.

6-2-2. Equal Exponents or Integral Exponent Differences.

Solution of the indicial equation, see **6-2**, has given $\Delta s = s_i - s_j = m$, where $m = 0$ or an integer, for at least one pair i, j. Arrange the exponents in the following scheme

$$s_1, s_2, \dots, s_{\alpha-1}$$
$$s_\alpha, s_{\alpha+1}, \dots, s_{\beta-1}$$
$$\dots \quad \dots \quad \dots$$
$$s_r, s_{r+1}, \dots, s_n$$

where the exponents in each set differ only by integers, including zero, and where they are so ordered that their real parts form a nonincreasing sequence. The first member of each set will yield a solution as in **6-2-1**. It is not the general solution of the differential equation, however, since $r < n$. Before seeking the remaining solutions, note that two kinds of difficulties can occur. Consider the set beginning with s_α. One or both of the following situations might arise.

i. Some exponent, say $s_{\alpha+i}$ equals s_α. The solutions for s_α and $s_{\alpha+i}$ are identical.

ii. The exponent $s_{\alpha+i}$ is less than s_α by a positive integer. The solution corresponding to the former cannot be obtained since the condition $f_0(s+k) \neq 0$, see **6-2-1**, cannot be satisfied when $k = s_\alpha - s_{\alpha+i}$. This difficulty can be avoided but then the solution for $s_{\alpha+i}$ will be a constant multiple of the solution for s_α; hence nothing has been gained.

In either case of the preceding paragraph, rearrange the set beginning with s_1, so that $s_1 = s_2 = \dots = s_i$; $s_{i+1} = s_{i+2} = \dots = s_j$; etc., until that set is used up. The first subset corresponds to a root of the indicial equation of multiplicity i; the second subset to a root of multiplicity j;

and so on. The equations which result in the most general case are quite complicated. They are given in detail by Ince-1. The following simplified treatment may be helpful in many cases.

a. $s_1 = s_2$; $s_2 = s_{\alpha-1}$; the exponent is a double root of the indicial equation. Differentiate $L(Y) = f(s)x^s$, see **6-2**, partially with respect to s, and get

$$L_s(Y) = [f_s(s) + f(s) \ln x]x^s$$

Differentiation is commutative for the left-hand side of this equation so that $L_s(Y) = L(Y_s)$. Since s_1 has been assumed to be a double root, both $f(s_1)$ and $f_s(s_1)$ vanish. Thus, Y_s evaluated at $s = s_1$ is a solution of the differential equation, which could be written as

$$Y_{11}(x) = Y_1 \ln x + Y_2$$

where $Y_1(x)$ is the series solution obtained according to **6-2-1** with $s = s_1$, and

$$Y_2(x) = x^{s_1}(X_1 x + X_2 x^2 + \ldots + X_k x^k + \ldots)$$

The quantities $X_k(x)$ are determined from

$$X_k(x) = \left[\frac{\partial A_k}{\partial s} \right]_{s=s_1}$$

b. $s_1 = s_2 = \ldots = s_i$; thus, s_1 is a root of the indicial equation of multiplicity i. If $(i-1)$ differentiations are performed, as in **a**, there will be i solutions of the differential equation.

c. $s_1 = s_2 = \ldots = s_i$; $s_{i+1} = s_j$; $s_i - s_j = q$, a positive integer. As stated in **ii**, the two solutions obtained with s_i and s_j can be determined but they are constant multiples of each other. To find a second independent solution, calculate

$$L\left[\frac{\partial^i Y}{\partial s^i} \right] = i! f(s)x^s + G(s)$$

where i is the multiplicity of the root s_1 and $G(s)$ contains $s - s_{i+1}$ as a factor. With $s = s_{i+1}$, one gets $L(Y_{i+1}) = 0$, where Y_{i+1} is $\partial^i Y / \partial s^i$ at $s = s_{i+1}$. Its leading term is $i!/x^{s_1+1}$ and the solution which results is different from any involving the root s_1.

d. The various cases in this section show that the following results will be obtained for the subset of exponents beginning with s_1.

$$y_1 = Y_1(x, s_1)$$
$$y_2 = Y_1(x, s_1) \ln x + Y_2(x, s_1)$$
$$y_3 = Y_1(x, s_1)(\ln x)^2 + 2 Y_2(x, s_1) \ln x + Y_3(x, s_1)$$
$$\ldots \quad \ldots \quad \ldots \quad \ldots \quad \ldots \quad \ldots \quad \ldots$$
$$y_i = Y_1(x, s_1)(\ln x)^i + i Y_2(x, s_1)(\ln x)^{i-1} + \ldots + Y_i(x, s_1)$$

Here, the quantities $Y_i(x, s_1)$ are infinite series in x, the lowest power of x in each series is s_1, and the coefficients A_{ij} are different for each of the series Y_1, Y_2, etc. Note further that i is an integer in these equations and that it does not mean $\sqrt{-1}$.

The remaining subsets of exponents beginning with s_1 should be treated in the same way to find further solutions of the differential equation. Finally, subject the sets s_α, s_β, ... , s_r to a similar procedure. Eventually, there will be n linearly independent solutions of the differential equation, which means that the general solution has been found. There will be r solutions as infinite series in x, with lowest terms in x raised to the powers s_1, s_α, s_β, ... , s_r, respectively. The remaining solutions, $(n-r)$ in number, will usually contain logarithmic factors, but see **e**.

e. From **d**, it was seen that the exponents s_1, s_α, s_β, ... , s_r always give nonlogarithmic solutions, since the requirements of **6-2-1** are met. Similarly, repeated roots of the indicial equation always give logarithmic solutions. When the exponent differences are integral, logarithmic solutions usually occur but exceptions may arise; see also **B1-8-2-3**.

The following treatment explains the exceptional cases and it also offers an alternative method for finding the logarithmic solutions. The method in **c**, however, could also be used for the exceptional cases where no logarithmic term appears.

Consider the set of exponents s_1, s_2, ... , $s_{\alpha-1}$, with integral differences, including zero, and differences from all other exponents by numbers which are not integers. The first member of the set will certainly give a solution, according to **6-2-1**, of the form $y_1(x) = x^{s_1}u_1(x)$, where $u_1(x)$ is analytic near $x = 0$. The differential equation can then be reduced in order from n to $(n-1)$, see **4-1-1**, with $y = y_1 \int v(x)dx$. Now

$$v(x) = \frac{d}{dx}\left(\frac{y}{y_1}\right)$$

hence the new equation in $v(x)$ of order $(n-1)$ has exponents at $x = 0$, which are $s_2 - s_1 - 1$, $s_3 - s_1 - 1$, ... , $s_{\alpha-1} - s_1 - 1$. All but the last of these is a negative integer. Since $s_2 \geqslant s_3$, there will be a solution

$$v(x) = x^{s_1 - s_2 - 1}\phi(x)$$

where $\phi(x)$ is analytic near $x = 0$. The second solution of the nth order equation is thus

$$y_2 = y_1 \int x^{s_2 - s_1 - 1}\phi(x)dx$$

There are two possibilities.

i. The preceding solution can be written as

$$y_2 = x^{s_1}[u_1(x) \ln x + u_{22}(x)]$$

where u_{22} is analytic near $x = 0$. The procedure is to be repeated, if necessary, so that finally

$$y_k = x^{s_1}[u_1(x)(\ln x)^k + u_{k1}(x)(\ln x)^{k-1} + \ldots + u_{kk}(x)]$$

with $k = 2, 3, \ldots, (\alpha - 1)$. This result, except for changes in notation, agrees with the conclusions in **d**. Repeat the procedure for the exponents beginning with $s_\alpha, s_\beta, \ldots, s_r$ until n linearly independent solutions of the equation have been found.

ii. An exceptional case arises if $\phi(x)$ does not contain a term $x^{s_1-s_2}$. No logarithmic factor will result when the integral containing $\phi(x)$ is evaluated. This is an unusual situation, not the general one, but see **f**. The second-order equation has been presented in more detail in **B1-8-2-3**; for the nth order equation, see Ince-1 or Forsyth-2.

f. Real and apparent singularities. The procedure of **6-2-1** will always give nonintegral exponents; hence the solution of the differential equation will have a branch point at the origin. If the case of **6-2-2** arises, there will be poles in the solution for the negative exponents. In the general case of **6-2-2**, the solution will also contain terms in $\ln x$. Solutions of these types are called regular solutions and the corresponding singular point at $x = 0$ is a real singularity. It can happen, however, that $x = 0$ is an ordinary point for the solution of the differential equation even though it is a singular point of the differential equation. The singularity is then said to be apparent, see also **B1-8-2**.

An apparent singularity can occur only when the following conditions are met. First, $P_1(0)$ must be a negative integer greater than zero. Next, the exponents must be unequal positive integers; hence case **6-2-2** must apply. Finally, there must be no logarithmic terms in the general solution. Let the exponents be $s_1, s_2, \ldots, s_n$, arranged as described earlier in this section, all differing by integers, and all unequal. The solution with exponent s_1 is certainly free from logarithms; one condition guarantees that s_2 is free from logarithms, two further conditions for s_3, and so on. Thus, $1 + 2 + \ldots + (n-1) = n(n-1)/2$ conditions are imposed to prevent logarithmic terms in the general solution. If any of the stated conditions cannot be met, the singularity at $x = 0$ is real and not apparent.

6-3. Series Solution Near an Irregular Singular Point.

Consider the standard equation (1), where the point of interest is at $x = 0$. If at least one of its coefficients $P_k(x)$ has a pole of order greater than k at $x = 0$, an irregular singular point occurs there. It may have one or more regular solutions; see **6-2-2f**. However, there may be no solutions of this kind; see also **B1-8-3**. There are two problems of interest in this case.

a. The possible number of regular solutions.

b. The nature of the remaining solutions of the differential equation.

a. Regular solutions. Let h_k be the order of the pole in $P_k(x)$ at $x = 0$, see also **A1-10-1**, and calculate

$$g_1 = h_1 + n - 1, \quad g_2 = h_2 + n - 2, \ldots, \quad g_{n-1} = h_{n-1} + 1, g_n = h_n$$

Call the largest of these n integers g_c. It may occur more than once; if so, make the choice

$$g_k < g_c; \quad k = 1, 2, \ldots, (c-1)$$

$$g_k \geqslant g_{c+k}; \quad k = 1, 2, \ldots, (n-c)$$

The number c is the class or characteristic index of the irregular singular point. If $g_k \leqslant n$ for every coefficient, then $c = 0$ and the singular point was regular; return to **6-2**. For an irregular singular point, $c \geqslant 1$ and there may be $r = (n - c)$ regular solutions, see **6-2-2f**, but possibly fewer than that number.

To proceed further, multiply (1) by x^g and it becomes

$$x^n Q_0(x) y^{(n)} + x^{n-1} Q_1(x) y^{(n-1)} + \ldots + x Q_{n-1}(x) y' + Q_n(x) y = 0 \qquad (5)$$

where

$$Q_0(x) = x^{g-n}, \quad Q_k(x) = x^{g-n+k} P_k(x); k = 1, 2, \ldots, n.$$

These coefficients are analytic near $x = 0$ and, since the origin is assumed to be an irregular singular point, $Q_0(0) = Q_1(0) = \ldots = Q_{r-1}(0) = 0$; $Q_r(0) \neq 0$, provided that $g = g_c$. The remaining coefficients are either zero or finite at $x = 0$. If a regular solution exists, the indicial equation, see **6-2**, becomes $[s]_{n-c} Q_r(0) + \ldots = 0$, where the unwritten terms are polynomials in s of degree less than $r = (n - c)$. It follows that there will be no more than r exponents for the differential equation and no more than r regular solutions. Note, also, that when $c = n$, $Q_n(0) = 0$, the indicial equation is independent of s, and there are no regular solutions; see also **6-2a**.

To determine the actual number of regular solutions, abbreviate (5) as $L(y) = 0$ and consider its adjoint $\bar{L}(u) = 0$; see **5-1**. Suppose that $L(y) = 0$ has the full number of r regular solutions and therefore its indicial equation is of degree r. The corresponding differential operator can be written as $L = RM$, where L is of order n, R is a linear operator of order c, and M an operator of order $r = (n - c)$. The r regular solutions must each satisfy the equation $M(y) = 0$. Let the operator adjoint to L be $\bar{L} = \bar{M}\bar{R}$. Since both $\bar{L}$ and $\bar{M}$ have indicial equations of degree r, it follows that the indicial equation for $\bar{R}$ is of degree zero. Therefore, if $L(y) = 0$ has exactly $r = (n - c)$ regular solutions, its adjoint equation $\bar{L}(u) = 0$ must be satisfied by the solutions of an equation $\bar{R}(u) = 0$, which is of order c but which has no indicial equation.

When $L(y) = 0$ has been shown to have $r \leqslant (n-c)$ regular solutions, they can be found by the methods of **6**. If all exponents are different and there are no integral differences between them, see **6-2-1**; with repeated roots and integral differences, logarithmic terms may occur in the solutions; see **6-2-2**. Unfortunately, even when there is an indicial equation of order r, the formal series which satisfy the differential equation may diverge for all values of x. They are not useless for they may represent an asymptotic solution to the equation. perhaps for large values of x; see Erdélyi-2. In general, it is an exceptional case where the full number of convergent regular solutions can exist.

b. Normal solutions. Assuming that the work of **a** has been completed, only $r \leqslant (n-c)$ solutions of the differential equation have been found. Since $c > 0$ and $r < n$, the general solution of the equation has not yet been obtained. It would be possible to insist on series solutions for the rest of the members in the general solution. However, they will usually involve infinite series in both ascending and descending powers of the independent variable; the recursion formulas, see **B1-8-1-1**, will contain all of the coefficients; and the difficulties of computing will be great.

It was first shown by Thomé that simpler solutions might exist of the form

$$y(x) = e^{\phi(x)}u(x)$$

These are called *normal solutions*. The quantity $\phi(x)$ is the determining factor, a polynomial in $1/x$ of degree $(\delta - 1)$, with properties such that the transformed equation in $u(x)$ has at least one regular solution. Note that $e^{\phi(x)}$ has an essential singularity at $x = 0$.

Irregular singular points often occur at $x = \infty$. For this reason, it may be convenient to take (1) as

$$y^{(n)} + p_1(x)y^{(n-1)} + \ldots + p_n(x)y = 0$$

where

$$p_k = x^{m_k}(A_{k0} + A_{k1}/x + A_{k2}/x^2 + \ldots).$$

For an irregular singular point, it is necessary that $m_k \geqslant (1-k)$ for at least one k, $0 \leqslant k \leqslant m$. The determining factor will then be a polynomial in x and $u(x)$ will be a regular solution in powers of $1/x$. This case has been discussed by Ince-1 and Wasow. In the following treatment, the irregular singular point will be kept at $x = 0$.

A given differential equation may not have a normal solution, but see **c**. To investigate the situation, let $d^k e^\phi/dx^k = w_k e^\phi$, so that $w_0 = 1$, $w_1 = \phi'$, $w_2 = w_1' + w_1\phi'$, $\ldots$, $w_{k+1} = w_k' + w_k\phi'$. Then,

$$y^{(k)} = e^\phi[w_k u + k w_{k-1} u' + \ldots + k w_1 u^{(n-1)} + u^{(n)}]$$

and the transformed equation becomes

$$u^{(n)} + q_1(x)u^{(n-1)} + \ldots + q_n(x)u = 0 \tag{6}$$

where

$$q_k(x) = p_k + (n-k+1)w_1 p_{k-1} + \binom{n-k+2}{2} w_2 p_{k-2} + \ldots + \binom{n}{k} w_k.$$

It is hoped that (6) will have at least one solution regular at $x = 0$. This means that it must have an indicial equation, defining one or more exponents. In the general case, it will have no indicial equation, for the leading terms in that equation will be of degrees greater than c; see **a**. Advantage can be taken, however, of the available parameters in $\phi(x)$ to remove the offending terms. The intermediate steps are rather tedious. If they are wanted, see Forsyth-2 or Ince-1. The conclusions, sufficient for finding a normal solution, follow.

Let h_k be the order of the pole at $x = 0$ in $P_k(x)$ and take g as the greatest of the numbers h_1, $h_2/2$, ..., h_n/n. It must be greater than unity since h_k must be greater than k for at least one k; otherwise, the singular point at $x = 0$ would have been regular, not irregular. Consideration of the indicial equation shows further that $\delta \leqslant g$ and $\delta \geqslant 2$; if these conditions fail there will be no indicial equation, hence no regular solution for $u(x)$. There are several cases.

i. $g < 2$. No value of δ is acceptable and no normal solution exists. See also **c** in this case.

ii. g is an integer greater than unity. In this case, try $\delta = g$. It follows that g must be found among the numbers h_1, $h_2/2$, ... , h_c/c, where c is the *class* of the irregular singular point at $x = 0$. It may occur more than once in this set. Reading from left to right, suppose that g is found for the first time at h_α/α and for the last time at h_β/β. It then follows that $h_\alpha + (n-\alpha)\delta = ng$; $h_\beta + (n-\beta)\delta = ng$; $h_k + (n-k)\delta < ng$, $k < \alpha$ or $k > \beta$. Remembering that the irregular singular point is of class c and that $w_1 = \phi'$, the leading terms in the indicial equation occur at $c = ng$, and they involve $w_1{}^c$, $P_\alpha w_1{}^{c-\alpha} + \ldots + P_\beta w_1{}^{c-\beta}$. Note further that $\phi(x)$ is to be a polynomial of degree $(\delta-1)$ in $1/x$. It contains δ constants but the coefficient of x^0 can be absorbed into the integration constant of the solution. There remain only $(\delta-1)$ constants to be calculated in $\phi(x)$. It has just been seen that the indicial equation involves $\phi' = w_1$, which also contains $(\delta-1)$ constants; hence $\phi(x)$ itself is known as soon as the constants in w_1 are known. Let the latter quantity be

$$w_1(x) = \frac{a_2}{x^2} + \frac{a_3}{x^3} + \ldots + \frac{a_\delta}{x^\delta}$$

The coefficients in the differential equation will have the form

$$P_k(x) = x^{-h_k}(b_{k0} + b_{k1}x + \dots)$$

and the coefficient of x^{-g} in w_1 is a_g. It is determined from

$$a_g\beta + b_{a0}a_g\beta^{-\alpha} + \dots + b_{\beta0} = 0$$

When one value of a_g is determined from this equation, the remaining $(g-2)$ coefficients of w_1 can be found by equating to zero the next $(g-2)$ terms in $w_1^c + P_1w_1^{c-1} + \dots + P_{n-1}w_1 + P_n$. The maximum number of different forms for w_1 is β. Thus, if $\beta > 1$, more than one normal integral can be obtained.

iii. In the preceding case it was assumed that $\delta = g$. However, g may be an integer greater than two and then other values of $\delta < g$ may be acceptable. Similarly, g may be greater than two but not an integer. For procedures in such cases, see Forsyth-2 or Ince-1.

The normal solution is said to be of *grade* $(\delta - 1)$. The *rank* of the differential equation is $(g-1)$. If the latter is an integer, it may be equal to $(\delta - 1)$ but, in general, the rank is greater than δ.

The final step, after obtaining $\phi(x)$, involves calculating the function $u(x)$. This work proceeds as directed in **6-2-1** or **6-2-2**. The result will have the form

$$y(x) = e^{\phi(x)}x^s[U_0(x) + U_1(x)\ln x + U_2(x)(\ln x)^2 + \dots]$$

where $U_k(x)$ is analytic at $x = 0$. The presence or absence of the logarithmic factors can be investigated as in **6-2-2**.

The normal solutions, secured by the procedures described, may satisfy the differential equation formally but diverge for all x. They are asymptotic solutions of the differential equation in such cases; see **a** for further comment.

c. Subnormal solutions. In some cases, where a normal solution does not exist, there may be a normal solution in the new independent variable $z = x^{1/m}$, where m is an integer. When a suitable value of m has been found, the transformed equation in z can be handled by the procedure of **b**. Such integrals, normal in the variable $x^{1/m}$ are called *subnormal integrals*. The determining factor is of degree $(\delta - 1)$ in $x^{1/m}$. Its grade is $(\delta - 1)/m$; its rank is $(g + 1) \geqslant (\delta - 1)/m$. If such a subnormal integral exists, there will be $(m - 1)$ others of the same type. Further details could be inferred from the procedures explained in **B1-8-3** or see Forsyth-2, Ince-1.

7. Fuchsian Equations and Others with Special Properties

A number of nth order equations with certain special properties have been studied by mathematicians. They are solved by methods similar to those presented in the preceding sections. The details are likely to become quite lengthy. Since their general properties are usually of more interest than their explicit solutions, they will be omitted here. Some types of equations which have been so treated can be inferred from those of second order listed in **B1-9-7**. For details about the nth order equations, refer to Forsyth-2 or Ince-1.

The only special case which will be discussed here is the Fuchsian equation of order n. Second-order equations of this type are of considerable importance; see **B1-9, 9-5**. Let the nth order equation be

$$y^{(n)} + P_1(x)y^{(n-1)} + \ldots + P_{n-1}(x)y' + P_n(x)y = 0 \qquad (1)$$

It is required that there be $(r+1)$ regular singular points at $x = a_1, a_2,$ $\ldots, a_r, \infty$. Ignore the point at infinity for the moment and take

$$P_k(x) = H^{-k}(x)f_k(x) \qquad (2)$$

where $H(x) = (x-a_1)(x-a_2) \ldots (x-a_r)$; $k \leqslant 1, 2, \ldots, n$. The coefficient $P_k(x)$ has r zeros—therefore a regular singular point or pole of order k or less, provided that $f_k(x)$ is analytic for every $x < \infty$.

To study the point at infinity, write (1) as

$$y^{(n)} + xp_1(x)y^{(n-1)} + \ldots + x^n p_n(x)y = 0$$

where the properties of $p_k(x)$ are to be determined. Use new variables $y(x) = u(z)$, $x = 1/z$, and shift the required singular point from $x = \infty$ to $z = 0$. Note further that

$$x^k y^{(k)}(x) = (-1)^k z^k u^{(k)}(z) + b_{k-1,\,k} z^{k-1} u^{(k-1)}(z) + \ldots + b_{2k} z^2 u''(z) + b_{1k} z u'(z)$$

where the b_{ik} are constants. The transformed equation is

$$u^{(n)} + zq_1(z)u^{(n-1)} + \ldots + z^n q_n(z)u = 0 \qquad (3)$$

Its coefficients can be calculated from the relations

$$(-1)^n q_1(z) = (-1)^{n-1} p_1(z) + b_{n-1,\,n} p_0(z)$$

$$(-1)^n q_2(z) = (-1)^{n-2} p_2(z) + b_{n-2,\,n-1} p_1(z) + b_{n-2,\,n} p_0(z)$$

$$\ldots \quad \ldots \quad \ldots \quad \ldots \quad \ldots \quad \ldots.$$

$$(-1)^n q_n(z) = p_n(z) + b_{01} p_{n-1}(z) + \ldots + b_{0n} p_0(z)$$

Since $z = 0$ is to be a regular singular point for (3), it is necessary that every $q_k(z)$ and $p_k(z)$ be analytic there, which in turn means that $p_k(x)$ must be analytic at $x = \infty$ and $p_k(x) = x^k P_k(x)$.

It follows that $f_k(x) = x^{-k} p_k(x) H^k(x)$, with $f_k(x)$ analytic for finite x and $p_k(x)$ finite at $x = \infty$. The last equation can also be written as

$$f_k(x) = x^{k(r-1)} p_k(x) G^k(x)$$

where $G(x) = (1 - a_1/x)(1 - a_2/x) \dots (1 - a_r/x)$, which must be analytic at infinity. Consequently, $f_k(x)$ is a polynomial in x of degree $k(r-1)$ or less.

In summary, (1) is a Fuchsian equation with $(r+1)$ regular singular points at $x = a_1, a_2, \dots, a_r, \infty$ provided that its coefficients are given by

$$P_k(x) = H^{-k}(x) f_{k(r-1)}(x)$$

with $f_{k(r-1)}(x)$ a polynomial in x of degree equal to or less than its subscript.

It is often useful to resolve (2) into partial fractions

$$P_k(x) = \frac{A_{k1}}{(x - a_1)^k} + \frac{A_{k2}}{(x - a_2)^k} + \dots + \frac{A_{kr}}{(x - a_r)^k} + \phi_k(x)$$

where $A_{ki} = [(a_i - a_1)(a_i - a_2) \dots (a_i - a_{i-1})(a_i - a_{i+1}) \dots (a_i - a_r)]^{-k} f_k(a_i)$ and $\phi_k(x) = Q_k(x) H^{1-k}(x)$. The quantity $Q_k(x)$ is a polynomial in x of degree no greater than $k(r-1) - r$ for $k > 1$, but $Q_1(x) = 0$.

There are some further relations of interest. Let the regular solution at $x = a_1$ be $y_1 = (x - a_1)^s X(x)$, where $X(x)$ is a series in ascending powers of x. Using the notation of **6-2**, the indicial equation is found to be

$$[s]_n + A_{11}[s]_{n-1} + \dots + A_{n1} = 0$$

and its roots, the exponents at $x = a_1$, can be called $\alpha_{11}, \alpha_{12}, \dots, \alpha_{1n}$. Setting this equation equal to its identity

$$(s - \alpha_{11})(s - \alpha_{12}) \dots (s - \alpha_{1n}) = 0$$

and comparing terms, it follows that

$$\alpha_{11} + \alpha_{12} + \dots + \alpha_{1n} = n(n-1)/2 - A_{11} \tag{4}$$

Additional, but more complicated, relations are sums of products of the exponents and the constants A_{21}, A_{31}, etc. Thus, if numerical values are selected for the n exponents at $x = a_1$, the n constants A_{i1} can be calculated. If the exponents at each singular point are selected beforehand, all of the constants A_{ik} might be fixed. However, there are relations between these constants as will now be shown.

Assume a solution $y = x^\sigma Y(x)$ at $x = \infty$, where $Y(x)$ is a series in descending powers of x, and let $\beta_1, \beta_2, \dots, \beta_n$ be the exponents calculated from the indicial equation. Proceeding as before, it is found that

$$\beta_1 + \beta_2 + \dots + \beta_n = A_{11} + A_{12} + \dots + A_{1r} - n(n-1)/2 \tag{5}$$

Sum the terms like (4) for each finite singular point, add the relation shown in (5), and get

$$\sum_{i.k} \alpha_{ik} + \sum_k \beta_k = n(n-1)(r-1)/2 \tag{6}$$

with $i = 1, 2, \dots, r; \; k = 1, 2, \dots, n$.

Summarizing these results, the differential equation (1) will contain three categories of constants.

a. The singular points $x = a_1, a_2, \ldots, a_r, \infty$. The number of these constants is $K_1 = (r+1)$.

b. There will be n exponents at each singular point, thus $K_2 = n(r+1)$ constants of this kind. There is one relation between them, see (6), so only $k_2 = n(r+1)-1$ of them are arbitrary.

c. The coefficients $P_k(x)$ in (1) involve polynomials of degree no greater than $k(r-1)$. Remembering that a polynomial of degree m contains $(m+1)$ constants and summing over k from 1 to n, it is found that there are $K_3 = n(n+1)(r-1)/2 + n$ constants of this type.

Choose, in any suitable way, numerical values for the singular points and the exponents. There remain undetermined constants

$$k_0 = K_3 - K_1 - k_2 = \tfrac{1}{2}(n-1)(nr-n-2)$$

which are completely arbitrary. If the equation is of second order, with $r = 2$, it is convenient to select $a_1 = 0$, $a_2 = 1$. The result is the Gauss hypergeometric equation, see **B1-9-5**, completely fixed when the exponents are also assigned. In other cases, there will remain $k_0 \geqslant 1$ arbitrary constants, in addition to the location of the singular points and the values of the exponents at each.

Fuchsian equations of order n could be treated like those of second order, letting singular points coalesce to produce degenerate cases with irregular singular points; see **B1-9-5**. No systematic study, in this way, seems to have been made for equations of order greater than two.

8. Integral Solutions

When the solution of a differential equation cannot be presented in terms of known functions, a solution as an infinite series is often useful. Such procedures have been given in **6** and **7**. Alternatively, there may be advantages with a solution as a definite integral; see **B1-7** and **B1-10** for comments about the second-order equation. Some methods in the latter section have been given in a form applicable to equations of order $n > 2$.

As examples, where definite integrals are especially convenient when $n > 2$, consider the following cases.

a. The Laplace equation. Its standard form is

$$A_0(x)y^{(n)} + A_1(x)y^{(n-1)} + \ldots + A_n(x)y = 0 \tag{1}$$

where $A_k(x) = a_k + b_k x$. It can also be written symbolically as

$$xF(D)y + G(D)y = 0,$$

with $D = d/dx$ and F, G as rational integral functions of order n. Assume a solution

$$y(x) = \int_a^b e^{xt}u(t)dt \tag{2}$$

where $u(t)$, the modulation factor, and the integration limits a, b are to be determined. The procedure can be inferred from the directions given in **B1-10-1** for $n = 2$.

b. Generalize the case of **a** to the equation

$$X_n(x)y^{(n)} + X_{n-1}(x)y^{(n-1)} + \ldots + X_0(x)y = 0 \tag{3}$$

where $X_k(x) = a_{k0} + a_{k1}x + a_{k2}x^2 + \ldots + a_{km}x^m$. Assume a solution like (2). It follows that

$$y^{(k)}(x) = \int e^{xt}t^k u(t)dt$$

Substitute this result in (3) and get

$$\int e^{xt}u(t)\phi(x, t)dt = 0 \tag{4}$$

where $\phi(x, t) = t^n X_n + t^{n-1}X_{n-1} + \ldots + X_0$. The latter may also be written as

$$\phi(x, t) = w_0(t) + w_1(t)x + \ldots + w_m(t)x^m$$

and the coefficients are

$$w_0 = a_{1n}t^n + a_{1, n-1}t^{n-1} + \ldots + a_{11}t + a_{10}$$
$$w_1 = a_{2n}t^n + a_{2, n-1}t^{n-1} + \ldots + a_{21}t + a_{20}$$
$$\ldots \quad \ldots \quad \ldots \quad \ldots \quad \ldots \quad \ldots$$
$$w_m = a_{m, n}t^n + a_{m, n-1}t^{n-1} + \ldots + a_{m1}t + a_{m0}$$

The left-hand side of (4) is the sum of $(m + 1)$ integrals like

$$\int e^{xt}u(t)w_k(t)x^k dt$$

Integrate each of these by parts until x no longer occurs, except in the exponential term. The result is found to be

$$e^{xt}(g_1 + g_2 + \ldots + g_m) + \int e^{xt}f(x, t)dt = 0$$

where

$$g_k = x^{k-1}uw_k - x^{k-2}(uw_k)' + \ldots + (-1)^{k-1}(uw_k)^{(k-1)}$$

and

$$f(x, t) = uw_0 - (uw_1)' + (uw_2)'' + \ldots + (-1)^m(uw_m)^{(m)} = 0.$$

All conditions are satisfied if the integration limits are chosen to make $e^{xt}(g_1 + g_2 + \ldots + g_m) = 0$. Since the equation which determines u is of order $m < n$, it will have m special solutions which are linearly independent. Each of them will give m special solutions of (1), when $u(t) = u_1$, $u_2, \ldots, u_m$ are substituted into (2).

9. The Linear Nonhomogeneous Equation

Take the standard form as

$$y^{(n)} + P_1(x)y^{(n-1)} + \ldots + P_n(x)y = R(x) \tag{1}$$

It is assumed that the general solution of the associated homogeneous equation has been found. This is the complementary function

$$Y(x) = C_1 y_1 + C_2 y_2 + \ldots + C_n y_n$$

Let any special solution of (1) be $F(x)$; then the general solution of (1) is

$$y(x) = Y(x) + F(x)$$

There are three cases.

a. All coefficients $P_k(x)$ in (1) are constants; $R(x)$ may be a constant or a function of x; see **9-1**.

b. The coefficients are functions of x but the equation is reducible to **b**; see **9-2**.

c. The general case, where **b** does not apply; see **9-3**.

9-1. The Nonhomogeneous Equation with Constant Coefficients. The standard form is

$$y^{(n)} + a_1 y^{(n-1)} + \ldots + a_{n-1} y' + a_n y = R(x)$$

where the a_k are constants and $R(x)$ may be a constant or a function of x. The operator form $f(D)y = R(x)$ is often useful, where

$$f(D) = D^n + a_1 D^{n-1} + \ldots + a_n$$

and $D = d/dx$; see also **1**.

Methods for finding a particular solution are generalizations of those used for second-order equations. The descriptions here will be brief; refer to **B1-12-1** for details which may be extended for $n > 2$.

a. If $R(x) = R_0$, a constant, the particular integral is one of the following.

i. $F(x) = R_0/a_n$, $a_n \neq 0$.

ii. $F(x) = R_0 x^k/k! a_{n-k}$, where a_{n-k} is the coefficient of the lowest-ordered derivative in the differential equation.

b. Reduction of order. Use the factored form of the equation

$$(D - r_1)(D - r_2) \ldots (D - r_n) = R(x)$$

The problem can then be reduced successively to the solution of n first-order linear differential equations; see **B1-12-1-2**. Omitting the complementary function, which presumably has been found according to 1, the particular integral involves n quadratures

$$F(x) = e^{r_n x} \int \phi_{n-1}(x)dx \int \dots \int \phi_1(x)dx \int e^{-r_1 x}R(x)dx$$

where $\phi_1(x) = \exp(r_1 - r_2)x$, ..., $\phi_{n-1}(x) = \exp(r_{n-1} - r_n)x$. The successive integrals may be difficult. It sometimes helps if the r_i are arranged in some special order.

c. Further possibilities include the method of undetermined coefficients, see **B1-12-1-1**; operator methods, see **B1-12-1-3**; the Laplace transform, see **B1-12-1-4**. Any of these can be generalized for $n > 2$, with the procedures given for $n = 2$. In most cases, the details will be lengthy and tedious.

9-2. The Equation Reducible to Type 9-1. Let the given equation be

$$x^n y^{(n)} + a_1 x^{n-1} y^{(n-1)} + \dots + a_n y = R(x)$$

Choose a new variable $z = \ln x$, $y(x) = u(x)$. Then, if

$$xD = \theta, \, x^2 D^2 = \theta(\theta - 1), \dots, x^n D^n = \theta(\theta - 1)\dots(\theta - n + 1)$$

where $D = d/dx$ and $\theta = d/dz$, the differential equation becomes of type **9-1**,

$$[\theta(\theta - 1)\dots(\theta - n + 1) + a_1\theta(\theta - 1)\dots(\theta - n + 2) + \dots + a_{n-1}\theta + a_n]u(z) = U(z)$$

The quantity $U(z)$ is the transformed function $R(x)$. Proceed as directed in **9-1** and then restore the original variables x and y.

Similarly, see **3-2**, the Legendre linear equation can be transformed into type **9-1**.

9-3. The Nonhomogeneous Equation With Variable Coefficients. The standard form is

$$y^{(n)} + P_1(x)y^{(n-1)} + \dots + P_n(x)y = R(x)$$

The case with $n = 2$ has been described in **B1-12-3**. Any of those methods can be generalized for $n > 2$ but the details will usually be rather complicated. It seems likely that **B1-12-3a** would be the easiest procedure in most cases.

C2. THE NONLINEAR EQUATION OF ORDER GREATER THAN TWO

The general equation is

$$f(x, y, y', y'', ..., y^{(n)}) = 0$$

but terms like $yy'^{(n)}$, $y'y''$, xy^3, etc., may occur. Read the general remarks in **B2** and then refer to the following sections. The simplest cases are those in which x or y do not appear explicitly. There are two possibilities.

1. The Dependent Variable Is Missing

The general equation is

$$f(x, y', y'', ..., y^{(n)}) = 0$$

There are two special cases, as in **B1-1**, but see also **2**.

1-1. Only One Derivative Occurs. The equation becomes

$$f(x, y^{(n)}) = 0$$

Solve it, if possible, to get $y^{(n)} = F(x)$. Successive integrations produce the general solution

$$y = \int_{x_0}^{x} dx \int_{x_0}^{x} dx ... \int_{x_0}^{x} F(x) dx + C_1 \frac{(x - x_0)^{n-1}}{(n-1)!} + ... + C_n$$

The lower limit of the integrals is chosen to make the work as simple as possible. Frequently $x = 0$ or $x = 1$ may be a suitable choice. The multiple integral can be replaced so that an equivalent solution is

$$y = \frac{1}{(n-1)!} \int_{x_0}^{x} (x-t)^{n-1} F(t) dt + C_1 \frac{(x - x_0)^{n-1}}{(n-1)!} + ... + C_n$$

Note that the linear nonhomogeneous equation may be of this type. The integral is a particular solution and the remaining terms constitute the complementary function. This procedure may be easier than that of **C1-9-1**.

1-2. There Are Only Two Derivatives. The equation is

$$f(x, y^{(n-1)}, y^{(n)}) = 0$$

Let $y^{(n-1)} = u(x)$. The equation in u and x is of first order. When it has been solved by some method of **A1** or **A2** to get $u = F(x)$, then $y^{(n-1)}(x) = F(x)$, which is type **1-1**. The general solution of the equation follows after $(n-1)$ further quadratures.

1-3. The General Case. The equation is

$$f(x, y^{(k)}, y^{(k+1)}, \dots, y^{(n)}) = 0 \tag{1}$$

where $k \geqslant 1$; y and its first $(k-1)$ derivatives do not occur. Use a new variable $u(x) = y^{(k)}$ and get an equation of order $(n-k)$

$$F(x, u, u', \dots, u^{(n-k)}) = 0 \tag{2}$$

There are two possibilities.

a. If (2) can be solved to get $u(x)$, replace $u(x)$ by $y^{(k)}$ and the result is **1-1**, which might be solved for y.

b. If the solution of (2) is $g(x, u) = 0$, an equation not readily solvable for u, use a parameter t, so that

$$y^{(k)} = u(t), \quad x = x(t)$$

Then, $dy^{(k-1)} = u(t)dx = u(t)x'(t)dt$. Integrate this result to get $y^{(k-1)}$. Repeat the procedure k times in all to produce the general solution of (1).

2. The Independent Variable Is Missing

The general equation is

$$f(y, y', y'', \dots, y^{(n)}) = 0$$

There are four types, in three of which the dependent variable is also missing. Note that they are similar to the cases of **B2-2**.

2-1. Two Successive Derivatives. The equation is

$$f(y^{(n-1)}, y^{(n)}) = 0 \tag{1}$$

Solve it to get $y^{(n)} = F(y^{(n-1)})$. Let $y^{(n-1)} = u(x)$ and get $u'(x) = F(u)$. This first-order equation, see **A1-1-3**, will have a solution

$$\phi(u) = \int \frac{du}{F(u)} = x + C \tag{2}$$

Solve (2) so that

$$u(x) = g(x, C) = y^{(n-1)} \tag{3}$$

which means that the problem has been reduced to type **1-1**. Now,

$$(y^{(n-2)})' = u(x); \quad y^{(n-2)} = \int u(x)dx = \int \frac{udu}{F(u)}$$

$$y^{(n-3)} = \int dx \int \frac{udu}{F(u)} = \int \frac{du}{F(u)} \int \frac{udu}{F(u)}$$

Finally, with n quadratures,

$$y = \int \frac{du}{F(u)} \int \frac{du}{F(u)} \cdots \int \frac{udu}{F(u)}$$

The integrals must be evaluated from right to left, remembering that a constant of integration must be added after each integration. Eventually, eliminate $u(x)$ between (2) and (3). The multiple integrals could be replaced by a single integral, as in **1-1**.

2-2. Two Derivatives, Differing in Order By Two.   The equation is

$$f(y^{(n-2)}, y^{(n)}) = 0$$

Solve it to get $y^{(n)} = F(y^{(n-2)})$ and let $y^{(n-2)} = u(x)$, so that $u''(x) = F(u)$. This is now case **B2-2-1**. Proceed as directed there and get

$$g(x, u, C_1, C_2) = 0 \tag{4}$$

There are two possibilities.

a. Solve (4) and get

$$u = G(x, C_1, C_2) \tag{5}$$

Integrate this expression $(n-2)$ times which yields the general solution of the differential equation.

b. If it is difficult to solve (4) for $u(x)$, take

$$u'(x) = [C_1 + 2 \int F(u)du]^{1/2} = \phi(u)$$

It follows that

$$y^{(n-3)} = \int u(x)dx = \int \frac{udu}{\phi(u)}; \quad y^{(n-4)} = \int \frac{du}{\phi(u)} \int \frac{udu}{\phi(u)}$$

Eventually, y is obtained as a function of u. Eliminate $u(x)$ to get the general solution of the differential equation as a function of x and the constants $C_1, C_2, \ldots, C_n$.

2-3. Three Successive Derivatives.   The equation is

$$f(y^{(n-2)}, y^{(n-1)}, y^{(n)}) = 0$$

Let

$$y^{(n-2)} = u(x), \qquad y^{(n-1)} = v(x), \qquad y^{(n)} = v\frac{dv}{du}$$

The result is an equation of first order in the variables u and v,

$$f(u, v, v\,dv/du) = 0$$

Use a method of **A1** or **A2** to get $F(u, v, C_1) = 0$. If this can be solved for $v = g(u, C_1)$, then $u'(x) = g(u, C_1)$. Let its solution be $u(x) = y^{(n-2)} = h(x, C_1, C_2)$. This is an equation of type **1-1**, which can be solved with $(n-2)$ further quadratures.

2-4. The General Case. No variable is lacking except x; thus the equation is

$$f(y, y', y'', \ldots, y^{(n)}) = 0 \tag{6}$$

Let

$$y' = p, y'' = pp'(y), y''' = p^2p''(y)+pp'^2(y), y^{\text{iv}} = p^3p'''+4p^2p'p''+pp'^3,$$

etc. Then, (6) becomes

$$F(y, p, p', \ldots p^{(n-1)}) = 0 \tag{7}$$

an equation of order $(n-1)$ in p and y. There are two possibilities.

a. Solve (7), if possible, to get

$$y'(x) = p = \phi(y, C_1, C_2, \ldots, C_{n-1})$$

One more quadrature gives the general solution

$$x + C_n = \int \frac{dy}{\phi(y)}$$

b. A parametric solution may be convenient

$$y = g_1(t, C_1, C_2, \ldots, C_{n-1}); \quad p = g_2(t, C_1, C_2, \ldots, C_{n-1})$$

With another integration,

$$x + C_n = \int \frac{dy}{p} = \int \frac{g_1'(t)}{g_2(t)}dt$$

3. Homogeneous Equations

The cases of **B2-3** can be generalized for equations of order n. There are several types.

3-1. Homogeneous in y and Its Derivatives. The equation can be written as

$$y^k f(x, y'/y, y''/y, \ldots, y^{(n)}/y) = 0$$

Use a new variable $y = \exp \int u(x)dx$, so that $y'/y = u$, $y''/y = u' + u^2$, ... , $y^{(n)}/y = U_n$, where U_n is a polynomial in u, u', ... , $u^{(n-1)}$. The transformed equation is of order $(n-1)$. Repeat, if necessary or possible. At the least, the procedure will give a first integral.

3-2. Homogeneous in x and dx.   The form of the equation is

$$f(y, xy', x^2y'', ... , x^ny^{(n)}) = 0$$

Use new variables $y(x) = u(z)$, $\ln x = z$, so that $xy' = u'$, $x^2y'' = u'' - u'$, ... , $x^ky^{(k)} = D(D-1) ... (D-k+1)u$, where $D = d/dz$. The transformed equation is

$$F(u, u', u'', ... , u^{(n)}) = 0$$

which is of type **2-4**.

3-3. The Isobaric Equation.   This case, see **B2-3-4**, is

$$f(x, y, y', y'', ... , y^{(n)}) = x^k f(1, y/x^m, y'/x^{m-1}, ... , y^{(n)}/x^{m-n})$$

If $m = 0$, the equation is of type **3-2**. If $m \neq 0$, use $y = x^m u(z)$, $z = \ln x$. A common factor e^{kz} can be eliminated and the result is an equation with z missing. Try a method of **2** to solve it.

4. The Exact Nonlinear Equation

Let the equation be $f(x, y, y', ... , y^{(n)}) = 0$. It is exact if $f dx$ is the exact differential of some function $F(x, y, y', ... , y^{(n-1)})$. Use the abbreviations $y_0 = y$, $y_1 = y'$, $y_2 = y''$, ... , $y_n = y^{(n)}$, let $D = d/dx$ meaning that the derivative with respect to x is taken with y, y_1, y_2, ... , y_n regarded as functions of x, and understand that $f_k = \partial f/\partial y_k$. The test for exactness becomes

$$f_0 - Df_1 + D^2f_2 \mp ... \pm D^nf_n = 0$$

When this condition is satisfied, it follows that

$$F_x dx + F_0 dy + F_1 dy_1 + ... + F_{n-1} dy_{n-1} = 0$$

and a first integral of the exact equation is $F(x, y, y', ... , y^{(n-1)}) = C$.

A general rule for the integration is the following. Integrate $f dx$ as if $y^{(n-1)}$ were the only variable and $y^{(n)}$ its differential coefficient. Call the result F_1. Then, $f dx - dF_1$ contains differential coefficients of order no greater than $(n-1)$. Repeat, getting eventually

$$f dx - dF_1 - dF_2 - ... = 0$$

and a first integral of the exact equation is

$$F_1 + F_2 + ... = C$$

If the highest differential coefficient at any stage is of greater than first degree, the differential equation was not exact. In such a case, it might be possible to find an integrating factor. There are no general rules which might help in the search for an integrating factor.

5. Other Procedures

The preceding methods of this part exhaust the processes for solving the nonlinear equation of order n, when the solution is wanted in an exact form. In some special cases, it might be possible to find a variable transformation, converting the equation into another of known type. See **B2-5** for the second-order equation, which may suggest something to try for an equation of order greater than two.

One might, of course, try to obtain a series solution, a solution as a definite integral, or an approximate solution; see **B2-6** and **A1-13**. Equations of order three or more, with fixed critical points, see **B2-7**, have not been studied exhaustively. See Ince-1 for references.

Part II

TABLES OF DIFFERENTIAL EQUATIONS
AND THEIR SOLUTIONS

The remainder of this book contains more than two thousand differential equations, together with their solutions and references to Part I for methods which could be used to find these solutions. To search for a given differential equation, first classify it as follows and consult the section indicated.

1. First Order and First Degree; (**A1**)
2. First Order and Higher Degree; (**A2**)
3. Second Order and Linear; (**B1**)
4. Second Order and Nonlinear; (**B2**)
5. Order Greater than Two and Linear; (**C1**)
6. Order Greater than Two and Nonlinear; (**C2**)

The symbols in parentheses are the corresponding sections of Part I, which could be used for definitions, general properties, and other information.

It will be found that each equation is preceded by an identifying number, starting again with one in each section. Similarly, a number following each equation refers to a method of Part I, which might be used to find the solution which is given. In some cases more than one method is cited but the first one will usually be the easiest to apply. Alternatively, if only one method is cited, it does not necessarily follow that this is the only method which could be used.

References to equations are always given in parentheses; to section numbers, without parentheses. Thus, for example, references to (10) and **2** in section 1 would mean the tenth equation of that section and the method of **A1-2** in Part I. Similarly, the references (3-10) and **B1-1** in section 1 would mean the tenth equation in section 3 of Part II and the method of section **B1-1** in Part I.

223

1. THE DIFFERENTIAL EQUATION IS OF FIRST ORDER AND OF FIRST DEGREE

The general equation of this type will have the form $f(x, y)y' = g(x, y)$ and the coefficients will usually appear as

$$f(x, y) = f_1(x, y) + f_2(x, y) + \dots; \quad g(x, y) = g_1(x, y) + g_2(x, y) + \dots.$$

The following equations have been arranged so that these coefficients become successively more complicated as the equation numbers increase. The most general form that any coefficient, either an f_i or a g_i, can take will be $\phi_i(x, y) = a_i x^{r_i} y^{s_i} F_i(x,y)$, where a_i, r_i, s_i are constants and $F_i(x, y)$ is some transcendental or more general function of one or both variables. If this term is less complicated than some other term $\phi_j(x, y)$, then the latter will be said to have a higher rank than the former.

Increasing order of complexity or rank is defined according to the following scheme:

$$1, 2, \dots, a; \quad x, 2x, \dots, ax; \quad x^2, 2x^2, \dots, ax^2; \quad \dots; \quad x^r, 2x^r, \dots, ax^r; \quad F(x)$$

Increasing rank in $F(x)$ is taken as functions which are irrational, trigonometric, inverse trigonometric, exponential, logarithmic, hyperbolic, of a more general type. Continuing in a similar way, with functions of y or of both x and y, increasing rank is defined as follows:

$$y, 2y, \dots, ay; \quad xy, \dots, axy; \quad \dots; \quad x^r y, \dots, ax^r y; \quad F(x)\, y; \quad y^2, \dots, ay^2;$$
$$xy^2, \dots; \quad \dots; \quad x^r y^2, \dots; \quad F(x)y^2; \quad \dots; \quad x^r y^s, \dots; \quad F(y); \quad xF(y), \dots, x^r F(y);$$
$$F_1(x)F_2(y); \quad F(x, y).$$

To locate a given equation in the collection, first clear it of fractions and then find the coefficient of y' which has the highest rank. Follow with the term of next lower rank and continue until all of these coefficients have been arranged. Go on to use the terms $g_1(x, y)$, $g_2(x, y)$, etc., if necessary.

An entirely satisfactory way of arranging the equations was not found and the preceding description of the arrangement actually used does not please the author. There will certainly be cases where the rules have not

224

been followed. However, there will usually be only a few variations of some particular type of equation and, with a little experience, the user of the tables will be able to determine whether or not a given equation is contained in them. The following further comments may be helpful.

i. The coefficient of y' has generally been made as simple as possible. Thus, $ay' + f(x, y) = 0$ would appear here as $y' + bf(x, y) = 0$. Similarly, $y' \sin x + g(x, y) = 0$ would be given as $y' + g(x, y) \csc x = 0$.

ii. The tables contain a considerable number of equations containing trigonometric functions. To arrange them, the order of increasing rank is taken as the alphabetical order, thus: cos, cot, csc, sec, sin, tan. Relations between the trigonometric functions, such as $\sin^2 x = 1 - \cos^2 x$; $\sin 2x = 2 \sin x \cos x$; $\tan x = 1/\cot x$; etc., have been freely used to simplify an equation. A given equation may often be found in the tables if such relations are used.

iii. A given equation with numerical coefficients may appear in the tables as special cases of equations where the coefficients are arbitrary constants. The same situation may occur with powers of x or y. However, when the solution assumes an especially simple form with definite values of constants or powers, this case is also included. Cross references have been used liberally to help.

iv. A constant $2a$ is generally regarded as of lower rank than the more general constant a. Thus, a term x^{2a} will appear before a term x^a. Similarly, if n is an integer and a is simply a constant, x^a is of higher rank than x^n.

v. When all terms of two equations are identical except for signs of some members, the plus sign is taken as of lower rank than the minus sign. Again, the plus sign occurs first if the term of highest rank in two equations is the same, except for sign.

If further information is needed for symbols used in the following equations, see Part I, Introduction-**4**. The integration constant in the general solution is always called C.

1    $y' = af(x)$ **1-1**
     $y = a \int f(x)dx + C$

2    $y' = x + \sin x + y$ **2**
     $y = Ce^x - 1 - x - (\cos x + \sin x)/2$

3    $y' = x^2 + 3 \cosh x \pm 2y$ **2**
     $y = Ce^{\pm 2x} \mp (2x^2 \pm 2x + 1)/4 - \sinh x \mp 2 \cosh x$

4    $y' = a + bx + cy; \quad c \neq 0$ **2**
     $c^2 y = Ce^{cx} - (ac + b) - bcx$

5    $y' = a \cos(bx+c)+ky$ **2**
     $y = Ce^{kx}+A[b \sin(bx+c)-k \cos(bx+c)]$
     $= Ce^{kx}+B \cos(bx+c-\delta); \quad A = a/(b^2+k^2);$
     $B = a/\sqrt{b^2+k^2}; \quad \tan \delta = -b/k$

6    $y' = a \sin(bx+c)+ky$ **2**
     $y = Ce^{kx}-A[b \cos(bx+c)+k \sin(bx+c)]$
     $= Ce^{kx}-B \sin(bx+c-\delta); \quad A = a/(b^2+k^2);$
     $B = a/\sqrt{b^2+k^2}; \quad \tan \delta = -b/k$

7    $y' = a+be^{kx}+cy$ **2**
     i. $(k-c)(a+cy) = Ce^{cx}+bce^{kx}; \quad k \neq c.$
     ii. $(a+ky) = e^{kx}(C+bkx); \quad k = c.$

8    $y' = x(x^2-2y)$ **2**
     $2y+1-x^2 = Ce^{-x^2}$

9    $y' = x(e^{-x^2}+ay)$ **2**
     i. $(a+2)y = Ce^{ax^2/2}-e^{-x^2}; \quad (a+2) \neq 0.$
     ii. $y = e^{-x^2}(C+x^2/2); \quad (a+2) = 0.$

10    $y' = x^2(ax^3+by)$ **2**
     $b^2y+a(3+bx^3) = Ce^{bx^3/3}$

11    $y' = ax^ny$ **1-2**
     i. $(n+1) \ln y = ax^{n+1}+C; \quad n \neq -1.$
     ii. $y = Cx^a; \quad n = -1.$

12    $y' = \cos x \sin x \pm y \cos x$ **2**
     $y = Ce^{\pm \sin x}-1 \mp \sin x$

13    $y' = e^{\pm \sin x} \pm y \cos x$ **2**
     $y = (C+x)e^{\pm \sin x}$

14    $y' = y \cot x$ **1-2**
     $y = C \sin x$

15    $y' = 1-y \cot x$ **2**
     $y = C \csc x-\cot x$

16    $y' = x \csc x-y \cot x$ **2**
     $2y \sin x = C+x^2$

17    $y' = (2 \csc 2x+ \cot x)y$ **1-2**
     $y = C \sin x \tan x$

18    $y' = \sec x-y \cot x$ **2**
     $y \sin x = C+\ln \sec x$

19    $y' = e^x \sin x+y \cot x$ **2**
     $y = (C+e^x) \sin x$

20    $y' + \csc x + 2y \cot x = 0$ 2
      $y \sin^2 x = C + \cos x$

21    $y' = 2 \csc 2x \sec^2 x - 2y \cot 2x$ 2
      $y = C \csc 2x + \sec^2 x$

22    $y' = 2(\cot^2 x \cos 2x - y \csc 2x)$ 2
      $y \tan x = C + \cos 2x + \ln \sin^2 x$

23    $y' = 2 \csc 2x(\sin^3 x + y)$ 2
      $y = C \tan x - \sin x$

24    $y' = 2 \csc 2x(1 - \tan^2 x + y)$ 2
      $y = C \tan x - \sec^2 x$

25    $y' = y \sec x$ 1-2
      $y = C(\sec x + \tan x)$

26    $y' + \tan x = (1 - y)\sec x$ 2
      $y(\sec x + \tan x) = C + x$

27    $y' = y \tan x$ 1-2
      $y = C \sec x$

28    $y' = \cos x + y \tan x$ 2

      $y = \left(C + \dfrac{x}{2} + \dfrac{1}{4} \sin 2x\right)\sec x$

29    $y' = \cos x - y \tan x$ 2
      $y = (C + x)\cos x$

30    $y' = \sec x - y \tan x$ 2
      $y = C \cos x + \sin x$

31    $y' = \sin 2x + y \tan x$ 2
      $y = C \sec x - (2/3) \cos^2 x$

32    $y' = \sin 2x - y \tan x$ 2
      $y = (C - 2 \cos x)\cos x$

33    $y' = \sin x + 2y \tan x$ 2
      $3y \cos^2 x = C - \cos^3 x$

34    $y' = 2(1 + \sec 2x + y \tan 2x)$ 2
      $y = (C + 2x) \sec 2x + \tan 2x$

35    $y' = \csc x + 3y \tan x$ 2
      $y = (C + \ln \sin x)\sec^3 x + (1/2) \sec x$

36    $y' = (a + \cos \ln x + \sin \ln x)y$ 1-2
      $\ln y = Cx(a + \sin \ln x)$

37    $y' = 6e^{2x} - y \tanh x$ 2
      $y \cosh x = C + 3e^x + e^{3x}$

38    $y' = f(x)f'(x) \pm f'(x)y$ 2
$$y = Ce^{\pm f(x)} \mp f(x) - 1$$

39    $y' = f(x) + g(x)y$ 2

40    $y' = x^2 - y^2$ 11-1
$$y = C - C^2 x + C^3 x^2 - (C^4 - 1/3)x^3 + C(C^4 - 1/6)x^4 \mp \quad \cdots$$

41    $y' + f^2(x) = f'(x) + y^2$ 3-1
$y_1 = f(x);$ $u'(x) = 1 + 2uf(x);$ see **3-1-1ai** and **2**.

42    $y' + 1 - x = (x+y)y$ 3-1
$y_1 = -1;$ $u'(x) + 1 + (x-2)u = 0;$ see **3-1-1ai** and **2**.

43    $y' = (x+y)^2$ 9-2, 3-1
$u(x) = x+y;$ $u'(x) = 1 + u^2;$ see (55).
$$x + y = \tan(C + x)$$

44    $y' = (x-y)^2$ 9-2, 3-1
$u(x) = x-y;$ $u'(x) = 1 - u^2;$ see (55).
$$x - y = \tanh(C + x)$$

45    $y' = 3(1 - x + y) + (x-y)^2$ 6-1
$$(x - y - 2)e^x = C(x - y - 1)$$

46    $y' = 2x - (1 + x^2)y + y^2$ 3-1
$y_1 = (1+x)^2;$ $u'(x) + 1 + (1 + x^2)u = 0;$ see **3-1-1ai** and **2**.

47    $y' = x(2 + x^3) - (2x^2 - y)y$ 3-1
$y = u + x^2;$ $u'(x) = u^2;$ see **3-1-3aii** and (55).
$$(C - x)y = 1 + x^2(C - x)$$

48    $y' = 1 + x(2 - x^3) + (2x^2 - y)y$ 3-1
$y = u + x^2;$ $u'(x) = 1 - u^2;$ see **3-1-3aii** and (55).
$$y - x^2 = \tanh(C + x)$$

49    $y' = \cos x - (\sin x - y)y$ 3-1
$y_1 = \sin x;$ $u'(x) + 1 + u \sin x = 0;$ see **3-1-1ai** and **2**.

50    $y' = \cos 2x + (\sin 2x + y)y$ 3-1
$y_1 = \tan x;$ $u'(x) + 1 + 2 \tan x(1 + \cos x)u = 0;$ see **3-1-1ai** and **2**.

51    $y' = f(x) + xf(x)y + y^2$ 3-1
$y_1 = -1/x;$ $u'(x) + 1 + u(xf + 2/x) = 0;$ see **3-1-1ai** and **2**.

52    $y' = (3 + x - 4y)^2$ 6-1
$$7 + 2x - 8y = Ce^{4x}(5 + 2x - 8y)$$

53    $y' = (1 + 4x + 9y)^2$ 6-1
$$3(1 + 4x + 9y) = 2 \tan(C + 6x)$$

54 $y' = 3(a + bx + by^2)$ **3-1**
$3ayu(x) + u' = 0$; $u'' - 3axu' + 9abu = 0$; see **3-1-1d** and (3-123).

55 $y' = a + by^2$ **1-3**
    i. $ry = a \tan(C + rx)$; $r = \sqrt{ab}$.
    ii. $sy = a \tanh(C + sx)$; $s = \sqrt{-ab}$.
    iii. $y(C - bx) = 1$; $a = 0$.
    iv. $y = ax + C$; $b = 0$.

56 $y' = ax + by^2$ **3-2**
$u'(x) = -byu$; $u'' + abxu = 0$; see **3-2c** and (3-34).

57 $y' = a + bx + cy^2$; $a \neq 0$ **3-1**
$cyu = -u'(x)$; $u'' - bxu' + acu = 0$; see **3-1-1d** and (3-123).

58 $y' = ax^{n-1} + bx^{2n} + cy^2$ **3-1**
    i. $n = -1$; see (59).
    ii. $n \neq -1$; $y = Ax^n u(z)$; $(1 + n)z = x^{n+1}$; $zu'(z)$
$+ a_0 + a_1 z + a_2 u + a_3 z u^2 = 0$; $a_0 = -a/A(1 + n)$; $a_1 = -b/A$; $a_2 = n/(1 + n)$; $a_3 = -cA$; see (182)

59 $y' = ax^n + by^2$ **3-2**

60 $y' = a_0 + a_1 y + a_2 y^2$ **1-3**
If y_1, y_2 are the real roots of the quadratic,
    i. $y - y_1 = (y - y_2)C \exp[a_2 x(y_1 - y_2)]$; $y_1 \neq y_2$.
    ii. $(y - y_1)(C - a_2 x) = 1$; $y_1 = y_2$.

61 $y' = f(x) + ay + by^2$ **3-1**
$u'(x) + byu = 0$; $u'' - au' + bfu = 0$; see **3-1-1d**.

62 $y' = 1 + a(x - y)y$ **.3-1**
$y_1 = x$; $u'(x) = a(1 + xu)$; see **3-1-1ai** and **2**.

63 $y' = f(x) + g(x)y + ay^2$ **3-1**
$ayu + u' = 0$; $u''(x) - gu' + afu = 0$; see **3-1-1d**

64 $y' = xy(3 + y)$ **5**
    $(3 + y) \exp 3x^2/2 = Cy$

65 $y' = 1 - x - x^3 + (1 + 2x^2)y - xy^2$ **3-1**
$y_1 = x$; $u'(x) - x + u = 0$ see **3-1-1ai** and (4).
    $(y - x)(Ce^{-x} - 1 + x) = 1$

66 $y' = x(2 + x^2 y - y^2)$ **3-1**
$y_1 = x^2$; $u'(x) = x + x^3 u$; see **3-1-1ai** and **2**.

67 $y' = x + (1 - 2x)y - (1 - x)y^2$ **3-1**
$y_1 = 1$; $u'(x) = 1 - x + u$; see **3-1-1ai** and (4).
    $(y - 1)(C + xe^{-x}) = e^{-x}$

68     $y' = axy^2$ **1-2**
        $y(C - ax^2) = 2$

69     $y' = x^n(a + by^2);$ $a \neq 0,$ $b \neq 0$ **1-2**
        i. $ry = a \tan[rx^{n+1}/(n+1) + C];$ $r = \sqrt{ab}.$
        ii. $sy = a \tanh[sx^{n+1}/(n+1) + C];$ $s = \sqrt{-ab}.$
        iii. $n = -1;$ see (169).

70     $y' = ax^m + bx^n y^2$ **3-1**
        i. $m = n;$ see (69)
        ii. $m \neq n;$ $y(x) = u(z),$ $(n+1)z = x^{n+1};$
   $u'(z) = Az^k + bu^2;$ $A = a(1+n)^k;$ $k = (m-n)/(n+1);$ see (59).

71     $y' = (a + by \cos kx)y$ **5**
        $y[Ce^{-ax} - b(a \cos kx + k \sin kx)] = a^2 + k^2$

72     $y' = \sin x(2 \sec^2 x - y^2)$ **3-1**
   $y_1 = \sec x;$ $u'(x) = \sin x + 2u \tan x;$ see **3-1-1ai** and (33).
        $(y - \sec x)(C - \cos^3 x) = 3 \cos^2 x$

73     $y' + 4 \csc x = (3 - \cot x)y + y^2 \sin x$ **3-1**
   $y \sin x = u(x);$ $u'(x) = u^2 + 3u - 4;$ see **3-1-2a** and (60).
        $y \sin x - 1 = Ce^{5x}(y \sin x + 4)$

74     $y' = y \sec x + (\sin x - 1)^2$ **5**
        $y(C + \sin x) = \tan x + \sec x$

75     $y' + \tan x(1 - y^2) = 0$ **1-2**
        $(y + 1) = C(y - 1) \cos^2 x$

76     $y' = f(x) + g(x)y + h(x)y^2$ **3-1**

77     $y' = (a + by + cy^2)f(x)$ **1-2**
   Let $F(x) = \int f(x)dx + C;$ $q = 4ac - b^2.$

        i. $2cy + b = \sqrt{q} \tan \dfrac{\sqrt{qF}}{2};$ $q > 0.$

        ii. $2cy + b = i^3\sqrt{q} \tanh \dfrac{\sqrt{-qF}}{2};$ $q < 0.$

        iii. $(2cy + b)F + 2c = 0;$ $q = 0.$

78     $y' + (ax + y)y^2 = 0$ **4-1**
   $u(x) = 1/y - ax^2/2;$ $x'(u) = ax^2/2 + u;$ see **9-2**, **9-1**, **3-2**,
   and (56).

79     $y' = (ae^x + y)y^2$ **4-1**
   $y(x) = u(z);$ $z = e^{-x};$ $z^2 u'(z) + zu^3 + au^2 = 0;$ see **4-1**.

80    $y' + 3a(2x+y)y^2 = 0$ **4-1**

$y = u'(x)$; $u'' + 3au'^3 + 6axu'^2 = 0$. Interchange the variables and get $x''(u) - 6axx' - 3a = 0$, which is the derivative of (54).

81    $y' = y(a+by^2)$ **5**

$\qquad y^2(Ce^{-2ax} - b) = a$

82    $y' = a_0 + a_1y + a_2y^2 + a_3y^3$ **1-3**

If y_1, y_2, y_3 are the roots of the cubic,

     i. $(C - 2x)(y - y_1)^2 = 1$; $y_1 = y_2 = y_3$.

    ii. $\ln Y_1/Y_2 = (y_3 - y_1)(C + x)$; $Y_1 = (y - y_3)^{y_3}$;

        $Y_2 = (y - y_1)^{y_1}$; $y_1 = y_2 \neq y_3$.

   iii. $(y - y_1)^{A_1}(y - y_2)^{A_2}(y - y_3)^{A_3} = Ce^x$;

        $A_1 = 1/(y_1 - y_2)(y_1 - y_3)$; $A_2 = 1/(y_2 - y_3)(y_2 - y_1)$;

        $A_3 = 1/(y_3 - y_1)(y_3 - y_2)$; $y_1 \neq y_2 \neq y_3$.

83    $y' = xy^3$ **1-2**

$\qquad y^2(x^2 + C) + 1 = 0$

84    $y' + y(1 - xy^2) = 0$ **5**

$\qquad 2/y^2 = Ce^{2x} + 2x + 1$

85    $y' = (a + bxy)y^2$ **4-1**

$u(z) = xy$; $z = \ln x$; $u'(z) = u + au^2 + bu^3$;   see **4-1g** and (82).

86    $y' + 3xy^2 + (a + 4b^2x + 3bx^2)y^3 = 0$ **4-1**

$y = u'(x)$; $u'' + (a + 4b^2x + 3bx^2)u'^3 + 3xu'^2 = 0$. Interchange the variables to get $x''(u) - 3xx' - (a + 4b^2x + 3bx^2) = 0$; see **B2**. Let $X(x) = x' - 3x^2/2 - 2bx$ and the second-order equation can be written as $X'(u) + 2bX = a$, which is linear; see **2**.

87    $y' = (1 + x^3y)y^2$ **4-1**

Solve $t^2x''(t) + x^3 = 0$ for $x(t)$ and $ty(x)x'(t) + 1 = 0$ for $y(x)$.

88    $y' + 2xy(1 \pm ax^2y^2) = 0$ **5**

$\qquad 2/y^2 = Ce^{2x^2} \mp a(1 + 2x^2)$

89    $y' = y^2 - ax(1 - x^{n-1})y^3$ **4-1**

Solve $t^2x''(t) = ax(1 - x^{n-1})$ for $x(t)$ and $ty(x)x'(t) + 1 = 0$ for $y(x)$.

90    $y' = ay^2 + xy^3(b + cx^{n-1})$ **4-1**

$y(x) = Au(z)$; $z = Aax$; $aA = (-c/b)^{1/(n-1)}$;

$\qquad u'(z) = u^2 + b(z - z^n)u^3/a^2$;   see (89).

91    $y' + (\tan x + y^2 \sec x)y = 0$ **5**

$\qquad 1/y^2 = C \sec^2 x + 2 \sec x \tan x$

92    $y' + y^3 \sec x \tan x = 0$ **1-2**

$\qquad 2y^2(C + \sec x) = 1$

93    $y' = f_0(x) + f_1(x)y + f_2(x)y^2 + f_3(x)y^3$ **4-1**

94    $y' = (\tan x + y^3 \sec x)y$ **5**
$$1/y^3 = C \cos^3 x + \sin x(2 \sin^2 x - 3)$$

95    $y' = ax^{n/(1-n)} + by^n$ **9-2**
$y = x^{1/(1-n)}u(x);$ $xu'(x) = bu^n + u/(n-1) + a;$ see **1-2**.

96    $y' = f(x)y + g(x)y^k$ **5**

97    $y' = f(x) + g(x)y + h(x)y^n$ **9-2**

98    $y' = f(x)y^m + g(x)y^n$ **9-2**

99    $y' = \sqrt{|y|}$ **1-3**
There are two real continuous solutions satisfying the initial conditions $x = 0$, $y = 0$.
      i. $y = 0$.
      ii. $4y = x^2$, $x \geqslant 0$; $4y = -x^2$, $x \leqslant 0$.

100    $y' = a + by \pm \sqrt{A + By}$ **1-3**
$u^2 = A + By;$ $uu'(x) = a_0 + u(a_1 + a_2 u);$ $a_0 = (aB - Ab)/2;$
$a_1 = \pm B/2;$ $a_2 = b/2;$ see (429).

101    $y' = ax + b\sqrt{y};$ see (95)   **9-2**

102    $y' + x^3 = x\sqrt{x^4 + 4y}$ **8-2**
$y = ux^4;$ $xu' + (1 + 4u) = \sqrt{1 + 4u};$ see **1-2**.
$$4y = C(C + 2x^2)$$

103    $y' + 2y(1 - x\sqrt{y}) = 0$ **5**
$$1/y = (Ce^x + 1 + x)^2$$

104    $y' = \sqrt{a + by^2}$ **1-3**
      i. $a = A^2B^2$, $b = B^2$, $y = A \sinh(C + Bx)$.
      ii. $a = -A^2B^2$, $b = B^2$, $y = A \cosh(C + Bx)$.
      iii. $a = A^2B^2$, $b = -B^2$, $y = A \sin(C + Bx)$.

105    $y' = y\sqrt{a + by}$ **1-3**
      i. $a + by = a \tanh^2\left(C - \dfrac{x\sqrt{a}}{2}\right);$ $a > 0$.

      ii. $a + by = -a \tan^2\left(\dfrac{x\sqrt{-a}}{2} + C\right);$ $a < 0$.

106    $y' + [f(x) - y]g(x)\sqrt{(y - a)(y - b)} = 0$ **9-2**
$(y - b)u^2(x) = (y - a);$ $2u'(x) = \pm g(x)[a - f(x) - u^2(b - f)];$
see **3-1**.

107 $y' = \sqrt{XY}$ **1-2**
$X(x) = a_0 + a_1 x + a_2 x^2 + a_3 x^3 + a_4 x^4$; $Y(y) = b_0 + b_1 y + b_2 y^2 + b_3 y^3 + b_4 y^4$. In the usual case, the integral will involve elliptic functions; see, for example, the references in **1-4**.

108 $y' = R_1(x, \sqrt{X})R_2(y, \sqrt{Y})$ **1-2**
The quantities R_i are rational functions of X, Y and the latter are defined as in (107). The integrals will usually involve elliptic functions.

109 $y' = \cos^2 x \cos y$ **1-2**
$\quad\quad 4\ln(\sec y + \tan y) = 2x + \sin 2x + C$

110 $y' = \sec^2 x \cot y \cos y$ **1-2**
$\quad\quad \sec y = C + \tan x$

111 $y' = a + b\cos(Ax + By)$ **9-2**
$u(x) = Ax + By$; $u'(x) = aB + A + bB\cos u$; see (114).

112 $y' = 1 + f'(x) - f(x)\sin y - [1 - f'(x)]\cos y$ **9-2**
$u(x) + f(x) = \tan y/2$; $u'(x) + f(x)u - u^2 = 0$;   see **5**.

113 $y' + f(x) + g(x)\sin ay + h(x)\cos ay = 0$ **9-2**
$u(x) = \tan ay/2$; $2u'(x) + a(f + h) + 2agu + a(f - h)u^2 = 0$;
see **3-1**.

114 $y' = a + b\cos y$ **1-3**
$\quad\quad$ i. $\tan^{-1}\sqrt{A}\tan y/2 = \sqrt{B}(x + C)/2$;
$A = (a - b)/(a + b)$; $B = (a^2 - b^2)$; $a > b$.
$\quad\quad$ ii. $\tanh^{-1}\sqrt{-A}\tan y/2 = \sqrt{-B}(x + C)/2$; $a < b$.

115 $y' + x(\sin 2y - x^2\cos^2 y) = 0$ **9-2**
$u(x) = \tan y$; $u'(x) + x(2u - x^2) = 0$;   see (8).
$\quad\quad 2\tan y + 1 - x^2 = Ce^{-x^2}$

116 $y' + \tan x \sec x \cos^2 y = 0$ **1-2**
$\quad\quad \sec x + \tan y = C$

117 $y' = \cot x \cot y$ **1-2**
$\quad\quad \sin x \cos y = C$

118 $y' + \cot x \cot y = 0$ **1-2**
$\quad\quad \sin x = C\cos y$

119 $y' = \sin x(\csc y - \cot y)$ **9-2, 1-2**
$u(x) = \cos y$; $u'(x) = \sin x(u - 1)$.
$\quad\quad \ln(\cos y - 1) + \cos x = C$

120 $y' = \tan x \cot y$ **1-2**
$\quad\quad \cos y = C\cos x$

121     $y' + \tan x \cot y = 0$ **1-2**
           $\cos x \cos y = C$

122     $y' + \sin 2x \csc 2y = 0$ **1-2**
           $\cos 2x + \cos 2y = C$

123     $y' = \tan x(\tan y + \sec x \sec y)$ **7-2**
      $I(x, y) = \cos x \cos y$
           $\cos x \sin y + \ln \cos x = C$

124     $y' = \cos x \sec^2 y$ **1-2**
           $2y + \sin 2y = 4 \sin x + C$

125     $y' = \sec^2 x \sec^3 y$ **1-2**
           $\sin y(\cos^2 y + 2) = C + 3 \tan x$

126     $y' = a + b \sin y$ **1-3**
           i. $\tan^{-1} A(a \tan y/2 + b) = (x + C)/2A$;
              $A = 1/\sqrt{a^2 - b^2}$; $a > b$.
           ii. $\tanh^{-1} B(a \tan y/2 + b) = (C - x)/2B$.
              $B = 1/\sqrt{b^2 - a^2}$; $a < b$.

127     $y' = a + b \sin(Ax + By)$ **9-2**
     $u(x) = Ax + By$; $u'(x) = aB + A + bB \sin u$;   see (126).

128     $y' = (1 + \cos x \sin y) \tan y$ **9-2**
     $u(x) = \sin y$; $u'(x) = u + u^2 \cos x$;   see (71).
           $2 \csc y + \cos x + \sin x = Ce^{-x}$

129     $y' + \csc 2x \sin 2y = 0$ **1-2**
           $\tan x \tan y = C$

130     $y' + f(x) + g(x) \tan y = 0$ **9-2**
     $u(x) = \tan y$; $u'(x) + f(x) + g(x)u + f(x)u^2 + g(x)u^3 = 0$; see **4-1**.

131     $y' = \sqrt{a + b \cos y}$ **1-3**
     A solution is $kx = 2F(y/2, p)$; $(a + b) = k^2$; $k^2 p^2 = 2b$, where F
     is Legendre's form of the elliptic integral of the first kind; see,
     for example, Peirce and Foster, pp. 71ff.

132     $y' = x + e^y$ **11-1**
           $y = C + e^C x + (1 + e^{2C})x^2/2 + e^C(1 + 2e^{2C})x^3/6 + $ ...

133     $y' = e^{x+y}$ **1-2**
           $e^x + e^{-y} = C$

134     $y' = e^x(a + be^{-y})$ **1-2**
           $y = \ln(Ce^{-u} - b/a)$; $u = e^x$

135     $y' + y \ln x \ln y = 0$ **1-2**
           $\ln (\ln y) = C + x(1 - \ln x)$

136    $y' = x^{m-1}y^{1-n}f(ax^m \pm by^n)$ 9-2

$u(x) = ax^m \pm by^n;$ $u'(x) = x^{m-1}[am \pm bnf(u)];$ see **1-2**.

137    $y' = af(y)$ 1-3

$$\int \frac{dy}{f(y)} = ax + C$$

138    $y' = f(a + bx + cy)$ 6-1

139    $y' = f(x)g(y)$ 1-2

$$\int \frac{dy}{g(y)} = \int f(x)dx + C$$

140    $2y' = \sec^2 x + y \sec x \csc x$ 2

$y = C \tan^{1/2} x + \tan x$

141    $2y' + 2 \csc^2 x = y \csc x \sec x - y^2 \sec^2 x$ 3-1

$y_1 = \cot x;$ see **3-1-1ai**; $2u'(x) = \sec^2 x + u \sec x \csc x;$

see (140).

$y \tan x (C + \tan^{1/2} x) = C + 2 \tan^{1/2} x$

142    $2y' = 2 \sin^2 y \tan y - x \sin 2y$ 9-2

$u(x) = \tan y;$ $u'(x) + xu - u^3 = 0;$ see **5**.

143    $2y' + ax = \pm \sqrt{a^2 x^2 - 4bx^2 - 4cy}$ 8-2

$y = ux^2;$ $xu'(x) + 2u = -[a \pm \sqrt{a^2 - 4b - 4cu}]/2;$ see **1-2**.

144    $3y' = x \pm \sqrt{x^2 - 3y}$ 7-2

$I(x, y) = 3(x \pm \sqrt{x^2 - 3y}).$

$x(2x^2 - 9y) \pm 2(x^2 - 3y)^{3/2} = C$

145    $xy' = \pm \sqrt{a^2 - x^2}$ 1-1

$$y = \pm X + \frac{a}{2} \ln \frac{a \mp X}{a \pm X} + C; \quad X = \sqrt{a^2 - x^2}$$

146    $xy' + x + y = 0$ 2

$x(x + 2y) = C$

147    $xy' + x^2 - y = 0$ 7-2

$I(x) = 1/x^2.$

$y = x(C - x)$

148    $xy' = x^3 - y$ 7-1, 2

$4xy = x^4 + C$

149    $xy' = 1 + x^3 + y$ 2

$2(y + 1) = x(C + x^2)$

150    $xy' = x^m + y$ **2**
        i. $(m-1)y = x(C + x^{m-1}); \quad m \neq 1$
        ii. $m = 1; \quad$ see (157)

151    $xy' = x \sin x - y$ **2**
        $xy = \sin x - x \cos x + C$

152    $xy' = x^2 \sin x + y$ **2**
        $y = x(C - \cos x)$

153    $xy' = x^n \ln x - y$ **2**
        $(n+1)^2 xy = C + x^n[(n+1)\ln x - 1]$

154    $xy' = \sin x - 2y$ **2**
        $x^2 y = C + \sin x - x \cos x$

155    $xy' = \pm ay$ **1-2**
        $y = Cx^{\pm a}$

156    $xy' = 1 + x + ay$ **2**

$$y = Cx^a + \frac{x}{1-a} - \frac{1}{a}; \quad a \neq 1$$

157    $xy' = ax + by$ **8-1**
        i. $(b-1)y + ax = Cx^b; \quad b \neq 1.$
        ii. $y = ax \ln Cx; \quad b = 1.$

158    $xy' = ax^2 + by$ **2**
        i. $(2-b)y = Cx^b + ax^2; \quad b \neq 2.$
        ii. $y = x^2(C + a \ln x); \quad b = 2.$

159    $xy' = a + bx^n + cy$ **2**
        i. $(a+cy)(n-c) = Cx^c + bcx^n; \quad n \neq c.$
        ii. $y = x^n(C + b \ln x) - a/n; \quad n = c.$

160    $xy' + 2 + (3 - x)y = 0$ **2**
        $x^3 y = Ce^x + 2(2 + 2x + x^2)$

161    $xy' + x + (2 + ax)y = 0$ **2**
        $a^2 x^2 (1 + ay) = Ce^{-ax} + 2(ax - 1)$

162    $xy' + (a + bx)y = 0$ **1-2**
        $x^a y = Ce^{-bx}$

163    $xy' = x^3 + (1 - 2x^2)y$ **2**
        $(2y - x) = Ce^{-x^2}$

164    $xy' = ax - (1 - bx^2)y$ **2**
        $bxy = Ce^{bx^2/2} - a$

165    $xy' + (2 - ax^2)y = 0$ **1-2**
        $x^2 y = Ce^{ax^2/2}$

166 $xy' + x^2 + y^2 = 0$ **3-3**

   $uy = xu'(x);$ $xu'' + u' + xu = 0;$ see **3-1-1d** and (3-199).

167 $xy' = x^2 + y(1 + y)$ **3-3**

   $y = ux,$ $u'(x) = 1 + u^2;$ see **3-1-3ai** and (55).

$$y = x \tan(C + x)$$

168 $xy' - y + y^2 = x^{2/3}$ **3-3**

   $(3x^{2/3} - y_2)y = 3x^{2/3}y_2;$ see **3-3aiii** and (249) for the differential equation for y_2.

$$\ln \frac{X_1}{X_2} = C - 6x^{1/3}$$

where $X_{1,2} = 3x^{1/3}y \mp 3x^{2/3} \mp y$.

169 $xy' = a + by^2$ **1-2**

      i. $r \ln Cx = \tan^{-1}\dfrac{ry}{a};$ $r = \sqrt{ab}.$

      ii. $sy(Cx^{2s} + 1) = a(Cx^{2s} - 1);$ $s = \sqrt{-ab}.$

170 $xy' = ax^2 + y + by^2$ **8-3, 3-3**

   $y = ux;$ $u'(x) = a + bu^2;$ see (55).

      i. $y = r_1x \tan(r_2x + C);$ $r_1 = \sqrt{a/b};$ $r_2 = \sqrt{ab}.$

      ii. $y = s_1x \tanh(s_2x + C);$ $s_1 = \sqrt{-a/b};$ $s_2 = \sqrt{-ab}.$

171 $xy' = ax^{2n} + (n + by)y$ **3-3**

   $y(x) = u(z);$ $z = x^n;$ $zu'(z) = az^2/n + u + bu^2/n;$ see (170).

172 $xy' = ax^n + by + cy^2$ **3-3**

173 $xy' = k + ax^n + by + cy^2$ **3-1**

   The equation is integrable if m is an integer, positive, negative, or zero, and $\sqrt{b^2 - 4kc} + n(m + 1/2) = 0$.

174 $xy' + a + xy^2 = 0$ See (59).   **3-2**

175 $xy' + (1 - xy)y = 0$ **5**

$$xy(C - \ln x) = 1$$

176 $xy' = (1 - xy)y$ **5**

$$y(C + x^2) = 2x$$

177 $xy' = (1 + xy)y$ **5**

$$y(C - x^2) = 2x$$

178 $xy' = ax^3 + (1 - xy)y$ **3-1**

   $y_1 = x\sqrt{A};$ $xu'(x) - x + (1 - 2x^2\sqrt{A})u = 0;$ $A = \sqrt{|a|};$ see **3-1-1ai** and **2**.

      i. $y = Ax \tanh(Ax^2/2 + C);$ $a > 0.$

      ii. $y = Ax \cot(Ax^2/2 + C);$ $a < 0.$

179     $xy' = x^3 + (1 + 2x^2)y + xy^2$ **3-1**
        $u'(x) = -yu;$ $xu'' - (1 + 2x^2)u' + x^3 u = 0;$ see **3-1-1d** and
        (3-221).
$$y(C + x^2) + x(C + 2 + x^2) = 0$$

180     $xy' = y(1 + 2xy)$ **5**
        $(C - x^2)y = x$

181     $xy' + bx + (2 + axy)y = 0$ **3-1**
        $y = u(x) - 1/ax;$ $u'(x) + au^2 + b = 0;$ see **3-1-3aii** and (55).

182     $xy' + a_0 + a_1 x + (a_2 + a_3 xy)y = 0$ **3-1**
        $u'(x) = a_3 yu;$ $xu'' + a_2 u' + a_3(a_0 + a_1 x)u = 0;$ see **3-1-1d** and
        (3-200).

183     $xy' + ax^2 y^2 + 2y = b$ **3-1**
        $u'(x) = axyu;$ $xu'' + u' - abxu = 0;$ see **3-1-1e** and (3-199).

184     $xy' + x^m + ay + x^n y^2 = 0;$ $2a = n - m$ **3-1**
    See **3-1-3bii**.

$$y = x^{-a} \tan[C - \frac{2}{m+n} x^{(m+n)/2}]$$

185     $xy' + (a + bx^n y)y = 0$ **5**
        i. $(n - a) = (Cx^a + bx^n)y;$ $n \ne a.$
        ii. $x^a y(C + b \ln x) = 1;$ $n = a.$

186     $xy' = ax^m - by - cx^n y^2$ **3-1**
        $x^b y = u(z);$ $z = x^{n-b};$ $(n - b)u'(z) + cu^2 = az^{k(n-b)};$
        $(n - m)k = 2b + m - n;$ see **3-2**. This is known as the Rawson
        form of the Riccati equation.

187     $xy' = 2x - y + ax^n(x - y)^2$ **3-1**
        $y_1 = x;$ $xu'(x) + ax^n - u = 0;$ see **3-1-1ai** and (159).
        $x(x - y)(C + ax^{n+1}) = (n + 1)$

188     $xy' + (1 - ay \ln x)y = 0$ **5**
         $1/y = Cx + a(1 + \ln x)$

189     $xy' = y + (x^2 - y^2)f(x)$ **3-1**
        $y_1 = x;$ $y_2 = -x;$ see **3-1-1b**.

190     $xy' = y(1 + y^2)$ **1-2**
        $x = y\sqrt{C - x^2}$

191     $xy' + (1 - xy^2)y = 0$ **5**
        $1/y^2 = x(Cx + 2)$

192     $xy' + y = a(1 \pm x^2)y^3$ **5**
        $y^2(Cx^2 + a \mp 2ax^2 \ln x) = 1$

193 $\quad xy' = ay + b(1 \pm x^2)y^3$ 5
  i. $\quad a(a+1)x^{2a} = y^2[C - bx^{2a}(1 + a \pm ax^2)]; \quad a \neq -1.$
  ii. $\quad a = -1; \quad$ see (192).

194 $\quad xy' + 2y = ax^{2k}y^k$ 5
  $\quad 2y^{(1-k)} = x^{2k}[C/x^2 + a(1-k)]$

195 $\quad xy' = 4(y - \sqrt{y})$ 1-2, 5
  $\quad y = (Cx^2 + 1)^2$

196 $\quad xy' + 2y = \pm\sqrt{1+y^2}$ 1-2
  $y + u = \pm\sqrt{1+y^2}; \quad x(1+u^2)u'(x) = u(1 - 3u^2).$
  $\quad x^3(1 - 3u^2)^2 = Cu^3$

197 $\quad xy' = y + \sqrt{x^2 + y^2}$ 8-1
  $\quad x^2 = C(2y + C)$

198 $\quad xy' = y + \sqrt{x^2 - y^2}$ 8-1
  $\quad y = x\sin(C + \ln x)$

199 $\quad xy' = y + x\sqrt{x^2 + y^2}$ 8-3
  $\quad y + \sqrt{x^2 + y^2} = Cxe^x$

200 $\quad xy' = y - x(x-y)\sqrt{x^2+y^2}$ 8-3
  $\quad 2\sqrt{x+y} = \sqrt{x-y}(C + x^2)$

201 $\quad xy' = y + a\sqrt{y^2 \pm b^2x^2}$ 8-1
  $\quad y + \sqrt{y^2 \pm b^2x^2} = Cx^{a+1}$

202 $\quad xy' + (\sin y - 3x^2\cos y)\cos y = 0$ 7-2
  $I(y) = \sec^2 y.$
  $\quad x(\tan y - x^2) = C$

203 $\quad xy' + x - y + x\cos y/x = 0$ 8-1
  $\quad \ln x + \tan y/2x = C$

204 $\quad xy' = y - x\cos^2 y/x$ 8-1
  $\quad \ln x + \tan y/x = C$

205 $\quad xy' = (1 - 2x^2)\cot y$ 1-2
  $\quad x\cos y = Ce^{x^2}$

206 $\quad xy' = y - x\cot^2 y/x$ 8-1
  $\quad y = x(C + \ln x + \tan y/x)$

207 $\quad xy' + y + 2x\sec xy = 0$ 7-2
  $I(x, y) = \cos xy.$
  $\quad x^2 + \sin xy = C$

208 $\quad xy' - y + x\sec y/x = 0$ 8-1
  $\quad \ln x + \sin y/x = C$

209     $xy' = y + x \sec^2 y/x$ 8-1

$$y = x\left(C - \sin\frac{y}{x} \cos\frac{y}{x} - 2\ln x\right)$$

210     $xy' = \sin(x - y)$ 9-2
$u(x) = x\tan(y - x)/2;$ $2xu'(x) + u^2 + x^2 = 0;$ see **3-1**.

211     $xy' = y + x \sin y/x$ 8-1
$\tan(y/2x) = Cx$

212     $xy' + \tan y = 0$ 7-2
$I(y) = \cos y.$
$x \sin y = C$

213     $xy' + x + \tan(x + y) = 0$ 9-2
$u(x) = x + y;$ $xu'(x) + \tan u = 0;$ see (212).
$x \sin(x + y) = C$

214     $xy' = y - x \tan y/x$ 8-1
$x \sin y/x = C$

215     $xy' = (1 + y^2)(x^2 - \tan^{-1} y)$ 9-2
$y = \tan u;$ $xu'(x) = x^2 - u;$ see (158).
$x(3\tan^{-1} y - x^2) = C$

216     $xy' = y + xe^{y/x}$ 8-1
$\ln x + e^{-y/x} = C$

217     $xy' = x + y + xe^{y/x})$ 8-1
$e^{y/x} = Cx(1 + e^{y/x})$

218     $xy' = y \ln y$ 1-2
$\ln y = Cx$

219     $xy' = (1 + \ln x - \ln y)y$ 8-1
$y = xe^{C/x}$

220     $xy' + (1 - \ln x - \ln y)y = 0$ 9-2
$u = xy;$ $xu'(x) = u \ln u;$ see **1-2**.
$Cx = \ln xy$

221     $xy' = y - 2x \tanh y/x$ 8-1
$x^2 \sinh y/x = C$

222     $xy' + ny = f(x)g(x^n y)$ 9-2
$u(x) = x^n y;$ $u'(x) = x^{n-1} f(x)g(u);$ see **1-2**.

223     $xy' = yf(x^m y^n)$ 9-2

224     $(1 + x)y' = x^3(4 + 3x) + y$ 2
$y = C(1 + x) + x^4$

225     $(1 + x)y' = (1 + x)^4 + 2y$ 2
$2y = (1 + x)^2[C + (1 + x)^2]$

226    $(1+x)y' = e^x(1+x)^{n+1}+ny$ **2**
$$y = (1+x)^n(C+e^x)$$

227    $(1-x)y' = ay+bxy^2$ **5**
     i. $y[C(1-x)^a+b(1-ax)] = a(a-1);\quad a \neq 1$
     ii. $y[C(1-x)-b(1-x)\ln x-b] = 1;\quad a = 1$

228    $(1+x)y'+y+(1+x)^4y^3 = 0$ **5**
$$1/y^2 = (1+x)^2[C+(1+x)^2]$$

229    $(1-x)y' = (1-xy^3)y$ **5**
$$y^3[C(1-x)^3+3x-1] = 2$$

230    $(1+x)y' = (1+y)+(1+x)\sqrt{1+y}$ **9-2**
   $u(x) = \sqrt{1+y};\quad 2(1+x)u'(x) = 1+x+u;\quad$ see **2.**
$$\sqrt{1+y} = 1+x+C\sqrt{1+x}$$

231    $(a+x)y' = bx$ **1-1**
$$y = C+bx-ab\ln(a+x)$$

232    $(a+x)y' = bx+y$ **2**
$$y = ab+(a+x)[C+b\ln(a+x)]$$

233    $(a+x)y'+bx^2+y = 0$ **2**
$$3y(a+x) = C-bx^3$$

234    $(a+x)y' = 2(a+x)^5+3y$ **2**
$$y = (a+x)^3[C+(a+x)^2]$$

235    $(a+x)y' = \pm(b+cy)$ **1-2**
$$cy+b = C(a+x)^{\pm c}$$

236    $(a+x)y' = bx+cy$ **2**
     i. $c(1-c)y = C(a+x)^c+b(a+cx);\quad c \neq 0, c \neq 1.$
     ii. $c = 0;$ see (231).
     iii. $c = 1;$ see (232).

237    $(a+x)y' = y(1-ay)$ **5**
$$y(C+ax) = a+x$$
This equation has a common primitive with (344).

238    $(a-x)y' = y+(b+cx)y^3$ **5**
$$1/y^2 = C(a-x)^2+2c(a-x)-(ac+b)$$

239    $2xy' = 2x^3-y$ **2**
$$7y = 2x^3+C/\sqrt{x}$$

240    $2xy'+1 = 4ixy+y^2;\quad i = \sqrt{-1}$ **3-1**
   $2xu'(x)+uy = 0;\quad 4x^2u''+4x(1-2ix)u'-u = 0;\quad$ see **3-1-1d**
   and (3-334).

241    $2xy' = y(1+y^2)$ **1-2**
$$y^2(1-Cx) = Cx$$

242     $2xy' + y(1+y^2) = 0$ **1-2**
         $y^2(x-C) = C$

243     $2xy' = (1+x-6y^2)y$ **5**
         $y^2(Ce^{-x}+6) = x$

244     $2xy' + 4y + a \pm \sqrt{a^2 - 4b - 4cy} = 0$ **1-2**
         $u^2(x) = a^2 - 4b - 4cy; \quad c \neq 0; \quad uu'(x) = U(x) = ac + a^2 - 4b$
         $\pm cu - u^2;$ see (429).

245     $(1+2x)y' = 2(8+16x-3y)$ **2**
         $(1+2x)^3[y - 2(1+2x)] = C$

246     $(1+2x)y' = 4e^{-y} - 2$ **1-2**

$$y = \ln \frac{(C+4x)}{(1+2x)}$$

247     $2(1-x)y' = 4x\sqrt{1-x} + y$ **2**
         $y\sqrt{1-x} = C + x^2$

248     $2(1+x)y' + 2y + (1+x)^4 y^3 = 0$ **5**
         $2/y^2 = (1+x)^2[C + (1+x)^2]$

249     $3xy' = 3x^{2/3} + (1-3y)y$ **3-3**

$$\ln \frac{(y-X)}{(y+X)} + 6X = C; \quad X = x^{1/3}$$

See also (168).

250     $3xy' = (2+xy^3)y$ **5**
         $y^3(C+x^3) + 3x^2 = 0$

251     $3xy' = (1+3xy^3 \ln x)y$ **5**
         $(4x + Cy^3) = 3x^2y^3(1 - 2\ln x)$

252     $x^2y' = a - y$ **1-2**
         $y = Ce^{1/x} + a$

253     $x^2y' = a + bx + cx^2 + xy$ **2**
         $2xy = x^2(C + 2c \ln x) - 2bx - a$

254     $x^2y' = a + bx + cx^2 - xy$ **2**
         $2xy = C + 2a \ln x + 2bx + cx^2$

255     $x^2y' + (1-2x)y = x^2$ **2**
         $y = x^2(1 + Ce^{1/x})$

256     $x^2y' = a + bxy$ **2**
         i. $(b+1)xy = Cx^{b+1} - a; \quad b \neq -1.$
         ii. $b = -1,$ see (254).

257    $x^2y' = (a+bx)y$ 1-2
       $y = Ce^{-a/x}x^b$

258    $x^2y' + x(2+x)y = x(1-e^{-2x}) - 2$ 2
       $x^2y = Ce^{-x} + (1+x)e^{-2x} + x - 3$

259    $x^2y' + 2x(1-x)y = e^x(2e^x - 1)$ 2
       $x^2y = 2e^{2x}(C+x) + e^x$

260    $x^2y' + x^2 + xy + y^2 = 0$ 8-1
       $x = (x+y)(C + \ln x)$

261    $x^2y' = (1 + 2x - y)^2$ 6-2
       $y - 4x - 1 = Cx^3(y - x - 1)$

262    $x^2y' = a + by^2$ 1-2

       i. $y = \sqrt{a/b}\, \tan\left(C - \dfrac{\sqrt{ab}}{x}\right); \quad ab > 0.$

       ii. If $ab < 0$, replace tan by tanh.

263    $x^2y' = (x + ay)y$ 8-1, 5
       $x = y(C - a \ln x)$

264    $x^2y' = (ax + by)y$ 8-1, 5
       i. $y(Cx^{1-a} - b) = (a-1)x; \quad a \neq 1.$
       ii. If $a = 1$, see (263).

265    $x^2y' + ax^2 + bxy + cy^2 = 0$ 8-1

       i. $\sqrt{q}\, \ln Cx = 2 \tan^{-1}\left[\dfrac{(b+1)x + 2cy}{x\sqrt{q}}\right];$

            $q = 4ac - (b+1)^2; \quad q > 0.$
       ii. If $q < 0$, replace $\tan^{-1}$ by $\tanh^{-1}$.
       iii. $q = 0, \quad a = b = c = 1; \quad$ see (260).
       iv. $q = 0, \quad a = 0, \quad b = -1; \quad$ see (263).
       v. $a = b = c = -1; \quad I(x, y) = 1/x(x^2 + y^2);$ see 7-2.

266    $x^2y' = a + bx^n + x^2y^2$ 3-1
       $yu(x) + u' = 0; \quad x^2u'' + (a + bx^n)u = 0; \quad$ see 3-1-1d and
       (3-259).

267    $x^2y' + 2 + xy(4 + xy) = 0$ 3-1
       $y_1 = -2/x; \quad u'(x) = 1; \quad$ see 3-1-1ai and 1-2.
       $xy(C + x) + (2C + x) = 0$

268    $x^2y' + 2 + ax(1 - xy) - x^2y^2 = 0$ 3-1
       $y_1 = 1/x; \quad xu'(x) + x + (2 + ax)u = 0; \quad$ see 3-1-1ai and (161).
       $(xy - 1)[Ce^{-ax} - (a^2x^2 - 2ax + 2)] = a^3x^3$

269 $x^2y' = a + bx^2y^2$ 8-2, 3-2
     $xy = u;$ $xu'(x) = a - u + bu^2;$ see **1-2**

270 $x^2y' = a + bx^n + cx^2y^2$ 3-1
     $u(x) = xy + A;$ $a = A(1-cA);$ $xu'(x) = bx^n + (1-2cA)u + cu^2;$
     see **3-3**.

271 $x^2y' = a + bxy + cx^2y^2$ 3-1
     $cyu + u'(x) = 0;$ $x^2u'' - bxu' + acu = 0;$ see **3-1-1e** and (3-311).

272 $x^2y' = a + bxy + cx^4y^2$ 3-1
     $cx^2yu + u'(x) = 0;$ $x^2u'' - (2+b)u' + acxu = 0;$ see **3-1-1e** and **B1**.

273 $x^2y' + (x^2 + y^2 - x)y = 0$ 7-2
     See **7-2-3c**, $k = 3$, $I(x, y) = 1/y(x^2 + y^2).$
     $y^2(Ce^{2x} - 1) = x^2$

274 $x^2y' = 2y(x - y^2)$ 5
     $(3C + 4x^3)y^2 = 3x^4$

275 $x^2y' = ax^2y^2 - ay^3$ 4-2
     $u(x) = ax + 1/y;$ $ax'(u) = x^2(u - ax);$ see (78).

276 $x^2y' + ay^2 + bx^2y^3 = 0$ 4-2
     $Ay = -u(z);$ $xz = B;$ $A^3 = ab;$ $aB^3 = b^2;$
     $z^2u'(z) + z^2u^2 - z^3 = 0;$ see (275).

277 $x^2y' = (ax + by^3)y$ 5
$$1/y^3 = C/x^{3a} + \frac{3b}{(1-3a)x};\quad a \neq 1/3$$

278 $x^2y' + xy + \sqrt{y} = 0$ 5
     $x^2y = (C\sqrt{x} + 1)^2$

279 $x^2y' = \sec y + 3x \tan y$ 9-2
     $u(x) = \sin y;$ $x^2u'(x) = 1 + 3ux;$ see (256).
     $4x \sin y + 1 = Cx^4$

280 $(1 - x^2)y' = 1 - x^2 + y$ 2
     $(y - 1)\sqrt{1 - x^2} = C + \sin^{-1}x$

281 $(1 - x^2)y' \pm 1 = xy$ 2
     $y\sqrt{1 - x^2} \pm \sin^{-1}x = C$

282 $(1 - x^2)y' = 5 - xy$ 2
     $y = 5x + C\sqrt{x^2 - 1}$

283 $(1 + x^2)y' \pm a + xy = 0$ 2
     $y\sqrt{1 + x^2} = C \mp a \ln(x + \sqrt{1 + x^2})$

284 $(1 + x^2)y' \pm a - xy = 0$ 2
     $y = C\sqrt{1 + x^2} \mp ax$

285    $(1-x^2)y' \pm a - xy = 0$ **2**
$$y\sqrt{1-x^2} = C \mp a \sin^{-1}x$$

286    $(1-x^2)y' - x + xy = 0$ **2**
$$y = 1 + C\sqrt{1-x^2}$$

287    $(1+x^2)y' - x^2 + xy = 0$ **2**
$$(y - x/2)\sqrt{1+x^2} = C - (1/2)\ln(x + \sqrt{1+x^2})$$

288    $(1-x^2)y' + x^2 + xy = 0$ **2**
$$x + y = \sqrt{x^2-1}[C + \ln(x + \sqrt{x^2-1})]$$

289    $(1+x^2)y' = x(1+x^2) - xy$ **2**
$$3y\sqrt{1+x^2} = C + (1+x^2)^{3/2}$$

290    $(1+x^2)y' = x(3x^2 - y)$ **2**
$$y\sqrt{1+x^2} = C + (x^2-2)\sqrt{1+x^2}$$

291    $(1-x^2)y' + 2xy = 0$ **1-2**
$$\ln[(1-x)^2 y] = C - \frac{2}{(1-x)}$$

292    $(1+x^2)y' = 2x(x-y)$ **2**
$$3y(1+x^2) = C + 2x^3$$

293    $(1+x^2)y' = 2x(1+x^2)^2 + 2xy$ **2**
$$y = (1+x^2)(C + x^2)$$

294    $(1-x^2)y' + \cos x = 2xy$ **7, 2**
$$(1-x^2)y + \sin x = C$$

295    $(1+x^2)y' = \tan x - 2xy$ **7, 2**
$$(1+x^2)y + \ln\cos x = C$$

296    $(1-x^2)y' = a + 4xy$ **2**
$$3(1-x^2)^2 y = C + ax(3-x^2)$$

297    $(1+x^2)y' = (a+2bx)y$ **1-2**
$$y = Ce^{at}\sec^{2b}t; \quad x = \tan t$$

298    $(1+x^2)y' = \pm(1+y^2)$ **1-2**
$$y(1 \mp Cx) = C \pm x$$

299    $(1-x^2)y' = \pm(1-y^2)$ **1-2**
$$y(x - C) = \pm(1 - Cx)$$

300    $(1-x^2)y' = 1 - (2x-y)y$ **3-1**
$y_1 = x; \quad (1-x^2)u'(x) = 1; \quad$ see **3-1-1ai** and **1-1**.
$$(y-x)\left(C + \ln\frac{1-x}{1+x}\right) = 2$$

301     $(1-x^2)y' = n(1-2xy+y^2)$ **3-1**
$y = Ax+B/u$; $An = 2n-1$; $Bn = 1-n$; $(1-x^2)u'(x)$
$= (n-1)(1+u^2-2xu)$. If n is a positive integer, repeat the
transformations until $(n-1)$ becomes unity. The result is (300).

302     $(1+x^2)y'+xy(1-y) = 0$ 5
$$1/y = 1+C\sqrt{1+x^2}$$

303     $(1-x^2)y' = xy(1+ay)$ 5
$$1/y = C\sqrt{1-x^2}-a$$

304     $(1+x^2)y' = 1+y^2-2xy(1+y^2)$ **4-2**
$x^4y = (1+x^2)u(x)+x^3$; $x^7u'(x)+2(1+x^2)u^3+5x^3u^2 = 0$;
see (383).

305     $(1+x^2)y'+x\sin y\cos y = x(1+x^2)\cos^2y$ **9-2**
$u(x) = \tan y$; $(1+x^2)u' = x(1+x^2)-xu$;   see (289).
$$3\tan y\sqrt{1+x^2} = C+(1+x^2)^{3/2}$$

306     $(1+x^2)y' = (1+x^2)-y\cot^{-1}x$ 2
$$2(x-y)\tan^{-1}x = C+\ln(1+x^2)$$

307     $(4-x^2)y'+4y = (2+x)y^2$ 5
$$(x-2) = y(x+2)[C+\ln(x+2)]$$

308     $(a^2+x^2)y' = b+xy$ 2
$$a^2y = bx+C\sqrt{a^2+x^2}$$

309     $(a^2+x^2)y' = (b+y)(x+\sqrt{a^2+x^2})$ **1-2**
$$y+b = C(a^2+x^2+x\sqrt{a^2+x^2})$$

310     $(x^2\pm a^2)y'+(x-y)y = 0$ 5
$$a^2/y = C\sqrt{x^2\pm a^2}\mp x$$

311     $(a^2+x^2)y' = a^2+3xy-2y^2$ **3-1**
$y_1 = x$; $(a^2+x^2)u'(x) = 2+ux$;   see **3-1-1ai** and (308).
$$2(y-x)(x+C\sqrt{a^2+x^2}) = a^2$$

312     $(x^2\pm a^2)y'+xy+bxy^2 = 0$ 5
$$1/y = C\sqrt{x^2\pm a^2}-b$$

313     $x(1-x)y' = a+(1+x)y$ 2
$$(1-x)^2y = Cx-a(1+x\ln x)$$

314     $x(1-x)y' = 2(1+xy)$ 2
$$(1-x)^2y = C+2(\ln x-1)$$

315     $x(1-x)y' = 2(xy-1)$ 2
$$(1-x)^2y = 2(x-\ln x+C)$$

316     $x(1+x)y' = (1-2x)y$ **1-2**
$$y(1+x)^3 = Cx$$

317   $x(1-x)y' + (1+2x)y = a$ **2**
      $xy = a + C(1-x)^3$

318   $x(1-x)y' = a + 2(2-x)y$ **2**
      $12(1-x)^2 y = Cx^4 + a(4x-3)$

319   $x(1-x)y' + (2-3xy+y) = 0$ **2**
      $(1-x)^2(1-xy) = C$

320   $x(1+x)y' = (x+1)(x^2-1) + (x^2+x-1)y$ **2**
      $xy = (Ce^x - x)(1+x)$

321   $(x-2)(x-3)y' + x^2 - 8y + 3xy = 0$ **7-2, 2**
   $I(x) = (x-2);$
      $12(x-2)^2(x-3)y + x^3(3x-8) = C$

322   $x(a+x)y' = (b+cy)y$ **1-2**
      $y^a(a+x)^b = Cx^b(b+cy)^a$

323   $(a+x)^2 y' = 2(a+x)(b+y)$ **7-2, 1-2**
   $I(y) = 1/(b+y)^2.$
      $y+b = C(a+x)^2$

324   $(x-a)^2 y' + k(x+y-a)^2 + y^2 = 0$ **3-1**
   $ku(x) = y + k(x+y); \quad (x-a)^2 u'(x) + k(u-a)^2 = 0;$ see (328).
      $[y + k(x+y-a)]^{-1} + (x-a)^{-1} = C/k$

325   $(x-a)(x-b)y' + ky = 0$ **1-2**

    i. $y = C\left(\dfrac{x-a}{x-b}\right)^{k/(b-a)} \quad ; a \neq b.$

    ii. $(x-a)(\ln y - C) = k; \quad a = b.$

326   $(x-a)(x-b)y' = (x-a)(x-b) + (2x-a-b)y$ **2**

    i. $\dfrac{(a-b)y}{(x-a)(x-b)} = C + \ln\dfrac{(x-a)}{(x-b)} \quad ; \quad a \neq b.$

    ii. $y = (x-a)[C(x-a)-1]; \quad a = b.$

327   $(x-a)(x-b)y' = cy^2$ **1-2**

    i. $cy \ln\dfrac{(x-a)}{(x-b)} = C(b-a); \quad a \neq b.$

    ii. $y[C(x-a)+c] = x-a; \quad a = b.$

328   $(x-a)(x-b)y' + k(y-a)(y-b) = 0$ **1-2**

    i. $\dfrac{y-a}{y-b} = C\left(\dfrac{x-b}{x-a}\right)^k; \quad a \neq b.$

    ii. $1/(y-a) + k/(x-a) = C; \quad a = b.$

329     $(x-a)(x-b)y' + k(x+y-a)(x+y-b) + y^2 = 0$ **3-1**
     $ku(x) = y + k(x+y);$ $(x-a)(x-b)u'(x) + k(u-a)(u-b) = 0;$
     see (328).

         i. $\dfrac{y + k(x+y-a)}{y + k(x+y-b)} = C\left(\dfrac{x-b}{x-a}\right)^k$; $a \neq b$, $k(k+1) \neq 0$.

         ii. $k = 0$;   see (327).
         iii. $k = -1$;   see (326).
         iv. $a = b$;   see (324).

330     $2x^2 y' = y$ **1-2**
     $2x \ln y = Cx - 1$

331     $2x^2 y' + x \cot x - 1 + 2x^2 y \cot x = 0$ **1-2**
     $x(2y - C \csc x) + 1 = 0$

332     $2x^2 y' + 1 + 2xy - x^2 y^2 = 0$ **8-2**
     $x(1 + xy) = C(1 - xy)$

333     $2x^2 y' = 2xy + (1 - x \cot x)(x^2 - y^2)$ **3-1**
     $y_1 = x;$ $2x^2 u'(x) + x \cot x - 1 + 2x^2 u \cot x = 0;$ see **3-1-1ai**
     and (331).
         $y(Cx - \sin x) = x(Cx + \sin x)$

334     $2(1 - x^2)y' = \sqrt{1 - x^2} + (1 + x)y$ **2**
     $y\sqrt{1 - x} = C + \sqrt{1 + x}$

335     $x(1 - 2x)y' + 1 + (1 - 4x)y = 0$ **2**
     $x(2x - 1)y = C + x$

336     $x(1 - 2x)y' = 4x - (1 + 4x)y + y^2$ **3-1**
     $y_1 = 1;$ $x(1 - 2x)u'(x) + 1 + (1 - 4x)u = 0;$ see **3-1-1ai** and (335).
         $y(C + x) = C + 2x^2$

337     $2x(1 - x)y' + x + (1 - 2x)y = 0$ **2**
     $(2y - 1)\sqrt{x(x-1)} = C + \ln\left[\sqrt{x} + \sqrt{x-1}\right]$

338     $2x(1 - x)y' + x + (1 - x)y^2 = 0$ **3-1**
     $2xu'(x) = yu;$ $x(1 - x)u'' + (1 - x)u' + u/4 = 0;$ see **3-1-1d** and
     (3-410).

339     $2(1 + x + x^2)y' = 1 + 8x^2 - (1 + 2x)y$ **2**
     $(y + 3 - 2x)\sqrt{1 + x + x^2} = C$

340     $4(1 + x^2)y' - 4xy - x^2 = 0$ **2**
     $x + 4y = \sqrt{1 + x^2}[C + \ln(x + \sqrt{1 + x^2})]$

341     $ax^2 y' = x^2 + axy + b^2 y^2$ **8-1**
     $a \tan^{-1} by/x = C + b \ln x$

342 $(a+bx^2)y' = \pm(A+By^2)$ 1-2

   i. $\sqrt{AB}\, \tan^{-1} \dfrac{y\sqrt{AB}}{A} = \pm\sqrt{ab}\, \tan^{-1}\dfrac{x\sqrt{ab}}{a}.$

   ii. If $ab < 0$ or $AB < 0$, replace $\tan^{-1}$ by $\tanh^{-1}$.

343 $(a+bx^2)y' = cxy \ln y$ 1-2
   $\ln y = C(a+bx^2)^{c\,/2b}$

344 $x(1+ax)y'+a-y = 0$ 2
   $Ca(xy-1)-ax+Cy = 0$
   The primitive also satisfies (237).

345 $(a+bx)^2 y'+cy^2+(a+bx)y^3 = 0$ 4-2

   $u(x) = \dfrac{1}{y} - \dfrac{(A+Bx)}{a+bx};\quad Ba-Ab = c;$

   $u'(x)[(a+bx)u+A+Bx] = 1;\quad x'(u) = (B+bu)x+au+A;$
   see **2**.

346 $x^3y' = a+bx^2y$ 2
   i. $(2+b)x^2y = Cx^{b+2}-a;\quad b \neq -2.$
   ii. $x^2y = C+a \ln x;\quad b = -2.$

347 $x^3y' = 3-x^2+x^2y$ 2
   $x^2y = Cx^3-1$

348 $x^3y' = x^4+y^2$ 3-1
   $(x^2-y)\ln Cx = x^2$
   A special case of (388).

349 $x^3y' = y(x^2+y)$ 5, 7-2
   $I(x, y) = 1/x^2y^2.$
   $y(Cx+1) = x^2$

350 $x^3y' = x^2(y-1)+y^2$ 9-2
   $(1-u)y = x(1+u);\quad x^3u'(x) = 2u;\quad$ see **1-2**.
   $y = x \coth (1/x+C)$

351 $x^3y' = (1+x)y^2$ 1-2
   $y(1+2x-Cx^2) = 2x^2$

352 $x^3y'+20+x^2y(1-x^2y) = 0$ 3-1
   $u'(x)+uxy = 0;\quad x^2u'' = 20u;\quad$ see **3-1-1d** and (3-250).
   $x^2y(C+x^9) = 4-5Cx^9$

353 $x^3y'+3+(3-2x)x^2y-x^6y^2 = 0$ 3-1
   $u'(x)+x^3yu = 0;\quad u''-2u'-3u = 0;\quad$ see **3-1-1d** and (3-102).

354 $x^3y' = (2x^2+y^2)y$ 8-1
   $x^2(x^2+y^2) = Cy^2$

355    $x^3y' = \cos y(\cos y - 2x^2 \sin y)$ 9-2
    $u(x) = \tan y; \quad x^3u'(x) = 1 - 2ux^2$; see (346).
       $x^2 \tan y = C + \ln x$

356    $x(1+x^2)y' = ax^2 + y$ 2
      $y\sqrt{1+x^2} = x(C + a \sinh^{-1} x)$

357    $x(1-x^2)y' = ax^2 + y$ 2
      $y\sqrt{1-x^2} = x(C + a \sin^{-1} x)$

358    $x(1+x^2)y' = ax^3 + y$ 2
      $(y - ax)\sqrt{1+x^2} = Cx$

359    $x(1+x^2)y' = a - x^2y$ 2

$$y\sqrt{1+x^2} + a \ln \frac{1 + \sqrt{1+x^2}}{x} = C$$

360    $x(1+x^2)y' = (1-x^2)y$ 1-2
      $y(1+x^2) = Cx$

361    $x(1-x^2)y' = (1-x+x^2)y$ 1-2
      $(x^2-1)^{3/2}y = Cx(x-1)$

362    $x(1-x^2)y' = ax^3 + (1-2x^2)y$ 2
      $y = ax + Cx\sqrt{1-x^2}$

363    $x(1-x^2)y' = x^3(1-x^2) + (1-2x^2)y$ 2
      $y = Cx\sqrt{1-x^2} - x(1-x^2)$

364    $x(1+x^2)y' = 2(1-2x^2y)$ 2
      $x^3y^4(C + e^x) = 1$

365    $x(1+x^2)y' = x - (3+5x^2)y$ 2
      $4x^3(1+x^2)y = C + x^4$

366    $x(1-x^2)y' + x^2 + (1-x^2)y^2 = 0$ 3-1
  $y(x) = u(z); \quad z = x^2; \quad 2z(1-z)u'(z) + (1-z)u^2 + z = 0$; see (338).

367    $x^2(1-x)y' = (2-x)xy - y^2$ 5
      $y[C(x-1) + 1] = x^2$

368    $2x^3y' = (x^2 - y^2)y$ 8-1, 5
      $x^2 + y^2 = Cxy^2$

369    $2x^3y' = (3x^2 + ay^2)y$ 8-1, 5
      $x^3 = (C - ax)y^2$

370    $6x^3y' = 4x^2y + (1-3x)y^4$ 5
      $2x^2 = y^3(C + 3x - \ln x)$

371 $\quad x(a+bx+cx^2)y' +x^2 -(a+bx+cx^2)y = y^2$ $\qquad$ **3-1**

$\quad y_1 = x;\quad y_2 = -x;\quad$ see **3-1-1b**.

$$y(C-U) = x(C+U);\quad \ln U(x) = 2\int \frac{dx}{X};$$

$\quad X(x) = a+bx +cx^2$

372 $\quad x^4 y' = (x^3+y)y$ $\qquad$ **5**

$\qquad y(Cx^2+1) = 2x^3$

373 $\quad x^4 y' +a^2 +x^4 y^2 = 0$ $\qquad$ **3-2**

$\quad x^2 y = u+x;\quad x^2 u'(x) +u^2 +a^2 = 0;\quad$ see (262).

$\qquad x^2 y = x+a \tan (C+a/x)$

374 $\quad x^4 y' +x^3 y +\csc xy = 0$ $\qquad$ **9-2**

$\quad u(x) = xy;\quad x^3 u'(x) +\csc u = 0;\quad$ see **1-2**.

$\qquad 2x^2 \cos xy = Cx^2 -1$

375 $\quad (1-x^4)y' = 2x(1-y^2)$ $\qquad$ **1-2**

$\qquad y(Cx^2+1) = C+x^2$

376 $\quad x(1-x^3)y' = 2x-(1-4x^3)y$ $\qquad$ **2**

$\qquad x(1-x^3)y = C+x^2$

377 $\quad x(1-x^3)y' = x^2 +(1-2xy)y$ $\qquad$ **3-1**

$\quad y_1 = x^2;\quad x(1-x^3)u'(x) = 2x-(1-4x^3)u;\quad$ see **3-1-1a** and (376).

$\qquad (y-x^2)(C+x^2) = x(1-x^3)$

378 $\quad x^2(1-x^2)y' = (x-3x^3 -y)y$ $\qquad$ **5**

$\qquad y \ln Cx = x(1-x^2)$

379 $\quad x(1-2x^3)y' = 2(1-x^3)y$ $\qquad$ **1-2**

$\qquad (1-2x^3)y^3 = Cx^6$

380 $\quad (a+bx+cx^2)^2(y' +y^2) +A = 0$ $\qquad$ **3-1**

$\quad uy = u'(x);\quad (a+bx+cx^2)^2 u'' +Au = 0;\quad$ see **3-1-1d** and (3-581).

381 $\quad x^5 y' = 1-3x^4 y$ $\qquad$ **2**

$\qquad x^4 y = Cx -1$

382 $\quad x(1-x^4)y' = 2x(x^2 -y^2) +(1-x^4)y$ $\qquad$ **9-2**

$\quad y = ux;\quad (1-x^4)u'(x) = 2x(1-u^2);\quad$ see (375).

$\qquad y(Cx^2+1) = x(C+x^2)$

383 $\quad x^7 y' +5x^3 y^2 +2(1+x^2)y^3 = 0$ $\qquad$ **4-1**

$\quad y = 1/u;\quad x^7 uu'(x) = 5x^3 u +2(1+x^2);\quad$ see **4-2b** and (593).

384 $\quad x^n y' = a+bx^{n-1}y$ $\qquad$ **2**

$\qquad$ i. $\quad (1-b-n)(y-Cx^b) = ax^{1-n};\quad b+n \neq 1.$

$\qquad$ ii. $\quad y = x^b(C+a \ln x);\quad b+n = 1.$

385     $x^n y' = x^{2n-1} - y^2$ **3-1**
$y(x) = u(z);$ $x^{1-n} = (1-n)z;$ $u'(z) + u^2 = [(1-n)z]^m;$
$m = (2n-1)/(n-1).$ If $n = 1$, see **3-3**.

386     $x^n y' + x^2 + (x^{n-1} + y)y$ **9-2**
$y(1-u) - x(1+u);$ $x^{n-1} u'(x) = 2u;$ see **1-2**.
      i. $n = 1;$ see (170).
      ii. $n = 2;$ see (265).
      iii. $n = 3;$ see (350).

387     $x^n y' + x^{2n-2} + y^2 + (1-n)x^{n-1} y = 0$ **3-1**
See **3-1-3ai** and **bii**.
$$y = x^{n-1} \tan(C - \ln x)$$

388     $x^n y' = a^2 x^{2n-2} + b^2 y^2$ **3-1**
$y = A x^{n-1} u(x);$ $bA = a;$ $xu'(x) + (n-1)u = ab(u^2 + 1);$
see **1-2**.

389     $x^n y' = x^{n-1}(ax^{2n} + ny - by^2)$ **9-2**
$y = ux^n;$ $u'(x) = x^{n-1}(a - bu^2);$ see (69).

390     $x^{2n} y' = 1 - nx^{n-1} + x^n y(1 - 3x^n y + x^{2n} y^2)$ **4-1**
$y_1 = 1/x^n;$ $x^n u'(x) + 2u - x^{2n} u^3 = 0;$ see **5**.

391     $x^k y' = ax^m + by^n$ **9-2**
$k = r(n-1) + n;$ $m = n(r+1);$ $y = A x^{r+1} u(x);$
$A = (a/b)^{1/n};$ $xu'(x) = B(u^n - \beta u + 1);$ $a\beta = (r+1)A;$
see **1-2**.

392     $y'\sqrt{1+x^2} = 2x - y$ **2**
$$(y-x)X(x) = C - \ln X(x); \quad X(x) = x + \sqrt{1+x^2}$$

393     $y'\sqrt{1-x^2} = 1 + y^2$ **1-2**
$$y(\sqrt{1-x^2} - Cx) = C\sqrt{1-x^2} + x$$

394     $(x - \sqrt{1+x^2})y' = (y + \sqrt{1+y^2})$ **1-2**
$$x^2 - y^2 + xX + yY + \ln(x+X)(y+Y) = C$$
$X(x) = \sqrt{1+x^2};$ $Y(y) = \sqrt{1+y^2}.$

395     $y'\sqrt{a^2+x^2} + x + y = \sqrt{a^2+x^2}$ **2**
$$y = (R-x)[C/a^2 + \ln(R+x)]; \quad R = \sqrt{a^2+x^2}$$

396     $y'\sqrt{x^2 \pm b^2} = \pm \sqrt{y^2 \pm a^2}$ **1-2**
$$y = C(x + \sqrt{x^2 \pm b^2}) - \sqrt{y^2 \pm a^2}$$

397     $y'\sqrt{b^2 - x^2} = \pm \sqrt{a^2 - y^2}$ **1-2**
$$y\sqrt{b^2 - x^2} = C \pm x\sqrt{a^2 - y^2}$$

398 $\quad xy'\sqrt{a^2 \pm x^2} = \pm y\sqrt{b^2 \pm y^2}$ **1-2**

$\qquad x(b + \sqrt{b^2 \pm y^2}) = \pm Cy(a + \sqrt{a^2 \pm x^2})$

399 $\quad xy'\sqrt{x^2 - a^2} = \pm y\sqrt{y^2 - b^2}$ **1-2**

$\qquad a\cos^{-1}b/y = \pm b\cos^{-1}a/x + C$

400 $\quad y'\sqrt{X} + \sqrt{Y} = 0$

$\qquad X(x) = a_0 + a_1x + a_2x^2; \quad Y(y) = a_0 + a_1y + a_2y^2$ **1-2**

$\qquad A_0(x^2 + y^2) + 2A_1xy + 2A_2(x + y) + C = 0$

$(A_1^2 - A_0^2)/a_2 = 2A_2(A_1 - A_0)/a_1 = (A_2^2 - A_0C)/a_0;\quad$ see

$\quad$ also **1-4**.

401 $\quad y'\sqrt{X} = \sqrt{Y}$

$\qquad X(x) = a_0 + a_1x + a_2x^2; \quad Y(y) = b_0 + b_1y + b_2y^2$ **1-2**

$\qquad$ i. $\quad \sinh^{-1}u = \sqrt{a_2/b_2}\sinh^{-1}v + C.$

$u\sqrt{r} = 2a_2x + a_1; \quad v\sqrt{s} = 2b_2y + b_1; \quad r = 4a_0a_2 - a_1^2;$

$s = 4b_0b_2 - b_1^2.$

$\qquad$ ii. $\quad$ If a_2, b_2, r, s are negative, replace $\sinh^{-1}$ by $\sin^{-1}$.

$\qquad$ iii. $\quad$ If $a_2 = b_2$, the solution is simplified

$\qquad\qquad u\sqrt{1 + v^2} = v\sqrt{1 + u^2} + C.$

$\qquad$ iv. $\quad$ If $a_i = b_i$, use the method of **1-4** to get an algebraic

$\qquad\qquad$ solution

$\qquad\qquad f(x, y) = c_0 + 2c_1(x + y) + 4c_2xy + c_3(x^2 + y^2) = 0.$

See **1-4di** for the coefficients and see also (400).

402 $\quad x^{3/2}y' = a + bx^{3/2}y^3$ **4-1**

$y\sqrt{x} = u(z); \quad z = \ln x; \quad u'(z) = bu^3 + u/2 + a; \quad$ see **1-3**.

403 $\quad y'\sqrt{1 + x^3} = \sqrt{1 + y^3}$ **1-4, 1-2**

$\qquad x^2y^2 - 4(x + y) + 2Cxy(x + y) + C^2(x - y)^2 + 4C = 0$

404 $\quad y'\sqrt{x(1 - x)(1 - ax)} = \pm\sqrt{y(1 - y)(1 - ay)}$ **1-4, 1-2**

$y = \pm u^2(z); \quad x = \pm z^2; \quad u'(z)\sqrt{(1 - z^2)(1 - az^2)}$

$\quad = \sqrt{(1 - u^2)(1 - au^2)}; \quad$ see also (409).

$\qquad \sqrt{x(1 - y)(1 - ay)} \mp \sqrt{y(1 - x)(1 - ax)} = C(1 - axy)$

405 $\quad y'\sqrt{1 - x^4} = \pm\sqrt{1 - y^4}$ **1-4, 1-2**

$\qquad x^2 + y^2 + 2xy\sin A = (1 - x^2y^2)\cos A$

$4C\tan A = 4 - C^2.$

406 $\quad y'\sqrt{1 + x^2 + x^4} = \pm\sqrt{1 + y^2 + y^4}$ **1-4, 1-2**

$\qquad 1 + Axy + B(x^2 + y^2) + x^2y^2 = 0$

$A = (C^2 + 3)/2C; \quad B = (1 + C)(3 - C)/4C.$

407 $\quad y'\sqrt{X} = 0; \quad X(x) = a_0 + a_1x + a_2x^2 + a_3x^3 + a_4x^4$ **1-1**
In the general case, the quadrature involves elliptic integrals;
see also **1-4**.

408 $\quad y'\sqrt{X} + \sqrt{Y} = 0$ **1-2, 1-4**
$X(x) = 1 + ax^2 + bx^4; \quad Y(y) = 1 + ay^2 + by^4.$
$\qquad C(x^2 + y^2) + 2Bxy = 1 + bx^2y^2$
$B^2 - b = C(C + a).$

409 $\quad y'\sqrt{X} = \pm\sqrt{Y}$ **1-4, 1-2**
$X(x) = a_0 + a_1x + a_2x^2 + a_3x^3 + a_4x^4; \quad Y(y) = b_0 + b_1y + b_2y^2$
$\quad + b_3y^3 + b_4y^4.$
$\qquad$ i. $\quad$ Elliptic integrals generally result.
$\qquad$ ii. $\quad$ If $a_i = b_i$, an algebraic solution is
$\qquad (\sqrt{Y} - \sqrt{X})^2 = (y-x)^2[C + a_3(x+y) + a_4(x+y)^2]$

410 $\quad y'(1+x^3)^{2/3} + (1+y^3)^{2/3} = 0$ **1-4, 1-2**
$\qquad (1+x^3)(1+y^3)(1+C^3) = (1+Cxy)^3$

411 $\quad y'(a_0 + a_1x + 4x^3)^{2/3} + (a_0 + a_1y + 4y^3)^{2/3} = 0$ **1-4, 1-2**
$\qquad (a_0 + a_1x + 4x^3)(a_0 + a_1y + 4y^3)(a_0 + a_1C + 4C^3)$
$\qquad = [4Cxy + (a_1/3)(C + x + y) + a_0]^3$

412 $\quad X^{2/3}y' = \pm Y^{2/3}$ **1-4, 1-2**
$X(x) = a_0 + a_1x + a_2x^2 + a_3x^3; \quad Y(y) = a_0 + a_1y + a_2y^2 + a_3y^3.$
Let x_0 be a simple root of $X(x)$ so that $X(x) = a_3(x - x_0)X_2(x)$;
$X_2(x) = x^2 + 2ax + b; \quad (x_0^2 + 2ax_0 + b)A = a^2 - b.$ $\quad$ Transform
to new variables with $X(x) = a_3(x - x_0)^3z^3; \quad Y(y) = a_3(y - x_0)^3u^3(z)$
and get $u'(z)\sqrt{z^3 + A} = \pm\sqrt{u^3 + A}$; see (403). The solution is
$\qquad uz + Bz + Bu = \pm 2\sqrt{(Buz + A)(u + z + B)}$
where B is the arbitrary integration constant. An equivalent
solution is
$\qquad XYC = [a_0cxy + (a_1/3)(xy + xc + yc) + (a_2/3)(x + y + c) + a_3]^3$
where $C = a_0 + a_1c + a_2c^2 + a_3c^3.$

413 $\quad y'[a + \cos^2(x/2)] = y\tan(x/2)[1 + a + \cos^2(x/2) - y]$ **9-3**
$y(x)u(z) = z; \quad z = \sec^2(2/x); \quad (1 + az)u'(z) + u = z; \quad$ see (236).

414 $\quad (1 - 4\cos^2 x)y' = \tan x(1 + 4\cos^2 x)y$ **1-2**
$\qquad y = C(4\cos x - \sec x)$

415 $\quad (1 - \sin x)y' + y\cos x = 0$ **1-2**
$\qquad y = C(1 - \sin x)$

416 $\quad (\cos x - \sin x)y' + y(\cos x + \sin x) = 0$ **1-2**
$\qquad y = C(\sin x - \cos x)$

417 $(a_0+a_1\sin^2 x)y'+a_2 x(a_3+a_1\sin^2 x)+a_1 y\sin 2x = 0$ **2**
$$8(a_0+a_1\sin^2 x)y = a_2[a_1\cos 2x+2a_1 x\sin 2x$$
$$-2(a_1+2a_3)x^2]+C$$

418 $(x-e^x)y'+xe^x+(1-e^x)y = 0$ **2**
$$y(x-e^x) = C+e^x(1-x)$$

419 $y'x\ln x = ax(1+\ln x)-y$ **2**
$$(y-ax)\ln x = C$$

420 $yy'+x = 0$ **1-2**
$$x^2+y^2 = C$$

421 $yy'+xe^{x^2} = 0$ **1-2**
$$y^2+e^{x^2} = C$$

422 $yy'+x^3+y = 0$ **4-2**
$y = 1/u;\quad u'(x) = u^2(1+ux^3);\quad$ see **4-2di** and (87).

423 $yy'+ax+by = 0$ **8-1**
  i. $\ln X_1 = C+bX_2;\quad q = 4a-b^2 > 0;$

$$X_1 = ax^2+bxy+y^2;\quad X_2 = \frac{2}{\sqrt{q}}\left[\tan^{-1}\frac{bx+2y}{x\sqrt{q}}\right].$$

  ii. $q < 0;$ change the sign of the term involving X_2
   and replace $\tan^{-1}$ by $\tanh^{-1}$.
  iii. $q = 0,\quad a = 1,\quad b = \pm 2.$

$$(x\pm y)\exp\frac{x}{(x\pm y)} = C$$

424 $yy'+xe^{-x}(1+y) = 0$ **2**
$$y-\ln(1+y) = C+e^{-x}(1+x)$$

425 $yy'+f(x) = g(x)y$ **7-2**
If $(n-1)g(x) = n^2(f/g)',\quad I(x,y) = (\phi+y)^{-n};\quad \phi(x) = -nf/g.$

426 $yy'+4(1+x)x+y^2 = 0$ **5**
$$y^2+4x^2 = Ce^{-2x}$$

427 $yy' = ax+by^2$ **5**
$$2b^2 y^2 = Ce^{2bx}-a(1+2bx)$$

428 $yy' = b\cos(x+c)+ay^2$ **5**
$$(1+4a^2)y^2 = Ce^{2ax}+2b[\sin(x+c)-2a\cos(x+c)]$$

429 $yy' = a_0+a_1 y+a_2 y^2$ **1-3**
  i. $a_0 = 0;\quad a_1+a_2 y = Cx^{a_2};\quad$ see also (4).
  ii. $a_0 \neq 0$ and $y_1 \neq y_2$, the two roots of the quadratic
   $(y-y_2)^{y_2} = C(y-y_1)^{y_1}\exp[x(y_2-y_1)]$
See also iv, v.

iii. $a_0 \neq 0$, $y_1 = y_2$
$\ln(y - y_1) = C + x + y_1/(y - y_1)$

See also vi.

iv. If y_1 and y_2 are complicated functions of the constants a_i, calculate $q = 4a_0a_2 - a_1^2$
$\ln CY = 2a_2x + a_1J$; $Y(y) = a_0 + a_1y + a_2y^2$;
$$J(y) = \frac{2}{\sqrt{q}}\left[\tan^{-1}\frac{a_1 + 2a_2y}{\sqrt{q}}\right];\quad q > 0.$$

v. If $q < 0$, $\ln CY = 2a_2x - a_1K(y)$, where $K(y)$ is like $J(y)$, with $\tan^{-1}$ replaced by $\tanh^{-1}$.

vi. If $q = 0$, $(a_1 + 2a_2y)[C - x + \ln(a_1 + 2a_2y)] + a_1 = 0$.

430    $yy' = ax + bxy^2$ 5
         $by^2 = Ce^{bx^2} - a$

431    $yy' = \csc^2 x - y^2 \cot x$ 5
         $y^2 \sin^2 x = C + 2x$

432    $yy' = \sqrt{a^2 \pm y^2}$ 1-3
         $a^2 \pm y^2 = (x + C)^2$

433    $yy' = \sqrt{y^2 - a^2}$ 1-3
         $y^2 - a^2 = (x + C)^2$

434    $yy' \pm x + f(x^2 \pm y^2)g(x) = 0$ 9-2
   $u(x) = x^2 \pm y^2$; $u'(x) \pm 2f(u)g(x) = 0$; see **1-2**

435    $(1 + y)y' = x + y$ 6-2
   $y + 1 = u$; $x = z + 1$; $uu'(z) = u + z$; see (423).

436    $(1 + y)y' = x^2(1 - y)$ 1-2
       $x^3 + 3y + 6\ln(1 - y) = C$

437    $(x + y)y' + y = 0$ 8-1
       $y(2x + y) = C$

438    $(x - y)y' = y$ 8-1
       $ye^{x/y} = C$

439    $(x + y)y' + (x - y) = 0$ 8-1
       $\ln(x^2 + y^2) + 2\tan^{-1}y/x = C$
   In polar coordinates, $re^\theta = A$.

440    $(x + y)y' = x - y$ 8-1
       $x^2 - 2xy - y^2 = C$

441    $(x - y)' = x + y$ 8-1
       $\ln(x^2 + y^2) = C + 2\tan^{-1}y/x$
   In polar coordinates, $r = Ae^\theta$

442    $(x-y)y' = (1+2xy)y$ 7-2
  $I(y) = 1/y^2.$
  $$y(C-x^2-\ln y) = x$$

443    $(x+y)y' + \tan y = 0$ 7-2
  $I(y) = \cos y.$
  $$(x+y)\sin y + \cos y = C$$

444    $(x-y)y' = (e^{-x/y}+1)y$ 7-2
  $I(x, y) = e^{x/y}/y.$
  $$x + ye^{x/y} = C$$

445    $(1+x+y)y' + 1 + 4x + 3y = 0$ 6-2
  $$(2x+y-1)[\ln(2x+y-1)+C] = 2-x$$

446    $(2+x+y)y' = 1-x-y$ 6-2
  $$(x+y)^2 = C + 2x - 4y$$

447    $(3-x-y)y' = 1+x-3y$ 6-2
  $$2(y-1) = (1-x+y)\ln C(x-y-1)$$

448    $(3-x+y)y' = 11 - 4x + 3y$ 6-2
  $$y+1 = 2(5-2x+y)\ln C(2x-5-y)$$

449    $(2x+y)y' + (x-2y) = 0$ 8-1
  $$\ln(x^2+y^2) + 4\tan^{-1}(y/x) = C$$
  In polar coordinates, $r = Ae^{-2\theta}.$

450    $(2+2x-y)y' + 3(1+2x-y) = 0$ 6-2
  $$5(C+3x+y) = 3\ln(7+10x-5y)$$

451    $(3+2x-y)y' + 2 = 0$ 6-2
  $$y + \ln(4+2x-y) = C$$

452    $(4+2x-y)y' + 5 + x - 2y = 0$ 6-2
  $$(1-x-y)^3 = C(3+x-y)$$

453    $(5-2x-y)y' + 4 - x - 2y = 0$ 6-2
  $$(1-x+y)^3 = C(3-x-y)$$

454    $(1-3x+y)y' = 2(x-y)$ 6-2
  $$(1-x-y)^4 = C(1-4x+2y)$$

455    $(2-3x+y)y' + 5 - 2x - 3y = 0$ 6-2
  $$2x^2 + 6xy - y^2 = C + 10x + 4y$$

456    $(4x-y)y' + 2x - 5y = 0$ 6-2
  $$(2x+y)^2 = C(x-y)$$

457    $(6-4x-y)y' = 2x - y$ 6-2
  $$(3-x-y)^3 = C(4-2x-y)^2$$

458    $(1+5x-y)y' + 5 + x - 5y = 0$ 6-2
  $$(x+y-1)^3 = C(x-y+1)^2$$

459    $(a+bx+y)y'+a-bx-y = 0$ 6-2

$$(1+b)(y-x)+2a\ln[(1+b)(y+bx)+a(b-1)] = C$$

460    $(x^2-y)y'+x = 0$ 9-1

$u(y) = x^2;\quad u'(y)+2u = 2y;\quad$ see **2**.

$$x^2+\tfrac{1}{2} = y+Ce^{-2y}$$

461    $(x^2-y)y' = 4xy$ 9-2

$y = x^2 u(x);\quad x(u-1)u'+2u(u+1) = 0;\quad$ see **1-2**.

$$(x^2+y)^2 = Cy$$

462    $(y-\cot x\csc x)y'+\csc x(1+y\cos x)y = 0$ 7-2

$I(x) = \sin^2 x.$

$$y^2\sin^2 x = C+2y\cos x$$

463    $2yy'+2x+x^2+y^2 = 0$ 7-2

$I(x) = e^x.$

$$(x^2+y^2)e^x = C$$

464    $2yy' = xy^2+x^3$ 5

$$x^2+2(1+y^2) = Ce^{x^2/2}$$

465    $(x-2y)y' = y$ 7-2, 8-1

$I_1(y) = 1/y^2;\quad I_2(x,\, y) = e^{x/y}.$

$$y^2 e^{x/y} = C$$

466    $(x+2y)y'+2x-y = 0$ 8-1

$$\ln(x^2+y^2) = \tan^{-1}(x/y)+C$$

467    $(x-2y)y'+2x+y = 0$ 8-1, 7-1

$$x^2+xy = C+y^2$$

468    $(1+x-2y)y' = 1+2x-y$ 7-1

$$x^2-xy+y^2+x-y = C$$

469    $(1+x+2y)y'+1-x-2y = 0$ 6-2

$$2\ln(6y+3x-1) = 3(x-y)+C$$

470    $(1+x+2y)y'+7+x-4y = 0$ 6-2

$$(4+x-y)^3 = C(5+x-2y)^2$$

471    $2(x+y)y'+x^2+2y = 0$ 7-1

$$3y(2x+y)+x^3 = C$$

472    $(3+2x-2y)y' = 1+6x-2y$ 6-2

$$3x^2-2xy+y^2+x-3y = C$$

473    $(1-4x-2y)y'+2x+y = 0$ 6-2

$$5x-10y+\ln(10x+5y-2) = C$$

474    $(6x-2y)y' = 2+3x-y$ 6-2

$$4\ln(5y-15x+2) = 10y-5x+C$$

475    $(19+9x+2y)y'+18-2x-6y = 0$ **6-2**
$$(x-2y+11)^2 = C(2+2x+y)$$

476    $(x^3+2y)y' = 3x(2-xy)$ **7-1**
$$y^2+x^3y = C+3x^2$$

477    $(\tan x \sec x - 2y)y' + \sec x(1+2y\sin x) = 0$ **7-2**
$I(x) = \cos^2 x.$
$$y\sin x - y^2\cos^2 x = C$$

478    $(xe^{-x}-2y)y' = 2xe^{-2x}-(e^{-x}+xe^{-x}-2y)y$ **7-2**
$I(x) = e^{2x}.$
$$y^2e^{2x}-xye^x+x^2 = C$$

479    $3yy'+5\cot x \cot y \cos^2 y = 0$ **1-2**
$$3\sec^2 y + 10\ln\sin x = C$$

480    $3(2-y)y'+xy = 0$ **1-2**
$$6y = x^2 + 12\ln Cy$$

481    $(x-3y)y'+4+3x-y = 0$ **6-2**
$$(1+x-y)(2+x+y)^2 = C$$

482    $(4-x-3y)y'+3-x-3y = 0$ **6-2**
$$2x+2y+C = \ln(2x+6y-5)$$

483    $(2+2x+3y)y' = 1-2x-3y$ **6-2**
$$x+y+3\ln(2x+3y-7) = C$$

484    $(5-2x-3y)y'+1-2x-3y = 0$ **6-2**
$$x+y = C+4\ln(7+2x+3y)$$

485    $(1+9x-3y)y'+2+3x-y = 0$ **6-2**
$$2x+6y+\ln(1+6x-2y) = C$$

486    $(x+4y)y'+4x-y = 0$ **8-1, 6-2**
$$2\ln(x^2+y^2)+\tan^{-1}(y/x) = C$$

487    $(3+2x+4y)y' = 1+x+2y$ **6-2**
$$5+4x+8y = C\exp(4x-8y-4)$$

488    $(5+2x-4y)y' = 3+x-2y$ **7-1, 6-2**
$$(x-2y)^2+6x-10y = C$$

489    $(5+3x-4y)y' = 2+7x-3y$ **7-1, 6-2**
$$7x^2+4x-6xy-10y+4y^2 = C$$

490    $4(1-x-y)y'+2-x = 0$ **6-2**
$$2(1+y)+(x+2y)\ln C(x+2y) = 0$$

491    $(11-11x-4y)y' = 62-8x-25y$ **6-2**
$$(y-4x-2)^3 = C(2y+x-5)$$

492    $(6+3x+5y)y' = 2+x+7y$ **6-2**
$$(2+x+5y) = C(2+x-y)^4$$

493     $(7x+5y)y'+10x+8y = 0$ **8-1**
           $(x+y)^2(2x+y)^3 = C$

494     $(x+4x^3+5y)y'+7x^3+3x^2y+4y = 0$ **7-2**
$I(x, y) = (x+y)^3.$
           $(x^3+y)(x+y)^4 = C$

495     $(5-x+6y)y' = 3-x+4y$ **6-2**
           $(1-x+2y)^2 = C(2-x+3y)$

496     $3(x+2y)y' = 1-x-2y$ **6-2**
           $x+3y+C = 3\ln(2+x+2y)$

497     $(3-3x+7y)y'+7-7x+3y = 0$ **6-2**
           $(1-x+y)^2(1-x-y)^5 = C$

498     $(1+x+9y)y'+1+x+5y = 0$ **6-2**
           $2y = (1+x+3y)\ln C(1+x+3y)$

499     $(8+5x-12y)y' = 3+2x-5y$ **7-1, 6-2**
           $(1+x-3y)(2+x-2y) = C$

500     $(140+7x-16y)y'+25+8x+y = 0$ **6-2**
           $(x+2y-10)^5(x-y+11)^3 = C$

501     $(3+9x+21y)y' = 45+7x-5y$ **6-2**
           $(11+x-3y)^4(x+y+3)^3 = C$

502     $(ax+by)y'+x = 0$ **9-1**
   $xx'(y)+ax+by = 0;$ see (423).

503     $(ax+by)y'\pm y = 0$ **9-1**
   $yx'(y)\pm ax+by = 0;$ see   (157).

504     $(ax+by)y'+bx+ay = 0$ **8-1, 7-1**
           $bx^2+2axy+ay^2 = C$

505     $(ax+by)y' = bx+ay$ **8-1, 6-2**
           $(x+y)^r(x-y)^s = C;$ $br = a-b;$ $bs = -(a+b).$

506     $(a_2+bx+c_2y)y'+(a_1+b_1x+by) = 0$ **6-2**
           $b_1x^2+2bxy+c_2y^2+2a_1x+2a_2y = C$

507     $(a_2+b_2x+c_2y)y' = (a_1+b_1x+c_1y)$ **6-2**

508     $xyy'+1+y^2 = 0$ **1-2**
           $x^2(1+y^2) = C$

509     $xyy' = x+y^2$ **7-2**
$I(x, y) = -1/x(2x+y^2).$
           $2x+y^2 = Cx^2$

510    $xyy' + x^2 + y^2 = 0$ **8-1**
$$x^2(x^2 + 2y^2) = C$$
See also (516).

511    $xyy' + x^4 - y^2 = 0$ **5**
$$y^2 = x^2(C - x^2)$$

512    $xyy' = ax^3 \cos x + y^2$ **5**
$$y^2 = x^2(C + 2a \sin x)$$

513    $xyy' = x^2 - xy + y^2$ **8-1**
$$(x - y) = Ce^{-y/x}$$

514    $xyy' + 2x^2 - 2xy - y^2 = 0$ **8-1**
$$(x - y) = Cx^3 e^{-y/x}$$

515    $xyy' = a + by^2$ **1-2**
$$a + by^2 = Cx^{2b}$$

516    $xyy' = ax^n + by^2$ **5**
i. $(n - 2b)y^2 = Cx^{2b} + 2ax^n; \quad n \neq 2b$
ii. $y^2 = x^{2b}(C + 2a \ln x); \quad n = 2b$

517    $xyy' = (1 + x^2)(1 - y^2)$ **1-2**
$$x^2(1 - y^2) = Ce^{-x^2}$$

518    $xyy' + x^2 \cot^{-1}(y/x) - y^2 = 0$ **8-1**
$$2x^2 \ln Cx = xy - (x^2 + y^2)\tan^{-1}(y/x)$$

519    $xyy' + x^2 e^{-2y/x} - y^2 = 0$ **8-1**
$$(x - 2y) = 4xe^{-2y/x} \ln Cx$$

520    $(1 + xy)y' + y^2 = 0$ **7-2**
$I(y) = 1/y.$
$$ye^{xy} = C$$

521    $x(1 + y)y' - (1 - x)y = 0$ **1-2**
$$x = Cye^{x+y}$$

522    $x(1 - y)y' + (1 + x)y = 0$ **1-2**
$$xy = Ce^{y-x}$$

523    $x(1 - y)y' + (1 - x)y = 0$ **1-2**
$$xy = Ce^{x+y}$$

524    $x(2 + y)y' + ax = 0$ **1-2**
$$y(4 + y) + 2ax = C$$

525    $(2 + 3x - xy)y' + y = 0$ **9-1**
$yx'(y) + 2 + 3x - xy = 0; \quad$ see (160).
$$xy^3 = 2y^2 + 4y + 4 + Ce^y$$

526      $x(4+y) = 2x + 2y + y^2$ **8-4**
       $y = ux;\ 2(1-u)x'(u) = 4x + ux^2$;   see (227).
            $(x-y)^2 = Cx(4-x+2y)$

527      $x(a+y)y' + bx + cy = 0$ **9-1**
         i. $x(a+y) + (bx+cy)x'(y) = 0;\ \ u(y) = (bx+cy)^{-1};$
            $u'(y) = (a-c+y)u^2 - cy(a+y)u^3;$ see **4-1**.
         ii. $2y(x) = azu'(z);\ \ x = z^2 e^u;$
            $a^2 zu'' + a(a+2c)u' + 4bze^u = 0;$ see (4-81).

528      $x(a+y)y' = y(A+Bx)$ **1-2**
         $y = Bx + \ln Cx^A/y^a$

529      $x(x+y)y' + y^2 = 0$ **8-1**
         $xy^2 = C(x+2y)$

530      $x(x-y)y' + y^2 = 0$ **8-1**
         $Cy = x \ln y$

531      $x(x+y)y' = x^2 + y^2$ **8-1**
         $e^{y/x}(x-y)^2 = Cx$

532      $x(x-y)y' + 2x^2 + 3xy - y^2 = 0$ **8-1, 7-2**
       $I(x) = x.$
          $x^2 y^2 - 2x^3 y - x^4 = C$

533      $x(x+y)y' - y(x+y) + x\sqrt{x^2 - y^2} = 0$ **8-1**
         $x \ln x - \sqrt{x^2 - y^2} + x \sin^{-1}(y/x) = Cx$

534      $[a + x(x+y)]y' = b + (x+y)y$ **9-3, 8-4**
       $x = u + v;\ \ y = ku - v;\ \ k = b/a;\ \ A = a+b;$
       $Auvdu = (Au^2 + a^2)dv;$ see **1-2**.
         $(x+y)^2 + A = C(bx - ay)^2$

535      $x(2x+y)y' = x^2 + xy - y^2$ **8-1**
         $x^3(x-2y)^5 = C(x+y)^2$

536      $x(4x-y)y' + 4x^2 - 6xy - y^2 = 0$ **8-1**
         $x(2x+y)^2 = C(x-y)$

537      $x(x^3 + y)y' = (x^3 - y)y$ **7-2**
       $I(x, y) = 1/x^2 y.$
         $x^3 + 2y = Cxy^2$

538      $x(2x^3 + y)y' = (2x^3 - y)y$ **7-2**
       $I(x, y) = 1/x^2 y^3.$
         $x^3 + y = Cxy^2$

539      $x(2x^3 + y)y' = 6y^2$ **9-1**
       See (277); $6y^2 x'(y) = x(2x^3 + y).$
         $(2x^3 - y)^2 = Cx^6 y$

540    $y(1-x)y' + x(1-y) = 0$ **1-2**
       $x + y + \ln(x-1)(y-1) = C$

541    $(a+x)(b+y)y' = xy$ **1-2**
       $x - y + C = \ln[(a+x)^a y^b]$

542    $2xyy' + 1 - 2x^3 - y^2 = 0$ **5**
       $y^2 = 1 + Cx + x^3$

543    $2xyy' + a + y^2 = 0$ **7-1**
       $x(a + y^2) = C$

544    $2xyy' = ax + y^2$ **5**
       $y^2 = x(C + a \ln x)$

545    $2xyy' + x^2 + y^2 = 0$ **8-1, 5**
       $x(x^2 + 3y^2) = C$

546    $2xyy' = x^2 + y^2$ **8-1, 5**
       $x^2 - y^2 = Cx$

547    $2xyy' = 4x^2(1+2x) + y^2$ **5**
       $y^2 = x(C + 4x + 4x^2)$

548    $2xyy' + x^2(1 + ax^3) = 6y^2$ **5**
       $4y^2 = x^2(1 + 4ax^3 + Cx^4)$

549    $(3 - x + 2xy)y' + 3x^2 - y + y^2 = 0$ **7-1**
       $x^3 + xy^2 - xy + 3y = C$

550    $x(x - 2y)y' + y^2 = 0$ **8-1**
       $Cx - xy + y^2 = 0$

551    $x(x + 2y)y' + (2x - y)y = 0$ **8-1**
       $y(3x + y)^5 = Cx^3$

552    $x(x - 2y)y' + (2x - y)y = 0$ **8-1**
       $xy(x - y) = C$

553    $x(1 + x - 2y)y' + (1 - 2x + y)y = 0$ **7-2**
   $I(x, y) = 1/(1 + x + y)^4.$
       $(1 + x + y)^3 = Cxy$

554    $x(1 - x - 2y)y' + (1 + 2x + y)y = 0$ **7-2**
   $I(x, y) = (xy)^{-4/3}.$
       $(1 - x + y)^3 = Cxy$

555    $2x(2x^2 + y)y' + (12x^2 + y)y = 0$ **7-1**
       $4x^3y + xy^2 = C$

556    $2(1 + x)yy' + 2x - 3x^2 + y^2 = 0$ **7-1**
       $(1 + x)y^2 = C - x^2 + x^3$

557    $x(2x + 3y)y' = y^2$ **8-1**
       $(x + y)y^2 = Cx$

558 $\quad x(2x+3y)y' + 3(x+y)^2 = 0$ $\qquad\qquad$ **7-2**
$I(x) = x.$
$$6x^2y^2 + 8x^3y + 3x^4 = C$$

559 $\quad (3+6xy+x^2)y' + 2x+2xy+3y^2 = 0$ $\qquad$ **7-1**
$$3xy^2 + x^2y + 3y + x^2 = C$$

560 $\quad 3x(x+2y)y' + x^3 + 3y(2x+y) = 0$ $\qquad$ **7-1**
$$x^4 + 12xy(x+y) = C$$

561 $\quad axyy' = x^2 + y^2$ $\qquad\qquad\qquad\qquad$ **8-1**
$$Cx = [(1-a)y^2 + x^2]^{a/2}$$

562 $\quad axyy' + x^2 - y^2 = 0$ $\qquad\qquad\qquad$ **8-1**
$$Cx = [(1-a)y^2 - x^2]^{a/2}$$

563 $\quad x(a+by)y' = cy$ $\qquad\qquad\qquad\qquad$ **1-2**
$$Cx^c = y^a e^{by}$$

564 $\quad x(x-ay)y' = y(y-ax)$ $\qquad\qquad\qquad$ **8-1**
$$(y-x)^{1-a} = Cxy$$

565 $\quad [a_0 + a_1x + a_2y + x(Ax+By)]y'$ $\qquad$ **8-5**
$$= [b_0 + b_1x + b_2y + y(Ax+By)]$$

566 $\quad [a_1 + b_1x + c_1y + x(a_2+b_2x+c_2y)]y'$ $\quad$ **8-5**
$$= (a_3+b_3x+c_3y) + y(a_2+b_2x+c_2y)$$

567 $\quad x(x^n+ay)y' + (b+cy)y^2 = 0$ $\qquad\qquad$ **9-2**
$y = 1/u; \quad (c+bu)x'(u) = ax+ux^{n+1}; \quad$ see **5**.

568 $\quad (1-x^2y)y' + 1 - xy^2 = 0$ $\qquad\qquad\quad$ **7-1**
$$x^2y^2 = C + 2(x+y)$$

569 $\quad (1-x^2y)y' - 1 + xy^2 = 0$ $\qquad\qquad\quad$ **8-4**
$y = ux; \quad (1-u)x'(u) = x - ux^4; \quad$ see (229).
$$C(x-y)^3 = 2 + x^2(x-3y)$$

570 $\quad x(1-xy)y' + (1+xy)y = 0$ $\qquad\qquad$ **7-2**
$I(x, y) = 1/x^2y^2.$

$$\ln \frac{x}{y} = C + \frac{1}{xy}$$

571 $\quad x(2+xy)y' = 3 + 2x^3 - 2y - xy^2$ $\qquad$ **7-1**
$$x(6+x^3 - 4y - xy^2) = C$$

572 $\quad x(2-xy)y' + 2y - xy^2(1+xy) = 0$ $\qquad$ **9-2**
$u(x) = xy; \quad x(u-2)u' + u^3 = 0; \quad$ see **1-2**.
$$1/x^2y^2 - 1/xy + \ln x = C$$

573    $x(3-xy)y' = y(xy-1)$ 7-2
$I(x, y) = 1/xy.$
$$xy = C + \ln xy^3$$

574    $x^2(1-y)y' + (1-x)y = 0$ 1-2
$$y = Cx \exp(y + 1/x)$$

575    $x^2(1-y)y' + (1+x)y^2 = 0$ 1-2
$$\ln x/y = C + (x+y)/xy$$

576    $(1+x^2)yy' + x(1-y^2) = 0$ 1-2
$$y^2 = C(x^2+1) + 1$$

577    $(1-x^2)yy' + 2x^2 + xy^2 = 0$ 5
$$y^2 = (1-x^2)[C + \ln(1-x) - \ln(1+x)] + 2x$$

578    $2x^2yy' = x^2(1+2x) - y^2$ 9-2, 5
$u(x) = y^2 - x^2;$ $x^2u'(x) + u = 0;$ see (252).
$$x^2 - y^2 = Ce^{1/x}$$

579    $x(1-2xy)y' + (1+2xy)y = 0$ 9-3
$ux = y;$ $v = xy;$ $2v^2u' = uv';$ see **1-2**.
$$2 \ln y/x + 1/xy = C$$

580    $x(1+2xy)y' + (2+3xy)y = 0$ 8-2
$$x^2y(1+xy) = C$$

581    $x(1+2xy)y' + (1+2xy-x^2y^2)y = 0$ 7-2
$I(x, y) = 1/x^3y^3.$
$$2 \ln x + 1/x^2y^2 + 4/xy = C$$

582    $x^2(x-2y)y' = 2x^3 - 4xy^2 + y^3$ 8-1
$$x^2 - y^2 = C(2x-y)^2$$

583    $2(1+x)xyy' = 1 + y^2$ 1-2
$$(1+x)(1+y^2) = Cx$$

584    $3x^2yy' + 1 + 2xy^2 = 0$ 5
$$xy^2 + 2 = Cx^{-1/3}$$

585    $x^2(4x-3y)y' = (6x^2 - 3xy + 2y^2)y$ 8-1
$$3x(x^2+y^2) \tan^{-1}(y/x) = 2 \ln Cy^2$$

586    $(1-x^3y)y' = x^2y^2$ 7-2
$I(y) = y.$
$$y^2(3 - 2x^3y) = C$$

587    $2x^3yy' + a + 3x^2y^2 = 0$ 7-1
$$x(a + x^2y^2) = C$$

588    $x(3 - 2x^2y)y' = 4x - 3y + 3x^2y^2$ 7-1
$$x(2x - 3y + x^2y^2) = C$$

589     $x(3+2x^2y)y' + (4+3x^2y)y = 0$ **7-2**
    $I(x, y) = x^3y^2.$
       $x^4y^3(2+x^2y) = C$

590     $8x^3yy' + 3x^4 - 6x^2y^2 - y^4 = 0$ **8-1**
      $y^2(C+x) = x^2(3C-x)$

591     $xy(a+bx^2)y' = A+By^2$ **1-2**
      $(a+bx^2)^{1/a}(A+By^2)^{1/B} = Cx^{2/a}$

592     $3x^4yy' = 1-2x^3y^2$ **7-2**
    $I(x) = x^{-8/3}.$
      $5x^3y^2+2 = Cx^{5/3}$

593     $x^7yy' = 2(1+x^2)+5x^3y$ **4-2**
    $xu(x) = 1+x^3y; \quad 2(1+u^2)x'(u)+1-xu = 0; \quad$ see **2.**

594     $yy'\sqrt{1\pm x^2}+x\sqrt{1\pm y^2} = 0$ **1-2**
      $\sqrt{1\pm x^2}+\sqrt{1\pm y^2} = C$

595     $(1+y)y'\sqrt{1+x^2} = y^3$ **1-2**
      $2y^2 \ln [C(x+\sqrt{1+x^2})]+1+2y = 0$

596     $[g_0(x)+yg_1(x)]y' = f_0(x)+f_1(x)y+f_2(x)y^2+f_3(x)y^3$ **4-2**

597     $y^2y'+x(2-y) = 0$ **1-2**
      $8 \ln (y-2)+(y+2)^2 = C+x^2$

598     $y^2y' = x(1+y^2)$ **1-2**
      $2y+C = 2 \tan^{-1} y+x^2$

599     $(x+y^2)y'+y = a+bx$ **7-1**
      $2y(3x+y^2) = 3x(2a+bx)+C$

600     $(x-y^2)y' = x^2-y$ **7-1**
      $x^3+y^3 = C+3xy$

601     $(x^2+y^2)y'+xy = 0$ **8-1**
      $y^2(2x^2+y^2) = C$

602     $(x^2+y^2)y' = xy$ **8-1**
      $x^2 = 2y^2 \ln Cy$

603     $(x^2-y^2)y' = 2xy$ **8-1**
      $x^2+y^2 = Cy$

604     $(x^2-y^2)y'+x(x+2y) = 0$ **7-1, 8-1**
      $x^3+3x^2y-y^3 = C$

605     $(x^2+y^2)y'+2x(2x+y) = 0$ **7-1, 8-1**
      $4x^3+3x^2y+y^3 = C$

606    $(1-x^2+y^2)y' = 1+x^2-y^2$ **7-2**
$I(x, y) = \exp[\tfrac{1}{2}(x+y)^2]$.
$(x-y)\exp[\tfrac{1}{2}(x+y)^2] = C$

607    $(a^2+x^2+y^2)y' + 2xy = 0$ **7-1**
$y^3 + 2x^2y + 3a^2y = C$

608    $(a^2+x^2+y^2)y' + b^2+x^2+2xy = 0$ **7-1**
$x^3 + y^3 + 3(x^2y + a^2y + b^2x) = C$

609    $(x+x^2+y^2)y' = y$ **7-2**
$I(x, y) = 1/(x^2+y^2)$.
$y = x\tan(C-y)$

610    $(3x^2-y^2)y' = 2xy$ **7-2**
$I(y) = 1/y^4$.
$x^2-y^2 = Cy^3$

611    $(x^4+y^2)y' = 4x^3y$ **7-2**
$I(y) = 1/y^2$.
$x^4-y^2 = Cy$

612    $y(1+y)y' = x(1+x)$ **1-2**
$3(x^2-y^2) + 2(x^3-y^3) = C$

613    $(x+2y+y^2)y' + y(1+y) + (x+y)^2y^2 = 0$ **9-2**
$(1+y)u(x) + (x+y)y = 0;\quad u'(x) = u^2;\quad$ see **1-3**.
$(1+y) = y(x+y)(C+x)$

614    $(x^2+2y+y^2)y' + 2x = 0$ **7-2**
$I(y) = e^y$.
$y + \ln(x^2+y^2) = C$

615    $(x^3+2y-y^2)y' + 3x^2y = 0$ **7-1**
$y(3x^3 + 3y - y^2) = C$

616    $(1+y+xy+y^2)y' + 1+y = 0$ **7-2**
$I(y) = e^y/(1+y)^2$.
$e^y(x+y) = C(1+y)$

617    $(x+y)^2y' = a^2$ **6-1**

$(x+y) = a\tan\dfrac{(C+y)}{a}$

618    $(x-y)^2y' = a^2$ **6-1**
$a^2-x+y = Ce^{2y/a}(a^2+x-y)$

619    $(x^2 \mp 2xy - y^2)y' \mp x^2 - 2xy \pm y^2 = 0$ **8-1**
$(y \pm x) = C(x^2+y^2)$

620     $(x-y)^2 y' = (1+x-y)^2$ **6-2**
$$2(x-y)^2 + 6x + 2y + \ln(1+2x-2y) = C$$

621     $(x+y)^2 y' = (2+x+y)^2$ **6-2**
$$x - y + \ln[(x+y)^2 + (2+x+y)^2] = C$$

622     $(x+y)^2 y' = x^2 - 2xy + 5y^2$ **6-2**
$$(x-y)^2 \ln C(x-y) = 2x(2y-x)$$

623     $(a+b+x+y)^2 y' = 2(a+y)^2$ **6-2**

$$\ln(a+y) + 2\tan^{-1}\left(\frac{a+y}{b+x}\right) = C$$

624     $(2x^2 + 4xy - y^2)y' = x^2 - 4xy - 2y^2$ **7-1, 8-1**
$$x^3 - 6x^2 y - 6xy^2 + y^3 = C$$

625     $(3x+y)^2 y' = 4(3x+2y)y$ **8-1**
$$y^3 = C(x+y)(y-3x)^3$$

626     $(1-3x-y)^2 y' = (1-2y)(3-6x-4y)$ **9-3**
$y(x) = u(z) + 1/2; \quad x = z + 1/6; \quad (u+3z)^2 u'(z) = 4u(2u+3z);$
see (625).
$$(3x+3y-2)(3x-y)^3 = C(2y-1)^3$$

627     $(\cot x - 2y^2)y' = y^3 \csc x \sec x$ **9-1**
$y^3 x'(y) = \cos x(\cos x - 2y^2 \sin x); \quad$ see (355).
$$y^2 \tan x = C + \ln y$$

628     $3y^2 y' = 1 + x + ay^3$ **5**
$$a^2 y^3 = Ce^{ax} - a(1+x) - 1$$

629     $(x^2 - 3y^2)y' + 1 + 2xy = 0$ **7-1**
$$x + y(x^2 - y^2) = C$$

630     $(2x^2 + 3y^2)y' + x(3x+4y) = 0$ **7-1, 8-1**
$$x^3 + y^3 + 2x^2 y = C$$

631     $3(x^2 - y^2)y' + 3e^x + 6xy(1+x) - 2y^3 = 0$ **9-2**
$u(x) = y^3 - 3x^2 y; \quad u'(x) + 2u = 3e^x; \quad$ see (7).
$$(y^3 - 3x^2 y)e^{2x} = C + e^{3x}$$

632     $(3x^2 + 2xy + 4y^2)y' + 2x^2 + 6xy + y^2 = 0$ **7-1, 8-1**
$$2x^3 + 9x^2 y + 3xy^2 + 4y^3 = C$$

633     $(1-3x+2y)^2 y' = (4+2x-3y)^2$ **6-2**
$$(6-4x+y)^5(9+x-4y)^5 = C(3+5x-5y)$$

634     $(1-3x^2 y + 6y^2)y' + x^2 - 3xy^2 = 0$ **7-1**
$$12y^3 - 9x^2 y^2 + 6y + 2x^3 = C$$

635     $(x-6y)^2 y' + a + 2xy - 6y^2 = 0$ **7-1**
$$x(a+xy-6y^2) + 12y^3 = C$$

636     $(x^2 + ay^2)y' = xy$ **8-1**
       $2ay^2(C + \ln y) = x^2$

637     $(x^2 + xy + ay^2)y' = ax^2 + xy + y^2$ **8-1**
       $(x^2 + xy + y^2)^{1-a} = C(x - y)^{2+a}$

638     $(ax^2 + 2xy - ay^2)y' + x^2 - 2axy - y^2 = 0$ **8-1**
       $x^2 + y^2 = C(x - ay)$

639     $[(a + 2b)x^2 + 2(c + 2b)xy + 3cy^2]y' + 3ax^2 + 2(a + 2b)xy$
       $+ (c + 2b)y^2 = 0$ **7-1, 8-1**
See also (640).
       $(x + y)(ax^2 + 2bxy + cy^2) = C$

640     $(ax^2 + 2bxy + cy^2)y' + kx^2 + 2axy + by^2 = 0$ **7-1, 8-1**
See also (639).
       $kx^3 + 3ax^2y + 3bxy^2 + cy^3 = C$

641     $x(1 - y^2)y' = (1 + x^2)y$ **1-2**
       $2 \ln x/y + x^2 + y^2 = C$

642     $x(3x - y^2)y' + (5x - 2y^2)y = 0$ **7-2**
   $I(x, y) = x^{-27}y^{-16}$.
       $13x - 5y^2 = Cx^{26}y^{15}$

643     $x(x^2 + y^2)y' = (x^2 + x^4 + y^2)y$ **8-3**
       $x^4 - y^2 = 2x^2 \ln (Cy/x)$

644     $x(1 - x^2 + y^2)y' + (1 + x^2 - y^2)y = 0$ **8-4**
   $y = ux;$ $2ux'(u) + x - (1 - u^2)x^3 = 0;$ see (193).
       $x^2 + y^2 = 1 + 4Cxy$

645     $x(a - x^2 - y^2)y' + (a + x^2 + y^2)y = 0$ **8-4**
   $y = ux;$ $2aux'(u) + ax = (1 + u^2)x^3;$ see (193).
       $x^2 - y^2 = Cxy + a$

646     $x(2x^2 + y^2)y' = (2x^2 + 3y^2)y$ **8-1**
       $x^3 = Cye^{-x^2/y^2}$

647     $[x(a - x^2 - y^2) + y]y' + x - (a - x^2 - y^2)y = 0$ **9-3**
   $x = r \cos \theta, \ y = r \sin \theta, \ r'(\theta) + r(a - r^2) = 0;$ see (81).
      i. $r^2 = a + Cr^2 e^{2a\theta}$.
      ii. $(x^2 + y^2 - a) = C(x^2 + y^2) \exp (2a \tan^{-1} y/x)$.

648     $x(a + y)^2 y' = by^2$ **1-2**
       $Cx^b = y^{2a} \exp(y - a^2/y)$

649     $x(x^2 - xy + y^2)y' + (x^2 + xy + y^2)y = 0$ **8-1**
       $\tan^{-1} y/x = \ln Cxy$

650     $x(x^2 - xy - y^2)y' = (x^2 + xy - y^2)y$ **7-2**
$I(x, y) = 1/x^2y^2.$
$$x/y + y/x + \ln xy = C$$

651     $x(x^2 + axy + y^2)y' = (x^2 + bxy + y^2)y$ **8-1**
$$y^a = Cx^b \exp (x/y - y/x)$$

652     $x(x^2 - 2y^2)y' = (2x^2 - y^2)y$ **8-1, 7-2**
$I(x, y) = xy.$
$$x^2y^2(x^2 - y^2) = C$$

653     $x(x^2 + 2y^2)y' = (2x^2 + 3y^2)y$ **8-1**
$$(x^2 + y^2)y^2 = Cx^6$$

654     $2x(5x^2 + y^2)y' = x^2y - y^3$ **8-1**
$$x^{3/2}y^5 = C(3x^2 + y^2)$$

655     $x(x^2 + axy + 2y^2)y' = (ax + 2y)y^2$ **8-1**
$$axy + y^2 + x^2 \ln Cy = 0$$

656     $3xy^2y' = 2x - y^3$ **5**
$$xy^3 = C + x^2$$

657     $(1 - 4x + 3xy^2)y' = (2 - y^2)y$ **7-2**
$I(x, y) = (1 + xy^2)y.$
$$y^2(1 - 4x + 2xy^2 - 2x^2y^2 + x^2y^4) = C$$

658     $x(x - 3y^2)y' + (2x - y^2)y = 0$ **7-1**
$$xy(x - y^2) = C$$

659     $3x(x + y^2)y' + x^3 - 3xy - 2y^3 = 0$ **7-2**
$I(x) = 1/x^3.$
$$x^3 + 3xy + y^3 = Cx^2$$

660     $x(x^3 - 3x^3y + 4y^2)y' = 6y^3$ **9-1**
$6y^3x'(y) = x(x^3 - 3x^3y + 4y^2);$ see (370).
$$2y^2 = x^3(C + 3y - \ln y)$$

661     $6xy^2y' + x + 2y^3 = 0$ **5**
$$x(x + 4y^3) = C$$

662     $x(x + 6y^2)y' + xy - 3y^3 = 0$ **7-2**
$I(x, y) = 1/x^2y.$
$$3y^2 + x \ln xy = Cx$$

663     $x(x^2 - 6y^2)y' = 4(x^2 + 3y^2)y$ **8-1**
$$x^4 + 6x^2y^2 = Cy$$

664     $x(3x - 7y^2)y' + (5x - 3y^2)y = 0$ **7-2**
$I(x, y) = \sqrt{xy}.$
$$x^3y^3(x - y^2)^2 = C$$

665    $x^2y^2y' + 1 - x + x^3 = 0$ **1-2**
$$2xy^3 + 3x^3 = 6(1 + x \ln Cx)$$

666    $(1 - x^2y^2)y' = xy^3$ **7-2**
   $I(y) = 1/y.$
$$x^2y^2 = \ln Cy^2$$

667    $(1 - x^2y^2)y' = (1 + xy)y^2$ **7-2**
   $I(x, y) = 1/y(1 + xy).$
$$y = Ce^{xy}$$

668    $x(1 + xy^2)y' + y = 0$ **7-2**
   $I(x, y) = 1/x^2y^2.$
$$xy^2 = 1 + Cxy$$

669    $x(1 + xy^2)y' = (2 - 3xy^2)y$ **7-2**
   $I(x, y) = x/y^2.$
$$Cy = x^2(1 - xy^2)$$

670    $x^2(a + y)^2y' = (1 + x^2)(a^2 + y^2)$ **1-2**
$$y + a \ln(a^2 + y^2) = C + x - 1/x$$

671    $(1 + x^2)(1 + y^2)y' + 2xy(1 - y^2) = 0$ **1-2**
$$y(1 + x^2) = C(1 - y^2)$$

672    $(1 + x^2)(1 + y^2)y' + 2xy(1 - y)^2 = 0$ **1-2**
$$1 + x^2 = Cy \exp[2/(1 - y)]$$

673    $(1 - x^3 + 6x^2y^2)y' = (6 + 3xy - 4y^3)x$ **7-1**
$$x^3y + x^2(3 - 2y^3) = C + y$$

674    $x(3 + 5x - 12xy^2 + 4x^2y)y' + (3 + 10x - 8xy^2 + 6x^2y)y = 0$ **7-1**
$$2x^3y^2 - 4x^2y^3 + 5x^2y + 3xy = C$$

675    $x^3(1 + y^2)y' + 3x^2y = 0$ **1-2**
$$2 \ln x^3y + y^2 = C$$

676    $x(1 - xy)^2y' + (1 + x^2y^2)y = 0$ **8-2**
   $u = xy;$ $x(u - 1)^2u'(x) + 2u^2 = 0;$ see (648).
$$y^2 = C \exp(xy - 1/xy)$$

677    $(1 - x^4y^2)y' = x^3y^3$ **7-2**
   $I(y) = y.$
$$y^2(2 - x^4y^2) = C$$

678    $(3x - y^3)y' = x^2 - 3y$ **7-1**
$$4x^3 - 36xy + 3y^4 = C$$

679    $(x^3 - y^3)y' + x^2y = 0$ **8-1**
$$y^3(2x^3 - y^3) = C$$

680    $(x^3 + y^3)y' + x^2(ax + 3y) = 0$ **7-1, 8-1**
$$ax^4 + 4x^3y + y^4 = C$$

681     $(x - x^2y - y^3)y' = x^3 - y + xy^2$ **7-1**
          $(x^2 + y^2)^2 = C + 4xy$

682     $[a^2x + y(x^2 - y^2)]y' + x(x^2 - y^2) = a^2y$ **9-3**
      $x = r \cos \theta, \ y = r \sin \theta, \ rr'(\theta) + a^2 \sec 2\theta = 0; \ \ \text{see } \mathbf{1\text{-}2}.$
         $r^2 + a^2 \ln(\tan 2\theta + \sec 2\theta) = C$

683     $(a \pm x^2 \pm y^2)yy' = x(a \mp x^2 \mp y^2)$ **7-1**
          $(x^2 + y^2)^2 \mp 2a(x^2 - y^2) = C$

684     $(3x^2 + y^2)yy' + x(x^2 + 3y^2) = 0$ **7-1**
          $x^4 + 6x^2y^2 + y^4 = C$

685     $(a - 3x^2 - y^2)yy' + x(a - x^2 + y^2) = 0$ **9-3**
      $x = r \cos \theta, \ y = r \sin \theta, \ (a - r^2)r'(\theta) = 2r^3 \cos \theta \sin \theta; \text{ see } \mathbf{1\text{-}2}.$
         $\ln r^2 + a/r^2 = C + \cos 2\theta$

686     $2y^3y' = x^3 - xy^2$ **7-2, 8-1**
    $I(x, y) = x^2 + y^2.$
          $(x^2 + y^2)^2(x^2 - 2y^2) = C$

687     $y(1 + 2y^2)y' = x(1 + 2x^2)$ **1-2**
          $y^2(1 + y^2) = x^2(1 + x^2) + C$

688     $(3x^2 + 2y^2)yy' + x^3 = 0$ **7-2, 8-1**
    $I(x, y) = (x^4 + 3x^2y^2 + 2y^4)^{-1}.$
          $x^2 + 2y^2 = C\sqrt{x^2 + y^2}$

689     $(5x^2 + 2y^2)yy' + x(x^2 + 5y^2) = 0$ **7-1, 8-1**
          $x^4 + 10x^2y^2 + 2y^4 = C$

690     $(x^2 - x^3 + 3xy^2 + 2y^3)y' + 2x^3 + 3x^2y + y^2 - y^3 = 0$ **7-2**
    $I(x, y) = 1/(x + y)^2.$
          $x^3 + xy + y^3 = C(x + y)$

691     $(3x^3 + 6x^2y - 3xy^2 + 20y^3)y' + 4x^3 + 9x^2y + 6xy^2 - y^3 = 0$ **7-1, 8-1**
      $x^4 + 3x^3y + 3x^2y^2 - xy^3 + 5y^4 = C$

692     $(x^3 + ay^3)y' = x^2y$ **8-1**
          $\ln y = C + x^3/3ay^3$

693     $(ax^2 - bx^3 + 3cxy^2 + 2cy^3)y' + 2bx^3 + 3bx^2y + ay^2 - cy^3 = 0$ **7-2**
    $I(x, y) = 1/(x + y)^2.$
          $bx^3 + axy + cy^3 = C(x + y)$

694     $xy^3y' = (1 - x^2)(1 + y^2)$ **1-2**
          $x^2 + y^2 = \ln[Cx\sqrt{1 + y^2}]$

695     $x(x - y^3)y' = (3x + y^3)y$ **7-2**
    $I(x, y) = x/y^2.$
          $x^2(2x + y^3) = Cy$

696 $x(2x^3+y^3)y' = (2x^3-x^2y+y^3)y$ **8-1**
    $2x^2y \ln Cx = 4x^3-y^3$

697 $x(2x^3-y^3)y' = (x^3-2y^3)y$ **7-2, 8-1**
  $I(x, y) = 1/x^3y^3.$
    $x^3+y^3 = Cx^2y^2$

698 $x(x^3+3x^2y+y^3)y' = (3x^2+y^2)y^2$ **8-1**
    $3x^3 \ln y = Cx^3-9x^2y-y^3$

699 $x(x^3-2y^3)y' = (2x^3-y^3)y$ **7-2**
  $I(x, y) = 1/x^2y^2.$
    $x^3+y^3 = Cxy$

700 $x(x^4-2y^3)y'+(2x^4+y^3)y = 0$ **7-2**
  $I(x) = 1/x^3.$
    $(2x^4-y^3)y = Cx^2$

701 $x(x+y+2y^3)y' = (x-y)y$ **7-2**
  $I(x, y) = 1/xy^2.$
    $y(C-y^2-\ln xy)+x = 0$

702 $(5x-y-7xy^3)y'+5y-y^4 = 0$ **7-2**
  $I(y) = y^3-5.$
    $2y^5-25y^2+10xy(y^3-5)^2 = C$

703 $x(1-2xy^3)y'+(1-2x^3y)y = 0$ **7-2**
  $I(x, y) = 1/x^2y^2.$
    $x^2+y^2 = C-1/xy$

704 $x(2-xy^2-2xy^3)y'+1+2y = 0$ **9-1**
  $(1+2y)x'(y) = x^2y^2(1+2y)-2x;$ see 5.
    $2y(y-1)+\ln(2y+1) = C-8/x(2y+1)$

705 $(2-10x^2y^3+3y^2)y' = x(1+5y^4)$ **7-1**
    $x^2+5x^2y^4 = C+4y+2y^3$

706 $x(a+bxy^3)y'+(a+cx^3y)y = 0$ **7-2**
  $I(x, y) = 1/x^2y^2.$
    $xy(cx^2+by^2+C) = 2a$

707 $x(1-2x^2y^3)y'+(1-2x^3y^2)y = 0$ **7-2**
  $I(x, y) = 1/x^3y^3.$
    $4(x+y)+1/x^2y^2 = C$

708 $x(1-xy)(1-x^2y^2)y'+(1+xy)(1+x^2y^2)y = 0$ **7-2, 8-2**
  $I(x, y) = 1/x^2y^2(1+xy).$
    $xy(xy-2 \ln Cy) = 1$

709     $(x^2 - y^4)y' = xy$ **9-1**

       $x = uy;$ $uu'(y) + y = 0;$ see **1-2**.

                 $x^2 = y^2(C - y^2)$

710     $(x^3 - y^4)y' = 3x^2 y$ **7-2**

    $I(y) = 1/y^2.$

                 $3x^3 + y^4 = Cy$

711     $[a^2 x^2 + (x^2 + y^2)^2]y' = a^2 xy$ **9-3**

       $x = r \cos \theta,\ y = r \sin \theta,\ rr'(\theta) + (a^2 + r^2) \cot \theta = 0;$ see **1-2**.

           i. $\sin^2 \theta(a^2 + r^2) = C.$

           ii. $(x^2 + y^2)(C + y^2) = a^2 x^2.$

712     $2(x - y^4)y' = y$ **7-2**

    $I(y) = 1/y^3.$

                 $x + y^4 = Cy^2$

713     $(4x - xy^3 - 2y^4)y' = (2 + y^3)y$ **7-2**

    $I(y) = 1/y^3.$

               $2x + xy^3 + y^4 = Cy^2$

714     $[ax^3 + (ax + by)^3]yy' + x[(ax + by)^3 + by^3] = 0$ **7-2**

    $I(x, y) = 1/(ax + by)^3.$

             $(ax + by)^2(x^2 + y^2 - C) + x^2 y^2 = 0$

715     $(x + 2y + 2x^2 y^3 + xy^4)y' + (1 + y^4)y = 0$ **7-2**

    $I(x, y) = 1/(xy^3 - 1)^2.$

             $xy + y^2 = C(xy^3 - 1)$

716     $2x(x^3 + y^4)y' = (x^3 + 2y^4)y$ **7-2**

    $I(x, y) = 1/x^3 y^3.$

             $x^3 = y^2(Cx^2 + y^2)$

717     $x(1 - x^2 y^4)y' + y = 0$ **7-2**

    $I(x, y) = 1/x^3 y^3.$

            $x^2 y^2(C - y^2) = 1$

718     $(x^2 - y^5)y' = 2xy$ **7-2**

    $I(x) = 1/y^2.$

               $4x^2 = y(C - y^4)$

719     $x(x^3 + y^5)y' = (x^3 - y^5)y$ **7-2**

    $I(y) = 1/y^5.$

             $x^4 = y^4(C + 4xy)$

720     $x^3(1 + 5x^3 y^7)y' + (3x^5 y^5 - 1)y^3 = 0$ **7-2**

    $I(x, y) = 1/x^3 y^3.$

               $y^2(1 + 2x^5 y^5) = x^2(1 + Cy^2)$

721    $[f_1(x, y) + xf_2(x, y)]y' = f_3(x, y) + yf_2(x, y)$ **8-6**
The Darboux equation. The functions $f_i(x, y)$ are polynomials in x and y of maximum degree m and at least one is actually of degree m.

722    $[1 + a(x + y)]^n y' + a(x + y)^n = 0$ **7-1**
      i. $(1 + n)y + a(x + y)^{n+1} = C; \quad n \neq -1.$
     ii. $y + a\ln(x + y) = C; \quad n = -1.$

723    $x(a + xy^n)y' + by = 0$ **9-1**
   $byx'(y) + x(a + xy^n) = 0; \quad$ see (186).
      $nb - a = x(Cy^{a/b} + y^n)$

724    $f(x)y^m y' + g(x)y^{m+1} + h(x)y^n = 0; \quad n \neq m+1$ **5**

725    $y'\sqrt{y^2 \pm b^2} = \pm\sqrt{x^2 \pm a^2}$ **1-2**
      $[y\sqrt{y^2 \pm b^2} \pm b^2 \ln(y + \sqrt{y^2 \pm b^2})]$
        $= C \pm [x\sqrt{x^2 \pm a^2} \pm a^2 \ln(x + \sqrt{x^2 \pm a^2})]$

726    $y'\sqrt{b^2 - y^2} = \pm\sqrt{a^2 - x^2}$ **1-2**
      $y\sqrt{b^2 - y^2} + b^2 \sin^{-1} y/b = C \pm x\sqrt{a^2 - x^2} \pm a^2 \sin^{-1} x/a$

727    $y'\sqrt{Y} = \pm\sqrt{X}$ **1-4, 1-2**
$X = a_0 + a_1 x + a_2 x^2 + a_3 x^3 + a_4 x^4; \quad Y = b_0 + b_1 y + b_2 y^2 + b_3 y^3 + b_4 y^4.$
In the general case, elliptic integrals will result from the quadrature.

728    $(1 + \sqrt{x+y})y' + 1 = 0$ **9-2**
   $u = x + y; \quad (1 + \sqrt{u})u'(x) = \sqrt{u}; \quad$ see **1-3**; $y + 2\sqrt{x+y} = C.$

729    $y'\sqrt{xy} + x - y = \sqrt{xy}$ **8-1**
      $\sqrt{x}/(\sqrt{x} - \sqrt{y}) + \ln(\sqrt{x} - \sqrt{y}) + \tfrac{1}{2}\ln(x - y) = C$

730    $(x - 2\sqrt{xy})y' = y$ **8-1**
      $\ln y + \sqrt{x/y} = C$

731    $(y + \sqrt{1+y^2})(1+x^2)^{3/2}y' = 1 + y^2$ **1-2**
      $x = \sqrt{1+x^2}[C + \ln(1 + y^2 + y\sqrt{1+y^2})]$

732    $(1+x^2)^{3/2}(y + \sqrt{1+y^2})y' = 1 + y^2$ **1-2**
      $x/\sqrt{1+x^2} = C + \tfrac{1}{2}\ln(1 + y^2) + \ln(y + \sqrt{1+y^2})$

733    $(x - \sqrt{x^2 + y^2})y' = y$ **7-2**
   $I(x, y) = 1/y\sqrt{x^2 + y^2}.$
      $y^2 = C(C - 2x)$

734    $x(1 - \sqrt{x^2 - y^2})y' = y$ **7-2**
   $I(x) = 1/x.$
      $y = x\sin(C + y)$

735     $x(x+\sqrt{x^2+y^2})y'+y\sqrt{x^2+y^2}=0$ 8-1
$$Cx = x\ln(\sqrt{x^2+y^2}-x)+\sqrt{x^2+y^2}$$

736     $xy(x+\sqrt{x^2-y^2})y' = xy^2-(x^2-y^2)^{3/2}$ 8-1
$$y^2+2x^2\ln Cx = 2x\sqrt{x^2-y^2}$$

737     $(x-y^2\sqrt{y^2-x^2})y' = (1+x\sqrt{y^2-x^2})y$ 7-2
$I(x, y) = 1/y\sqrt{y^2-x^2}.$
$$x^2+y^2+2\sin^{-1}x/y = C$$

738     $[x\sqrt{1+x^2+y^2}-y(x^2+y^2)]y' = x(x^2+y^2)+y\sqrt{1+x^2+y^2}$ 7-2
$I(x, y) = 1/(x^2+y^2)\sqrt{1+x^2+y^2}.$
$$\sqrt{1+x^2+y^2}+\tan^{-1}x/y = C$$

739     $(1\pm x\sec x\cos y)y'-y\tan x\pm\sec x\sin y = 0$ 7-2
$I(x) = \cos x.$
$$y\cos x\pm x\sin y = C$$

740     $y'\cos y(\cos y-\sin A\sin x)+\cos x(\cos x-\sin A\sin y) = 0$ 7-1
$$2(x+y)+\sin 2x+\sin 2y = C+4\sin A\sin x\sin y$$

741     $[a\cos(bx+ay)-b\sin(ax+by)]y'$ 7-1
$\qquad +b\cos(bx+ay)-a\sin(ax+by) = 0$
$$\cos(ax+by)+\sin(bx+ay) = C$$

742     $[x\sin xy+\cos(x+y)-\sin y]y'+y\sin xy$ 7-1
$\qquad +\cos(x+y)+\cos x = 0$
$$\cos xy-\sin(x+y)-\sin x-\cos y = C$$

743     $(x+\cos x\sec y)y'+\tan y-y\sin x\sec y = 0$ 7-2
$I(y) = \cos y.$
$$x\sin y+y\cos x = C$$

744     $(x^2+2y\sec y\sin x)y'+2x\tan y+y^2\cos x\sec y = 0$ 7-2
$I(y) = \cos y.$
$$x^2\sin y+y^2\sin x = C$$

745     $(2-6xy+x^2\sec^2 y)y'+2x\tan y-3y^2 = 0$ 7-1
$$x^2\tan y+2y = C+3xy^2$$

746     $[1+(x+y)\tan y]y'+1 = 0$ 7-2
$I(y) = \sec y.$
$$(x+y) = C\cos y$$

747     $x(x-y\tan y/x)y'+(x+y\tan y/x)y = 0$ 8-1
$$xy\cos y/x = C$$

748     $(e^x+xe^y)y'+ye^x+e^y = 0$ 7-1
$$xe^y+ye^x = C$$

749 $(1 - 2x - \ln y)y' + 2y = 0$ **7-2**

$I(y) = 1/y^2.$

$Cy = 2x + \ln y$

750 $(\sinh x + x \cosh y)y' + y \cosh x + \sinh y = 0$ **7-1**

$y \sinh x + x \sinh y = C$

751 $y'(1 + \sinh x)\sinh y + \cosh x(\cosh y - 1) = 0$ **7-1**

$(1 + \sinh x)\cosh y = C + \sinh x$

2. THE DIFFERENTIAL EQUATION IS OF FIRST ORDER AND OF SECOND OR HIGHER DEGREE

Most of the equations here will have the form

$$X_0(x, y)p^n + X_1(x, y)p^{n-1} + \dots + X_n(x, y) = 0$$

where $p = dy/dx$. More complicated ones, toward the end of the section, will be $f(x, y, p) = 0$. See 1 for a description of the rank of a term, which fixes the order in which the equations are arranged. The first determining factor will be $X_0(x, y)$, followed by $X_1(x, y)$, $X_2(x, y)$, etc.

In addition to a general solution, singular solutions are often given. They are easily recognized because they contain no integration constant C. When a singular solution is not given, it does not necessarily mean that none exists. In a number of cases, further functions, not solutions, have also been listed. They have been identified by the symbols CL, NL, TL meaning cuspidal, nodal, tac locus, respectively. See **A2-10-3**, for more details.

A general solution in explicit algebraic form is sometimes impossible. In such cases, a parametric solution may be presented. The symbol $p = dy/dx$ is then always replaced by the parameter t. See Part I, **A-2** for further details.

1    $p^2 = ax^n$ **1-1-1**

$$(n+2)y = \pm 2\sqrt{ax^{n+2}} + C$$

2    $p^2 = y$ **1-2-2**

$$4y = (x+C)^2; \quad y = 0$$

3    $p^2 = x - y$ **2-2**

$(1-p)y'(p) = 2p^2$;   see **A1-1-1**.

$$x = C - 2[t + \ln(t-1)]; \quad y = C - [t(t+2) + 2\ln(t-1)]$$

4    $p^2 = x^2 + y$ **3-2**

$y = ux^2$; $z = \ln x$; $u'^2(z) + 4uu' = 1 + u - 4u^2$;   see **1-1-1**.

$$C(2y \pm x\sqrt{x^2+y})^{\sqrt{17}} = \frac{\pm 4\sqrt{x^2+y} - x(\sqrt{17}-1)}{\pm 4\sqrt{x^2+y} + x(\sqrt{17}+1)}$$

$$x^4 + x^2y = 4y^2; \quad x^2 + y = 0(\text{CL}).$$

278

5 $p^2 + x^2 = 4y$ **2-3**
$(2p - x)x'(p) = p;$ see (1–502).
$$x = (t - x)[C + \ln(t - x)];\quad 4y = x^2 + t^2$$

6 $p^2 + 3x^2 = 8y$ **2-3**
$(4p - 3x)x'(p) = p;$ see (1–502).
$$(t - 3x)^3 = C(t - x);\quad 8y = 3x^2 + t^2$$

7 $p^2 + ax^2 + by = 0$ **2-3**
$(p - 2rx)x'(p) = 2sp;\quad br = -a;\quad bs = -1;$ see $(1 - 502)$

8 $p^2 = 1 + y^2$ **1-2-1**
$$2y^2 + \cosh 2x = C$$

9 $p^2 = 1 - y^2$ **1-2-1**
$$y = \sin(x + C) \cdot \quad y^2 = 1$$

10 $p^2 = a^2 - y^2$ **1-2-1**
$$(1 + C^2)y = a(1 - C^2)\sin x + 2Ca \cos x: \quad y = \pm a$$
$y + a \sin x = 0.$

11 $p^2 = a^2 y^2$ **1-2-1**
$$y = Ce^{\pm ax}$$

12 $p^2 = a + by^2$ **1-2-1**
$p = \pm\sqrt{a^2 + by^2};$ see (1–104).

13 $p^2 = x^2 y^2$ **2-1**
$$x^2 = \pm 2 \ln Cy$$

14 $p^2 = (y - 1)y^2$ **1-2-1**
$p = \pm y\sqrt{y - 1};$ see (1–105).
$$y = \sec^2(C + x/2);\quad y = 0;\quad y = 1.$$

15 $p^2 = (y - a)(y - b)(y - c)$ **1-2-1**
The general solution will usually involve elliptic integrals.

16 $p^2 = a^2 y^n$ **1-2-1**
  i. $\pm 2y^{1-n/2} = (2 - n)(ax + C);\quad n \neq 2.$
  ii. $n = 2,$ see (11).

17 $p^2 = a^2(1 - \ln^2 y)y^2$ **6**
$u(x) = \ln y;\quad u'^2(x) = a^2(1 - u^2);$ see (12).
$$\ln y = \sin(C + ax);\quad y = e;\quad \ln y = \pm 1$$

18 $p^2 + f(x)(y - a)(y - b) = 0$ **9-4**
See also (24).

19 $p^2 + f(x)(y - a)^2(y - b) = 0$ **9-4**
See also (24).

20 $p^2 + f(x)(y - a)(y - b)(y - c) = 0$ **9-4**
See also (24).

21    $p^2 + f(x)(y-a)^2(y-b)(y-c) = 0$ **9-4**
    See also (23) and (24).

22    $p^2 + f(x)(y-a_1)(y-a_2)(y-a_3)(y-a_4) = 0$ **9-4**
    See also (24).

23    $p^2 = f^2(x)(y-a)(y-b)(y-c)^2$ **6**
    See (24); $2v'(x) = \pm f(x)(a_0 - a_1 v^2)$; $a_0 = (a-c)$; $a_1 = (b-c)$;
    see also **A1-1-2**.

24    $p^2 = f^2(x)[y-u(x)]^2(y-a)(y-b)$ **6**
        i. $(y-b)v^2(x) = (y-a)$;
              $2v'(x) = \pm f(x)[a - u(x) - (b-u)v^2]$;   see **A1-3-1**.
        ii. If $u(x)$ is a constant, see (23).

25    $p^2 + 2p + x = 0$ **2-1**
        $9(x + y - C)^2 = 4(1 - x^3)$

26    $p^2 - 2p + a(x-y) = 0$ **2-3**
    $ax'(p) = 2$;   see **A1-1-1**.
        $a(C + x)^2 = 4(C + y)$; $ay = 1 + ax$

27    $p^2 - 2p - y^2 = 0$ **1-2-1**
    $p = 1 \pm \sqrt{1 + y^2}$.
        $y \ln [\sqrt{1 + y^2} \pm y] \mp \sqrt{1 + y^2} = (C + x)y - 1$

28    $p^2 - 5p + 6 = 0$ **1-3**
        $y = 2x + C$; $y = 3x + C$

29    $p^2 - 7p + 12 = 0$ **1-3**
        $y = 3x + C$; $y = 4x + C$

30    $p^2 + ap + b = 0$ **1-3**

31    $p^2 + ap + bx = 0$ **1-1-2**
        $bx + t(a + t) = 0$; $6by = C - t^2(3a + 4t)$

32    $p^2 + ap + by = 0$ **1-2-2**
        $bx = C - 2t - a \ln t$; $by + t(a + t) = 0$

33    $p^2 + xp + 1 = 0$ **1-1-2**
        $xt + 1 + t^2 = 0$; $y = \ln t - t + C$

34    $p^2 + xp - y = 0$ **4-1**
        $y = C(C + x)$; $x^2 + 4y = 0$

35    $p^2 - xp + y = 0$ **4-1**
        $y = C(x - C)$; $x^2 = 4y$

36    $p^2 - xp - y = 0$ **2-3, 4-3**
    $2px'(p) = 2p - x$;   see (1-157).
        $3x = 2t + C/\sqrt{t}$; $3y = t^2 - C\sqrt{t}$

37    $p^2 + xp + x - y = 0$ **4-3**
     $x'(p) + 2p + x = 0$;   see (1-4).
         $x = 2(1-t) + Ce^{-t}$; $y = 2 - t^2 + (1+t)Ce^{-t}$

38    $p^2 + (1-x)p + y = 0$ **4-1**
         $y = C(x-1) - C^2$; $4y = (x-1)^2$

39    $p^2 - (1+x)p + y = 0$ **4-1**
         $y = Cx + C(1-C)$; $4y = (1+x)^2$

40    $p^2 - (2-x)p + 1 - y = 0$ **4-1**
         $y = C(x-2) + C^2 + 1$; $4y = x(4-x)$

41    $p^2 + (a+x)p - y = 0$ **4-1**
         $y = C(x+a) + C^2$; $4y + (a+x)^2 = 0$

42    $p^2 - 2xp + 1 = 0$ **1-1-2**
         $2x = t + 1/t$; $4y = t^2 - 2 \ln t + C$

43    $p^2 + 2xp - 3x^2 = 0$ **1-1-1**
         $(2y - x^2 + C)(2y + 3x^2 + C) = 0$; $x = 0(TL)$

44    $p^2 \pm 2xp \mp y = 0$ **4-3, 2-3**
     $px'(p) + 2(p \pm x) = 0$; $p^2(2p \pm 3x) = C$;   see (1-157).
         $(2x^3 \pm 3xy + C)^2 = 4(x^2 \pm y)^3$; $x^2 \pm y = 0(CL)$

45    $p^2 + 2xp - y = 0$ **6**
     $y(x) = -u(x)$; $u'^2(x) - 2xu' + u = 0$;   see (44).

46    $p^2 - 2xp + 2y = 0$ **4-1**
         $2y = C(2x - C)$; $2y = x^2$

47    $p^2 - (1+2x)p - x(1-x) = 0$ **1-1-1**
         $144(2y - x^2 - x + C)^2 = (1 + 8x)^3$

48    $p^2 + 2(1-x)p - 2(x-y) = 0$ **2-3**
         $x = t + Ce^{-t}$; $y = t^2/2 + Ce^{-t}(1+t)$

49    $p^2 + 3xp - y = 0$ **2-3**
     $2px'(p) + 3x + 2p = 0$;   see (1-157).
         $t^3(5x + 2t)^2 = C$; $y = t(3x + t)$

50    $p^2 - 4(1+x)p + 4y = 0$ **4-2**
         $y = C(1 + x - C/4)$; $y = (1+x)^2$

51    $p^2 + axp = b + cx^2$ **1-1-1**

       i. $y = C - \dfrac{ax^2}{4} + \dfrac{x}{4}\sqrt{(a^2 + 4c)x^2 + 4b}$; $a^2 + 4c > 0$.

       ii. $y = C - \dfrac{ax^2}{4} + (b/\sqrt{4a^2 + c})\ln X(x)$; $a^2 + 4c < 0$;

         $X(x) = x + \sqrt{x^2 + 4b/(a^2 + 4c)}$.

52    $p^2 - axp + ay = 0$ 4-1
$$ay = C(ax - C); \quad 4y = ax^2$$

53    $p^2 + axp + bx^2 + cy = 0$ 2-1, 6
    i. $c = 0$; see (51).
    ii. $c \neq 0$; $y = x^2\phi(x)$; $u^2(x) = a^2 - 4b - 4c\phi$;
       $xuu'(x) = F(u)$; $F(u) = u^2 \pm cu - (ac + c^2 - 4b)$;
    see **A1-1-2**.

For conditions under which the solution is algebraic, see iii; for
conditions under which a singular solution can occur, see iv.
    iii. Let u_1, u_2 be the roots of $F(u) = 0$, with $2u_1 = \pm c$
$+ \sqrt{k}$, $2u_2 = \pm c - \sqrt{k}$. The general solution of the equation is

$$\left(\frac{u - u_1}{u - u_2}\right)^{\pm c/\sqrt{k}} (u - u_1)(u - u_2)x^2 = C^2$$

and this result is algebraic, provided that a, b, c, r are rational
numbers, where $k = (c + 2a)^2 - 16b = r^2$.
    iv. Call the differential equation $f(x, y, p) = 0$. Then,
a singular solution exists, see **10-1**, provided that $f_p = 0$ and
that $f_x + pf_y = 0$. These conditions require that $4b = a(a + c)$,
the general solution is $(cx - C)^2 + c(ax^2 + 4y) = 0$ and the singular
solution is $ax^2 + 4y = 0$. The general solution is thus algebraic.
If the conditions of both iii and iv are met, it follows that
$r^2 = c^2$.

54    $p^2 + (a + bx)p + c = by$ 4-1
    i. $by = (a + bx)C + C^2 + c$; $4by = 4c - (a + bx)^2$;
      $b \neq 0$.
    ii. $b = 0$, see (30).

55    $p^2 - 2x^2p + 2xy = 0$ 2-3, 3-2
$p^2x'(p) = 2x(p - x^2)$; see (1-274) or (56).
    $(3y^2 - C)^2 = 4x^3y^3 + 4Cx^3(x^3 - 3y)$

56    $p^2 + ax^2p + bxy = 0$ 3-2
$y = x^3u(z)$; $z = \ln x$; $u'^2(z) + (a + 6u)u' + (3a + b + 9u)u = 0$;
see (69).

57    $p^2 + ax^3p - 2ax^2y = 0$ 6, 3-2
    i. $y = u(z)$; $z = x^2$; $2y'^2(z) + azu' = au$; see **4-1**.
      $y = aC(x^2 + 2C)$; $8y + ax^4 = 0$; $x = 0$(TL)
    ii. $y = x^4u(z)$; $z = \ln x$; $u'^2(z) + (a + 8u)u'$
      $+ 2(a + 8u)u = 0$; see **1-2**.

58    $p^2 - 2ax^3p + 4ax^2y = 0$ 6
$y(x) = u(z)$; $ax^2 = z$; $au'^2(z) - zu' + u = 0$; see (52).
    $y = Ca(x^2 - C)$; $4y = ax^4$

59 $p^2 + 4x^5 p - 12x^4 y = 0$ **2-3**
$2px'(p) = x$;   see **A1-1-2**.
$\qquad 12y = C(4x^3 + C)$; $x^6 + 3y = 0$

60 $p^2 - 2p \cosh x + 1 = 0$ **1-1-1**
$\qquad (y - e^x + C)(y + e^{-x} + C) = 0$

61 $p^2 + yp = x(x + y)$ **2-1**
$\qquad x^2 - 2y + C = 0$; $x + y = Ce^{-x} + 1$

62 $p^2 - yp + e^x = 0$ **2-3**
$px'(p) = 1$;   see **A1-1-1**.
$\qquad Cy = C^2 e^x + 1$; $y^2 = 4e^x$

63 $p^2 \pm (x + y)p + xy = 0$ **2-1**
$(p \pm y)(p \pm x) = 0$.
$\qquad y = Ce^{\mp x}$; $2y = C \mp x^2$

64 $p^2 - 2yp - 2x = 0$ **2-2**
$(1 + p^2)y'(p) = p(p - y)$;   see (1-287).
$\qquad 2x = t(t - 2y)$; $(2y - t)\sqrt{1 + t^2} = C - \ln(t + \sqrt{1 + t^2})$

65 $p^2 + (1 + 2y)p + y(y - 1) = 0$ **1-2-3**
$y = u(u - 1)/(u + 1)^2$; $p = y/u$.
$\qquad x + C = \ln (u + 1)^2 (u - 1)$

66 $p^2 - 2(x - y)p - 4xy = 0$ **2-1**
$(p - 2x)(p + 2y) = 0$.
$\qquad y = C + x^2$; $\ln Cy + 2x = 0$

67 $p^2 - (1 + 4y)p + (1 + 4y)y = 0$ **1-2-1**
See (1-100).
$\qquad y = Ce^x(Ce^x + 1)$; $y = -1/4$

68 $p^2 - 2(1 - 3y)p - (4 - 9y)y = 0$ **1-2-1**
See (1-100); $u = \sqrt{1 - 2y}$.
$\qquad \ln(3u - 1) + 3\ln(u + 1) = C - 6x$

69 $p^2 + (a + 6y)p + y(3a + b + 9y) = 0$ **1-2-1**
$2p = -(a + 6y) \pm \sqrt{a^2 - 4by}$;   see (1-100).

70 $p^2 + ayp - ax = 0$ **4-3**
$ap(1 - p^2)x'(p) = ax + p^2$;   see (1-357).
$\qquad ax\sqrt{1 - t^2} = t(C + \sin^{-1} t)$; $aty = ax - t^2$

71 $p^2 - ayp - ax = 0$ **4-3**
$ap(1 + p^2)x'(p) = ax + p^2$;   see (1-356).
$\qquad ax\sqrt{1 + t^2} = t(C + \sinh^{-1} t)$; $a(x + yt) = t^2$

72     $p^2 + (ax + by)p + abxy = 0$ **2-1**
$(p + ax)(p + by) = 0.$
$$2y + ax^2 = C; \quad ye^{bx} = C$$

73     $p^2 - xyp + y^2 \ln ay = 0$ **2-2**
$py'(p) = y; \quad p = Cy.$
$$\ln ay = C(x - C); \quad \ln ay = x^2/4$$

74     $p^2 - (1 + 2xy)p + 2xy = 0$ **2-1**
$(p - 1)(p - 2xy) = 0.$
$$y = C + x; \quad Cy = e^{x^2}$$

75     $p^2 - (4 + y^2)p + 4 + y^2 = 0$ **1-2-3**
$p = 1 + u^2; \quad y + u = 1/u.$
$$(x - C)y = (x - C)^2 - 1$$

76     $p^2 - (x - y)yp - xy^3 = 0$ **2-1**
$(p + y^2)(p - xy) = 0.$
$$y(C + x) = 1; \quad ye^{-x^2/2} = C$$

77     $p^2 + xy^2p + y^3 = 0$ **2-2**
$2py'(p) = y.$
$$Cy(x - C) = 1; \quad x^2y = 4$$

78     $p^2 - 2x^3y^2p - 4x^2y^3 = 0$ **6**
$u(z) = 1/y; \quad 2z = x^2; \quad u(z) = zu' + u'^2/4; \quad \text{see } \mathbf{4\text{-}1}.$
$$C(x^2 + C) = 1/y; \quad x^4y + 4 = 0; \quad y = 0$$

79     $p^2 - xy(x^2 + y^2)p + x^4y^4 = 0$ **2-1**
$(p - x^3y)(p - xy^3) = 0.$
$$x^4 = 4 \ln Cy; \quad y^2(C + x^2) + 1 = 0$$

80     $p^2 + 2xy^3p + y^4 = 0$ **2-2**
$3py'(p) = y.$
$$Cy^2(C + 2x) + 1 = 0; \quad xy = \pm 1$$

81     $p^2 + 2yp \cot x - y^2 = 0$ **2-1**
$p + y \csc x(\cos x \mp 1) = 0.$
$$y(1 \pm \cos x) = C; \quad y = 0$$

82     $p^2 - 3xy^{2/3}p + 9y^{5/3} = 0$ **6**
$y = u^3(x); \quad u(x) = xu' - u'^2; \quad \text{see } \mathbf{4\text{-}1}.$
$$y = C^3(x - C)^3; \quad y = (x/2)^6$$

83     $p^2 = e^{4x - 2y}(p - 1) = 0$ **6**
$2y = \ln u(z); \quad 2x = \ln z; \quad u'^2(z) + zu' = u; \quad \text{see } \mathbf{4\text{-}1}.$
$$e^{2y} = C(e^{2x} + C)$$

84     $2p^2 + xp - 2y = 0$ **4-3**
$px'(p) = 4p + x; \quad \text{see } (1\text{-}157).$
$$x = 4t \ln Ct; \quad y = t^2(1 + 2 \ln Ct)$$

85    $2p^2-(1-x)p-y=0$ **4-1**
       $y=Cx+C(2C-1);\quad 8y+(1-x)^2=0$

86    $2p^2-2x^2p+3xy=0$ **3-2**
       $y=x^3u(z);\quad z=\ln x;\quad 2u'^2(z)+2(6u-1)u'+3u(6u-1)=0;$
       see (87).
                 $(3y+C)^2=2Cx^3;\quad 6y=x^3;\quad x=0\ (\mathrm{CL})$

87    $2p^2+2(6y-1)p+3y(6y-1)=0$ **1-2-1**
       $2p=1-6y\pm\sqrt{1-6y};\quad$ see (1-100).
             $y=Ce^{3x/2}(Ce^{3x/2}+1)$

88    $3p^2-2xp+y=0$ **2-1**
       $3p=x\pm\sqrt{x^2-3y};\quad$ see (1-144).
                $x(2x^2-9y)\pm2(x^2-3y)^{3/2}=C$

89    $3p^2+4xp+x^2-y=0$ **6**
       $3y=x^2(u^2-1);\quad xu'(x)+u=1/2;\quad$ see **1-2**.
               $y+(C+x/2)^2=4C^2$

90    $4p^2=9x$ **1-1-1**
                $(y+C)^2=x^3;\quad x=0\ (\mathrm{CL})$

91    $4p^2+2xe^{-2y}p-e^{-2y}=0$ **6**
       $2y=\ln u;\quad u'^2(x)+xu'=u;\quad$ see **4-1**.
               $2y=\ln C(x+C)$

92    $4p^2+2e^{2x-2y}p-e^{2x-2y}=0$ **6**
       $2y=\ln u;\quad x=\ln z;\quad u'^2(z)+zu'=u;\quad$ see **4-1**.
             $e^{2y}=C(C+e^x)$

93    $5p^2+3xp-y=0$ **2-3**
       $2px'(p)+10p+3x=0;\quad$ see (1-157).
              $t^3(x+2t)^2=C;\quad y=t(3x+5t)$

94    $5p^2+6xp-2y=0$ **2-3**
       $2px'(p)+5p+3x=0;\quad$ see (1-157).
               $t^3(x+t)^2=C;\quad t(2y+t^2)^2=36C^2$

95    $9p^2+3xy^4p+y^5=0$ **2-2**
       $4py'(p)=y;\quad$ see **A1-1-2**.
                $Cy^3(C+x)+1=0;\quad x^2y^3=4$

96    $xp^2=a$ **1-1-1**
       $p=\pm\sqrt{a/x};\quad$ see also (1).
                $y=\pm2\sqrt{ax}+C$

97    $xp^2=(a-x)^2$ **1-1-1**
                $9(y+C)^2=4x(x-3a)^2;\quad x=0;\quad x=a\ (\mathrm{TL});$
                $x=3a\ (\mathrm{NL})$

98     $xp^2 = y$ **2-1**
$$(x-y)^2 + 2C(x+y) + C^2 = 0$$

99     $xp^2 + x - 2y = 0$ **2-3**
$(1-p^2)x'(p) + 2xp = 0$;   see (1-291).
$$\ln(1-t)^2x = C - 2/(1-t); \quad 2y = x(1+t^2); \quad y = x$$

100     $xp^2 + p = y$ **4-3**
$p(p-1)x'(p) = 1 + 2px$;   see **A1-2**.
$$(t-1)^2x = C - t + \ln t; \quad (t-1)^2y = t + t^2(C - 2 + \ln t)$$

101     $xp^2 + 2p - y = 0$ **4-3**
$p(1-p)x'(p) = 2(1+xp)$;   see (1-314).
$$x(1-t)^2 = C + 2(\ln t - t); \quad y(1-t)^2 = (C - 4 + 2\ln t)t^2 + 2t;$$
$$y = x + 2.$$

102     $xp^2 - 2p - y = 0$ **4-3**
$p(1-p)x'(p) = 2(xp-1)$;   see (1-315).
$$(t-1)^2x = 2t - 2\ln t + C; \quad y = t(tx - 2); \quad y = 0,$$
$$y = 2 + x$$

103     $xp^2 + 4p - 2y = 0$ **2-2**
$p(p-2)y'(p) = 4(p-y)$;   see **A1-2**.
$$y(t-2)^2 = t(Ct + 4t\ln t + 8); \quad xt^2 = 2(y - 2t);$$
$$y = 2x + 4$$

104     $xp^2 + xp - y = 0$ **2-3**
$p^2x'(p) + x(2p+1) = 0$;   see (1-257).
$$t^2x = Ce^{1/t}; \quad y = xt(t+1); \quad y = 0$$

105     $xp^2 - (1+x^2)p + x = 0$ **1-1-1**
$(p-x)(xp-1) = 0$.
$$x^2 = 2(C+y); \quad y = \ln Cx$$

106     $xp^2 + yp + a = 0$ **4-3**
$2p^3x'(p) = a - xp^2$;   see **A1-2**.
$$x = C/\sqrt{t} - a/3t^2; \quad y + C\sqrt{t} + 2a/3t = 0.$$

107     $xp^2 - yp + a = 0$ **4-1**
$$Cy = C^2x + a; \quad y^2 = 4ax$$

108     $xp^2 - yp + ax = 0$ **2-3, 3-1-1**
$apx'(p) = x(a - p^2)$;   see **A1-1-2**.
$$x = Ct\exp(-t^2/2a); \quad ty = x(t^2+a)$$

109     $xp^2 + yp - x^2 = 0$ **3-2**
$y = x^{3/2}u(z); \quad z = \ln x; \quad u'^2(z) + 4uu' + 15u^2/4 = 1$
$$2u' + 4u = \pm\sqrt{4+u^2}; \quad \text{see } \textbf{A1-1-3}.$$

110     $xp^2 + yp + x^3 = 0$ 3-2
$y = x^2 u(z);$ $z = \ln x;$ $u'^2(z) + 5uu' + 6u^2 + 1 = 0;$
$2u' + 5u = \pm \sqrt{u^2 - 4};$ see **A1-1-3**.

111     $xp^2 - yp + ay = 0$ 2-2
$apy'(p) = y(2a - p);$ see **A1-1-2**.
$x = C(t - a)e^{-t/a};$ $y = Ct^2 e^{-t/a}$

112     $xp^2 + yp - y^4 = 0$ 2-2
$2py'(p) = y;$ $p^2 x = y(y^3 - p);$ $y^2 + Cp = 0.$
$y(x - C^2) = C;$ $y = 0;$ $4xy^2 + 1 = 0$

113     $xp^2 + (a - y)p + b = 0$ 4-2
$C(Cx - y + a) + b = 0;$ $(y - a)^2 = 4bx$

114     $xp^2 + (x - y)p + 1 - y = 0$ 4-2
$C^2 x + C(x - y) + 1 - y = 0;$ $(x + y)^2 = 4x$

115     $xp^2 + (a \pm x - y)p \mp y = 0$ 4-2
$C^2 x + (a \pm x - y)C \mp y = 0;$ $(x \pm y)^2 \pm 2a(x \mp y) + a^2 = 0$

116     $xp^2 - (3x - y)p + y = 0$ 4-3
$2p(p + 1)x'(p) + x(p + 3) = 0;$ see **A1-1-2**.
$xt^{3/2} = C(t + 1);$ $yt^{1/2} = C(3 - t);$ $y = 0;$ $y = x$

117     $xp^2 + (a \pm bx - y)p \mp by = 0$ 4-2
$(y - Cx)(b + C) = \pm aC;$ $4bxy \pm (a \pm bx - y)^2 = 0$

118     $xp^2 - 2yp + a = 0$ 2-3
$p^3 x'(p) = xp^2 - a;$ see (1-346).
$16ax^3 - 12x^2 y^2 - 12Caxy + 8Cy^3 + C^2 a^2 = 0;$
$y^2 = ax$(CL)

119     $xp^2 + 2yp - x = 0$ 3-1-1
$y = ux;$ $xu'(x) + 2u = \pm \sqrt{1 + u^2};$ see (1-196).
$x^2(x^2 - 3y^2)^2 - 2Cy(y^2 - 3x^2) = C^2$

120     $xp^2 - 2yp + ax = 0$ 3-1-2
$2Cy = C^2 x^2 + a;$ $y^2 = ax^2$

121     $xp^2 - 2yp + x + 2y = 0$ 6
$y - x = u(z);$ $x^2 = z;$ $2u'(z)(u'z - u) + 1 = 0;$ see **4-1**.
$y - x = Cx^2 + 1/2C;$ $(x - y)^2 = 2x^2$

122     $xp^2 - 3yp + 9x^2 = 0$ 2-3
$2px'(p) = x;$ see **A1-1-2**.
$Cy = C^2 x^3 + 1;$ $y^2 = 4x^3$

123     $xp^2 - (2x + 3y)p + 6y = 0$ 2-1
$(p - 2)(xp - 3y) = 0.$
$y = 2x + C;$ $y = Cx^3$

124    $xp^2 - ayp + b = 0$ **2-3**

      $(1-a)p^3 x'(p) = b - xp^2$;   see **A1-2**.

        i. $x = Ct^k + b/(2a - 1)t^2$; $xt^2 + b = ayt$;

             $k = 1/(a-1)$; $a \neq 1$.

        ii. $C(y - Cx) = b$;   see **4-1**; $a = 1$.

125    $xp^2 + ayp + bx = 0$ **2-3, 3-1-1**

      $p(Ap^2 + b)x'(p) = x(b - p^2)$; $A = a + 1 \neq 0$;   see **A1-2**.

        i. $x = Ct(At^2 + b)^{-n}$; $2An = A + 1$;

             $aty = -x(b + t^2)$.

        ii. $a = -1$;   see (108).

        iii. $a = -2$;   see (120).

126    $xp^2 - (1 + xy)p + y = 0$ **2-1**

      $(p - y)(xp - 1) = 0$.

          $x = \ln Cy$; $y = \ln Cx$

127    $xp^2 + (1 - x)yp - y^2 = 0$ **2-1**

      $(p - y)(xp + y) = 0$.

          $x = \ln Cy$; $xy = C$

128    $xp^2 + (1 - x^2 y)p - xy = 0$ **2-1**

      $(p - xy)(xp + 1) = 0$.

          $y = Ce^{x^2/2}$; $xe^y = C$

129    $(1 + x)p^2 = y$ **2-3, 2-1**

      $(1 - p)x'(p) = 2(1 + x)$;   see **A1-1-2**.

          $(1 + x - y)^2 + 2C(1 + x + y) + C^2 = 0$; $y = 0$

130    $(1 + x)p^2 - (x + y)p + y = 0$ **4-2**

      $(y - xp)(1 + p) + p^2 = 0$.

          $(C + 1)(y - Cx) = C^2$; $4y(1 + x) = (x + y)^2$

131    $(a - x)p^2 + yp - b = 0$ **4-2**

      $p(y - xp) + ap^2 = b$.

          $Cy = C^2(x - a) + b$; $y^2 = 4b(x - a)$

132    $(a + x)p^2 + (a_1 + b_1 x + c_1 y)p + (a_2 + b_2 x + c_2 y) = 0$ **6**

      See (212) and **A1-9-3-1**.

133    $2xp^2 + (2x - y)p + 1 - y = 0$ **4-3**

      $p(1 + p)^2 x'(p) = 1 - 2x(1 + p)^2$;   see **A1-2**.

           $xt^2 = 1/(1 + t) + \ln C(1 + t)$;

             $yt = 1 + 1/(1 + t) + 2\ln C(1 + t)$

134    $3xp^2 - 6yp + x + 2y = 0$ **2-3**

      $(3p - 1)x'(p) = 3x$;   see **A1-1-2**.

          $x^2 + C(x - 3y) + C^2 = 0$; $(x + 3y)(x - y) = 0$

135    $(1+3x)p^2 - 3(2+y)p + 9 = 0$ 4-2
   $3p(y-xp) = (p-3)^2.$
            $3Cy = 3C^2x + (C-3)^2;\quad y^2 = 4(3x-y)$

136    $(5+3x)p^2 - (x+3y)p + y = 0$ 4-2
            $(y-Cx)(3C-1) = 5C^2;\quad 4y(5+3x) = (x+3y)^2$

137    $4xp^2 = (a-3x)^2$ 1-1-1
   $2p\sqrt{x} = \pm(a-3x);\quad$ see **A1-1-1**.
            $(y+C)^2 = x(a-x)^2;\quad x = 0:\quad x = a(\text{NL});$
            $3x = a(\text{TL})$

138    $4xp^2 + 2xp - y = 0$ 2-3
   $px'(p) + 2x = 0;\quad$ see **A1-1-2**.
            $(y-C)^2 = Cx;\quad x + 4y = 0$

139    $4xp^2 - 3yp + 3 = 0$ 4-3
   $p^3x'(p) = 3 - 4xp^2;\quad$ see (1-346).
            $2xt^4 = 3t^2 + C;\quad 3yt^3 = 9t^2 + 2C$

140    $4xp^2 + 4yp = 1$ 4-3, 2-3
   See (124).
            $C^2 + 2Cy(3x-y^2) - x(x-3y^2)^2 = 0;\quad x + y^2 = 0\ (\text{CL})$

141    $4xp^2 + 4yp - y^4 = 0$ 2-2
   $2py'(p) = y;\quad$ see **A1-1-2**.
            $y(C^2x - 1) = 2C;\quad xy^2 + 1 = 0$

142    $4(2-x)p^2 + 1 = 0$ 1-1-1
            $(y+C)^2 = x - 2;\quad x = 2,\quad$ an envelope but not a
            singular solution.

143    $16xp^2 + 8yp + y^6 = 0$ 2-2
   $3py'(p) = y;\quad$ see **A1-1-2**.
            $y^2(C^2x + 1) = 2C;\quad xy^4 = 1$

144    $x^2p^2 = a^2$ 1-1-1
            $y = C \pm a\ln x$

145    $x^2p^2 = y^2$ 2-1
            $xy = C;\quad y = Cx$

146    $x^2p^2 + x^2 - y^2 = 0$ 3-1-1, 2-1
            $y\sqrt{y^2-x^2} - x^2\ln\dfrac{y+\sqrt{y^2-x^2}}{x} = y^2 + x^2\ln Cx^2;\quad x = 0$

147    $x^2p^2 = (x-y)^2$ 2-1, 3-1-1
   See (1-157).
            $x(x-2y) = C;\quad y + x\ln Cx = 0$

148     $x^2p^2 + y^2 - y^4 = 0$ **2-1**
$$1/y = \pm \cos \ln Cx$$

149     $x^2p^2 - xp + y(1 - y) = 0$ **2-1**
$$(xp - y)(xp - 1 + y) = 0.$$
$$y = Cx; \quad x(y - 1) = C$$

150     $x^2p^2 + 2axp + a^2 + x^2 - 2ay = 0$ **2-3**
$$(p^2 + 1)x'(p) + a + px = 0; \quad \text{see (1-283)}.$$
$$x\sqrt{1 + t^2} = C - a \ln (t + \sqrt{1 + t^2}); \quad 2ay = x^2 + (xt + a)^2$$

151     $x^2p^2 - 2xyp - x + y(1 + y) = 0$ **6**
$$y = ux; \quad x^3u'^2(x) = 1 - u; \quad x(1 - u) = (1 + C\sqrt{x})^2; \quad \text{see } \textbf{2-1}.$$
$$y = x - (1 + C\sqrt{x})^2; \quad y = x$$

152     $x^2p^2 - 2xyp - x^4 + (1 - x^2)y^2 = 0$ **6**
$$y = ux; \quad u'^2(x) = 1 + u^2; \quad u = \pm \sinh(x + C); \quad \text{see } \textbf{1-2-1}.$$
$$y = \pm x \sinh(C + x)$$

153     $x^2p^2 - (1 + 2xy)p + 1 + y^2 = 0$ **4-2**
$$(y - xp)^2 = p - 1.$$
$$(y - Cx)^2 = C - 1; \quad 4x(x - y) = 1$$

154     $x^2p^2 - (a + 2xy)p + y^2 = 0$ **4-2**
$$(xp - y)^2 = ap.$$
$$(Cx - y)^2 = Ca; \quad 4xy + a = 0$$

155     $x^2p^2 - x(x - 2y)p + y^2 = 0$ **6**
$$xy = u(x); \quad u'^2 - xu' + u = 0; \quad \text{see (35)}.$$
$$xy - Cx + C^2 = 0; \quad 4y = x$$

156     $x^2p^2 + 2x(2x + y)p - 4a + y^2 = 0$ **6**
$$u(x) = xy + x^2 + a; \quad u'^2(x) = 4u; \quad \text{see } \textbf{1-2-1}.$$
$$xy + a = C(C + 2x)$$

157     $x^2p^2 + x(x^3 - 2y)p - (2x^3 - y)y = 0$ **6**
$$y = ux; \quad u'^2(x) + xu' - u = 0; \quad \text{see } \textbf{4-1}.$$
$$y = Cx(C + x)$$

158     $x^2p^2 + 3xyp + 2y^2 = 0$ **3-1-1**
$$y = ux; \quad p^2 + 3up + 2u^2 = 0; \quad (p + u)(p + 2u) = 0$$
$$xy = C; \quad x^2y = C$$

159     $x^2p^2 - 3xyp + x^3 + 2y^2 = 0$ **6**
$$y = xu(x); \quad xu'^2(x) - uu' = 1 = 0; \quad \text{see } \textbf{4-1}.$$
$$C^2x^2 - Cy + x = 0$$

160     $x^2p^2 + 4xyp - 5y^2 = 0$ **2-1**
$$(xp + 5y)(xp - y) = 0.$$
$$x^5y = C; \quad y = Cx$$

161 $x^2p^2 - 4x(2+y)p + 4(2+y)y = 0$ **2-1**

$xp = 2(2+y) \pm 2\sqrt{2(2+y)}$;   see **A1-1-2**.

$2y = C^2x^2 \pm 4Cx$; $y + 2 = 0$

162 $x^2p^2 - 5xyp + 6y^2 = 0$ **2-1**

$(xp - 2y)(xp - 3y) = 0$.

$y = Cx^2$; $y = Cx^3$

163 $x^2p^2 + x(x^2 + xy - 2y)p + (1-x)(x^2 - y)y = 0$ **6**

$y = ux$; $(u' + u)(u' + 1) = 0$;   see **A1-1**.

$y = Cxe^{-x}$; $y = x(C-x)$; $y = 0$

164 $x^2p^2 + (2x+y)yp + y^2 = 0$ **6**

$u = xy$; $y = z$; $u'^2(z) + zu' = u$;   see **4-1**.

$xy = C(C+y)$; $y + 4x = 0$

165 $x^2p^2 + (2x-y)yp + y^2 = 0$ **2-2**

$px + y = \pm y\sqrt{p}$; $2py'(p) = y$; $y^2 = C^2p$;   see **A1-1-2**.

$y(C-x) = C^2$; $y = 4x$

166 $x^2p^2 + (a + bx^2y^3)p + aby^3 = 0$ **2-1**

$(p + by^3)(x^2p + a) = 0$;   see **A1-1**.

$1/y^2 = 2bx + C$; $x(y - C) = a$

167 $(1-x^2)p^2 = 1 - y^2$ **2-1**

See (1-397).

$x^2 + y^2 + C^2 = 1 + 2Cxy$; $x = \pm 1$; $y = \pm 1$

168 $(1-x^2)p^2 + 2xyp + 4x^2 = 0$ **2-3**

$xp[p^2(x^2-1) + 4x^2][px'(p) - x] = 0$;   see **A1-1-2**.

$x^2 = Cy + C^2 + 1$; $y^2 = 4(1-x^2)$

169 $(a^2 + x^2)p^2 = b^2$ **1-1-1**

$x = \pm a \sinh(C+y)/b$

170 $(a^2 - x^2)p^2 + b^2 = 0$ **1-1-1**

$x = \pm a \cosh(C+y)/b$

171 $(a^2 - x^2)p^2 = b^2$ **1-1-1**

$x = \pm a \sin(C+y)/b$

172 $(a^2 - x^2)p^2 = x^2$ **1-1-1**

$(a^2 - x^2) = (C+y)^2$; $x = \pm a$

173 $(a^2 - x^2)p^2 + 2xyp + x^2 = 0$ **2-3**

$px'(p) = x$;   see **A1-1-2**.

$C^2 + 2Cy + a^2 = x^2$; $x^2 + y^2 = a^2$; $x = 0$ (TL)

174 $(a^2 - x^2)p^2 - 2xyp - y^2 = 0$ **2-1**

$[(a-x)p - y][(a+x)p + y] = 0$;   see **A1-1-2**.

$y(a \pm x) = C$

175     $(a^2 \pm x^2)p^2 \mp 2xyp + b \pm y^2 = 0$ **4-2**
$(y - xp)^2 \pm (a^2 p^2 + b) = 0.$
$$(y - Cx)^2 \pm (a^2 C^2 + b) = 0; \quad \pm bx^2 + a^2(b \pm y^2) = 0$$

176     $(1 + 2x^2)p^2 + (2 + x^2 + 2xy + y^2)p + 1 + 2y^2 = 0$ **6**
$u = xy; \quad z = x + y; \quad u(z) = zu' + 1 + u'^2; \quad \text{see } \textbf{4-1}$
$$xy = C(x + y) + C^2 + 1; \quad x^2 + y^2 + 6xy = 4; \quad x = y \text{ (TL)}$$

177     $4x^2 p^2 - 4xyp = 8x^3 - y^2$ **2-1**
$(2xp - y)^2 = 8x^3; \quad \text{see } \textbf{A1-2}.$
$$y^2 = 2x(x + C)^2$$

178     $ax^2 p^2 - 2axyp + a(1 - a)x^2 + y^2 = 0$ **3-1-1**
$p = u \pm \sqrt{u^2 - u - a - 1}.$
$$y = Cx^{m+1} \pm \sqrt{ax^2 + y^2}; \quad m^2 = (a - 1)/a$$

179     $(1 - a^2)x^2 p^2 - 2xyp - a^2 x^2 + y^2 = 0$ **2-3**
$$x = C(1 + t^2)^{-1/2}(t + \sqrt{1 + t^2})^{-1/a}; \quad y = xt \pm ax\sqrt{1 + t^2}$$

180     $x^3 p^2 = a$ **1-1-1**
$p = \pm \sqrt{a/x^3}; \quad \text{see also } (1).$
$$y + C = \pm 2\sqrt{a/x}$$

181     $x^3 p^2 + xp - y = 0$ **2-3**
$3xp^2 x'(p) + 1 + 2x^2 p = 0; \quad \text{see } (1\text{-}584).$
$$tx^2 + 2 = Ct^{-1/3}; \quad y = xt(1 + x^2 t)$$

182     $x^3 p^2 + x^2 yp + a = 0$ **2-3**
$(x^3 p^2 - a)(p' x^2 + 2px) = 0; \quad \text{see } \textbf{A1-1-2}.$
$$Cxy = C^2 x + a; \quad xy^2 = 4a$$

183     $x^3 p^2 - (1 + 2x^2 y)p + xy^2 = 0$ **6**
$Y^2 P = X; \quad \text{see also } \textbf{A1-9-3-1}.$
$$x = X(3X^2/2 - C)^{-2/3}; \quad y = (C - X^2/2)(3X^2/2 - C)^{-2/3}$$

184     $x(1 - x^2)p^2 - 2(1 - x^2)yp + x(1 - y^2) = 0$ **6**
$y = ux; \quad x^2(1 - x^2)u'^2(x) = u^2 - 1; \quad \text{see } \textbf{A1-1-2}.$
$$(y - C)^2 = (1 - x^2)(C^2 - 1)$$

185     $4x(a - x)(b - x)p^2 = [ab - 2x(a + b) + 3x^2]^2$ **6**
$y(x) = u(z); \quad z = x(a - x)(b - x); \quad 4zu'^2 = 1; \quad \text{see } (96).$
$$(y + C)^2 = x(a - x)(b - x); \quad x(a - x)(b - x) = 0;$$
$$3x = a + b \pm (a^2 - ab + b^2)^{1/2} \text{ (TL)}.$$

186     $x^4 p^2 - xp - y = 0$ **3-2**
$x^2 y = u(z); \quad z = \ln x; \quad u'^2 - (1 + 4u)u' + (1 + 4u)u = 0;$
$2u' = 1 + 4u \pm \sqrt{1 + 4u}; \quad \text{see } (1\text{-}100).$
$$xy = C(Cx + 1); \quad 1 + 4x^2 y = 0; \quad x = 0 \text{ (TL)}$$

187    $x^4p^2 + 2x^3yp - 4 = 0$ **2-3**
$3px'(p) + x = 0$;   see **A1-1-2**.
$$x^2(1 + Cy) = C^2$$

188    $x^4p^2 + xy^2p - y^3 = 0$ **6**
$y = 1/u(z)$; $x = 1/z$; $u'^2(z) + zu' - u = 0$;   see **4-1**.
$$Cy(Cx + 1) = x; \quad 4x^2 + y = 0; \quad x = 0 \text{ (TL)}.$$

189    $x^2(a^2 - x^2)p^2 + 1 = 0$ **1-1-1**
$$x = a\sec(C + ay)$$

190    $3x^4p^2 - xy - y = 0$ **2-3**
$(xp' + 2p)(6x^3p - 1) = 0$;   see **A1-1-2**.
$$xy = C(3Cx - 1); \quad 12x^2y + 1 = 0$$

191    $4x^5p^2 + 12x^4yp + 9 = 0$ **2-3**
$(xp' + 4p)(4x^5p^2 - 9) = 0$;   see **A1-1-2**.
$$x^3(2Cy - 1) = C^2; \quad x^3y^2 = 1$$

192    $x^6p^2 - 2xp - 4y = 0$ **2-3**
$(xp' + 3p)(px^5 - 1) = 0$;   see **A1-1-2**.
$$x^2(y - C^2) = C; \quad 4x^4y + 1 = 0$$

193    $x^8p^2 + 3xp + 9y = 0$ **2-3**
$(xp' + 4p)(3 + 2px^7) = 0$;   see **A1-1-2**.
$$x^3(C^2 + y) + C = 0; \quad 4x^6y = 1$$

194    $yp^2 = a$ **1-2-1**
$$4y^3 = 9(C + ax)^2$$

195    $yp^2 = a^2x$ **2-1**
$$y^{3/2} = \pm ax^{3/2} + C$$

196    $yp^2 = e^{2x}$ **6**
$u(x) = y^{3/2}$; $u'(x) = \pm 3e^x/2$;   see **A1-1-1**.
$$4y^3 = 9(C + e^x)^2$$

197    $yp^2 \pm 2axp \mp ay = 0$ **6, 3-1**
$y^2 = u(x)$; $u'^2 \pm 4axu' \mp 4au = 0$;   see **4-1**.
$$ay^2 = 4C(ax \pm C); \quad ax^2 + y^2 = 0$$

198    $yp^2 - 4a^2xp + a^2y = 0$ **2-2, 6, 3-1**
    i. $p(3a^2 - p^2)y'(p) = y(p^2 - a^2)$;   see **A1-1-2**;
        $y^3p(3a^2 - p^2) = C$; $y^6 - 3a^2x^2y^4 + 6Caxy^2$
        $-16Ca^3x^3 + C^2 = 0$; $y^2 = 4a^2x^2$ (CL);   see
        also (199).
    ii. $y^2 = u(x)$; $a^2u'^2(x) - 8xu' + 4u = 0$;   see **4-3**.

199     $yp^2 + axp + by = 0$ **2-2, 6, 3-1**

      i. $p(a+b+p^2)y'(p) = y(b-p^2);$ $axt + y(b+t^2) = 0;$

          $Cy(t^2+a+b)^m = t^{b\,/(a+b)};$ $m = (a+2b)/2(a+b);$

          $m \neq 0.$

      ii. $y^2 = u(x);$ $u'^2(x) + 2axu' + 4bu = 0;$ see **4-3**.

      iii. $m = 0$ see (197).

200     $yp^2 - (a-2bx)p - by = 0$ **6**

    $y^2 = u(x);$ $u'^2(x) - 4(a-2bx)u' - 4bu = 0;$ see **4-3**.

       $4by^2 = C^2 - 2C(a-2bx);$ $(a-2bx)^2 + 4by^2 = 0$

201     $yp^2 + x^3p - x^2y = 0$ **6**

   $x^2 = z;$ $y^2 = u(z);$ $u'^2(z) + z - u = 0;$ see **4-1**.

       $y^2 = C(C+x^2);$ $x^4 + 4y^2 = 0$

202     $yp^2 + (x-y)p - x = 0$ **2-1**

   $(p-1)(yp+x) = 0.$

       $x^2 + y^2 = C;$ $y = C + x$

203     $yp^2 - (x+y)p + y = 0$ **2-2**

   $(p-1)[y(p+1)p' + p^2] = 0;$ see **A1-1-2**.

       $tx = y(t^2 - t + 1);$ $ty = Ce^{1/t};$ $y = x$

204     $yp^2 - (1+xy)p + x = 0$ **2-1**

   $(p-x)(yp-1) = 0.$

       $(2x - y^2 + C)(2y - x^2 + C) = 0$

205     $yp^2 + (x-y^2)p - xy = 0$ **2-1**

   $(p-y)(yp+x) = 0.$

       $y = Ce^x;$ $x^2 + y^2 = C$

206     $yp^2 + y = a$ **1-2-3**

   $p = \cot u;$ $y = a\sin^2 u;$ $x = a(u - \cos u \sin u) + C.$

207     $(x+y)p^2 + 2xp - y = 0$ **2-3**

   $p(1-p^2)x'(p) + 2x = 0;$ $p^2x = C(1-p^2);$ see **A1-1-2**.

       $y^2 - 2C(2x+y) - 3C^2 = 0;$ $y = 0$

208     $(2x-y)p^2 - 2(1-x)p + 2 - y = 0$ **2-3**

   $p(p^2+1)x'(p) = 2(1-x);$ see **A1-1-2**.

       $t^2(1-x) = C(t^2+1);$ $(t^2+1)y = 2[xt(t+1) - t + 1];$

       $y = 2$

209     $2yp^2 + (5-4x)p + 2y = 0$ **2-3**

   $(1-p^2)[(4x-5)p'(x) + 2p(p^2+1)] = 0;$ see **A1-1-2**.

       $4y^2 = C(4x - 5 - C);$ $4y = \pm(4x-5)$

210     $9yp^2 + 4x^3p - 4x^2y = 0$ **6**

   $y^2 = u(z);$ $z = x^2;$ $9u'^2(z) + 4zu' = 4u;$ see **4-1**.

       $y^2 = C(2x^2 + 9C)$

211    $(1-ay)p^2 = ay$ **1-2-3**
$p = \tan u.$
$$ay = \sin^2 u; \quad x = u + \cos u \sin u + C$$

212    $(a_0 + b_0 x + c_0 y)p^2 + (a_1 + b_1 x + c_1 y)p + a_2 + b_2 x + c_2 y = 0$ **6**
$x = P(X); \; X = p; \; Y = xp - y;$ see **A1-9-3-1**. The transformed
equation is $(f + Xg)P - gY + h = 0; \quad f(X) = b_2 + b_1 X + b_0 X^2;$
$g(X) = c_2 + c_1 X + c_0 X^2; \quad h(X) = a_2 + a_1 X + a_0 X^2;$ see **A1-2** and
also (132).

213    $(x^2 - ay)p^2 - 2xyp + y^2 = 0$ **6**
$x = yu(y); \quad y^3 u'^2(y) = a$
$$(x + Cy)^2 = 4ay$$

214    $xyp^2 + (x + y)p + 1 = 0$ **2-1**
$(xp + 1)(yp + 1) = 0;$ see **A1**.
$$y + \ln Cx = 0; \quad y^2 = 2(C - x)$$

215    $xyp^2 + (x^2 + y^2)p + xy = 0$ **2-1**
$(xp + y)(yp + x) = 0;$ see **A1-1-2**.
$$xy = C; \quad x^2 + y^2 = C^2; \quad y = 0$$

216    $xyp^2 + (x^2 - y^2)p - xy = 0$ **2-1**
$(xp - y)(yp + x) = 0;$ see **A1-1-2**.
$$y = Cx; \quad x^2 + y^2 = C^2$$

217    $xyp^2 - (x^2 - y^2)p - xy = 0$ **2-1**
$(xp + y)(yp - x) = 0;$ see **A1-1-2**.
$$xy = C; \quad x^2 - y^2 = C^2$$

218    $xyp^2 + (a \pm x^2 - y^2)p \mp xy = 0$ **6**
$y^2 = u(z); \; x^2 = z; \; zu'^2(z) + (a \pm z - u)u' \mp u = 0;$ see **4-1**.
   i. $x^2(a \pm C) + Cy^2 = C(a \pm C); \quad a \neq 0; \quad y = 0.$
   ii. $a = 0,$ see (216).

219    $xyp^2 - (a - bx^2 + y^2)p - bxy = 0$ **6, 5**
   i. $y^2 = u(z); \; x^2 = z; \; (zu' - u)(u' + b) = au'(z);$
see **4-2**; $(C + b)(Cx^2 - y^2) = Ca; \quad (a + bx^2 + y^2)^2 = 4abx^2.$
   ii. $xf = yp; \; g = y(y - xp)$ and the differential equation
becomes $af + by + fg = 0.$ The common primitive of $f = C_1$
and $g = C_2$ is $y^2 - C_1 x^2 = C_2;$ see **A1-1**. This is also the
solution of the second-degree equation, provided that
$aC_1 + bC_2 + C_1 C_2 = 0.$

220    $xyp^2 + (3x^2 - 2y^2)p - 6xy = 0$ **2-1, 3-1**
$(xp - 2y)(yp + 3x) = 0;$ see **A1-1-2**.
$$y = Cx^2; \quad y^2 + 3x^2 = C$$

221     $x(x-2y)p^2 - 2xyp - 2xy + y^2 = 0$ **3-1-1**
$y = ux;$ $(2u-1)p^2 + 2up + u(2-u) = 0;$
$(2u-1)p = -u \pm (1-u)\sqrt{2u}.$
$$x^2 + y^2 + 2C(x+y) + C^2 = 0$$

222     $x(x-2y)p^2 + 6xyp - 2xy + y^2 = 0$ **6, 3-1**
$xy = u(z);$ $y-x = z;$ $u'(z) = \pm \sqrt{2u};$ see **A1-1-3**.
$$2xy = (x-y+C)^2; \quad y = 0$$

223     $y^2 p^2 = a^2$ **1-2-1**
$$y^2 = C \pm 2ax$$

224     $y^2 p^2 - a^2 + y^2 = 0$ **1-2-2**
$$y^2 + (C+x)^2 = a^2; \quad y = \pm a; \quad y = 0 \text{ (TL)}$$

225     $y^2 p^2 - 3xp + y = 0$ **2-2**
$2py'(p) + y = 0.$
$$y^3 = C(3x - C); \quad 9x^2 = 4y^3$$

226     $y^2 p^2 - 6x^3 p + 4x^2 y = 0$ **6**
$y^3 = u(z);$ $z = x^2;$ $u'^2(z) = 9(zu' - u);$ see **4-1**.
$$y^3 = C(3x^2 - C); \quad 4y^3 = 9x^4$$

227     $y^2 p^2 - 4ayp + 4a^2 - 4ax + y^2 = 0$ **6**
$y^2 = 4ax - u(x);$ $u'^2 = 4u.$
$$4ax - y^2 = (C+x)^2; \quad y^2 = 4ax$$

228     $y^2 p^2 - (1+x)yp + x = 0$ **2-1**
$(yp-1)(yp-x) = 0.$
$$y^2 = 2(x-C); \quad x^2 - y^2 = C$$

229     $y^2 p^2 + 2xyp + x^2 = 0$ **3-1-1**
$y = ux;$ $(1+up)^2 = 0.$
$$x^2 + y^2 = C^2$$

230     $y^2 p^2 + 2xyp + a - y^2 = 0$ **6**
$y^2 = u(x);$ $u'^2(x) + 4(xu' + a - u) = 0;$ see **4-1**.
$$4(y^2 - a - Cx) = C^2; \quad x^2 + y^2 = a$$

231     $y^2 p^2 - 2xyp - x^2 + 2y^2 = 0$ **6**
$y^2 = x^2 + u(x);$ $u'^2(x) + 8u = 0;$ see **(16)**.
$$x^2 + y^2 + 4Cx + 2C^2 = 0; \quad y = \pm x$$

232     $y^2 p^2 - 2xyp + a - x^2 + 2y^2 = 0$ **6**
$y^2 = x^2 + u(x);$ $u'^2 + 8u + 4a = 0;$ see **1-2-1**
$$2y^2 = (C^2 - a) - 2(C+x)^2; \quad 2x^2 = a + 2y^2$$

233     $y^2 p^2 + 2axyp + (a-1)b + ax^2 + (1-a)y^2 = 0$ **6, 3-1-3**
$y^2 = u + b - ax^2;$ $u'^2(x) = 4(a-1)u;$ see **(16)**.
$$y^2 + ax^2 - b = (a-1)(C+x)^2; \quad y^2 + ax^2 = b$$

234 $(1-y^2)p^2 = 1$ **1-2-1**
$$y\sqrt{1-y^2}+\sin^{-1}y = 2x+C; \quad y = \pm 1 \text{ (CL)}$$

235 $(a^2-y^2)p^2 = y^2$ **1-2-1**
$$a \ln[a \pm \sqrt{a^2-y^2}]-a \ln y \mp \sqrt{a^2-y^2} = C+x$$

236 $(a^2-2ax+y^2)p^2+2ayp+y^2 = 0$ **2-2**
$$p(1+p^2)y'(p) = ap+y; \quad \text{see } \mathbf{A1\text{-}2}.$$
$$2axt^2 = t^2(a^2+y^2)+2ayt+y^2; \quad y\sqrt{1+t^2}$$
$$=t[C+a \ln t/(1+\sqrt{1+t^2})].$$

237 $(a^2x^2-y^2)p^2-2xyp+(a^2-1)x^2 = 0$ **2-3**
$$p(1+p^2)x'(p) = x; \quad \text{see } \mathbf{A1\text{-}1\text{-}2}.$$
$$x\sqrt{1+t^2} = Ct; \quad (Ca-y)\sqrt{1+t^2} = C$$

238 $[(1-a)x^2+y^2]p^2+2axyp+x^2+(1-a)y^2 = 0$ **3-1-1**
$$x = r \cos \theta, \; y = r \sin \theta.$$
i. $\ln Cr = \pm\theta\sqrt{a-1}; \quad a > 1.$
ii. $a = 1, \quad \text{see (229)}.$
iii. $a < 1, \quad \text{no real solution.}$

239 $[(1-4a^2)x^2+y^2]p^2-8a^2xyp+x^2+(1-4a^2)y^2 = 0$ **3-1-1**
$$x = r \cos \theta, \; y = r \sin \theta; \quad (1+p^2) = 4a^2(p \cos \theta - \sin \theta)^2.$$
$$\ln Cr = \pm\theta\sqrt{4a^2-1}$$

240 $[(1-a^2)x^2+y^2]p^2+2a^2xyp+x^2+(1-a^2)y^2 = 0$ **3-1-1**
$$x = r \cos \theta, \; y = r \sin \theta; \quad (1+p^2) = a^2(p \cos \theta - \sin \theta)^2.$$
$$\ln Cr = \pm\theta\sqrt{a^2-1}$$

241 $(x+y)^2p^2 = y^2$ **2-1**
$$[(x+y)p+y][(x+y)p-y] = 0; \quad \text{see (1-503)}.$$
$$x = y \ln Cy; \quad y(2x+y) = C$$

242 $(x+y)^2p^2-(x^2-xy-2y^2)p-(x-y)y = 0$ **2-1**
$$[(x+y)p+y][(x+y)p-(x-y)] = 0; \quad \text{see (1-503), (1-507)}.$$
$$y(2x+y) = C; \quad y(2x+y) = C+x^2$$

243 $[a^2-(x-y)^2]p^2+2a^2p+a^2-(x-y)^2 = 0$ **2-2**
$$(x-y)\sqrt{1+p^2} \pm a(p+1) = 0; \quad (1+p^2)^{3/2}y'(p) \pm ap = 0;$$
$$(y+C)\sqrt{1+p^2} = \pm a.$$
$$(x-C)^2+(y-C)^2 = a^2; \quad y = x \pm a.$$

244 $2y^2p^2+2xyp-1+x^2+y^2 = 0$ **6**
$$x^2+y^2 = 1+u(x); \quad u'^2(x)-2xu'+2u = 0; \quad \text{see } \mathbf{4\text{-}1}.$$
$$(x-C)^2+y^2 = 1-C^2; \quad x^2+2y^2 = 2; \quad y = 0 \text{ (TL)}$$

245     $3y^2p^2 - 2xyp - x^2 + 4y^2 = 0$ **3-1-3**
      $x = -y(p \pm 2\sqrt{p^2+1})$;   see also (233).
           $3(x^2+y^2) - 4Cx + C^2 = 0$; $x^2 = 3y^2$

246     $4y^2p^2 + 2(1+3x)xyp + 3x^3 = 0$ **2-1**
     $(2yp + x)(2yp + 3x^2) = 0$.
         $x^3 + y^2 = C$; $x^2 + 2y^2 = C$

247     $(x^2 - 4y^2)p^2 + 6xyp - 4x^2 + y^2 = 0$ **2-1, 3-1-1**
    $[(x+2y)p - (2x+y)][(x-2y)p + (2x-y)] = 0$;   see (1-505).
      $(x-y)^3(x+y) = C$; $(x+y)^3(x-y) = C$

248     $9y^2p^2 - 3xp + y = 0$ **2-2**
    $(yp' + 2p)(9yp^2 - 1) = 0$;   see **A1-1-2**.
       $y^3 = C(x-C)$; $x^2 = 4y^3$

249     $(2 - 3y)^2p^2 = 4(1-y)$ **1-2-1**
      $y^2(1-y) = (C+x)^2$; $y = 1$; $y = 0$ (NL);
       $3y = 2$ (TL)

250     $(1 - a^2)y^2p^2 - 2a^2xyp - a^2x^2 + y^2 = 0$ **6**
    $u(x) = x^2 + y^2$; $(1-a^2)u'^2 - 4xu' + 4u = 0$;   see **4-1**.
      $y^2 + (C-x)^2 = a^2C^2$; $(1-a^2)y^2 = a^2x^2$

251     $(a-b)y^2p^2 - 2bxyp - ab - bx^2 + ay^2 = 0$ **6**
    $u(x) = x^2 + y^2$; $(a-b)u'^2 - axu' + au - ab = 0$;   see **4-1**.
$$x^2 + y^2 = Cx + b - C^2\frac{(a-b)}{4a}; \quad (a-b)y^2 = b(x^2 + a - b)$$

252     $a^2[b^2 - (cx - ay)^2]p^2 + 2ab^2cp + c^2[b^2 - (cx - ay)^2] = 0$ **4-3**
    $(cx - ay)^2(c^2 + a^2p^2) = b^2(c + ap)^2$; $(ap - c)[(c^2 + a^2p^2)^{3/2}x'(p)$
     $\pm abc] = 0$;   see **A1-1-1**.
       $(cx - C)^2 + (ay - C)^2 = b^2$; $ay - cx = \pm c\sqrt{2}$;
      $ay - cx = 0$ (TL)

253     $xy^2p^2 - y^3p + a^2x = 0$ **6**
    $y^2 = u(z)$; $x^2 = z$; $zu'^2(z) - uu' + a^2 = 0$;   see **4-1**.
      $Cy^2 = C^2x^2 + a^2$

254     $xy^2p^2 + (a - x^3 - y^3)p + x^2y = 0$ **6**
    $y^3 = u(z)$; $x^3 = z$; $zu'^2(z) + (a - u - z)u' + u = 0$.
$$y^3 = C\left(x^3 + \frac{a}{C-1}\right); \quad (x^3 - y^3)^2 + a^2 = 2a(x^3 + y^3)$$

255     $xy^2p^2 - 2y^3p - x(x^2 - 2y^2) = 0$ **6**
    $y^2 = u(x)$; $(u' - 2x)(xu' - 4u + 2x^2) = 0$;   see **A1-1-1** and
    (1-158).
       $y^2 = C + x^2$; $y^2 = x^2(Cx^2 + 1)$

256 $\quad 2xy^2p^2 - y^3p - a = 0$ $\qquad\qquad$ **2-2**
$\quad 2y^2p(2a + y^3p)(py' + yp) = 0;\quad$ see **A1-1-2**.
$\qquad 2C^2x = Cy^2 + a;\quad 8ax + y^4 = 0$

257 $\quad 4x^2y^2p^2 = (x^2 + y^2)^2$ $\qquad\qquad$ **2-1**
$\quad (2xyp - x^2 - y^2)(2xyp + x^2 + y^2) = 0;\quad$ see (1-561).
$\qquad x^2 - y^2 = Cx;\quad x(x^2 + 3y^2) = C$

258 $\quad 4x^2y^2p^2 - 2xy(x^3 + 2y^2)p + (2x^3 + y^2)y^2 = 0$ $\qquad\qquad$ **6**
$\quad y^2 = ux;\quad u'^2(x) - xu' + u = 0;\quad$ see **4-1**.
$\qquad y^2 = Cx(x - C)$

259 $\quad 4y^3p^2 - 4xp + y = 0$ $\qquad\qquad$ **2-2**
$\quad (yp' + 3p)(4y^2p^2 - 1) = 0;\quad$ see **A1-1-2**.
$\qquad y^4 = 4C(x - C);\quad y^2 = x$

260 $\quad xy(x^2 + y^2)p^2 - (x^4 + x^2y^2 + y^4)p - xy(x^2 + y^2) = 0$ $\qquad\qquad$ **3-1-1**
$\quad [(1 + u^2)p + u][up - (1 + u^2)] = 0;\quad y = ux;\quad$ see **A1-8-1**.
$\qquad y^2(2x^2 + y^2) = C;\quad y^2 = 2x^2 \ln Cx$

261 $\quad x[a^2x + (x^2 - y^2)y]p^2 + [2a^2xy + (x^2 - y^2)^2]p$
$\qquad\qquad + a^2y^2 - xy(x^2 - y^2) = 0$ $\qquad\qquad$ **6**
$\quad x = r \cos \theta,\ y = r \sin \theta;\ r^3r'(\theta) \cos 2\theta + a^2[r'(\theta) \sin 2\theta + r \cos 2\theta]^2$
$\quad = 0;\quad$ see also (262).

262 $\quad x[a^2x + (x^2 - y^2)y]p^2 - [2a^2xy - (x^2 - y^2)^2]p$
$\qquad\qquad + a^2y^2 - xy(x^2 - y^2) = 0$ $\qquad\qquad$ **6**
$\quad (xp - y)[a^2(xp - y) + (x^2 - y^2)(yp + x)] = 0;\quad$ see (1-155)
$\quad$ and (1-682).
$\qquad y = Cx;\quad r^2 + a^2 \ln(\tan 2\theta + \sec 2\theta) = C$
$\quad$ where $x = r \cos \theta,\ y = r \sin \theta$.

263 $\quad [x^2 - (x^2 + y^2)y^2]p^2 - 2xyp + y^2 = 0$ $\qquad\qquad$ **6**
$\quad y = ux;\quad u'^2(y) = u^2(u^2 + 1);\quad$ see **1-2-1**.
$\qquad x = \pm y \sinh(C + y);\quad y = 0$

264 $\quad [x^4 + (x^2 - y^2)y^2]p^2 - 2xy(x^2 + 2y^2)p + y^4 = 0$ $\qquad\qquad$ **3-1-1**
$\quad x = r \cos \theta,\quad y = r \sin \theta;\quad r'^2(\theta) \sin^2 \theta = r^2;\quad$ see **2-1**.
$\qquad (C - y)[x^2 + (C - y)^2] + C[x^2 - (C - y)^2] = 0$

265 $\quad 3xy^4p^2 - y^5p + 1 = 0$ $\qquad\qquad$ **6**
$\quad y^3 = u(x);\quad xu'^2(x) - uu' + 3 = 0;\quad$ see (113).
$\qquad C(y^3 - Cx) = 3;\quad 12x = y^6$

266 $\quad 9xy^4p^2 - 3y^5p - a = 0$ $\qquad\qquad$ **2-2**
$\quad 9y^4p(2a + 3y^5p)[2py'(p) + y] = 0;\quad$ see **A1-1-2**;$\quad y^2p = C$.
$\qquad C(Cx - y^3) = a;\quad 4ax + y^6 = 0$

267     $9(1-x^2)y^4p^2 + 6xy^5p + 4x^2 = 0$ **6**
     $y^3 = u(x);$ $(1-x^2)u'^2(x) + 2xuu' + 4x^2 = 0;$ see (168).
         $x^2 = C(C+y^3)+1;$ $y^6 = 4(1-x^2)$

268     $[a^2R(x,y)-x^2]p^2 + 2xyp + a^2R(x,y) - y^2 = 0$ **6-1**
     $R(x,y) = \sqrt{x^2+y^2};$ $x = r\cos\theta,$ $y = r\sin\theta;$
     $a^2r(p^2+1) = (y-xp)^2.$

$$r = a^2 \sec^2 \frac{(\theta+C)}{2}$$

269     $[aR(x,y)-x^2]p^2 + 2xyp + aR(x,y) - y^2 = 0$ **6-1**
     $R(x,y) = (x^2+y^2)^{3/2};$ $x = r\cos\theta,$ $y = r\sin\theta;$
     $ar^3(1+p^2) = (y-xp)^2.$

$$ar = \sin^2\frac{(\theta+C)}{2}$$

270     $p^3 = a + bx$ **1-1-1**
       $4by = 3(a+bx)^{4/3} + C$

271     $p^3 = ax^n$ **1-1-1**
       $(3+n)^3(C+y)^3 = 27ax^{n+3}$

272     $p^3 + x - y = 0$ **2-2**
       $x = 3t^2/2 + 3t + 3\ln(t-1) + C;$ $y = t^3 + 3t^2/2$
         $+ 3t + 3\ln(t-1) + C$

273     $p^3 = (a + by + cy^2)f(x)$ **2-1**
     $u^3(x) = a + by + cy^2;$ $3u'(x) \pm (4cu^3 + b^2 - 4ac)^{1/2}f^{1/3} = 0;$
     see **A1-1-2**.

274     $p^3 = (y-a)^2(y-b)^2$ **1-2-1**
     $p = u^2;$ $u^3(x) = (y-a)(y-b);$ $3u'(x) \pm [(a-b)^2 + 4u^3]^{1/2} = 0;$
     see **A1-1-3**.

275     $p^3 + f(x)(y-a)^2(y-b)^2 = 0$ **9-4**

276     $p^3 + f(x)(y-a)^2(y-b)^2(y-c)^2 = 0$ **9-4**

277     $p^3 + p + a - bx = 0$ **1-1-2**
       $bx = a + t(1+t^2);$ $4by = t^2(2+3t^2) + C$

278     $p^3 + p - y = 0$ **1-2-2**
       $x = C + 3t^2/2 + \ln t;$ $y = t(t^2+1)$

279     $p^3 + p = e^y$ **1-2-2**
       $x = 2\tan^{-1}t - 1/t + C;$ $y = \ln t(t^2+1)$

280     $p^3 - 7p + 6 = 0$ **1-3**
     $(p-1)(p-2)(p+3) = 0.$
         $y = C + x;$ $y = C + 2x;$ $y = C - 3x$

281 $p^3 - xp + ay = 0$ **2-3**

     i. $a \neq 1$; $(a-1)px'(p) = x - 3p^2$;   see (1-158).
        $(2a-3)x = Ct^{1/(a-1)} + 3t^2$; $ay = t(x - t^2)$
     ii. $a = 1$;   see **4-1**.

282 $p^3 + 2xp - y = 0$ **2-3**

   $px'(p) + 2x + 3p^2 = 0$;   see (1-158).
     $t^2(4x + 3t^2) = C$; $t(2y + t^3) = C$

283 $p^3 - 2xp - y = 0$ **2-3**

   $3px'(p) + 2x - 3p^2 = 0$;   see (1-158).
     $t^{2/3}(8x - 3t^2) = C$; $4y = t^3 - Ct^{1/3}$

284 $p^3 - axp + x^3 = 0$ **1-1-3**

     i. $a \neq 0$; $p = xu(x)$; $x(u^3 + 1) = au$; $6y = C$
        $+ a^2(4u^3 + 1)/(u^3 + 1)^2$; $27x^3 = 4a^3$ (CL).
     ii. $a = 0$;   see (271).

285 $p^3 + axp - ay = 0$ **4-1**

     $ay = C(C^2 + ax)$; $4ax^3 + 27y^2 = 0$

286 $p^3 - (a + bx)p + by = 0$ **4-1**

     $by = C(a + bx) - C^3$; $4(a + bx)^3 = 27by^2$

287 $p^3 - yp - x = 0$ **4-3**

   $p(1 + p^2)x'(p) = 2p^3 + x$;   see (1-358); $p = \tan t$.
     $x = 2\tan t + C\sin t$; $y = \tan^2 t - 2 - C\cos t$

288 $p^3 - (3 + y)p + x = 0$ **2-2**

     $x = 2t + Ct(t^2 - 1)^{-1/2}$; $y = t^2 - 1 + C(t^2 - 1)^{-1/2}$

289 $p^3 - 2yp + y^2 = 0$ **1-2-2**

     $x = C \pm 3\sqrt{1-t} + 2\ln(1 \mp \sqrt{1-t})$; $y = t(1 \pm \sqrt{1-t})$

290 $p^3 - axyp + 2ay^2 = 0$ **2-2**

   $(p^3 - ay^2)(py' - 2y) = 0$; $y' = dy/dp$;   see **A1-1-2**.
     $4y = aC(x - C)^2$; $27y = ax^3$

291 $p^3 - (x^2 + xy + y^2)p + (x + y)xy = 0$ **2-1**

   $(p - x)(p - y)(p + x + y) = 0$.
     $(2y - x^2 - C)(y - Ce^x)(y - 1 + x - Ce^{-x}) = 0$

292 $p^3 - xy^4p - y^5 = 0$ **2-2**

   $(2p^3 + y^5)(2py' - y) = 0$;   see **A1-1-2**.
     $y(C^2x - 1) = C^3$; $4x^3y^2 = 27$

293 $p^3 + e^{(3x-2y)}(p - 1) = 0$ **6**

   $x = \ln z$; $y = \ln u$; $u'^3(z) + zu' - u = 0$;   see (285).
     $e^y = C(e^x + C^2)$

294    $p^3 + e^{-2y}(e^{2x} + e^{3x})p - e^{(3x-2y)} = 0$ **6**
   $x = \ln z; \quad y = \ln u; \quad u'^3(z) = (1+z)u' + u; \quad$ see (286).
     $e^y = C(e^x + 1 + C^2)$

295    $p^3 + p^2 - y = 0$ **1-2-2**
     $(2x + C)^3 + (2x + C)^2 = 18(2x + C)y = y(16 + 27y)$

296    $p^3 - p^2 + y^2 = 0$ **1-2-3**
   $p = 1 - u^2; \quad y = u(1 - u^2).$
$$x = C + 3u + \ln\frac{u-1}{u+1}$$

297    $p^3 - p^2 + xp - y = 0$ **4-1**
     $y = C(x - C + C^2);$ a singular solution in parametric
     form is $x = t(2 - 3t); \quad y = t^2(1 - 2t).$

298    $p^3 + ap^2 + by + abx = 0$ **2-3**
   $b(a + p)x'(p) + p(2a + 3p) = 0; \quad$ see **A1-1-1**.
     $2bx = C - 2a^2 \ln(a + t) + 2at - 3t^2;$
     $by + abx + at^2 + t^3 = 0.$

299    $p^3 + a_0p^2 + a_1p + a_2 + a_3y = 0$ **1-2-2**
     $2a_3x + 2a_1 \ln y + 4a_1t + 3t^2 = C;$
     $a_3y + a_2 + a_1t + a_0t^2 + t^3 = 0.$

300    $p^3 + xp^2 - y = 0$ **4-3, 2-3**
   $(1 - p)x'(p) = 2x + 3p; \quad$ see **A1-2**.
     $2x(1 - t)^2 = C + t^2(3 - 2t); \quad y = t^2(x + t); \quad y = 0$

301    $p^3 + (1 - 3x)p^2 - x(1 - 3x)p - 1 - x^3 = 0$ **1-1-3**
   $p = x + u; \quad ux = 1 - u^2 - u^3.$
     $6u^2y = 6u^2(C - \ln u - u) + 2u^5 + 3(1 + u^6)$

302    $p^3 - yp^2 + y^2 = 0$ **1-2-2**
     $x = t \pm r \mp \ln(t + r - 2) + C; \quad 2y = t(t \pm r);$
     $r = \sqrt{t(t - 4)}.$

303    $p^3 + (\cos x \cot x - y)p^2 - (1 + y \cos x \cot x)p + y = 0$ **2-1**
   $(p - y)(p - \sin x)(p + \csc x) = 0.$
     $y = Ce^x; \quad y = C - \cos x; \quad e^y \tan x/2 = C$

304    $p^3 + (2x - y^2)p^2 - 2xy^2p = 0$ **2-1**
   $p(p + 2x)(p - y^2) = 0.$
     $y = C; \quad x^2 + y = C; \quad xy + Cy + 1 = 0$

305    $p^3 - (2x + y^2)p^2 + (x^2 - y^2 + 2xy^2)p - (x^2 - y^2)y^2 = 0$ **2-1**
   $(p - y^2)(p - x - y)(p - x + y) = 0; \quad$ see (1-4) and **A1-1-3**.
     $xy + 1 = Cy; \quad x + y + 1 = Ce^x; \quad x - y - 1 = Ce^{-x}$

306 $\quad p^3 - (x^2 + xy + y^2)p^2 + xy(x^2 + xy + y^2)p - x^3y^3 = 0$ **2-1**
$(p - x^2)(p - y^2)(p - xy) = 0.$
$\quad 3y = C + x^3; \quad y(C + x) + 1 = 0; \quad y = Ce^{x^2/2}$

307 $\quad p^3 - (x^2 + xy^2 + y^4)p^2 + xy^2(x^2 + xy^2 + y^4)p - x^3y^6 = 0$ **2-1**
$(p - x^2)(p - xy^2)(p - y^4) = 0.$
$\quad x^3 = C + 3y; \quad y(C + x^2) + 2 = 0; \quad y^3(C + 3x) + 1 = 0$

308 $\quad 2p^3 + xp - 2y = 0$ **4-3**
$px'(p) = x + 6p^2; \quad$ see (1-158).
$\quad x = t(C + 6t); \quad y = t^2(C + 8t)$

309 $\quad 2p^3 + p^2 - y = 0$ **1-2-2**
$\quad x = t(2 + 3t) + C; \quad y = t^2(1 + 2t)$

310 $\quad 3p^3 - x^4p + 2x^3y = 0$ **2-3**
$(x^4 - 9p^2)(px' - x) = 0.$
$\quad 2y = C(x^2 - 3C^2); \quad 9y = \pm x^3$

311 $\quad 4p^3 + 4p = x$ **1-1-2**
$\quad x = 4t(1 + t^2); \quad y = t^2(2 + 3t^2) + C$

312 $\quad 8p^3 + 12p^2 = 27(x + y)$ **2-3**
$9x'(p) = 8p.$
$\quad (x + C)^3 = (y - C)^2$

313 $\quad xp^3 - yp^2 + a = 0$ **4-1**
$\quad C^2(y - Cx) = a; \quad 4y^3 = 27ax^2$

314 $\quad xp^3 + (2x - y)p^2 + (x - 2y)p + 1 - y = 0$ **4-2**
$(y - xp)(1 + p)^2 = 1.$
$\quad (y - Cx)(1 + C)^2 = 1; \quad 4(x + y)^3 = 27x^2$

315 $\quad xp^3 - (x + x^2 + y)p^2 + (x^2 + y + xy)p - xy = 0$ **2-1**
$(px - y)(p - 1)(p - x) = 0.$
$\quad y = Cx; \quad y = C + x; \quad 2y = C + x^2$

316 $\quad xp^3 - 2yp^2 + 4x^2 = 0$ **2-3**
$(p^3 - 8x)(px' - x) = 0; \quad$ see also (334).
$\quad x^2 = 4C(y - 8C^2); \quad 8y^3 = 27x^4$

317 $\quad 2xp^3 - 3yp^2 - x = 0$ **4-3**
$px'(p) = 2x.$
$\quad (3Cy + 1)^2 = 4C^3x^3; \quad x + y = 0$

318 $\quad 4xp^3 - 6yp^2 - x + 3y = 0$ **2-3**
$(2p^2 - 1)x'(p) = 4px.$
$\quad x = C(2t^2 - 1); \quad 3y = C(4t^3 - 1)$

319      $8xp^3 - 12yp^2 + 9y = 0$ **2-2**
     $py'(p) = 3y.$
$$3Cy^2 = (C+x)^3; \quad y = 0; \quad 2y = \pm 3x$$

320      $x^2p^3 - 2xyp^2 + y^2p + 1 = 0$ **4-2**
     $p(y - xp)^2 + 1 = 0.$
$$C(y - Cx)^2 + 1 = 0; \quad 27x + 4y^3 = 0$$

321      $(a^2 - x^2)p^3 + bx(a^2 - x^2)p^2 - p - bx = 0$ **1-1-1**
     $(p + bx)[(a^2 - x^2)p^2 - 1] = 0; \quad$ see (171).
$$2y + bx^2 = C; \quad x = \pm a \sin(y + C)$$

322      $x^3p^3 - 3x^2yp^2 + x(x^5 + 3y^2)p - 2x^5y - y^3 = 0$ **6**
     $(y - xp)^3 = x^5(xp - 2y); \quad y = xu(x); \quad u'^3(x) + xu' - u = 0;$
     see (285).
$$y = Cx(C^2 + x); \quad 27y^2 + 4x^5 = 0$$

323      $2x^3p^3 + 6x^2yp^2 - (1 - 6xy)yp + 2y^3 = 0$ **6**
     $2(xp + y)^3 = yp; \quad y = u^2(x); \quad (2xu' + u)^3 = u'; \quad$ see (324).
$$(2xt + u)^3 = t; \quad xt^{2/3} = C + (\ln t)/9; \quad u'(x) = t$$

324      $8x^3p^3 + 12x^2yp^2 - (1 - 6xy^2)p + y^3 = 0$ **4-3**
     $(2xp + y)^3 = p; \quad 9p^{5/3}x'(p) = 1 - 6xp^{2/3}; \quad$ see (1-384).
$$t^{2/3}x = C + (\ln t)/9; \quad y + 2xt = t^{1/3}$$

325      $x^4p^3 - x^3yp^2 - x^2y^2p + xy^3 = 1$ **6**
     $x(xp - y)^2(xp + y) = 1; \quad y = ux; \quad x^2 = 1/z;$
     $8u'^2(z)(u - zu') = 1; \quad$ see **4-1**.
$$x^2 - 2C^2xy + C^3 = 0; \quad 32xy^3 = 27$$

326      $x^6p^3 - xp - y = 0$ **2-3**
     $2px'(p) + x = 0; \quad$ see **A1-1-2**.
$$xy = C(C^2x - 1); \quad 27x^3y^2 = 4$$

327      $yp^3 - 3xp + 3y = 0$ **2-2**
     $p^4y'(p) = y(3 - 2p^3); \quad$ see **A1-1-2**.
$$3tx = y(3 + t^3); \quad \ln y = C - 1/t^3 - 2\ln t$$

328      $2yp^3 - 3xp + 2y = 0$ **2-2**
     $py'(p) + 2y = 0; \quad$ see **A1-1-2**.
$$4y^3 = C(3x - 2C)^2$$

329      $2yp^3 + 3yp + x = 0$ **2-2**
     $(1 + p^2)y'(p) + 3py = 0.$
$$(x^2 + y^2 - 4C)^3 + 27Cy^4 = 0$$

330      $2yp^3 - yp^2 + 2xp - x = 0$ **2-1**
     $(2p - 1)(yp^2 + x) = 0; \quad$ see (195).
$$2y = C + x; \quad y^{3/2} + x^{3/2} = C$$

331 $(x+2y)p^3+3(x+y)p^2+(2x+y)p = 0$ **2-1**
$p(p+1)[p(x+2y)+2x+y] = 0.$
$$y = C; \quad x+y = C; \quad xy+x^2+y^2 = C$$

332 $y^2p^3-xp+y = 0$ **2-2**
$2p^4y'(p) = 1-2yp^3; \quad$ see (1-384).
$$tx = y(1+t^3y); \quad 4t^2(C-ty) = 1$$

333 $y^2p^3+2xp-y = 0$ **6**
$y^2 = u(x); \quad u'^3(x)+8xu'-8u = 0; \quad$ see (285).
$$y^2 = C(2x+C^2); \quad 32x^3+27y^4 = 0$$

334 $4y^2p^3-2xp+y = 0$ **2-2**
$py'(p)+y = 0; \quad$ see **A1-1-2**.
$$y^2 = 2C(x-2C^2); \quad 8x^3 = 27y^4$$

335 $16y^2p^3+2xp-y = 0$ **6**
$y^2 = u(x); \quad 2u'^3(x)+xu'-u = 0; \quad$ see (285).
$$y^2 = C(x+2C^2); \quad 27y^4+2x^3 = 0$$

336 $xy^2p^3-y^3p^2+x(1+x^2)p-x^2y = 0$ **6**
$(y-xp)(x^2+y^2p^2) = xp; \quad y^2(x) = u(z); \quad x^2 = z;$
$(1+u'^2)(u-zu') = u'; \quad$ see **3-1**.
$$(C^2+1)(y^2-Cx^2) = C; \quad 4[3y^4-(1+x^2)^2]$$
$\times [3x^2(1+x^2)-y^4] = y^4(1-8x^2)^2.$ In parametric form, with
$t = u'(z)$, the singular solution is $(t^2+1)^2x^2 = (t^2-1);$
$(t^2+1)(y^2-x^2t) = t.$

337 $x^7y^2p^3+(1-3x^6y^3)p^2+3x^5y^4p-x^4y^5 = 0$ **6**
$x^4y^2(y-xp)^3 = p^2; \quad y^3(x) = u(z); \quad x^3 = z; \quad (u-zu')^3 = u'^2;$
see **4-1**.
$$y^3 = C^2(Cx^3+1); \quad 27x^6y^3 = 4$$

338 $y^3p^3-xp+y = 0$ **2-2**
$3yp^4y'(p) = 1-2y^2p^3; \quad$ see (1-592).
$$5xt = y(3+Ct^{5/3}); \quad 5y^2t^3 = Ct^{5/3}-2$$

339 $y^3p^3-(1-3x)y^2p^2+3x^2yp+x^3-y^2 = 0$ **6**
$(x+yp)^3 = (1+p^2)y^2; \quad 2u(x) = x^2+y^2;$
$u'^3(x)-u'^2+2xu'-2u = 0; \quad$ see **4-1**.
$$x^2+y^2 = C(2x-C+C^2); \quad 27(x^2+y^2)^2$$
$$-4x(x^2+9y^2)+4y^2 = 0$$

340 $y^4p^3-6xp+2y = 0$ **2-2**
$2py'(p)+y = 0; \quad$ see **A1-1-2**.
$$y^3 = 2C(3x-2C^2); \quad y^2 = 2x$$

341 $p^4 = (y-a)^3(y-b)^2$ **6**
$y-a = u^2(x); \quad 2u'(x) = \pm[u(u^2+a-b)]^{1/2}; \quad$ see **A1-1-3**.

342 $p^4+f(x)(y-a)^3(y-b)^2 = 0$ **9-4**

343     $p^4 + f(x)(y-a)^3(y-b)^3 = 0$ **9-4**

344     $p^4 + f(x)(y-a)^3(y-b)^3(y-c)^2 = 0$ **9-4**

345     $p^4 + xp - 3y = 0$ **2-3, 2-2**
$$2px'(p) = x + 4p^3; \quad \text{see (1-159)}.$$
$$5x = 4t^3 + C\sqrt{t}; \quad 15y = t(9t^3 + C\sqrt{t})$$

346     $p^4 - 3(1-x)p^2 + 3(1-2y)p + 3x = 0$ **4-3**
$$px' = x + p^2; \quad \text{see (1-159)}.$$
$$x = t(C+t); \quad 6ty = t^4 + 3t(1-t) + 3x(t^2+1)$$

347     $p^4 - 4x^2yp^2 + 16xy^2p - 16y^3 = 0$ **2-2**
$$p^4 = 4y(xp - 2y)^2; \quad (p^2 - 4y^{3/2})[py'(p) - 2y] = 0; \quad \text{see } \mathbf{A1\text{-}1\text{-}2}.$$
$$y = C^2(x - C)^2; \quad 16y = x^4$$

348     $p^4 + 4yp^3 + 6y^2p^2 - (1 - 4y^3)p - (3 - y^3)y = 0$ **1-2-3**
$$(y+p)^4 = 3y + p; \quad up = y.$$
$$x = C + (4/3)\ln(u+1) - (1/9)\ln(3u+1);$$
$$(u+1)^{4/3}y = u(3u+1)^{1/3}$$

349     $2p^4 - yp - 2 = 0$ **1-2-2**
$$x + C = 3t^2 - 1/t^2; \quad y = 2t^3 - 2/t$$

350     $xp^4 - 2yp^3 + 12x^3 = 0$ **2-3**
$$(p^4 - 36x^2)[x'(p) - x] = 0; \quad \text{see } \mathbf{A1\text{-}1\text{-}3}$$
$$2C^3y = C^4x^2 + 12; \quad 3y^2 = 8x^3$$

351     $p^5 + ap^3 + bp^2 = cy$ **1-2-2**
$$4cx = t(8b + 6at + 5t^3) + C; \quad cy = t^2(b + at + t^3)$$

352     $p^5 + ap^4 + bp^3 + cxp^2 = cy$ **4-3**
$$c(1-p)x'(p) = p(3b + 4ap + 5p^2) + 2cx; \quad \text{see } \mathbf{A1\text{-}2}.$$
$$c(1-t)^2x = C + t^2\left[\frac{3b}{2} + \frac{(4a-3b)}{3}t + \frac{(5-4a)}{4}t^2 - t^3\right];$$
$$cy = t^2(cx + bt + at^2 + t^3); \quad cy = a + b + 1 + cx$$

353     $3p^5 - yp + 1 = 0$ **1-2-2**
$$x = 4t^3 + 1/2t^2 + C; \quad y = 3t^4 + 1/t$$

354     $p^6 = (y-a)^4(y-b)^3$ **6**
$$y - a = u^3(x); \quad 3u'(x) = \pm (u^3 + a - b)^{1/2}; \quad \text{see } \mathbf{A1\text{-}1\text{-}3}.$$

355     $p^6 + f(x)(y-a)^4(y-b)^3 = 0$ **9-4**

356     $p^6 + f(x)(y-a)^5(y-b)^3 = 0$ **9-4**

357     $p^6 + f(x)(y-a)^5(y-b)^4 = 0$ **9-4**

358     $p^6 + f(x)(y-a)^5(y-b)^4(y-c)^3 = 0$ **9-4**

359     $x^2(p^6 + 3p^4 + 3p^2 + 1) = a^2$ **1-1-2**
$$x^2(t^2+1)^3 = a^2; \quad (y-C)^2(t^2+1)^3 = a^2t^6$$

360 $p^n = ax^r + by^s$ **6**

$y = u^k(x)$; $[ku^{k-1}u'(x)]^n = ax^r + bu^{sk}$.   If $n(r-s) = rs$, take $ks = r$ and the equation in u, x has become type **3-1**.

361 $p^n = f^n(x)(y-a)^{n+1}(y-b)^{n-1}$ **9-4, 6**

$(y-a)u^n(x) = \pm(y-b)$; $nu'(x) = (b-a)f(x)$;   see **A1-1-1**.

362 $p^n + f(x)(y-a)^{n+1} = 0$ **9-4**

363 $p^n + f(x)(y-a)^{n-1} = 0$ **9-4**

364 $p^n + f(x)g(y) = 0$ **9-2, 9-4**

365 $p^n + f(x, y) = 0$ **9-2**

366 $p^n + ap = by$ **1-2-2**

$b(n-1)x + C = a(n-1)\ln t + nt^{n-1}$; $by = at + t^n$.

367 $p^n + xp - y = 0$ **4-1**

$y = Cx + C^n$; $x^n(n-1)^{n-1} + n^n y^{n-1} = 0$

368 $p^n + ap^m = by$; $n > m$ **1-2-2**

  i. $b(m-1)(n-1)x = C + am(n-1)t^{m-1} + n(m-1)t^{n-1}$;

    $by = t^n + at^m$; $m \neq 1$.

  ii. $m = 1$;   see (366).

369 $p^n + Y_1(y)p^{n-1} + \quad \dots \quad + Y_n(y) = 0$ **9-1**

370 $p^n + X_1(x, y)p^{n-1} + \quad \dots \quad + X_n(x, y) = 0$ **9**

371 $x^{n-1}p^n - nxp + y = 0$ **2-3**

$(x^{n-2}p^{n-1} - 1)[nxp'(x) + (n-1)p] = 0$;   see **A1-1-2**.

  $y = C(nx^{1/n} - C^{n-1})$; $y = (n-1)x^{1/(n-1)}$

372 $X_0(x, y)p^n + X_1(x, y)p^{n-1} + \quad \dots \quad + X_n(x, y) = 0$ **8**

373 $2\sqrt{ap} + xp - y = 0$ **4-1**

  $y = Cx + 2\sqrt{Ca}$; $xy + a = 0$

374 $(x-y)\sqrt{p} = a(1+p)$ **2-3**

  $(p-1)(2p^{3/2} + ap') = 0$; $\sqrt{p}(x-C) = a$;   see **A1-1-3**.

  $(y-C)(C-x) = a^2$

375 $2(1+p)^{3/2} + 3xp - 3y = 0$ **4-1**

  $3y = 3Cx + 2(1+C)^{3/2}$; $3y = x(x^2 - 3)$

376 $\sqrt{1+p^2} + ap = x$ **1-1-2**

  $x = at + \sqrt{1+t^2}$; $2y = t(at + \sqrt{1+t^2})$

   $- \ln(t + \sqrt{1+t^2}) + C$.

377 $\sqrt{1+p^2} + ap = y$ **1-2-2**

  $x + C = \ln t^a(t + \sqrt{1+t^2})$; $y = at + \sqrt{1+t^2}$

378    $\sqrt{1+p^2} = xp$ **1-1-1**
        $(1-x^2)p^2 + 1 = 0;$ see (170)
        $x = \pm \cosh(y+C)$

379    $\sqrt{1+p^2} - ayp - ax = 0$ **2-2, 4-3**
       $a(1+p^2)^{3/2}y'(p) = p(p - ay\sqrt{1+p^2});$ see **A1-2**.
          $a(x+yt) = \sqrt{1+t^2};$ $ay\sqrt{1+t^2} = C + t - \tan^{-1}t$

380    $\sqrt{1+p^2} - xp^2 + y = 0$ **4-3**
       $(p-1)\sqrt{p^2+1}\,x'(p) = 1 - 2x\sqrt{p^2+1};$ see **A1-2**.
         $(t-1)^2 x = \sqrt{1+t^2} - \ln(t + \sqrt{1+t^2}) + C;$
          $y = xt^2 - \sqrt{1+t^2}.$

381    $\sqrt{a^2 \pm b^2 p^2} + xp - y = 0$ **4-1**
         $y = Cx + \sqrt{a^2 \pm b^2 C^2};$ $a^2 x^2 \pm b^2 y^2 = \pm a^2 b^2$

382    $\sqrt{a + 2bp + cp^2} + (xp - y)\sqrt{ac - b^2} = 0$ **4-1**
         $\sqrt{ac - b^2}(Cx - y) = \sqrt{a + 2bC + cC^2};$
         $ax^2 + 2bxy + cy^2 = 1.$

383    $x\sqrt{1+p^2} + xp - y = 0$ **2-1**
    $2xyp + x^2 - y^2 = 0;$ see (1-562).
         $x^2 + y^2 = Cx$

384    $ax\sqrt{1+p^2} + xp - y = 0$ **4-3, 2-3**
    $a(1+p^2)x'(p) + x(ap + \sqrt{1+p^2}) = 0;$ see **A1-2**.
      i. $a \neq 1;$ $x^a(t + \sqrt{1+t^2})(1+t^2)^{a/2} = C.$
      ii. $a = 1,$ see (383).

385    $y\sqrt{1+p^2} - ayp - ax = 0$ **2-3, 5**
      i. $(1-a^2)y^2 p^2 - 2a^2 xyp - a^2 x^2 + y^2 = 0;$ see (233);
         $x^2 + y^2 - 2Cx + C^2(1-a^2) = 0;$ $(1-a^2)y^2 = a^2 x^2.$
      ii.   See also (386).

386    $y\sqrt{1+p^2} = f(yp + x)$ **5**
    The equation can be written as $F(x, y, p) = G(x, y, p)$, where
$F = yp + x = C_1$ and $G = y\sqrt{1+p^2} = C_2$ are derivable from a
common primitive, $y^2 + (x - C_1)^2 = C_2^2$. The solution of the
given equation, see also (421), is
        $y^2 + (x - C_1)^2 = f^2(C_1)$

387    $[(ax^2 + y^2)(1+p^2)]^{1/2} - yp - ax = 0$ **3-1-1**
   $p = u \pm [(a-1)(a + u^2)/a]^{1/2};$ see **A1-8-1**;
     $y + \sqrt{ax^2 + y^2} = Cx^k;$ $k = 1 \pm \sqrt{(a-1)/a}.$

388 $\quad a(1+p^3)^{1/3}+xp-y=0$ $\qquad\qquad$ **4-1**

$\qquad y=Cx+a(C^3+1)^{1/3};\quad x^{3/2}+y^{3/2}=a^{3/2}$

389 $\quad p[a+x\sqrt{1+p^2})=y\sqrt{1+p^2}$ $\qquad\qquad$ **4-2**

$\quad (y-xp)\sqrt{1+p^2}+ap=0.$

$\qquad (y-Cx)\sqrt{1+C^2}+Ca=0;\quad x^{2/3}+y^{2/3}=a^{2/3}$

390 $\quad \cos p+xp=y$ $\qquad\qquad$ **4-1**

$\qquad y=Cx+\cos C;\quad (y-x\sin^{-1}x)^2=1-x^2$

391 $\quad a\cos p+bp+x=0$ $\qquad\qquad$ **1-1-2**

$\qquad x+a\cos t+bt=0;\quad 2(y-a\sin t)$

$\qquad\qquad +t(2a\cos t+bt)=C$

392 $\quad \sin p+p=x$ $\qquad\qquad$ **1-1-2**

$\qquad x=t+\sin t;\quad 2(y-\cos t)=t(t+2\sin t)+C$

393 $\quad p\sin p+\cos p=y$ $\qquad\qquad$ **1-2-2**

$\qquad x=C+\sin t;\quad y=t\sin t+\cos t$

394 $\quad p^2\sin p=y$ $\qquad\qquad$ **1-2-2**

$\qquad x=t\sin t-\cos t+C;\quad y=t^2\sin t$

395 $\quad p^2(x+\sin p)=y$ $\qquad\qquad$ **2-3**

$\quad (1-p)x'(p)=2(x+\sin p)+p\cos p;\quad$ see **A1-2**.

$\qquad x(1-t)^2=C-\cos t+t\sin t(1-t);\quad y=(x+\sin t)t^2$

396 $\quad (1+p^2)\sin^2(y-xp)=1$ $\qquad\qquad$ **4-2**

$\qquad (1+C^2)\sin^2(y-Cx)=1;\quad (1+t^2)x=1;$

$\qquad y=xt+\cot^{-1}t$

397 $\quad p(\cos^{-1}p-x)-\sqrt{1-p^2}+y=0$ $\qquad\qquad$ **4-1**

$\qquad C(\cos^{-1}C-x)-\sqrt{1-C^2}+y=0;\quad y=\sin x$

398 $\quad (1+p^2)(\tan^{-1}p+ax)+p=0$ $\qquad\qquad$ **1-1-2**

$\qquad (1+t^2)(\tan^{-1}t+ax)+t=0;\quad a(1+t^2)(C+y)=1$

399 $\quad e^{p-y}-p^2+1=0$ $\qquad\qquad$ **1-2-2**

$\qquad x=\ln t(t+1)-\ln(t-1)+C;\quad y=t-\ln(t^2-1)$

400 $\quad \ln p+p=x$ $\qquad\qquad$ **1-1-2**

$\qquad x+1=\pm\sqrt{C+2y}+\ln(\pm\sqrt{C+2y}-1)$

401 $\quad \ln p+xp+a=0$ $\qquad\qquad$ **1-1-2**

$\qquad xt+a+\ln t=0;\quad 2y=C+2(a-1)\ln t+(\ln t)^2$

402 $\quad \ln p+xp+a=y$ $\qquad\qquad$ **4-1**

$\qquad y=Cx+\ln C+a;\quad y=\ln(-1/x)+a-1$

403 $\quad \ln p+xp+a+by=0$ $\qquad\qquad$ **4-3**

$\quad (b+1)p^2x'(p)+1+xp=0;\quad$ see **A1-2**.

$\qquad bxt=Ct^{-1/(b+1)}+1;\quad by+xt+\ln t+a=0$

404     $\ln p + 4xp - 2y = 0$ **4-3**
        $2p^2 x'(p) + 1 + 4xp = 0$;   see **A1-2.**
              $t(2xt+1) = C$; $t(2y - \ln t) = 2(C - t)$

405     $\ln p + a(xp - y) = 0$ **4-2**
           $ay = aCx + \ln C$; $ay + 1 + \ln(-ax) = 0$

406     $a(\ln p - p) - x + y = 0$ **4-3**
      $(p-1)[px'(p) - a] = 0$;   see **A1-1-1.**
          $a \ln(C + y) = C + x$; $y = a + x$

407     $y \ln p + p - y \ln y - xy = 0$ **2-2**
     $(y^2 + yp + p^2)y'(p) = y(y + p)$;   see **A1-8-1.**
        $x = \ln t/y + t/y$; $2y^2 \ln Cy = t(2y + t)$

408     $p \ln p - (1+x)p + y = 0$ **4-1**
        $y = C(x + 1 - \ln C)$; $y = e^x$

409     $\ln(px - y) = p$ **2-3, 4-1**
        $y = Cx - e^C$; $y = x(\ln x - 1)$

410     $p \ln[p + \sqrt{1+p^2}] - \sqrt{1+p^2} - xp + y = 0$ **4-2**
      $y = Cx + \sqrt{1 + C^2} - C \ln[C + \sqrt{1 + C^2}]$; $y = \cosh x$

411     $\ln \cos p + p \tan p = y$ **2-3**
        $x = C + \tan t$; $y = t \tan t + \ln \cos t$

412     $f(p) = 0$ **1-3**

413     $f(x, p) = 0$ **1-1**

414     $f(xp^2) = y - 2xp$ **6**
   $y(x) = u(z)$; $x = z^2$; $u(z) = zu' + f(u'^2/4)$;   see **4-1.**
         $[y - f(C)]^2 = 4Cx$

415     $f(y, p) = 0$ **1-2**

416     $f(p) + xp = y$ **4-1**

417     $f(p) + xg(p) = y$ **4-3**

418     $f(p, y - xp) = 0$ **4-2**

419     $f(xp, y) = 0$ **3-2**

420     $x^n f(p, y/x) = 0$ **3-1**

421     $f(x + yp) = (1 + p^2)y^2$ **6**
   $2u = x^2 + y^2$; $u'^2(x) - 2xu' + 2u = f(u')$;   see **4-1.**
        $(x - C)^2 + y^2 = f(C)$
   There is also a singular solution.

422     $yf(p/y, x) = 0$ **3-3**

423     $f(x, y, p) = 0$ **2, 7**

3. THE DIFFERENTIAL EQUATION IS LINEAR AND OF SECOND ORDER

The general equation is

$$A_0(x)y'' + A_1(x)y' + A_2(x)y = f(x)$$

A given equation is located in the collection by the rank of the coefficients, beginning with $A_0(x)$. See 1 for further details. The general solution of the equation will be

$$y(x) = Y(x) + F(x)$$

where $Y(x) = C_1y_1 + C_2y_2$ and $F(x) = 0$, if $f(x) = 0$. When $f(x) \neq 0$, the tables will give $F(x)$ and refer to the appropriate equation for the rest of the solution $Y(x)$.

A number of equations in this section have been studied exhaustively and they are known by the names of famous mathematicians. Typical examples, together with the corresponding equation numbers, are:

Bessel—(194), (274), (275), (276), (454)
Gauss—(410)
Gegenbauer—(377), (378)
Hermite—(112), (117)
Heun—(523)
Jacobi—(376), (408)
Kummer—(211)
Laguerre—(204), (205)
Legendre—(366), (367), (369), (462), (463), (554), (555), (577), (578)
Mathieu—(43), (467)
Weber—(176), (177)
Whittaker—(450)

More than one equation number is necessary in most cases since alternative forms of the equation occur. For further information about such named equations refer to Erdélyi-1 or to Magnus-Oberhettinger.

For a general description of symbols used in this section see Part I, Introduction-4. Further symbols used frequently here include Γ (a), the gamma function; $\mathscr{P}(x)$, the Weierstrassian elliptic function; sn (x), the

311

Jacobi elliptic function; $_1F_1(a, b; x)$, the Kummer series, see (211); $_2F_1(a, b, c; x)$, the hypergeometric series, see (410). The letter p is always a constant and does not mean dy/dx here.

1    $y'' = 0$ **1, 9-1; B2-1-1, 2-1**
$$y = C_1 + C_2 x$$

2    $y'' = x + \sin x$ **12-1**
See (1); $F(x) = (x^3/6) - \sin x$.

3    $y'' = c_1 \cos ax + c_2 \sin bx$ **12-1**
See (1); $F(x) = A_1 \cos ax + A_2 \sin bx$; $A_1 = -c_1/a^2$, $A_2 = -c_2/b^2$.

4    $y'' = xe^x$ **12-1**
See (1); $f(x) = (x-2)e^x$.

5    $y'' = c_1 e^{ax} + c_2 e^{-bx}$ **12-1**
See (1); $F(x) = A_1 e^{ax} + A_2 e^{-bx}$; $A_1 = c_1/a^2$, $A_2 = c_2/b^2$.

6    $y'' + y = 0$ **1; B2-2-1**
$$y = C_1 \cos x + C_2 \sin x$$
For alternative forms of the solutions, see **1**.

7    $y'' - y = 0$ **1, 9-1; B2-2-1**
$$y = C_1 e^x + C_2 e^{-x}$$
For other forms of the solutions, see **1**.

8    $y'' + y = ax$ **12-1**
See (6); $F(x) = ax$.

9    $y'' + y = a \cos bx$ **12-1**
See (6).
     i. $b^2 \neq 1$; $F(x) = A \cos bx$; $A = a/(1-b^2)$.
     ii. $b = \pm 1$; $F(x) = (a/2)x \sin x$.

10    $y'' + y = 8 \cos x \cos 2x$ **12-1**
See (6); $F(x) = 2x \sin x - \frac{1}{2} \cos 3x$.

11    $y'' + y = \sec x$ **12-1**
See (6); $F(x) = x \sin x + \cos x \ln \cos x$.

12    $y'' + y = a \sin bx$ **12-1**
See (6).
     i. $b^2 \neq 1$; $F(x) = A \sin bx$; $A = a/(1-b^2)$.
     ii. $b = \pm 1$; $F(x) = \mp (a/2)x \cos x$.

13    $y'' + y = \sin ax \sin bx$ **12-1**
See (6).
     i. $|a \pm b| \neq 1$; $F(x) = F_1 - F_2$;
$$F_1 = \frac{\cos(a-b)x}{2 - 2(a-b)^2}; \quad F_2 = \frac{\cos(a+b)x}{2 - 2(a+b)^2}.$$

ii. $|a+b| = 1$; $F(x) = F_1 + \dfrac{x \sin x}{4}$.

iii. $|a-b| = 1$; $F(x) = \dfrac{x \sin x}{4} - F_2$.

14 $y'' + y = 4x \sin x$ **12-1**
See (6); $F(x) = x(\sin x - x \cos x)$.

15 $y'' + y = x(\cos x - x \sin x)$ **12-1**
See (6); $F(x) = (1/6)x^3 \cos x$.

16 $y'' + y = \tan^2 x$ **12-1**
See (6); $F(x) = \frac{1}{2} \sin x \ln \dfrac{1+\sin x}{1-\sin x} - 2$.

17 $y'' + y = e^{-x}$ **12-1**
See (6); $F(x) = \frac{1}{2}e^{-x}$.

18 $y'' + y = e^x(x^2 - 1)$ **12-1**
See (6); $f(x) = xe^x(\frac{1}{2}x - 1)$.

19 $y'' + y = e^x \sin 2x$ **12-1**
See (6); $F(x) = -(1/10)e^x(\sin 2x + 2 \cos 2x)$.

20 $y'' + y = e^{2x} \cos x$ **12-1**
See (6); $f(x) = (1/8)e^{2x}(\cos x + \sin x)$.

21 $y'' - 2y = 0$ **1; B2-2-1**
$$y = C_1 e^{x\sqrt{2}} + C_2 e^{-x\sqrt{2}}$$
See also (26).

22 $y'' - 2y = 4x^2 e^{x^2}$ **12-1**
See (21); $F(x) = e^{x^2}$.

23 $y'' + 4y = 0$ **1; B2-2-1**
$$y = C_1 \cos 2x + C_2 \sin 2x$$
See also (26).

24 $y'' + 4y = x \sin^2 x$ **12-1**
See (23); $F(x) = \dfrac{x}{8} - \dfrac{x}{32} \cos 2x - \dfrac{x^2}{16} \sin 2x$.

25 $y'' + 4y = 2 \tan x$ **12-1**
See (23); $F(x) = \sin 2x \ln \cos x - x \cos 2x$.

26 $y'' + a^2 y = 0$ **1; B2-2-1**
     i. $a^2 = 0$, see (1).
     ii. $a^2 > 0$, $y = C_1 \cos ax + C_2 \sin ax$.
     iii. $a^2 < 0$, $y = C_1 e^{ax} + C_2 e^{-ax}$.
For alternative solutions, see **1**.

27 $y'' - a^2 y = 1 + x$ **12-1**
See (26); $F(x) = -(1 + x)/a^2$.

28 $y'' = ax + by$ **4-1**
    $u = ax + by$; $u''(x) = bu$; see (26).

29 $y'' + a^2 y = 1 + x + x^2$ **12-1**
See (26); $F(x) = (1 + x + x^2)/a^2 - 2/a^4$.

30 $y'' + a^2 y = \cos bx$ **12-1**
See (26).

$$\text{i. } a \neq b;\ \ F(x) = \frac{\cos bx}{a^2 - b^2}.$$

$$\text{ii. } a = b;\ \ F(x) = \frac{x \sin ax}{2a}.$$

31 $y'' + a^2 y = \cot ax$ **12-1**
See (26); $F(x) = \dfrac{\sin ax}{a^2} \ln\!\left(\dfrac{1 - \cos ax}{\sin ax}\right).$

32 $y'' + a^2 y = \sin bx$ **12-1**
See (26).

$$\text{i. } a \neq b;\ \ F(x) = \frac{\sin bx}{a^2 - b^2}.$$

$$\text{ii. } a = b;\ \ F(x) = -\frac{x \cos ax}{2a}.$$

33 $y'' + xy = 0$ **9-1**
$y(x) = u(z)\sqrt{x}$; $3z = 2x^{3/2}$; $z^2 u'' + zu' - (1/9 - z^2)u = 0$;
see (274).
$$y_{1,2} = J_{\pm 1/3}(z)\sqrt{x}, \text{ where } J_k \text{ is a Bessel function of}$$
order k.

34 $y'' + (a + bx)y = 0$ **4-2-2, 9-1**
$y(x) = u(z)$; $b^{2/3}z = a + bx$; $u''(z) + zu = 0$; see (33) and (41).

35 $y'' + (a + x^2)y = 0$ **9-1**
A solution, see (177), is
$$y_1 = D_p(z);\ \ p = -(1 + ia)/2;\ \ z = \pm(1 + i)x$$

36 $y'' + (a - x^2)y = 0$ **4-1**
$y = e^{-x^2/2}u(x)$; $u''(x) - 2xu' + 2pu = 0$; $a = 1 + 2p$;
see (117).

37 $y'' = (a + x^2)y$ **4-3**
$$\text{i. } y(x) = u(z);\ \ z = x\sqrt{2};\ \ 4u''(z) = (2a + z^2)u;$$
see (176).

ii. $y = e^{-x^2/2}u(x)$; $u''(x) - 2xu' - (1+a)u = 0$;
see (117).

38 $y'' + (a + bx^2)y = 0$ **9-1**

i. $y = e^{-z/2}u(z)$; $z = ix^2\sqrt{b}$;
$zu'' + (1/2 - z)u' - ku = 0$; $4k = (ia/\sqrt{b} + 1)$;
see (211). A solution is
$y_1 = e^{-z/2}{}_1F_1(k, 1/2; z)$

ii. $y(x) = u(z)$; $cx^2 = z^2$; $u''(z) + (k + 1/2 - z^2/4)u = 0$;
$2a = c(2k + 1)$; $4b + c^2 = 0$; see (177).

39 $y'' + (a + bx + cx^2)y = 0$ **9-1**
$y(x) = u(z)$; $2c(z - x) = b$; $u''(z) + (a + bz)^2 u = 0$; see (38).

40 $y'' + (a_0 + a_1 x^2 + x^4)y = 0$ **9-2**
There is an ordinary point at at $x = 0$. Use **8-1** to find two
infinite series solutions.

41 $y'' + ax^k y = 0$ **9-1**
See also **A1-3-2c**.

i. $y = \sqrt{x}J_{1/p}\left(\dfrac{2\sqrt{a}}{p}x^{p/2}\right)$; $p = k + 2$ and $J_{1/p}$ is a

Bessel function of order $1/p$; see (274).

ii. $y(x) = xu(z)$; $x = 1/z$; $z^{k+4}u''(z) = au$.

iii. If $k = -2$, see **3-1** and (250).

42 $y'' + (a_0 + a_1 x + a_2 x^2 + ... + a_m x^m)y = 0$ **9-1**

43 $y'' + (a + b\cos 2x)y = 0$ **9-2, 9-3**
Mathieu's equation. The quantities a, b are real or complex
constants. There seems to be no standard form for the equation,
various writers taking the constants in different ways. Following Erdélyi-1, we choose $a = h$, $b = -2\theta$.

Since the differential equation has periodic coefficients,
Floquet's theorem predicts that it will have solutions of the
form $y_1 = e^{kx}f(x)$ and $y_2 = e^{-kx}f(-x)$, where $f(x)$ is a function
of period π and k is a constant, called the characteristic exponent. These solutions, said to be of the first kind, are linearly
independent and the general solution of the equation is $y = C_1 y_1 + C_2 y_2$, unless $m = ik$ is an integer. The characteristic
exponents can be calculated in a number of ways. In one method,
a trial solution is assumed

$$y = \sum_{n=-\infty}^{\infty} A_n e^{(k+2in)x}$$

When it is substituted into the differential equation, the recursion relation for the coefficients is found to be

$$A_n + c_n(k)(A_{n+1} + A_{n-1}) = 0; \quad c_n(k) = \theta/[(2n - ik)^2 - h];$$

$n = 0, \pm 1, \pm 2, \dots$. It leads to an infinite determinant, $\Delta(h, \theta)$ and k is found from $\Delta(h, \theta) = 0$.

If h, θ are both real, there are three possibilities:

  i. k is imaginary, ik is not an integer, every solution of the equation is bounded on the real x-axis. This is called a stable region of the (h, θ)-plane.

  ii. k or $(k - i)$ real and not zero. There is no bounded solution on the real axis and the region is called unstable.

  iii. $\cosh kn = \pm 1$. Characteristic curves separate stable and unstable regions, one solution of the equation is bounded and periodic but the general solution is unbounded.

If $ik = m$, an integer, the solution of the first kind is a Mathieu function. Its period is π if m is an even integer and 2π if m is odd. Such solutions are often of interest in physical problems. In those cases, θ is usually given and characteristic values of h are calculated in order to find the periodic solutions. There are four types of these solutions, frequently designated as ce_{2m}, ce_{2m+1}, se_{2m+1}, se_{2m+2}. Each is an infinite series with terms $A_{2r} \cos 2rx$, $A_{2r+1} \cos(2r + 1)x$, $B_{2r+1} \sin(2r + 1)x$, $B_{2r+2} \sin(2r + 2)x$, respectively.

When $m = ik$ is an integer and $e(x)$ is a Mathieu function of the first kind, another solution of the differential equation is $y_2 = xe(x) + g(x)$. It is a Mathieu function of the second kind. If $e(x)$ is a cosine series, $g(x)$ is a sine series and the reverse. There are also Mathieu functions of the third kind, which are linear combinations of those of first and second kinds.

44 $y'' + (a + b \cos 2x + k \cos 4x)y = 0$ 9-3
  A special case of (45).

45 $y'' + (a_0 + a_1 \cos 2x + \dots + a_m \cos 2mx)y = 0$ 9-3
  A special case of Hill's differential equation, which is $y'' + [a + \phi(x)]y = 0$, where $\phi(x)$ is a periodic function. Its solutions are similar to those of (43), which is a simpler case.

46 $y'' = 2y \csc^2 x$ 4-1-1
  $y_1 = \cot x$.
    $y = C_1 \cot x + C_2(1 - x \cot x)$

47    $y'' + ay \csc^2 x = 0$ **4-2-2**
$y(x) = u(z)$; $z = \cot x$; $(1+z^2)u'' + 2zu' + au = 0$;   see (368).

48    $y'' + (a_0 + a_1 \cos^2 x + a_2 \csc^2 x)y = 0$ **9-3**
The normal form of (143);   see also **4-1-2**.

49    $y'' = [a^2 + p(p-1)\csc^2 x + q(q-1)\sec^2 x]y$ **4-3**
    i. $y = \cos^q x \sin^p x u(z)$; $z = \sin^2 x$;
        $z(1-z)u'' + [\alpha - (1+\beta+\gamma)z]u' - \beta\gamma u = 0$;
        $\alpha = p+1/2$; $\beta, \gamma = \frac{1}{2}(p+q \pm ia)$;   see (410).
    ii. $a = 0, q = 0$, see (47).

50    $y'' + (a + b \sin^2 x)y = 0$ **9-6**
A more convenient form is $y'' + (A + B \cos 2x)y = 0$;
$A = a + b/2$; $B = -b/2$;   see (43).

51    $y'' = (1 + 2\tan^2 x)y$ **4-1-1**
$y_1 = \sec x$.
        $y = C_1 \sec x + C_2(\sin x + x \sec x)$

52    $y'' - (a^2 - be^x)y = 0$ **4-2**
$y(x) = u(z)$; $z = 2e^{x/2}\sqrt{b}$; $z^2u'' + zu' + (z^2 - 4a^2)u = 0$;
see (274).

53    $y'' - (a^2 - e^{2x})y = 0$ **4-2**
$y(x) = u(z)$; $z = e^x$; $z^2u'' + zu' + (z^2 - a^2)u = 0$;   see (274).

54    $y'' + (a + be^x + ce^{2x})y = 0$ **4-2**
$y(x) = e^{-x/2}u(z)$; $z = e^x$; $z^2u'' + (1/4 + a + bz + cz^2)u = 0$;
see (258).

55    $y'' + ae^{bx}y = 0$ **4-2-2**
$y(x) = u(z)$; $bz = 2e^{bx/2}\sqrt{a}$; $zu'' + u' + zu = 0$;   see 199).

56    $y'' + (a + b \cosh^2 x)y = 0$ **4-2**
$y(x) = u(z)$; $x = iz$; $u''(z) - (a + b\cos^2 z)u = 0$.   A more
convenient form is $u'' - (\alpha + \beta \cos 2z)u = 0$; $\alpha = a + b/2$;
$\beta = b/2$;   see (43).

57    $y'' + (a + b \sinh^2 x)y = 0$ **9-6**
$y(x) = u(z)$; $x = iz$; $u''(z) = (a - b \sin^2 z)u$;   see (50).

58    $y'' + (a + b \, \mathrm{sn}^2 x)y = 0$ **9-4**
The Jacobian form of the Lamé equation.

59    $y'' + [a + b\mathscr{P}(x)]y = 0$ **9-4**
The Weierstrassian form of the Lamé equation.

60    $y'' - y' + xy = 0$ **8-1**

i. $y = C_1 y_1 + C_2 y_2;$ $y_1 = 1 - \dfrac{1}{6}x^3 - \dfrac{1}{24}x^4 - \dfrac{1}{120}x^5$

$+ \dfrac{1}{240}x^6 + \dfrac{1}{630}x^7 + \dots;$ $y_2 = x\left(1 + \dfrac{1}{2}x + \dfrac{1}{6}x^2 - \dfrac{1}{24}x^3 - \dfrac{1}{30}x^4\right.$

$\left. - \dfrac{1}{90}x^5 - \dfrac{1}{1680}x^6 + \dots\right).$ The recursion relations, see **8-1-1**, are

$k(k-1)A_k - (k-1)A_{k-1} + A_{k-3} = 0;$ $A_0 = 1,$ $A_1 = A_2 = 0$ for y_1 and $A_0 = 0,$ $A_1 = 1,$ $A_2 = 1/2$ for y_2.

ii. $y = e^{x/2}u(x);$ $u'' + (x - 1/4)u = 0;$ see **4-1-2, 9-1**, and (34).

61    $y'' \pm 2y' + y = 0$ **1**

$y = e^{\mp x}(C_1 + C_2 x)$

62    $y'' - 2y' + y = x^2(x - 6)$ **12-1**

See (61); $F(x) = x^3 - 6x - 12.$

63    $y'' - 2y' + y = e^x$ **12-1**

See (61); $F(x) = x^2 e^x / 2.$

64    $y'' - 2y' + y = e^x(1 + 2x + 3x^2)$ **12-1**

See (61); $F(x) = x^2 e^x \left(\dfrac{1}{2} + \dfrac{1}{3}x + \dfrac{1}{4}x^2\right).$

65    $y'' - 2y' + y = e^x \sin x$ **12-1**

See (61); $F(x) = -e^x \sin x.$

66    $y'' + 2y' + y = x^2 - \cos x + 3e^{2x}$ **12-1**

See (61); $F(x) = \dfrac{1}{3}e^{2x} - \dfrac{1}{2}\sin x + (x^3 - 6x^2 + 18x - 24).$

67    $y'' - 2y' + y = 8x^2 e^{3x}$ **12-1**

See (61); $F(x) = e^{3x}(2x^2 - 4x + 3).$

68    $y'' - 2y' + y = 50 \cos x \cosh x$ **12-1**

See (61); $F(x) = e^{-x}(3 \cos x - 4 \sin x) - 25e^x \cos x.$

69    $y'' + 2y' + 3y = 0$ **1**

$y = e^{-x}(C_1 \cos x\sqrt{2} + C_2 \sin x\sqrt{2})$

70    $y'' + 2y' + 3y = e^{-x} \cos x$ **12-1**

See (69); $F(x) = e^{-x} \cos x.$

71    $y'' + 2y' + 5y = 0$ **1**

$y = e^{-x}(C_1 \cos 2x + C_2 \sin 2x)$

72    $y'' + 2y' + 5y = 8 \sinh x$ **12-1**

See (71); $F(x) = \frac{1}{2}e^x - e^{-x}.$

73 $\quad y'' - 2y' \tan a + y \csc^2 a = 0$ $\qquad\qquad\qquad$ **1**
$\qquad y = e^{x \tan a}(C_1 \cos x + C_2 \sin x)$

74 $\quad y'' - 2y' \tan a + y \csc^2 a = x^2 e^{x \tan a}$ $\qquad\qquad$ **12-1**
$\quad$ See (73); $\quad F(x) = e^{x \tan a}(x^2 - 2) \sec^2 a.$

75 $\quad y'' \pm 3y' + 2y = 0$ $\qquad\qquad\qquad\qquad\qquad$ **1**
$\qquad y = C_1 e^{\mp x} + C_2 e^{\mp 2x}$

76 $\quad y'' + 3y' + 2y = \cos ax$ $\qquad\qquad\qquad\qquad$ **12-1**
$\quad$ See (75); $\quad F(x) = \dfrac{3a \sin ax - (a^2 - 2) \cos ax}{9a^2 + (a^2 - 2)^2}$

77 $\quad y'' + 3y' + 2y = \sin x + e^x$ $\qquad\qquad\qquad$ **12-1**
$\quad$ See (75); $\quad F(x) = \dfrac{1}{6}e^x - \dfrac{3}{10} \cos x + \dfrac{1}{10} \sin x.$

78 $\quad y'' - 3y' + 2y = x^2 + 2e^{-x}$ $\qquad\qquad\qquad$ **12-1**
$\quad$ See (75); $\quad F(x) = \dfrac{x^2}{2} + \dfrac{3x}{2} + \dfrac{7}{4} + \dfrac{1}{3}e^{-x}.$

79 $\quad y'' - 3y' + 2y = xe^{ax}$ $\qquad\qquad\qquad\qquad$ **12-1**
$\quad$ See (75); $\quad F(x) = Ae^{ax}[(a-1)(a-2)x - (2a-3)];$
$\quad A = 1/(a-1)^2(a-2)^2.$

80 $\quad y'' - 3y' - 4y = 0$ $\qquad\qquad\qquad\qquad\qquad$ **1**
$\qquad y = C_1 e^{-x} + C_2 e^{4x}$

81 $\quad y'' - 3y' - 4y = 10 \cos 2x$ $\qquad\qquad\qquad$ **12-1**
$\quad$ See (80); $\quad F(x) = -\dfrac{4}{5} \cos 2x - \dfrac{3}{5} \sin 2x.$

82 $\quad y'' - 4y' + 4y = 0$ $\qquad\qquad\qquad\qquad\qquad$ **1**
$\qquad y = e^{2x}(C_1 + C_2 x)$

83 $\quad y'' - 4y' + 4y = e^{2x} \cos^2 x$ $\qquad\qquad\qquad$ **12-1**
$\quad$ See (82); $\quad F(x) = \tfrac{1}{8}e^{2x}(2x^2 - \cos 2x).$

84 $\quad y'' + 4y' + 5y = 0$ $\qquad\qquad\qquad\qquad\qquad$ **1**
$\qquad y = e^{-2x}(C_1 \cos x + C_2 \sin x).$

85 $\quad y'' + 4y' + 5y = \sin x$ $\qquad\qquad\qquad\qquad$ **12-1**
$\quad$ See (84); $\quad F(x) = \tfrac{1}{8}(\sin x - \cos x).$

86 $\quad y'' - 4y' + 13y = 0$ $\qquad\qquad\qquad\qquad\qquad$ **1**
$\qquad y = e^{2x}(C_1 \cos 3x + C_2 \sin 3x)$

87 $\quad y'' - 5y' + 6y = 0$ $\qquad\qquad\qquad\qquad\qquad$ **1**
$\qquad y = C_1 e^{2x} + C_2 e^{3x}$

88 $\quad y'' - 5y' + 6y = 4x^2 e^x$ $\qquad\qquad\qquad\qquad$ **12-1**
$\quad$ See (87); $\quad F(x) = e^x(2x^2 + 6x + 7).$

89    $y'' - 5y' + 6y = e^{ax}$ **12-1**
See (87).
      i. $(a-2)(a-3)F(x) = e^{ax};$ $a \neq 2;$ $a \neq 3.$
      ii. $a = 2;$ $F(x) = -xe^{2x}.$
      iii. $a = 3;$ $F(x) = xe^{3x}.$

90    $y'' + 6y' + 9y = 0$ **1**
      $y = e^{-3x}(C_1 + C_2 x)$

91    $y'' + 6y' + 9y = e^{-3x} \cosh x$ **12-1**
See (90); $F(x) = e^{-3x} \cosh x.$

92    $y'' - 7y' + 12y = 0$ **1**
      $y = C_1 e^{3x} + C_2 e^{4x}$

93    $y'' - 7y' + 12y = x$ **12-1**
See (92); $144F(x) = 12x + 7.$

94    $y'' + 8y' + 16y = 0$ **1**
      $y = e^{-4x}(C_1 + C_2 x)$

95    $y'' + 8y' + 16y = 4e^x - e^{2x}$ **12-1**
See (94); $F(x) = 4e^x/25 - e^{2x}/36.$

96    $y'' - 9y' + 20y = 0$ **1**
      $y = C_1 e^{4x} + C_2 e^{5x}$

97    $y'' - 9y' + 20y = x^2 e^{3x}$ **12-1**
See (96); $4F(x) = e^{3x}(7 + 6x + 2x^2).$

98    $y'' + 2ay' + b^2 y = 0$ **1**
      i. $b > a, y = e^{-ax}(C_1 \cos \sqrt{X} + C_2 \sin \sqrt{X});$
         $X = b^2 - a^2 x.$
      ii. $b = a, y = e^{-ax}(C_1 + C_2 x).$
      iii. $b < a, y = C_1 e^{-rx} + C_2 e^{-sx};$ $r, s = a \pm \sqrt{a^2 - b^2}.$

99    $y'' + 2ay' + b^2 y = c \sin kx$ **12-1**
See (98); $F(x) = K[c(b^2 - k^2) \sin kx - 2ack \cos kx];$
$1/K = (b^2 - k^2) + 4a^2 k^2.$

100    $y'' - 2ay' + a^2 y = e^x$ **12-1**
See (98).
      i. $a \neq 1;$ $F(x) = e^x/(a-1)^2.$
      ii. $a = 1;$ $F(x) = e^x x^2/2.$

101    $y'' - 4aby' + (a^2 + b^2)^2 y = 0$ **1**
      $y = e^{2abx}[C_1 \cos(a^2 - b^2)x + C_2 \sin(a^2 - b^2)x]$

102    $y'' + ay' + by = 0$ **1, 9-1**

103     $y'' + ay' + by = f(x)$ **12-1**
See (102).

104     $y'' + ay' + (b + cx)y = 0$ **4-1-2**
$y = uv;$ $v = e^{-ax/2};$ $u'' + (b + cx - a^2/4)u = 0;$ see (34).

105     $y'' + ay' + (b + cx^2)y = 0$ **4-1-2**
$y = uv;$ $v = x^{-a/2};$ $u'' + (b - a^2/4 + cx^2)u = 0;$ see (35).

106     $y'' + ay' + (b + ce^x)y = 0$ **4-1-2**
$y = uv;$ $v = e^{-ax/2};$ $u'' + (b - a^2/4 + ce^x)u = 0;$ see (54). A
solution is $y = e^{-ax/2}Z_p(z);$ $z = 2e^{x/2}\sqrt{c};$ $p = \sqrt{a^2 - 4b}$, where
$Z_p(z)$ is a Bessel function of order $p;$ see (274).

107     $y'' + ay' + be^{2ax}y = 0$ **4-2**
$y = e^{-ax}u(z);$ $z = e^{ax};$ $a^2u''(z) + bu = 0;$ see (26).

108     $y'' + ay' + be^{kx}y = 0$ **4-2**
$y(x) = u(z);$ $z = e^{kx/2};$ $zu''(z) + \alpha u' + \beta zu = 0;$ $\alpha = 1 + 2a/k;$
$\beta = 4b/k^2;$ see (199).

109     $y'' + xy' + y = 0$ **4-1-1**
$y_1 = e^{-x^2/2};$ see also (123).

110     $y'' + xy' - y = 0$ **4-1-1**
$y_1 = x;$ see also (123).

111     $y'' - xy' + 2y = 0$ **4-1-1**
$y_1 = (x^2 - 1);$ see also (113) and (123).

112     $y'' - xy' + ny = 0$ **8-1**
Hermite's equation. One solution is a Hermite polynomial.
$$y_1 = (-1)^n e^{x^2/2} D^n(e^{-x^2/2}) = H_n(x)$$
where $D = d/dx$. Equivalent definitions are
$$\exp[t(2x - t)/2] = \sum_{n=0}^{\infty} H_n(x)\frac{t^n}{n!}$$
$$H_{2n}(x) = \frac{(-1)^n(2n)!}{2^n n!} {}_1F_1\left(-n, \frac{1}{2}; \frac{x^2}{2}\right)$$
$$H_{2n+1}(x) = \frac{(-1)^n(2n+1)!}{2^n n!} x {}_1F_1\left(-n, \frac{3}{2}; \frac{x^2}{2}\right)$$

The quantities ${}_1F_1(a, b; z)$ are Kummer functions, see (211).
The Hermite polynomials are often defined in other ways; see
Erdélyi-1, Vol. 2.

The second solution of the differential equation is an infinite series, $y_2 = h_p(x)$, where

$$h_{2n}(x) = (-1)^n 2^n n! x_1 F_1\left(\frac{1}{2} - n, \frac{3}{2}; \frac{x^2}{2}\right)$$

$$h_{2n+1}(x) = (-1)^{n+1} 2^n n! {}_1 F_1\left(-\frac{1}{2} - n, \frac{1}{2}; \frac{x^2}{2}\right)$$

If n is other than a positive integer, see (113).

113     $y'' - xy' - ay = 0$ **4-1-2**

$y = uv;\ v = e^{x^2/4};\ u'' + \left(\dfrac{1}{2} - a - \dfrac{x^2}{4}\right)u = 0$; see (38) and (123).

114     $y'' - xy' - (1-x)y = 0$ **4-1-1**
$y_1 = e^x$;   see also (125).

115     $y'' - 2xy' + 6y = 0$ **4-1-1**
$y_1 = x(1 - 2x^2/3)$.

116     $y'' + 2xy' - 8y = 0$ **4-1-1**
$y_1 = 1 + 4x^2 + (4/3)x^4$.

117     $y'' - 2xy' + 2ny = 0$ **8-1**
Hermite's equation, according to some authors, but see also (112). One solution is a Hermite polynomial,

$$y_1 = H_n(x) = (-1)^n e^{x^2} D^n e^{-x^2}$$

where $D = d/dx$. Another definition is

$$\exp[t(2x - t)] = \sum_{n=0}^{\infty} \frac{H_n(x)}{n!} t^n$$

If $n = p$, not an integer, both solutions of the equation are infinite series

$$y_1 = \sum_{k=0}^{\infty} A_k x^{2k}; \quad y_2 = \sum_{k=0}^{\infty} B_k x^{2k+1};$$

$$A_k = \frac{(-1)^k 2^k p(p-2)...(p-2k+2)}{(2k)!};$$

$$B_k = \frac{(-1)^k 2^k (p-1)(p-3)...(p-2k+1)}{(2k+1)!}$$

118     $y'' - (1 + 2x)y' - (1 - x - x^2)y = 0$ **4-1-1**
$y_1 = e^{x^2/2}$.
$$y = C_1 e^{x^2/2} + C_2 e^{(x+1)^2/2}$$

119 $\quad y'' + 4xy' + 2(1 + 2x^2)y = 0$ $\hfill$ **4-1-1**
$y_1 = e^{-x^2}.$
$$y = e^{-x^2}(C_1 + C_2 x)$$

120 $\quad y'' - 4xy' - (3 - 4x^2)y = 0$ $\hfill$ **4-1-2**
$y = uv; \quad v = e^{x^2}; \quad u''(x) = u; \quad$ see (7).
$$y = e^{x^2}(C_1 e^x + C_2 e^{-x})$$

121 $\quad y'' - 4xy' - (3 - 4x^2)y = e^{x^2}$ $\hfill$ **12-1**
See (120); $\quad F(x) = -e^{x^2}.$

122 $\quad y'' - 2axy' + a^2 x^2 y = 0$ $\hfill$ **4-1-2**
$y = uv; \quad v = e^{ax^2/2}; \quad u''(x) + au = 0; \quad$ see (26).
$$y = e^{ax^2/2}(C_1 \cos x\sqrt{a} + C_2 \sin x\sqrt{a})$$

123 $\quad y'' + axy' + by = 0$ $\hfill$ **4-2**

$y(x) = u(z); \quad 2z = -ax^2; \quad zu''(z) + \left(\dfrac{1}{2} - z\right)u' - \dfrac{b}{2a}u = 0;$

see (211).

124 $\quad y'' + (a + bx)y' + cy = 0$ $\hfill$ **4-2**
$y(x) = u(z); \quad z = a + bx; \quad u''(z) + Azu' + Bu = 0; \quad A = 1/b;$
$B = c/b^2; \quad$ see (123).

125 $\quad y'' + (a_0 + b_0 x)y' + (a_1 + b_1 x)y = 0$ $\hfill$ **4-1-3**
$y = uv; \quad v = e^{-b_1 x/b_0}; \quad u'' + (A_0 + B_0 x)u' + A_1 u = 0;$
$A_0 = a_0 - 2b_1/b_0; \quad B_0 = b_0; \quad A_1 = b_1^2/b_0^2 - a_0 b_1/b_0 + a_1;$
see (124).
$\qquad$ i. If $b_1 = 0$, see (124).
$\qquad$ ii. If $a_0 = b_0 = 0$, see (34).
$\qquad$ iii. If $b_0 = b_1 = 0$, see (102).
$\qquad$ iv. If $A_1 = 0$, $v = y_1$ is a special solution; see **4-1-1**.

126 $\quad y'' + (a_0 + b_0 x)y' + (a_1 + b_1 x + c_1 x^2)y = 0$ $\hfill$ **4-1-3**
$y = uv; \quad v = e^{kx^2}; \quad 4k^2 + 2b_0 k + c_1 = 0;$
$u''(x) + [a_0 + (b_0 + 4k)x]u' + [(a_1 + 2k) + (b_1 + 2a_0 k)x]u = 0;$
see (125).

127 $\quad y'' - 4axy' - 2a(1 - 2ax^2)y = 0$ $\hfill$ **4-1-2, 4-1-1**
$\qquad$ i. $y = uv; \quad v = e^{ax^2}; \quad u''(x) = 0; \quad$ see (1).
$\qquad$ ii. $y_1 = e^{ax^2}; \quad y = e^{ax^2}(C_1 + C_2 x).$
$\qquad$ iii. See also (126).

128 $\quad y'' - x^2 y + xy = 0$ $\hfill$ **4-1-1**
$y_1 = x.$

129 $\quad y'' - x^2 y + xy = x$ $\hfill$ **12-1**
See (128); $\quad F(x) = 1.$

130     $y'' + x^2 y' - 4xy = 0$ **4-1-1**
        $y_1 = x(1 + x^3/4)$.

131     $y'' + x^4 y' - x^3 y = 0$ **4-1-1**
        $y_1 = x$;   see also (135).

132     $y'' + ax^k y' + a(k+1)x^{k-1} y = 0$ **4-1-1**

$$y_1 = x \exp\left[-\frac{ax^{k+1}}{k+1} \right]; \quad \text{see also (135)}$$

133     $y'' + ax^k y' + akx^{k-1} y = 0$ **4-1-1**

$$y_1 = \exp\left[-\frac{ax^{k+1}}{k+1} \right]; \quad \text{see also (135)}.$$

134     $y'' + ax^k y' - ax^{k-1} y = 0$ **4-1-1**
        $y_1 = x$;   see also (135).

135     $y'' + ax^k y' + bx^{k-1} y = 0$ **4-1-2**

$$y = uv; \quad v = \exp\left[-\frac{ax^{k+1}}{2(k+1)} \right];$$

$$u'' + \left[\left(b - \frac{ak}{2} \right)x^{k-1} - \frac{a^2 x^{2k}}{4} \right] u = 0.$$

The solutions are simpler in certain special cases.
        i. $b = -a$, see (134).
       ii. $b = a(k+1)$, see (132).
      iii. $b = ak$, see (133).
      iv. $2b = ak$, see (174).

136     $y'' - y' \cot x + 2y = 0$ **4-1-1**
        $y_1 = \sin^2 x$.
               $y = C_1 \sin^2 x + C_2 (\cos x - \sin^2 x \ln \tan (x/2)]$

137     $y'' + y' \cot x + k(k+1)y = 0$ **4-2-1**
        $y(x) = u(z)$; $z = \cos x$;   see (369);
             $(1 - z^2)u'' - 2zu' + k(k+1)u = 0$.

138     $y'' + y' \cot x - y \csc^2 x = 0$ **4-1-1**
        $y_1 = \cot x$.
               $y = C_1 \cot x + C_2 \csc x$

139     $y'' + y' \cot x + [p(p+1) - k^2 \csc^2 x]y = 0$ **4-2-1**
        $y(x) = u(z)$; $z = \cos x$; $(1 - z^2)^2 u'' - 2z(1 - z^2)u'$
       $- [k^2 - p(p+1)(1 - z^2)]u = 0$;   see (555).

140     $y'' + y' \cot x + (a_0 + 4a_1 \sin^2 x - a_2 \csc^2 x)y = 0$ **9-3**
The trigonometric form of the spheroidal wave equation;
see also (557).

141 $\quad y'' + 2y' \cot x + 3y = 0$ $\qquad\qquad$ **4-1-1**
$y_1 = \cos x.$
$$y = C_1 \cos x + C_2(\cos x \cot x - \sin x)$$

142 $\quad y'' + 2y' \cot x + 3y = e^x \csc x$ $\qquad\qquad$ **12-1**
See (141); $\quad F(x) = (1/5)e^x \csc x.$

143 $\quad y'' + ay' \cot x + (b + k^2 \cos^2 x)y = 0$ $\qquad\qquad$ **9-3**
The associated Mathieu equation; see also (43) and (48).

144 $\quad y'' + ky' \cot x + (a \cot^2 x + b \cot x \csc x + c \csc^2 x)y = 0$ $\quad$ **4-2-2**
$y(x) = u(z); \quad z = \cos x; \quad (1 - z^2)^2 u'' - (1 + k)z(1 - z^2)u'$
$+ (az^2 + bz + c)u = 0; \quad$ see (560).

145 $\quad y'' - y' \cot 2x + 2y = 0$ $\qquad\qquad$ **4-1-1**
$y_1 = \cos 2x.$

146 $\quad y'' - 2y' \cot 2x + ay \tan^2 x = 0$ $\qquad\qquad$ **4-2**
$y(x) = u(x); \quad z = \cos x; \quad z^2 u'' - zu' + au = 0; \quad$ see (311).

147 $\quad y'' + ay' \cot bx + cy = 0$ $\qquad\qquad$ **4-2**
$y(x) = u(z); \quad z = bx + \pi/2; \quad b^2 u'' - abu' \tan z + cu = 0;$
see (167).

148 $\quad y'' + 2ay' \cot ax + (b^2 - a^2)y = 0$ $\qquad\qquad$ **4-1-2**
$u = y \sin ax; \quad u''(x) + b^2 u = 0; \quad$ see (26).
$$y \sin ax = C_1 \cos bx + C_2 \sin bx$$

149 $\quad y'' - y' \csc x + ay \tan^2 (x/2) = 0$ $\qquad\qquad$ **4-2-2**
$y(x) = u(z); \quad z = \cos (x/2); \quad z^2 u'' + zu' + 4au = 0; \quad$ see (311).

150 $\quad y'' + (\cot x + \csc x)y' = 1 + a \csc x$ $\qquad\qquad$ **5-2**
$I(x) = \sin x.$ A first integral is
$$y' \sin x + y = C + ax - \cos x$$

151 $\quad y'' - y' \csc 2x + \csc^2 x(2 + \sin^2 x)y = 0$ $\qquad\qquad$ **4-1-1**
$y_1 = \sin x.$
$$y = \sin x(C_1 + C_2 \tan x)$$

152 $\quad y'' + y' \csc x(2 + \cos x) + ay \csc^2 x = 0$ $\qquad\qquad$ **4-2-1**
$y(x) = u(z); \quad e^z = \tan (x/2); \quad u''(z) + 2u' + au = 0; \quad$ see (102).

153 $\quad y'' - y' \csc x(2 + 3 \cos x) - 2y \sec x(1 + \cos x) = 0$ $\qquad\qquad$ **4-1-1**
$y_1 = \cos x$
$$y = C_1 \cos x + C_2(\sin^2 x + 2 \cos x \ln \cos x)$$

154 $\quad y'' - (\cot x - \sin x)y' + y \sin^2 x = 0$ $\qquad\qquad$ **4-2-1**
$y(x) = u(z); \quad z = \cos x; \quad u''(z) - u' + u = 0; \quad$ see (102).

155 $\quad y'' - y' \sin x - y \cos x = a - x + x \ln x$ $\qquad\qquad$ **5-1**
A first integral is
$$y' - y \sin x = C + ax + \tfrac{1}{2}x^2 \ln x - \tfrac{3}{4}x^2$$

156     $y'' - 2y' \csc 2x(1 - a \sin^2 x) + by \tan^2 x = 0$ **4-2-1**
$y(x) = u(z)$; $e^z = \cos x$; $u''(z) + au' + bu = 0$;   see (102).

157     $y'' + y' \tan x + ay \cos^2 x = 0$ **4-2-1**
$y(x) = u(z)$; $z = \sin x$; $u''(z) + au = 0$;   see (26).

158     $y'' + y' \tan x + ay \cot^2 x = 0$ **4-2-1**
$y(x) = u(z)$; $z = \sin x$; $z^2 u'' + au = 0$;   see (250).

159     $y'' - y' \tan x - a(1 + a)y \csc^2 x = 0$ **4-2-1**
$y(x) = u(z)$; $z = \sin x$; $z^2(1 - z^2)u'' - 2z^3 u' - a(1 + a)u = 0$;
see (550).

160     $y'' - y' \tan x + (a \cos^2 x - \sec^2 x)y = 0$ **4-1**
$y = u(x) \sec x$; $u'' + u' \tan x + au \cos^2 x = 0$;   see (157).

161     $y'' + 2y' \tan x - y = 0$ **4-1-1**
$y_1 = \sin x$.
$$y = C_1 \sin x + C_2(\cos x + x \sin x)$$

162     $y'' + 2y' \tan x - y = \sec x(1 + x)$ **12-3**
See (161); $F(x) = -\frac{1}{2}(1 + x) \cos x$.

163     $y'' + 2y' \tan x + 3y = 0$ **4-1-1**
$y_1 = \cos^3 x$;   see also (167).
$$y = C_1 \cos^3 x + C_2 \sin x(1 + 2 \cos^2 x).$$

164     $y'' - 2y' \tan x + by = 0$ **4-2-1**
$u(x) = y \cos x$; $u'' + (b + 1)u = 0$;   see (26) and (167).

165     $y'' - 2y' \tan x - (1 + a^2)y = 0$ **4-1-2**
$y = uv$; $v = \sec x$; $u''(x) = a^2 u$;   see (26).
$$y = \sec x(C_1 e^{ax} + C_2 e^{-ax})$$

166     $y'' - 2y' \tan x - (1 + a^2)y = \sin x$ **12-3**
See (165); $F(x) = -(\sin x)/(4 + a^2)$.

167     $y'' + ay' \tan x + by = 0$ **4-2-1**
$y(x) = u(z)$; $z = \sin x$; $(1 - z^2)u'' - (1 - a)zu' + bu = 0$; see (382).

168     $y'' - (1 \pm 2e^x)y' + e^{2x}y = 0$ **4-2-1**
$y(x) = u(z)$; $z = e^x$; $u''(z) \mp 2u' + u = 0$;   see (102).

169     $y'' + y' \coth x + (a_0 + 4a_1 \sinh^2 x - a_2 \operatorname{csch}^2 x)y = 0$ **4-2**
$y(x) = u(z)$; $x = iz$; $u'' + u' \cot z - (a_0 - 4a_1 \sin^2 z + a_2 \csc^2 z)u$
$= 0$;   see (140).

170     $y'' + y' \tanh x + (a_0 + 4a_1 \cosh^2 x - a_2 \operatorname{sech}^2 x)y = 0$ **4-2**
$y(x) = u(z)$; $x = i(z - \pi/2)$; $u'' + u' \cot z - (a_0 + 4a_1 \sin^2 z$
$- a_2 \csc^2 z)u = 0$;   see (140).

171     $y'' + 2y' \tanh x + by = 0$ **4-1-2**
$u(x) = y \cosh x$; $u'' + (b - 1)u = 0$;   see (26) and (172).

172 $\quad y'' + ay' \tanh x + by = 0$ $\hspace{4cm}$ **4-2-1**
$y(x) = u(z);\quad z = \sinh x;\quad (1+z^2)u'' + (1+a)zu' + bu = 0;$
see (381).

173 $\quad y'' + f(x)y' = 0$ $\hspace{5.5cm}$ **B2-1-2**
$\hspace{1.5cm} y = C_1 e^{-\phi};\quad \phi(x) = \int f(x)dx + C_2$

174 $\quad 2y'' + 2ax^k y' + akx^{k-1}y = 0$ $\hspace{3.5cm}$ **4-1-2**
$y = uv;\quad v = \exp\left[-\dfrac{ax^{k+1}}{2(k+1)}\right];\quad 4u'' = a^2 x^{2k}u;\quad$ see (41) and
(135).

175 $\quad 3y'' - 10y' + 3y = 0$ $\hspace{6cm}$ **1**
$\hspace{1.5cm} y = C_1 e^{3x} + C_2 e^{x/3}$

176 $\quad 4y'' = (a+x^2)y$ $\hspace{6cm}$ **4-3**
A form of Weber's equation, see (177); $y\sqrt{x} = u(z);\quad 2z = x^2;$
$16z^2 u'' + (3 - 2az - 4z^2)u = 0;\quad$ see (450); $\quad p = 1/4,\ k = -a/8.$

177 $\quad 4y'' + (2 + 4a - x^2)y = 0$ $\hspace{4cm}$ **9-1, 9-2**
Weber's equation. Its solutions are parabolic cylinder or
Weber-Hermite functions. The equation can be converted into
the Whittaker equation, see (450), or into the Kummer equation,
see (211). Solutions are $D_a(\pm x),\ D_r(\pm ix),\ r = -(a+1).$ If
$k + p = 2a,\ 4p + 1 = 0,$

$$D_a(x) = 2^k x^{-1/2} W_{k,p}\left(\frac{x^2}{2}\right)$$
$$= 2^{a/2} e^{-x^2/4}\left[A_1 F_1\left(-\frac{a}{2}, \frac{1}{2}; \frac{x^2}{2}\right) + Bx_1 F_1\left(\frac{1-a}{2}, \frac{3}{2}; \frac{x^2}{2}\right)\right]$$

where
$$A = \Gamma(1/2)/\Gamma\left(\frac{1-a}{2}\right);\qquad B = 2^{-1/2}\Gamma(-1/2)/\Gamma(-a/2).$$

For definitions of $W_{k,p}(z)$ and $_1F_1(a, b; z)$ see (450) and (211).

178 $\quad 4y'' - 8y' + 3y = 0$ $\hspace{6cm}$ **1**
$\hspace{1.5cm} y = C_1 e^{x/2} + C_2 e^{3x/2}$

179 $\quad xy'' + y = 0$ $\hspace{6.5cm}$ **9-2**
See (198).

180 $\quad xy'' + (a+x)y = 0$ $\hspace{5cm}$ **4-3**
$y = e^{ix}u(z);\quad z = -2ix;\quad zu'' - zu' + (ai/2)u = 0;\quad$ see (215).

181 $\quad xy'' + y' = 0$ $\hspace{6cm}$ **B2-1-2**
See also (193).
$\hspace{1.5cm} y = C_1 + C_2 \ln x$

182 $xy'' + y' = x^n$ **12-3**
See (181); $F(x) = x^{n+1}/(n+1)^2$.

183 $xy'' + y' - y = 0$ **8-2-2**

$$y_1 = 1 + x + \frac{x^2}{4} + \frac{x^3}{(3!)^2} + \dots + \frac{x^k}{(k!)^2} + \dots;$$

$$y_2 = y_1 \ln x - 2(X_1 + X_2 + \dots + X_k + \dots);$$

$$X_k = \frac{x^k}{(k!)^2}(1 + 1/2 + \dots + 1/k).$$

184 $xy'' + y' - (x \pm 1)y = 0$ **4-1-1**
$y_1 = e^{\pm x}$; see also (216).

185 $xy'' - y' + 4x^3 y = 0$ **4-1-1**
$y_1 = e^{ix^2}$.
$$y = C_1 \cos x^2 + C_2 \sin x^2$$

186 $xy'' - y' - a^2 x^3 y = 0$ **4-2-1, 4-1-2**
$y(x) = u(z)$; $2z = ax^2$; $u''(z) = u$; see (7).

187 $xy'' - y' + x^3(e^{x^2} - k^2)y = 0$ **4-2**
$y(x) = u(z)$; $z = e^{x^2/2}$; $z^2 u'' + zu' + (z^2 - k^2)u = 0$; see (274).

188 $xy'' + 2y' = 0$ **B2-1-2**
See also (193).
$$y = C_1 + C_2/x$$

189 $xy'' + 2y' = x$ **12-3**
See (188); $F(x) = x^2/6$.

190 $xy'' + 2y' - xy = e^x$ **12-3**
See (191).
$$2xy = xe^x + C_1 e^x + C_2 e^{-x}$$

191 $xy'' + 2y' + axy = 0$ **4-1-2**
$y = uv$; $v = 1/x$; $u''(x) + au = 0$; see (26).

192 $xy'' + 2y' + ax^2 y = 0$ **4-1-2**
$xy = u(x)$; $u'' + axu = 0$; see (34) and (41). A solution is
$$y\sqrt{x} = Z_{-1/3}\left(\pm \frac{2\sqrt{a}}{3}x^{3/2}\right)$$
where $Z_p(z)$ is a solution of the Bessel equation; see (274).

193 $xy'' + ay' = 0$ **9-2, B2-1-2**
i. $a = 1$; see (181).
ii. $a \neq 1$; $y = C_1 + C_2 x^{1-a}$.

194 $\quad xy'' + (1+a)y' + y = 0$ $\qquad\qquad$ **9-2**
The Bessel-Clifford equation; $u(z) = x^{a/2}y$; $z = 2\sqrt{x}$; see
(274); $\quad z^2u'' + zu' + [z^2 - 2a(1+a)]u = 0$
$\qquad y = x^{-a/2}[C_1 J_a(z) + C_2 Y_a(z)]$

195 $\quad xy'' + (1-a)y' + y = 0$ $\qquad\qquad$ **9-2**
$y_1 = x^a C_a(x)$, where $C_a(x)$ is a solution of (194). If $a = n + 1/2$,
and n is an integer, the solutions are polynomials; see (454).

196 $\quad xy'' + (1\pm a)y' - y = 0$ $\qquad\qquad$ **9-2**
See (195). If $a = n + 1/2$ and n is an integer, the solutions are
polynomials and functions of $\cosh x$, $\sinh x$; see (454).

197 $\quad xy'' + 2ny' + axy = 0$ $\qquad\qquad$ **4**
If n is a positive integer, $y = \left(\dfrac{1}{x}\dfrac{d}{dx}\right)^n u(x)$, where $u(x)$ satisfies
the equation $u''(x) + au = 0$; see (26).

198 $\quad xy'' + ay' + by = 0$ $\qquad\qquad$ **4-2**
$\qquad$ i. $y(x) = u(z)$; $z = 2\sqrt{bx}$; $zu''(z) + (2a-1)u' + zu = 0$;
see (199). A solution is $y = z^{1-a}Z_p(z)$, where $Z_p(z)$ is a Bessel
function of order $p = 1 - a$; see (274).
$\qquad$ ii. $a = 1/2$, $b = \pm c$; see (233) or (234).

199 $\quad xy'' + ay' + bxy = 0$ $\qquad\qquad$ **4-3**
$y = x^{(1-a)/2}u(z)$; $\quad z = x\sqrt{b}$; $\quad z^2u'' + zu' + (z^2 - k^2)u = 0$; $\quad$ see
(274). A solution is a Bessel function of order $k = (1-a)/2$.
$\qquad y = x^k Z_k(z)$
See also (202), and if a is an even integer, see (197).

200 $\quad xy'' + ay' + (b_1 + b_2x)y = 0$ $\qquad\qquad$ **9-2**
$y = e^{kx}u(x)$; $\quad xu'' + (a + 2kx)u' + (ak + b_1)u = 0$; $\quad k^2 + b_2 = 0$;
see (215).

201 $\quad xy'' + ay' + (a_1 + b_1x + c_1x^2)y = 0$ $\qquad\qquad$ **8-2**
There is a regular singular point at $x = 0$. Use the method of
8.2 to find two series solutions.

202 $\quad xy'' + ay' + bx^ky = 0$ $\qquad\qquad$ **4-3**
$\qquad$ i. $y = x^r u(z)$; $\quad z = Ax^s$; $\quad z^2u'' + zu' + (z^2 - p^2)u = 0$;
$2r = 1-a$; $A(1+k) = \pm 2\sqrt{b}$; $2s = 1+k$; $(1+k)p = 1-a$;
see (274). A solution is $y = x^r Z_p(z)$.
$\qquad$ ii. If $k = 1 - 2a$; $b + \beta(a-1)^2 = 0$; $y = C_1 e^X + C_2 e^{-X}$;
$X = x^{1-a}\sqrt{\beta}$.

203    $xy'' - (1+x)y' + y = 0$ **4-1-1**
   $y_1 = e^x$;   see also (205) and (211).
      $y = C_1(1+x) + C_2 e^x$

204    $xy'' + (1-x)y' + ny = 0$ **9-1, 9-2**
The Laguerre differential equation, a special case of (211). Provided that $n \geqslant 0$, an integer, a solution is a Laguerre polynomial

$$y_1 = L_n(x) = {}_1F_1(-n, 1; x)$$

Equivalent definitions are

$$n! L_n(x) = e^x D^n(x^n e^{-x})$$

where $D = d/dx$, and, in terms of a generating function

$$\exp\left(\frac{xt}{t-1}\right) = (1-t) \sum_{n=0}^{\infty} L_n(x) t^n.$$

Still other definitions of these polynomials are often given.

The second solution of the equation will involve a logarithm.

The results for (211) can be used to get such a solution and also for the case where n is not an integer. These more general solutions are Laguerre functions.

205    $xy'' + (1+k-x)y' + ny = 0$ **9-1, 9-2**
The associated Laguerre equation, a special case of (211); see also (204). If n is a positive integer, a solution is an associated Laguerre polynomial

$$y_1 = L_n^k(x) = \binom{n+k}{n} {}_1F_1(-n, 1+k; x)$$

It can also be defined by the relation

$$n! L_n^k(x) = e^x x^{-k} D^n(x^{n+k} e^{-x})$$

where $D = d/dx$, or by the generating function

$$\exp\left(\frac{xt}{t-1}\right) = (1-t)^{k+1} \sum_{n=0}^{\infty} L_n^k(x) t^n$$

If the general solution of the equation is needed, use the results of (211). They can also be used for associated Laguerre functions, when n is not an integer.

206    $xy'' - (1+x)y' + 2(1-x)y = 0$ **4-1-1**
   $y_1 = e^{2x}$;   see also (216).
      $y = C_1 e^{2x} + C_2 e^{-x}(1+3x)$

207 $xy'' - (2-x)y' - y = 0$ **4-1-1**
$y_1 = 2-x;$ see also (210).
$$y = C_1(2-x) + C_2(2+x)e^{-x}$$

208 $xy'' - (3+x)y' + y = 0$ **4-1-1**
$y_1 = 3+x;$ see also (210).
$$y = C_1(3+x) + C_2(x^2 - 4x + 6)e^x$$

209 $xy'' - (3+x)y' + 3y = 0$ **4-1-1**
$y_1 = e^x;$ see also (210).
$$y = C_1 e^x + C_2(x^3 + 3x^2 + 6x + 6)$$

210 $xy'' + (a+x)y' + by = 0$ **4-1-2**
$y(x) = u(z);$ $z = -x;$ $zu'' + (a-z)u' - bu;$ see (211). Special
solutions in certain cases are:
> i. $a = 0, b = \pm 1; y_1 = xe^{-x}.$
> ii. $a = b = 1; y_1 = e^{-x}.$
> iii. $a = 2, b = 1; y_1 = 1/x.$
> iv. $a = b = 2; y_1 = e^{-x}.$

211 $xy'' + (c-x)y' - ay = 0$ **9-1, 9-2**
The confluent hypergeometric differential equation; also called
the Kummer equation and the Pochhammer-Barnes equation.
A solution of it is a confluent hypergeometric function, a Kummer function, or a Pochhammer function.

Use (410), replace the independent variable x by x/b and
let $b \to \infty$. The result of this limiting process is the Kummer
equation. It has a regular singular point at $x = 0$ and an
irregular one at $x = \infty$. The latter has resulted by confluence
or coalescence of the regular singular point at $x = 1$ in (410)
with the regular singular point at $x = \infty$. The solutions (211)
can be found from those of (410) by a limiting process. For
other methods of solving it, see a. Alternatively, convert (211)
to its normal form, see **4-1-2**, and solve that; see b. For further
information about the equation, see c.

     a. Use the methods of **8-2** to find the general solution
$y = C_1 y_1 + C_2 y_2$. Provided that $c \neq \pm n$, an integer including
zero,
$$y_1 = {}_1F_1(a, c; x); \quad y_2 = x^{1-c} {}_1F_1(1+a-c, 2-c; x)$$
where
$${}_1F_1(a, c; x) = \sum_{k=0}^{\infty} A_k x^k; \quad A_k = \frac{a(a+1)\ldots(a+k-1)}{c(c+1)\ldots(c+k-1)k!}$$

The second series is similar with $(1+a-c)$, $(2-c)$ in place of
a, c, respectively.

The notation $_1F_1$ suggests that the series contains one factorial-like term in both numerator and denominator. Other symbols used for the series are $M(a, c; x)$ and Humbert's symbol $\Phi(a, c; x)$. The coefficients in the series are often designated by Pochhammer's symbol or in terms of gamma functions

$$(a)_k = a(a+1)...(a+k-1) = \frac{\Gamma(a+k)}{\Gamma(a)}; \quad k = 1, 2, ... ; \quad (a)_0 = 1.$$

There are a number of exceptional case, when the parameters a, c are specialized.

i. $c = n+1$, $n \geqslant 1$. One solution is
$$y_1 = {_1F_1}(a, 1+n; x)$$

The second solution will contain a zero factor in the denominator at the term beginning with $k = n$, unless $1 \leqslant a \leqslant n$, which produces companion zero terms in the numerator to cancel the offending zeros in the denominator. In that event, y_1 is an infinite series and y_2 is a polynomial. Otherwise, use a method of **8-2-3**, to get

$$y_2 = y_1 \ln x + Y_1 + Y_2$$

$$Y_1 = \sum_{k=1}^{\infty} B_k x^k; \quad B_k = \frac{n!\Gamma(a+k)H_k}{k!(n+k)!\Gamma(a)};$$

$$H_k = \sum_{r=0}^{k-1} \left[\frac{1}{a+r} - \frac{1}{n+r+1} - \frac{1}{r+1} \right]$$

$$Y_2 = \sum_{k=0}^{n-1} C_k x^{k-n}; \quad C_k = (-1)^{n+k+1} \frac{n!(n-k-1)!\Gamma(a-n+k)}{k!\Gamma(a)}$$

ii. $c = 1$. Use the results of i but omit the polynomial Y_2.

iii. $c = 1-n$, a negative integer. The two solutions y_1 and y_2 of a become proportional to each other. Use y_2, which becomes $x^n {_1F_1}(a+n, 1+n; x)$, call it y_1, and the result of i will apply. Compensating zeros will occur as in that case, provided $(1-n) \leqslant a \leqslant 0$ and then the second solution becomes a polynomial. Otherwise, terms from $k = n$ onwards contain zero denominators and the second solution will involve a logarithm.

iv. If $a-c = n$, an integer (including zero), y_1 of a becomes $e^x {_1F_1}(-n, c; -x)$ and the series has become a polynomial. The other solution is an infinite series. Similarly, if $a-1 = n$, the polynomial solution is $y_2 = x^{1-c}e^x {_1F_1}(-n, 2-c; -x)$.

b. The normal form of the equation. From the results of
4-1-2, one gets $y = uv$; $u''(x) + I(x)u \doteq 0$; $v = x^{-c/2}e^{x/2}$;
$I(x) = (1-4p^2)/4x^2 + k/x - 1/4$; $a = 1/2 + p - k$; $c = 1 + 2p$.
This form of the confluent equation, known as Whittaker's
equation, see (450), is frequently useful since its solutions are
more symmetric in the parameters than those of (211).

c. Related equations. Many integral solutions of the
equation and further properties of the solutions are known.
Suitable references are Erdélyi-1 and Tricomi.

Special cases of Kummer functions are the incomplete gamma
functions, the exponential integral, the error functions, and
solutions of the differential equations of Hermite (112), (117);
Weber (177); Laguerre (204), (205); Bessel (274). By suitable
variable transformations, a number of other differential equations can be converted into (211).

212 $xy'' + (1-2x)y' - (1-x)y = 0$ **4-1-1**
$y_1 = e^x$.
$$y = e^x(C_1 + C_2 \ln x)$$

213 $xy'' - (1+2x)y'' + (1+x)y = 0$ **4-1-1**
$y_1 = e^x$.
$$y = e^x(C_1 + C_2 x^2)$$

214 $xy'' - (1+2x)y' + (1+x)y = x^2 - x - 1$ **12-3**
See (213); $F(x) = x$.

215 $xy'' + (a+bx)y' + cy = 0$ **4-2, 9-2**
$y(x) = u(z)$; $z = -bx$; $zu'' + (a-z)u' - (c/b)u = 0$; see (211).

216 $xy'' + (a_1 + b_1 x)y' + (a_2 + b_2 x)y = 0$ **4-1**
  i. $y = e^{kx}u(x)$; $k^2 + b_1 k + b_2 = 0$; $xu'' + (A_1 + B_1 x)u'$
$+ A_2 u = 0$; $A_1 = a_1$; $B_1 = 2k + b_1 = \pm\sqrt{b_1^2 - 4b_2}$; A_2
$= a_1 k + a_2$; see (215).
  ii. If $b_1 = b_2 = 0$, see (198).

217 $xy'' - 2(a+bx)y' + b(2a+bx)y = 0$ **4-1-1**
$y_1 = e^{bx}$; see also (216).
$$y = e^{bx}(C_1 + C_2 x^{1+2a})$$

218 $xy'' + [m+n+(a+b)x]y' + (an+bm+abx)y = 0$ **4-1**
$a \neq b$; $m \neq n$; m, n integers.
  i. $y = u(x)e^{-ax}$; $xu'' + [m+n+(b-a)x]u' + m(b-a)u$
$= 0$; see (215).
  ii. $y = u(x)e^{-bx}$; $xu'' + [m+n+(a-b)x]u' + n(a-b)u$
$= 0$; see (215).

219 $xy'' - (1 - x^2)y' = 0$ **B2-1-2**
$$y = C_1 + C_2 e^{-x^2/2}$$

220 $xy'' - (4 - x^2)y' + 2xy = a$ **5-1**
A first integral, see **A1-2**, is
$$xy' - (5 - x^2)y = ax + C$$

221 $xy'' - (1 + 2x^2)y' + x^3 y = 0$ **4-2-1**
$y(x) = u(z);$ $2z = x^2;$ $u''(z) - 2u' + u = 0;$ see (102).
$$y = e^{x^2/2}(C_1 + C_2 x^2)$$

222 $xy'' - (1 + 2x^2)y' - 8x^3 y = 0$ **4-2-1**
$y(x) = u(z);$ $z = x^2;$ $u''(z) - u' - 2u = 0;$ see (102).
$$y = C_1 e^{2x^2} + C_2 e^{-x^2}$$

223 $xy'' - (1 + 2x^2)y' - 8x^3 y = 4x^3 e^{-x^2}$ **12-3**
See (222); $3F(x) = -x^2 e^{-x^2}.$

224 $xy'' + (1 + 4x^2)y' + 4x(1 + x^2)y = 0$ **4-1-1**
$y_1 = e^{-x^2}.$
$$y = e^{-x^2}(C_1 + C_2 \ln x)$$

225 $xy'' - (1 - 2ax^3)y' + a(1 + ax^3)x^2 y = 0$ **4-1-3**
$y = e^{-ax^3/3}u(x);$ $xu'' - u' = 0;$ see (193).
$$y = e^{-ax^3/3}(C_1 + C_2 x^2)$$

226 $xy'' + [2 + xf(x)]y' + f(x)y = 0$ **4-1-1**
$y_1 = 1/x.$

227 $(1 - x)y'' + xy' - y = 0$ **4-1-1**
$y_1 = x.$
$$y = C_1 x + C_2 e^x$$

228 $(1 - x)y'' + xy' - y = (1 - x)^2$ **12-3**
See (227); $F(x) = 1 + x^2.$

229 $(3 - x)y'' - (9 - 4x)y' + 3(2 - x)y = 0$ **4-1-1**
$y_1 = e^x.$
$$y = C_1 e^x + C_2 e^{3x}(4x^3 - 42x^2 + 150x - 183)$$

230 $(a - x)y'' - 2y' = 0$ **9-1; B2-1-2**
$$(a - x)(y + C_1) = C_2$$

231 $(a + x)y'' + (a_1 + b_1 x)y' + (a_2 + b_2 x)y = 0$ **4-2, 9-2**
$y(x) = u(z);$ $b_2 z = a_2 + b_2 x;$ $zu''(z) + (A_1 + B_1 z)u'$
$+ (A_2 + B_2 z)u = 0;$ $b_2^2 A_i = a_i b_2 - a_2 b_i;$ $b_2 B_i = b_i;$
see (216).

232 $2xy'' + y' = 0$ **9-2; B2-1-2**
$$y = C_1 + C_2 \sqrt{x}$$

233    $2xy'' + y' + ay = 0$ **4-2-1, 9-2**

$y(x) = u(z);$ $z^2 = 2ax;$ $u''(z) + u = 0;$ see (6) and (198).

        $y = C_1 \cos \sqrt{2ax} + C_2 \sin \sqrt{2ax}$

234    $2xy'' + y' - ay = 0$ **4-2-1, 9-2**

$y(x) = u(z);$ $z^2 = 2ax;$ $u''(z) - u = 0;$ see (7) and (198).

        $y = C_1 \cosh \sqrt{2ax} + C_2 \sinh \sqrt{2ax}$

235    $2xy'' + y' + (a + bx)y = 0$ **9-2**

$y(x) = u(z);$ $x = z^2;$ $2u'' + (a + bz^2)u = 0;$ see (38).

236    $2xy'' - (1 + 2x^2)y' - xy = 0$ **4-1-1**

$y_1 = e^{x^2/2}.$

237    $(1 - 2x)y'' - (2 + x)y' - y = a$ **5-1**

A first integral, see **A1-2**, is

        $(1 - 2x)y' - xy = ax + C$

238    $(1 - 2x)y'' - (4 - 3x)y' + (3 - x)y = 0$ **4-1-1**

$y_1 = e^x$

239    $4xy'' + 2y' + y = 0$ **4-2-1**

$y(x) = u(z);$ $x = z^2;$ $u''(z) + u = 0;$ see (6) and (198).

        $y = C_1 \cos \sqrt{x} + C_2 \sin \sqrt{x}$

240    $4xy'' - 2y' - y = 0$ **4-2-1**

$y(x) = u(z); x = z^2;$ $zu'' - 2u' - zu = 0;$ see (199).

        $y = C_1 e^{\sqrt{x}}(\sqrt{x} - 1) + C_2 e^{-\sqrt{x}}(\sqrt{x} + 1).$

241    $4xy'' + 4y' \coth x + y = 0$ **4-2**

See (462).

242    $16xy'' + 8y' + (a + bx)y = 0$ **9-2**

$y(x) = u(z);$ $x = z^2;$ $4u''(z) + (a + bz^2)u = 0;$ see (38).

243    $(a + bx)y'' + cy' = 0$ **B2-1-2**

        $y = C_1 + C_2(a + bx)^k;$ $k = (b - c)/b.$

244    $(a_0 + b_0x)y'' + (a_1 + b_1x)y' + (a_2 + b_2x)y = 0$ **9-2, 10**

Laplace's linear equation of second order.

     i. $b_0 = b_1 = b_2 = 0;$ see (102).

     ii. Divide by b_0 and see (231). Proceed as directed there. After a number of successive transformations, the final result will be (211). A special form of the Bessel equation might also result; see (274).

     iii. $y(x) = e^{kx}u(z);$ $x = A + Bz;$ $B \neq 0;$ $(A_0 + B_0z)u'' + (A_1 + B_1z)u' + (A_2 + B_2z)u = 0.$ The new equation has the same form as the original one in x, y and the coefficients are rather complicated functions of a_i, b_i. There are enough relations between the various constants so that the equation in u, z might be converted into (211) or (274). In some cases, a new independent variable may also be required.

iv. Integral solutions are readily obtainable with the Laplace transform; see **10-1**.

245    $(1-x\cot x)y'' - xy' + y = 0$ **4-1-1**
$y_1 = x$.
$$y = C_1 x + C_2 \sin x.$$

246    $x^2 y'' = a + bx$ **12-1, 12-2; B2-1-1**
$$y = C_1 + C_2 x - a \ln x + bx \ln x$$

247    $x^2 y'' = 2y$ **3-1**
$$xy = C_1 + C_2 x^3$$

248    $x^2 y'' = 6y$ **3-1**
$$x^2 y = C_1 + C_2 x^5$$

249    $x^2 y'' = 12y$ **3-1**
$$x^3 y = C_1 + C_2 x^7$$

250    $x^2 y'' + ay = 0$ **3-1**
$$y = \sqrt{x}(C_1 y_1 + C_2 y_2)$$
     i. $a - 1/4 = r^2 > 0$; $y_1 = \cos r \ln x$; $y_2 = \sin r \ln x$.
     ii. $r^2 < 0$; $y_1 = x^r$, $y_2 = x^{-r}$.
     iii. $r^2 = 0$; $y_1 = 1$, $y_2 = \ln x$.
     iv. See also (41).

251    $x^2 y'' + (a + bx)y = 0$ **4-1**
$y = x^k u(x)$; $k^2 - k + a = 0$; $xu''(x) + 2ku' + bu = 0$;   see (198).

252    $x^2 y'' - (2 - x^2)y = 0$ **4**
See also (257).
$$xy = C_1 x \sin(x + C_2) + C_1 \cos(x + C_2).$$

253    $x^2 y'' - (2 - x^2)y = x^4$ **12-3**
See (252); $F(x) = x^2$.

254    $x^2 y'' - (2 + a^2 x^2)y = 0$ **4**
See also (257).
$$y = C_1 e^{ax}(a - 1/x) + C_2 e^{-ax}(a + 1/x)$$

255    $x^2 y'' - (6 - a^2 x^2)y = 0$ **4**
See also (257).
$$y = C_1 \left[\frac{3}{ax} \cos(ax + C_2) + \left(1 - \frac{3}{a^2 x^2}\right) \sin(ax + C_2) \right]$$

256 $\quad x^2 y'' - [n(n+1) \pm a^2 x^2] y = 0$ **4**

$$x^{n+1} y = (x^3 D)^n \left[\frac{C_1 \cos ax + C_2 \sin ax}{x^{2n-1}} \right]$$

$$= (x^3 D)^n \left[\frac{C_1 e^{ax} + C_2 e^{-ax}}{x^{2n-1}} \right]; \quad D = d/dx.$$

257 $\quad x^2 y'' - [n(n-1) - a^2 x^2] y = 0$ **4**

$$y = x^n (1/x\, D)^n (C_1 e^{iax} + C_2 e^{-iax}); \quad D = d/dx.$$

258 $\quad x^2 y'' + (a + bx + cx^2) y = 0$ **4-1-3**

$y = x^k u(x); \quad k^2 - k + a = 0; \quad xu''(x) + 2ku' + (b+cx)u = 0;$
see (200).

259 $\quad x^2 y'' - [a(a-1) - bx^k] y = 0$ **4-3**

$y = x^a u(z); \quad z = x^{1-2a}; \quad (1-2a)^2 u'' + bz^r u = 0;$
$r = k/(1-2a) - 2; \quad$ see (41).

260 $\quad x^2 y'' + x^k (a + bx^k) y = 0$ **4-2-2**

$y(x) = u(z); \quad z = x^k; \quad zu'' + A_1 u' + (A_2 + B_2 z)u = 0;$
$A_1 = (k-1)/k; \quad A_2 = a/k^2; \quad B_2 = b/k^2; \quad$ see (200).

261 $\quad x^2 y'' + ay' - b(a + bx^2) y = 0$ **4-1-1**

$y_1 = e^{bx}.$

262 $\quad x^2 y'' + xy' + y = 0$ **3-1**

$$y = C_1 \cos \ln x + C_2 \sin \ln x.$$

263 $\quad x^2 y'' + xy' - y = 0$ **3-1**

$$xy = C_1 + C_2 x^2$$

264 $\quad x^2 y'' - xy' + y = 0$ **3-1**

$$y = C_1 x + C_2 x \ln x$$

265 $\quad x^2 y'' + xy' - y = ax^2$ **12-2**

See (263); $\quad F(x) = ax^2/3.$

266 $\quad x^2 y'' - xy' + y = x^2 (3+x)$ **12-2**

See (264); $\quad F(x) = 3x^2 + x^3/4.$

267 $\quad x^2 y'' - xy' + y = 3x^3$ **12-2**

See (264); $\quad F(x) = 3x^3/4.$

268 $\quad x^2 y'' + xy' + y = \ln x$ **12-2**

See (262); $\quad F(x) = \ln x.$

269 $\quad x^2 y'' - xy' + 2y = 0$ **3-1**

$$y = x(C_1 \cos \ln x + C_2 \sin \ln x)$$

270 $\quad x^2 y'' - xy' + 2y = x \ln x$ **12-2**

See (269); $\quad F(x) = x \ln x.$

271     $x^2y'' - xy' - 3y = 0$ **3-1, 5-2**
       $I(x) = 1/x^4.$
           $xy = C_1 + C_2 x^4$

272     $x^2y'' + xy' - a^2y = 0$ **9-2, 3-1**
          $y = C_1 x^a + C_2 x^{-a}$

273     $x^2y'' + xy' + (a+bx)y = 0$ **9-2**
       $y(x) = x^k u(x); \; x^2 u'' + (1+2k)xu' + (k^2+a+bx)u = 0;$ see (312).

274     $x^2y'' + xy' - (p^2 - x^2)y = 0$ **9-2**
Bessel's equation. Any solution of it is a cylindrical function and the general solution is

$$y = C_1 Z_1(x) + C_2 Z_2(x)$$

where the $Z_i(x)$ are two linearly independent cylindrical functions.

      i. If p is not an integer, the $Z_i(x)$ are usually taken as one of the pairs: $J_p, J_{-p}; \; J_p, Y_p; \; H_p^{(1)}, H_p^{(2)}.$ These functions are defined as follows:

$$J_p(x) = \sum_{k=0}^{\infty} (-1)^k \frac{1}{k!\Gamma(1+k+p)} \left(\frac{x}{2}\right)^{p+2k}$$

$$Y_p(x) = \csc p\pi (J_p \cos p\pi - J_{-p})$$

$$H_p^{(1)}(x) = J_p + iY_p$$

$$H_p^{(2)}(x) = J_p - iY_p$$

They are Bessel functions of order p and of the first, second, third kind, respectively. Alternatively, Y_p is a Neumann function (often denoted by N_p) and the $H^{(i)}$ are Hankel functions of the first and second kind.

      The solutions called $J_i(x)$ are obtainable by **8-2**, since $x = 0$ is a regular singular point.

      ii. If $p = n$, an integer, $J_{-n} = (-1)^n J_n$, hence the pair $J_{\pm n}(x)$ accounts for only one solution of the equation. The general solution can be taken as

$$y = C_1 J_n(x) + C_2 Y_n(x)$$

In this case, $Y_n(x) = \lim_{p \to n} Y_p(x)$. Explicitly, it contains a term in $J_n(x) \ln(x/2)$, a polynomial in $2/x$, and an infinite series in $x/2$.

      iii. If n is an integer (positive, negative, or zero) and $p = n+1/2$, see (454).

      iv. For other special cases, see (275), (276), (277).

275 $x^2y'' + xy' - (p^2 + x^2)y = 0$ **4-2-2**

The modified Bessel equation.

    i. $y(x) = u(z);$ $x = iz;$ $z^2u'' + zu' - (p^2 - z^2)u = 0;$

see (274).

    ii.   Define a modified Bessel function of the first kind

$$I_p = i^{-p}J_p(ix)$$

and a modified Bessel function of the third kind (also called one of the second kind) or a Basset function

$$K_p(x) = \frac{\pi}{2}i^{n+1}[J_p(ix) + iY_p(ix)]$$

The general solution of the differential equation is

$$y = C_1 I_p(x) + C_2 I_{-p}(x); \quad p \text{ not an integer}$$
$$y = C_1 I_n(x) + C_2 K_n(x); \quad p = n, \text{ an integer}$$

In the last case, $K_n(x) = \lim_{p \to n} K_p(x)$.

276 $x^2y'' + xy' - (p^2 + ix^2)y = 0$ **4-2-2**

    i. $y(x) = u(z);$ $z = xi^{3/2};$ $z^2u'' + zu' - (p^2 - z^2)u = 0;$

see (274).

    ii.   The general solution can be given in terms of Bessel functions or modified Bessel functions; see (274) and (275). Engineers frequently find the following solutions useful

$$ber_p(x) \pm ibei_p(x) = J_p(xe^{\pm 3\pi i/4})$$
$$ker_p(x) \pm ikei_p(x) = e^{\mp ip\pi/2}K_p(xe^{\pm i\pi/4})$$
$$her_p(x) + ihei_p(x) = H_p^{(1)}(xe^{3i\pi/4})$$
$$her_p(x) - ihei_p(x) = H_p^{(2)}(xe^{-3i\pi/4})$$

The notation b, k, h refers to Bessel, Kelvin, Hankel and r, i indicate the real and imaginary parts of the function.

277 $x^2y'' + xy' - (p^2 - a^2x^2)y = 0$ **9-2, 4-2-2**

$y(x) = u(z);$ $z = ax;$ $z^2u'' + zu' - (p^2 - z^2)u = 0;$ see (274).

278 $x^2y'' + xy' + (a + bx + cx^2)y = 0$ **9-2**

$y = x^k u(x);$ $x^2u'' + (1 + 2k)xu' + (k^2 + a + bx + cx^2)u = 0;$

see (315).

279 $x^2y'' + xy' - (n^2 + 4ax^2 - x^4)y = 0$ **4-3**

$xy = u(z);$ $z = \pm ix^2;$ $4z^2u'' + (1 - n^2 \pm 4aiz - z^2)u = 0;$ see (450), with $k = \pm ia$, $p = n/2$.

280 $x^2y'' + xy' - (a^2 + b^2x^2 + c^2x^4)y = 0$ **9-6**

$y = x^{\pm a}u(x);$ $x^2u'' + (1 \pm 2a)xy' - x^2(b^2 + c^2x^2)y = 0;$ see (316).

281     $x^2y'' + xy' + (a_0 + a_1x + \ldots + a_nx^n)y = 0$ **9-2**
Use **8-2** and get two series solutions at $x = 0$, a regular singular
point. See (279) and (280) for special cases.

282     $x^2y'' + (a + x)y' - y = 0$ **4-1-1**
$y_1 = xe^{ax}$.

283     $x^2y'' - 2xy' + 2y = 0$ **3-1**
$$y = x(C_1 + C_2x)$$

284     $x^2y'' - 2xy' + 2y = 4x^3$ **12-2**
See (283); $F(x) = 2x^3$.

285     $x^2y'' - 2xy' + 2y = x^3 \sin x$ **12-2**
See (283); $F(x) = -x \sin x$.

286     $x^2y'' - 2xy' + 2y = 2x \ln x$ **12-2**
See (283); $F(x) = -2x \ln x - x(\ln x)^2$.

287     $x^2y'' - 2xy' + 2y = x^5 \ln x$ **12-2**
See (283); $F(x) = \dfrac{x^5}{12}\left(\ln x - \dfrac{7}{12}\right)$

288     $x^2y'' + 2xy' - 6y = 0$ **3-1**
$$x^3y = C_1 + C_2x^5$$

289     $x^2y'' + 2xy' - 6y = 2 - x$ **12-2**
See (288); $F(x) = \dfrac{x}{4} - \dfrac{1}{3}$.

290     $x^2y'' - 2xy' + (2 + a^2x^2)y = 0$ **4-1-2**
$y = xu(x)$; $u'' + a^2u = 0$;   see (26).
$$y = C_1x \cos ax + C_2x \sin ax$$

291     $x^2y'' + 2xy' - [n(n+1) - a^2x^2]y = 0$ **4-3**
$u(z) = y\sqrt{x}$; $ax = z$; $4z^2u'' + 4zu' - [(2n+1)^2 - 4z^2]u = 0$;
see (454).

292     $x^2y'' + 2xy' + (a + bx^2)y = 0$ **4-1-3**
$y = x^ku(x)$; $k^2 + k + a = 0$; $xu'' + 2(k+1)u' + bxu = 0$;
see (199).

293     $x^2y'' - 2(1-x)y' + ay = 0$ **4-2**
$y(x) = x^{-1/2}e^{-1/x}u(z)$; $z = i/x$; $z^2u'' + zu' - (p^2 - z^2)u = 0$;
$p^2 + a = 1/4$;   see (274) and (318).

294     $x^2y'' + 3xy' + y = 0$ **3-1, 5-1**
$$xy = C_1 + C_2 \ln x$$

295     $x^2y'' + 3xy' + y = x$ **12-2**
See (294); $F(x) = x/4$.

296 $\quad x^2y'' + 3xy' + y = a - x + x \ln x$ $\qquad$ **12-2**

See (294); $\quad F(x) = a + \dfrac{x}{4} \ln x - \dfrac{x}{2}.$

297 $\quad x^2y'' - 3xy' + 4y = 0$ $\qquad$ **3-1**

$\quad\quad y = x^2(C_1 + C_2 \ln x)$

298 $\quad x^2y'' - 3xy' + 4y = 5x$ $\qquad$ **12-2**

See (297); $\quad F(x) = 5x.$

299 $\quad x^2y'' - 3xy' - 5y = 0$ $\qquad$ **3-1**

$\quad\quad xy = C_1 + C_2 x^6$

300 $\quad x^2y'' - 3xy' - 5y = x^2 \ln x$ $\qquad$ **12-2**

See (299); $\quad F(x) = -(x^2/9) \ln x.$

301 $\quad x^2y'' + 4xy' + 2y = 0$ $\qquad$ **3-1**

$\quad\quad x^2y = C_1 + C_2 x$

302 $\quad x^2y'' + 4xy' + 2y = e^x$ $\qquad$ **12-2**

See (301); $\quad F(x) = e^x/x^2.$

303 $\quad x^2y'' + 4xy' + 2y = \ln(1 + x)$ $\qquad$ **12-2**

See (301); $\quad F(x) = \dfrac{1}{2}\left(1 + \dfrac{1}{x}\right)^2 \ln(1 + x) - \dfrac{3}{4}.$

304 $\quad x^2y'' - 4xy' + 6y = 0$ $\qquad$ **3-1**

$\quad\quad y = x^2(C_1 + C_2 x)$

305 $\quad x^2y'' - 4xy' + 6y = x^2(x^2 - 1)$ $\qquad$ **12-2**

See (304); $\quad F(x) = x^4/2 + x^2 \ln x.$

306 $\quad x^2y'' + 4xy' + (2 - x^2)y = 0$ $\qquad$ **4-1-2**

$\quad u(x) = x^2y; \quad u'' = u; \quad$ see (7).

$\quad\quad x^2y = C_1 e^x + C_2 e^{-x}$

307 $\quad x^2y'' - 4xy' + (6 + x^2)y = 0$ $\qquad$ **4-1-2**

$\quad y = x^2 u(x); \quad u'' + u = 0; \quad$ see (6).

$\quad\quad y = x^2(C_1 \cos x + C_2 \sin x)$

308 $\quad x^2y'' + 5xy' + 13y = 0$ $\qquad$ **3-1**

$\quad\quad x^2y = C_1 \cos(3 \ln x) + C_2 \sin(3 \ln x)$

309 $\quad x^2y'' - 7xy' + 16y = 0$ $\qquad$ **3-1**

$\quad\quad y = x^4(C_1 + C_2 \ln x)$

310 $\quad x^2y'' - 2axy' + \lfloor a(a+1) + b^2x^2 \rfloor y = 0$ $\qquad$ **4-1-2**

$\quad y = x^n u(x); \quad u'' + a^2 u = 0; \quad$ see (26).

$\quad\quad y = x^n(C_1 \cos ax + C_2 \sin ax)$

311 $\quad x^2y'' + a_1 xy' + a_2 y = 0$ $\qquad$ **3-1, 9-2**

312 $\quad x^2y'' + a_1xy' + (a_2 + b_2x)y = 0$ $\qquad\qquad$ **4-3, 9-2**

$y = x^k u(z); \quad z = 2i\sqrt{x}; \quad 2k = 1 - a_1; \quad z^2u'' + zu + zu'$
$- (p^2 - z^2)u = 0; \quad p^2 = (1 - a_1)^2 - 4a_2; \quad$ see (274).

313 $\quad x^2y'' + a_1xy' + (a_2 + b_2x^2)y = 0$ $\qquad\qquad$ **4-3, 9-2**

$y = x^k u(z); \quad z = x\sqrt{b_2}; \quad 2k = 1 - a_1; \quad z^2u'' + zu' - (p^2 - z^2)u = 0;$
$p^2 + 4a_2 = (1 - a_1)^2; \quad$ see (274).

314 $\quad x^2y'' + a_1xy' + (a_2 + b_2x + c_2x^2)y = 0$ $\qquad$ **4-1-2, 4-1-3, 9-2**

$\qquad$ i. $\; y = x^{-a_1/2}u(x); \quad x^2u'' + (A + b_2x + c_2x^2)u = 0;$
$A = a_2 + a_1(2 - a_1)/4; \quad$ see (258).

$\qquad$ ii. $\; y = x^k u(x); \quad k^2 + (a_1 - 1)k + a_2 = 0; \quad xu'' + Au'$
$+ (b_2 + c_2x)u = 0; \quad A = a_1 + 2k; \quad$ see (200).

315 $\quad x^2y'' + axy' + (b + cx^3)y = 0$ $\qquad\qquad$ **4-3**

$y = x^{(1-a)/2}u(z); \quad 3z = 2x^{3/2}\sqrt{c}; \quad z^2u'' + zu' - (p^2 - z^2)u = 0;$
$9p^2 - (a - 1)^2 + 4b = 0; \quad$ see (274) and (317).

316 $\quad x^2y'' + axy' + x^2(a_1 + b_1x^2)y = 0$ $\qquad\qquad$ **4-2**

$y(x) = u(z); \quad 2z = x^2; \quad zu'' + Au' + (A_1 + B_1z)u = 0;$
$A = (1 + a)/2; \quad A_1 = a_1/2; \quad B_1 = b_1; \quad$ see (200).

317 $\quad x^2y'' + axy' + (b + cx^{2k})y = 0$ $\qquad\qquad$ **4-3**

$y = x^{(1-a)/2}u(z); \quad kz = x^k\sqrt{c}; \quad p^2k^2 + b = \tfrac{1}{4}(a - 1)^2; \quad z^2u''$
$+ zu' + (z^2 - p^2)u = 0; \quad$ see (274).

318 $\quad x^2y'' + (a + bx)y' + cy = 0$ $\qquad\qquad$ **4-2**

$y(x) = e^z z^k u(z); \quad z = 1/x; \quad k^2 + k(1 - b) + c = 0; \quad zu'' + (A_1$
$+ B_1z)u' + (A_2 + B_2z)u = 0; \quad A_1 = 2k + 2 - b; \quad B_1 = 2 - a;$
$A_2 = k(2 - a) + 2 - b; \quad B_2 = 1 - a; \quad$ see (216).

319 $\quad x^2y'' - 2axy' + a(a + 1)y = 0$ $\qquad\qquad$ **3-1**

$\qquad\qquad y = C_1x^a + C_2x^{a+1}$

320 $\quad x^2y'' - 2axy' + a(a + 1)y = e^x x^{a+2}$ $\qquad\qquad$ **12-2**

See (319); $\; F(x) = e^x x^a$.

321 $\quad x^2y'' - 2axy' + [a(a + 1) + b^2x^2]y = 0$ $\qquad\qquad$ **4-1-2**

$y = x^a u(x); \quad u'' + b^2u = 0; \quad$ see (26).

$\qquad\qquad y = x^a(C_1 \cos bx + C_2 \sin bx)$

322 $\quad x^2y'' \pm x^2y' + (a + bx)y = 0$ $\qquad\qquad$ **4-1-2**

$y = e^{\mp x/2}u(x); \quad x^2u'' + (a + bx - \tfrac{1}{4}x^2)u = 0; \quad$ see (258).

323 $\quad x^2y'' - x^2y' - 2x^2y = 1 + x + 2x^2 \ln x$ $\qquad\qquad$ **12-1**

See (98).

$\qquad\qquad y = C_1e^{2x} + C_2e^{-x} - \ln x$

324 $\quad x^2y'' + x^2y' + (a + bx^2)y = 0$ $\qquad\qquad$ **4-1-2**

$y = e^{-x/2}u(x); \quad x^2u'' + (a + Bx^2)u = 0; \quad B = b - 1/4; \quad$ see (258).

325 $x^2y'' - (1-x^2)y' - y = 0$ **4-1-1**
$y_1 = e^{-x}$.

326 $x^2y'' \pm x(1-x)y' \mp (1-x)y = 0$ **4-1-1**
$y_1 = x$.

327 $x^2y'' - x(2+x)y' + (2+x)y = 0$ **4-1-1**
$y_1 = x$.
$$y = x(C_1 + C_2e^x)$$

328 $x^2y'' - x(2+x)y' + (2+x)y = x^3$ **12-3**
See (327); $F(x) = -x^2$.

329 $x^2y'' + x(2-x)y' - (2+3x)y = 0$ **4-1-1**
$y_1 = xe^x$.

330 $x^2y'' + x(3+x)y' - y = 0$ **4-1-2**
$y = x^{-3/2}e^{-x/2}u(x)$; $4x^2u'' = (x^2+6x+7)u$; see (450).

331 $x^2y'' - 2x(1+x)y' + 2(1+x)y = 0$ **4-1-1**
$y_1 = x$.
$$y = C_1x + C_2xe^{2x}$$

332 $x^2y'' + ax^2y' - 2y = 0$ **4-3**
$zy = u$; $ax = z$; $zu'' - (2-z)u' - u = 0$; see (207).
$$axy = C_1(ax-2) + C_2(ax+2)e^{-ax}$$

333 $x^2y'' - x(5+ax)y' + (5+3ax)y = 0$ **4-1-1**
$y_1 = x(6+4ax+a^2x^2)$.

334 $x^2y'' + x(a_1+b_1x)y' + (a_2+b_2x+c_2x^2)y = 0$ **4-1-2, 9-2**
$y = x^ku(x)$; $k^2 + (a_1-1)k + a_2 = 0$; $xu'' + (A_1+b_1x)u'$
$+ (A_2+c_2x)u = 0; A_1 = a_1+2k$; $A_2 = b_2+b_1k$; see (216).

335 $x^2y'' + x^3y' - (2-x^2)y = 0$ **4-1-1**
$y_1 = 1/x$.

336 $x^2y'' + x(1-x^2)y' - (1+x^2)y = 0$ **4-1-1**
$y_1 = 1/x$.
$$xy = C_1 + C_2e^{x^2/2}$$

337 $x^2y'' + 4x^3y' + (1+2x^2+4x^4)y = 0$ **4-1-2**
$y = e^{-x^2}u(x)$; $x^2u'' + u = 0$; see (250).
$$yx^{-1/2}e^{x^2} = C_1\cos(A\ln x) + C_2\sin(A\ln x)$$
$A = \sqrt{3}/2$.

338 $x^2y'' + x(a_0+b_0x^k)y' + (a_1+b_1x^k+c_1x^{2k})y = 0$ **4-2**
$y(x) = u(z); z = x^k; z^2u'' + z(A_0+B_0z)u' + (a_2+b_2z+c_2z^2)u = 0$;
$kA_0 = k+a_0-1$; $kB_0 = b_0$; $k^2a_2 = a_1$; $k^2b_2 = b_1$; $k^2c_1 = c_2$;
see (334).

339 $x^2y'' + x(a_0 + a_1x^r + a_2x^s)y' + (b_0 + b_1x^r + b_2x^{2r} + b_3x^s + b_4x^{2s}$
$$+ b_5x^{r+s})y = 0 \qquad\qquad \textbf{4-1-3}$$
$y = uv; \quad v = kx^s; \quad$ see (344). The result is (338) in u, x, if
$2b_3 = a_0(a_0 + s - 1); \quad 4b_4 = a_2{}^2.; \quad 2b_5 = a_1a_2.$

340 $x^2y'' + 2x^2y' \cot x + ay = 0 \qquad\qquad \textbf{4-1-2}$
$y = u(x) \csc x; \quad x^2u'' + (a + x^2)u = 0; \quad$ see (258).

341 $x^2y'' + (1 + 2x \cot x)xy' - (a - x \cot x)y = 0 \qquad\qquad \textbf{4-1-3}$
$y = u(x) \csc x; \quad x^2u'' + xu' - (a^2 - x^2)u = 0; \quad$ see (274).

342 $x^2y'' - 2x^2y' \tan x + ay = 0 \qquad\qquad \textbf{4-1-2}$
$y = u(x) \sec x; \quad x^2u'' + (a + x^2)u = 0; \quad$ see (258).

343 $x^2y'' + (1 - 2x \tan x)xy' - (a + x \tan x)y = 0 \qquad\qquad \textbf{4-1-3}$
$y = u(x) \sec x; \quad x^2u'' + xu' - (a^2 - x^2)u = 0; \quad$ see (274).

344 $x^2y'' + x[a_1 + b_1x^k + 2f(x)]y' + [a_2 + b_2x^k + c_2x^{2k}$
$$+ (a_1 + b_1x^k - 1)f + f^2 + xf']y = 0 \qquad\qquad \textbf{4-1-3}$$
$y = uv; \quad v = e^{-\phi(x)}; \quad \phi(x) = \displaystyle\int \frac{f(x)}{x}dx; \quad x^2u'' + x(a_1 + b_1x^k)u'$
$+ (a_2 + b_2x^k + c_2x^{2k})u = 0; \quad$ see (338).

345 $(1 + x^2)y'' - 2y = 0 \qquad\qquad \textbf{4-1-1}$
$y_1 = 1 + x^2.$
$$y = C_1(1 + x^2) + C_2[x + (1 + x^2) \tan^{-1} x]$$

346 $(1 - x^2)y'' - xy' \pm a = 0 \qquad\qquad \textbf{B2-1-2}$
See (1-285).
$$y = C_1 + C_2 \sin^{-1} x \mp (a/2)(\sin^{-1} x)^2$$

347 $(1 - x^2)y'' + xy' = x \qquad\qquad \textbf{B2-1-2}$
See (1-286).
$$y = C_1 + x + C_2[x\sqrt{1 - x^2} + \sin^{-1} x]$$

348 $(1 + x^2)y'' - xy' + y = 0 \qquad\qquad \textbf{4-1-1}$
$y_1 = x.$

349 $(1 - x^2)y'' + xy' - y = 0 \qquad\qquad \textbf{4-1-1}$
$y_1 = x.$
$$y = C_1x + C_2[x \sin^{-1} x + \sqrt{1 - x^2}]$$

350 $(1 - x^2)y'' - xy' + y = 0 \qquad\qquad \textbf{4-1-1}$
$y_1 = x.$
$$y = C_1x + C_2\sqrt{1 - x^2}$$

351 $(1 - x^2)y'' - xy' - y = 0 \qquad\qquad \textbf{4-1-1}$
$\ln y_1 = \cos^{-1} x.$
$$y = C_1e^{\cos^{-1}x} + C_2e^{\sin^{-1}x}$$

352 $(1-x^2)y'' + xy' - y = x(1-x^2)^{3/2}$ **12-3**

See (349); $F(x) = -(x/9)(1-x^2)^{3/2}.$

353 $(1-x^2)y'' + xy' + 3y = 0$ **4-1-1**

$y_1 = (1-x^2)^{3/2}.$

$$y = C_1(1-x^2)^{3/2} + C_2x(3-2x^2)$$

354 $(1 \pm x^2)y'' \pm xy' \mp 4y = 0$ **4-2-1**

$y(x) = u(z);$ $x = \sinh z(\sin z);$ $u'' \mp 4u = 0;$ see (26).

$$y = C_1(1 \pm 2x^2) + C_2x\sqrt{1 \pm x^2}$$

355 $(1+x^2)y'' + xy' - 9y = 0$ **4-1-1**

$y_1 = x(3+4x^2).$

356 $(1-x^2)y'' - xy' + n^2y = 0$ **9-3**

In this equation n is an integer. For the nonintegral case, see
(358). The general solution is a linear combination of Tchebichef
(also spelled Tschebyscheff) polynomials of the first and second
kind; see also (370) and (408);

$$y = C_1T_n(x) + C_2U_n(x)$$

$$T_n(x) = \cos(n \cos^{-1} x) = x^n - \binom{n}{2}x^{n-2}(1-x^2)$$

$$+ \binom{n}{4}x^{n-4}(1-x^2)^2 \mp \dots$$

$$U_n(x) = \sin(n \cos^{-1} x) = \sqrt{1-x^2}\left[\binom{n}{1}x^{n-1} - \binom{n}{3}x^{n-3}(1-x^2)\right.$$

$$\left. + \binom{n}{5}x^{n-5}(1-x^2)^2 \mp \dots\right].$$

357 $(1+x^2)y'' + xy' \pm a^2y = 0$ **4-2-1**

$y(x) = u(z);$ $x = \sinh z;$ $u''(z) \pm a^2u = 0;$ see (26).

358 $(1-x^2)y'' - xy' \pm a^2y = 0$ **4-2-1**

$y(x) = u(z);$ $x = \sin z;$ $u''(z) \pm a^2u = 0;$ see (26) and also
(385).

359 $(1-x^2)y'' - xy' + (a+bx^2)y = 0$ **9-3**

$y(x) = u(z); x = \sin z; u'' + (A+B \cos 2z)u = 0; A = a+b/2;$
$B = -b/2;$ see (43).

360 $(1-x^2)y'' - xy' + (a_0 + a_1x^2 + \dots + a_nx^{2n})y = 0$ **9-3**

361 $(1-x^2)y'' - 2xy' = 0$ **B2-1-2**

$$y = C_1 + C_2 \ln\left(\frac{1+x}{1-x}\right)$$

362     $(1-x^2)y'' - 2xy' + a = 0$ **12-3**
See (361); $F(x) = a\ln(1+x)$.

363     $(1+x^2)y'' + 2xy' - 2y = 0$ **4-1-1**
$y_1 = x$.
$$y = C_1 x + C_2(1 + x\tan^{-1} x)$$

364     $(1 \pm x^2)y'' \mp 2xy' \pm 2y = 0$ **4-1-1**
$y_1 = x$.
$$y = C_1 x + C_2(1 \mp x^2)$$

365     $(1-x^2)y'' + 2xy' - 2y = (1-x^2)^2$ **12-3**
See (364); $F(x) = (x^2/6)(3 - x^2)$.

366     $(1-x^2)y'' - 2xy' + n(n+1)y = 0$ **9-3**
A special case of the Legendre equation; see (369). The results
from (369) may be used, replacing p by an integer n or replacing
$2p$ by n. However, in some cases only one solution would then
result. With the definitions $y_1 = P_p(x)$, $y_2 = Q_p(x)$, as given
for (369), the following possibilities occur.

      i. $n \geqslant 0$; y_1 is a polynomial, see a; y_2 is an infinite
series, convergent for $|x| > 1$.

      ii. $n < 0$; y_2 is a polynomial; y_1 is an infinite series,
convergent for $|x| > 1$. See a, replacing n by $-n$.

      iii. $2n = 2m+1$; $m \geqslant 0$; y_2 is a solution but y_1 be-
comes meaningless because of zeros in its denominators; see b.

      iv. $2n = -(2m+1)$; $m > 0$; y_1 is a solution but y_2
becomes meaningless as in iii; see c. The special case of $2n = -1$ is also treated there.

For some further properties of the solutions, see d.

      a. $n \geqslant 0$. Use the definitions of (369), replacing p by n.

      i. The first solution is a Legendre polynomial of the
first kind or a zonal spherical harmonic

$$y_1 = P_n(x) = \frac{(2n)!}{2^n(n!)^2} \left[x^n - \frac{n(n-1)}{2(2n-1)} x^{n-2} \right.$$
$$\left. + \frac{n(n-1)(n-2)(n-3)}{2 \cdot 4(2n-1)(2n-3)} x^{n-4} \pm \cdots \right]$$

If n is even, the last term in the bracket is
$$\frac{(-1)^{n/2}(n!)^3}{[(n/2)!]^2(2n)!}$$

If n is odd, the last term is
$$\frac{(-1)^{(n-1)/2}(n!)^2(n-1)!}{[(n/2 - 1/2)!]^2(2n-1)!}$$

The number of terms in the two cases is $(n+2)/2$, $(n+1)/2$, respectively. The constant multipliers are chosen so that $P_n(1) = 1$, for all values of n.

Further representations of y_1 are

$$P_{2n}(x) = \frac{(-1)^n 1 \cdot 3 \cdot 5 \ldots (2n-1)}{2 \cdot 4 \ldots (2n)} \left[1 - \frac{2n(2n+1)}{2!} x^2 \right.$$

$$+ \frac{2n(2n-2)(2n+1)(2n+3)}{4!} x^4 \mp \ldots \Big]$$

$$P_{2n+1}(x) = \frac{(-1)^n 3 \cdot 5 \ldots (2n+1)}{2 \cdot 4 \ldots (2n)} x \left[1 - \frac{2n(2n+3)}{3!} x^2 \right.$$

$$+ \frac{2n(2n-2)(2n+3)(2n+5)}{5!} x^4 \mp \ldots \Big]$$

$$P_n(\cos \theta) = \frac{(2n)!}{2^{2n}(n!)^2} \left[\cos n\theta + \frac{n}{2n-1} \cos(n-2)\theta \right.$$

$$+ \frac{1 \cdot 3n(n-1)}{1 \cdot 2(2n-1)(2n-3)} \cos(n-4)\theta + \ldots \Big]$$

The last series ends at $\cos(-n\theta)$. There are $(n+1)$ terms but if n is odd, they are equal in pairs.

For $m = -(1+n)$, $P_m(x) = P_n(x)$ and $P_n(-x) = (-1)^n P_n(x)$.

ii. The second solution is an infinite series; see (369). However, from **8-2-3**, $\Delta = 2n$; hence the methods of that section show that the second solution is related to y_1 and that it contains a logarithmic term. The form of the second solution can be found according to **8-2-3**. Alternatively, assume that

$$y_2 = \frac{1}{2} P_n \ln \left(\frac{x+1}{x-1} \right) - Y(x)$$

is a particular integral. It is found that, for $n \geqslant 0$, $Y(x)$ is a solution of the nonhomogeneous Legendre equation, see (367). The result is

$$Y(x) = \frac{(2n-1)}{1 \cdot n} P_{n-1}(x) + \frac{(2n-5)}{3(n-1)} P_{n-3}(x) + \frac{2n-9}{5(n-2)} P_{n-5}(x) + \ldots$$

The last term is $\dfrac{6P_1}{(n-1)(n+2)}$, if n is even; $\dfrac{2}{n(n+1)}$, if n is odd.

b. $2n = 2m+1$; $m \geqslant 0$. According to **8-2-3**, $\Delta = 2m+3$, an integer. The methods of that section give the two linearly independent solutions. They are

$$y_1 = y_2 \ln x + Y_1(x) + Y_2(x)$$

$$y_2 = Q_n(x)$$

$$= \frac{2^n(n!)^2}{(2n+1)!} x^{-n-1} {}_2F_1\left(\frac{1+n}{2}, \frac{2+n}{2}, \frac{3+2n}{2}; 1/x^2\right)$$

$$Y_1(x) = B\left[x^n - \frac{n(n-1)}{2(2n-1)} x^{n-2} + \ldots\right.$$

$$\left. - n(n-1)\left\{\frac{1/2 \cdot 3/2 \ldots (n-2)}{2 \cdot 4 \ldots (2n-1)}\right\}^2 x^{-n+1}\right]$$

$$B = \left[\frac{4 \cdot 8 \cdot 12 \ldots (4n-2)}{1 \cdot 3 \cdot 5 \ldots (2n)}\right]^2$$

$$Y_2(x) = Bx^{-n-1}$$

$$\times \sum_{k=1}^{\infty} \left[\frac{(n+1)(n+2)\ldots(n+2k)}{2 \cdot 4 \ldots 2k(2n+3)\ldots(2n+5)\ldots(2n+2k+1)} B_k x^{-2k}\right]$$

$$B_k = \sum_{r=1}^{k} \left[\frac{1}{2r} + \frac{1}{2n+2r+1} - \frac{1}{n+2r-1} - \frac{1}{n+2r}\right]$$

The quantity ${}_2F_1(a, b, c; 1/x^2)$ in y_2 is a Gauss hypergeometric series; see (410).

When $m = 0$, it follows that $2n = 1$ and $Y_1(x) = 8\sqrt{x}$. The other terms remain unchanged.

c. $2n = -(2m+1)$; $m \geqslant 0$. Exclude the case $m = 0$, $2n = -1$, for the moment. The solution y_1 is valid but y_2 contains vanishing terms in the denominators. Procedures like those in b show that

$$y_1 = P_n(x)$$

$$y_2 = y_1 \ln x + Y_1(x) + Y_2(x)$$

$$Y_1(x) = B\left[x^{-n-1} + \frac{(n+1)(n+2)}{2(2n+3)} x^{-n-3} + \ldots\right.$$

$$\left. - (n+1)(n+2)\left\{\frac{1/2 \cdot 3/2 \ldots (-n-3)}{2 \cdot 4 \ldots (-2n-3)}\right\}^2 x^{n+2}\right]$$

$$B = \left[\frac{4 \cdot 8 \cdot 12 \ldots (-4n-6)}{1 \cdot 3 \cdot 5 \ldots (-2n-2)}\right]^2 (-8n-4)$$

$$Y_2(x) = Bx^n \sum_{k=1}^{\infty} \frac{(-1)^k n(n-1)...(n-2k+1)}{2 \cdot 4...2k(2n-1)(2n-3)...(2n-2k+1)} B_k x^{-2k}$$

$$B_k = \sum_{r=1}^{k} \left[\frac{1}{2r} + \frac{1}{2r-2n-1} - \frac{1}{2r-n-2} - \frac{1}{2r-n-1} \right]$$

When $m = 0$, so that $2n = -1$, the results are

$$y_1 = x^{-1/2}\left[1 + \frac{1/2 \cdot 3/2}{2 \cdot 2}x^{-2} + \frac{1/2 \cdot 3/2 \cdot 5/2 \cdot 7/2}{2 \cdot 4 \cdot 2 \cdot 4}x^{-4} + ...\right]$$

$$y_2 = y_1 \ln x - Y_1(x)$$

$$Y_1(x) = x^{-1/2} \sum_{k=1}^{\infty} \frac{1/2 \cdot 3/2...(4k-1)/2}{(k!)^2 2^{2k}} B_k x^{-2k}$$

$$B_k = \sum_{r=1}^{k} \left[\frac{1}{2k+2r-1} + \frac{1}{2r-1} - \frac{1}{2r} \right]$$

d. The following properties of $P_n(x)$ and $Q_n(x)$ are often useful.

i. Generating functions determine the polynomials for a given value of n

$$(1-2xt+t^2)^{-1/2} = \sum_{n=0}^{\infty} P_n(x)t^n$$

$$(1-2xt+t^2)^{-1/2} \cosh^{-1}\left(\frac{t-x}{\sqrt{x^2-1}}\right) = \sum_{n=0}^{\infty} Q_n(x)t^n$$

ii. Recurrence formulas relate polynomials of different order

$$P_{n+1}'(x) - xP_n'(x) = (n+1)P_n(x)$$
$$(n+1)P_{n+1}(x) - x(2n+1)P_n(x) + nP_{n-1}(x) = 0$$
$$xP_n'(x) - P_{n-1}'(x) = nP_n(x)$$
$$P_{n+1}'(x) - P_{n-1}'(x) = (2n+1)P_n(x)$$
$$(x^2-1)P_n'(x) = nxP_n(x) - nP_{n-1}(x)$$

The same relations hold if $P_n(x)$ is replaced by $Q_n(x)$.

iii. Polynomials of the first kind can also be calculated by Rodrigues' formula

$$P_n(x) = \frac{1}{2^n n!} \frac{d^n(x^2-1)^n}{dx^n}$$

367    $(1-x^2)y'' - 2xy' + n(n+1)y = 2P_n'(x)$ 12-3
The nonhomogeneous Legendre equation, where $P_n(x)$ is a Legendre polynomial of the first kind and of the first degree; see (366).

A solution is

$$y_1 = \sum_{k=1}^{n} \frac{P_{k-1}(x)P_{n-k}(x)}{k}$$

$$= \frac{(2n-1)}{1 \cdot n}P_{n-1}(x) + \frac{(2n-5)}{3(n-1)}P_{n-3}(x) + \frac{(2n-9)}{5(n-2)}P_{n-5}(x) + \dots$$

The last term in the series is $\dfrac{6P_1}{(n-1)(n+2)} = \dfrac{6x}{(n-1)(n+2)}$ for n

even and $\dfrac{P_0}{n(n+1)} = \dfrac{2}{n(n+1)}$ for n odd.

368 $\qquad (1+x^2)y'' + 2xy' - p(p+1)y = 0$ $\qquad\qquad$ **4-2**
$y(x) = u(z); \quad z = ix; \quad (1-z^2)u'' - 2zu' + p(p+1)u = 0;$
see (369).

369 $\qquad (1-x^2)y'' - 2xy' + p(p+1)y = 0$ $\qquad\qquad$ **9-3**
The Legendre differential equation. If $p = \pm n$, or if $2p = \pm n$,
where n is an integer, see (366).

In the general case, the solution is

$$y = C_1 y_1 + C_2 y_2$$

The equation has regular singular points at $x = \pm 1$, ∞ with
exponents 0, 0; 0, 0; $p+1$, $-p$, respectively. It thus can be
transformed into the Gauss hypergeometric equation, see (410),
in a number of different ways. If such a procedure is desired,
see b. Alternatively, solutions can be given for the ordinary
point $x = 0$, see a.

a. Use the method of **8-1**. There will be two linearly independent solutions, convergent for $-1 < x < 1$,

$$y_1 = 1 - \frac{p(p+1)}{2!}x^2 + \frac{p(p-2)(p+1)(p+3)}{4!}x^4 \mp \quad \dots$$

$$+ (-1)^k \frac{p(p-2) \dots (p-2k+2)(p+1) \dots (p+2k-1)}{(2k)!}x^{2k} \pm \dots$$

$$y_2 = x\left[1 - \frac{(p-1)(p+2)}{3!}x^2 + \frac{(p-1)(p-3)(p+2)(p+4)}{5!}x^4 \mp \quad \dots\right.$$

$$\left. + (-1)^k \frac{(p-1)(p-3) \dots (p-2k+1)(p+2) \dots (p+2k)}{(2k+1)!}x^{2k} \pm \dots\right]$$

b. When solutions are wanted in terms of hypergeometric
series, there are a number of possibilities. Only a few are
listed here.

i. Refer to (555) and set $k = 0$.

ii. Let $y(x) = u(z)$; $2z = 1-x$. This transformation of the independent variable shifts the singular points of the equation from $x = \pm 1$, ∞ to $z = 0$, 1, ∞. The new equation in u, z, see (400), has solutions in terms of hypergeometric series. In this case, assume x to be real, $x = \cos\theta$, $2z = 1-x$; $z = \sin^2\theta/2$, $-1 < x < 1$. The results can be generalized if x is complex.

iii. Let $y(x) = u(z)$; $z = x^2$. The result is (443). The linearly independent solutions, identical with those in a, are

$$y_1 = {}_2F_1\left(-\frac{p}{2}, \frac{1+p}{2}, \frac{1}{2}; \ x^2\right)$$

$$y_2 = x {}_2F_1\left(\frac{1-p}{2}, \frac{2+p}{2}, \frac{3}{2}; \ x^2\right)$$

See (410) for the meaning of the symbols.

It is generally more useful to give these solutions in descending powers of x. They would then apply to the singular point $x = \infty$ and both series would converge for $|x| > 1$. The two linearly independent solutions are

$$y_1 = Ax^p {}_2F_1\left(-\frac{p}{2}, \frac{1-p}{2}, \frac{1-2p}{2}; \ 1/x^2\right) = P_p(x)$$

$$y_2 = Bx^{-p-1} {}_2F_1\left(\frac{1+p}{2}, \frac{2+p}{2}, \frac{3+2p}{2}; \ 1/x^2\right) = Q_p(x)$$

$$A = \frac{2p\Gamma(p+1/2)}{\sqrt{\pi}\Gamma(p+1)}; \ B = \frac{\sqrt{\pi}\Gamma(p+1)}{2^{p+1}\Gamma(p+3/2)}.$$

The constant factors A and B are inserted in order to obtain $P_p(x)$, $Q_p(x)$, Legendre functions of the first and second kinds, respectively, and as usually defined; see (366).

370    $(1-x^2)y'' - 3xy' + n(2+n)y = 0$ **4-1-1**
A solution is $y_1 = Y_n(x)$, often called a Tchebichef (also spelled Tschebyscheff) polynomial of the second kind; but see also (356),

$$Y_n(x) = \frac{\sin[(1+n)\cos^{-1}x]}{\sqrt{1-x^2}} = \frac{U_{n+1}(x)}{\sqrt{1-x^2}}$$

371    $(1-x^2)y'' - 3xy' - ay = 0$ **4-1**
$y(1-x^2)^{1/2} = u(x)$; $(1-x^2)u'' - xu' + (1-a)u = 0$;   see (358).

372 $(1+x^2)y'' + 4xy' + 2y = 2(\cos x - x)$ **5-1**
$$(1+x^2)y = C_1 + C_2 x - x^3/3 - 2\cos x$$

373 $(1+x^2)y'' - 4xy' + 6y = 0$ **4-1-1**
$y_1 = 1 - 3x^2.$
$$y = C_1(1 - 3x^2) + C_2 x(3 - x^2)$$

374 $(1-x^2)y'' - 4xy' - (1+x^2)y = 0$ **4-1-2**
$y(1-x^2) = u(x);$ $u'' + u = 0;$ see (6).
$$y(1-x^2) = C_1 \cos x + C_2 \sin x$$

375 $(1-x^2)y'' - 6xy' - 4y = 0$ **5-1**
A first integral is $(1-x^2)y' = C_1 + 4xy;$ see (1-296).
$$3(1-x^2)^2 y = C_1 x(3 - x^2) + C_2$$

376 $(1-x^2)y'' + [b - a - (2+a+b)x]y' + n(1+a+b+n)y = 0$ **4-2**
One form of the equation for Jacobi polynomials. It can be converted into the usual form with $y(x) = u(z);$ $2z = 1 - x;$ $z(1-z)u'' + [1 + a - (2+a+b)z]u' + n(1+a+b+n)u = 0;$ see (408). A solution is

$$P_n^{(a,\,b)}(x) = 2^{-n} \sum_{k=0}^{n} \binom{n+a}{k}\binom{n+b}{n-k}(x-1)^{n-k}(x+1)^k$$

$$= \binom{n+a}{n} {}_2F_1\left(-n,\ 1+a+b+n,\ 1+a;\ \frac{1-x}{2}\right)$$

$$P_n^{(a,\,b)}(-x) = (-1)^n P_n^{(b,\,a)}(x)$$

See (410) for the meaning of the symbol ${}_2F_1$.

A second solution, not a polynomial but an infinite series, is a Jacobi function of the second kind

$$Q_n^{(a,\,b)}(x)\Gamma(2n+a+b+2) = 2^{n+a+b}\frac{\Gamma(1+n+a)\Gamma(1+n+b)}{(x-1)^{n+a+1}(x+1)^b}$$

$$\times {}_2F_1\left(1+n,\ 1+a+n,\ 2+a+b+2n;\ \frac{2}{1-x}\right)$$

377 $(1-x^2)y'' - (1+2k)xy' + p(p+2k)y = 0$ **9-3**
The Gegenbauer equation. A solution is a Gegenbauer function, $C_p^k(x).$
    a. $y(x) = u(z); x = 1 - 2z; z(1-z)u'' + [a_0 - (1+b_0+c_0)z]u'$ $- b_0 c_0 u = 0; a_0 = k+1/2; b_0 = 2k+p; c_0 = -p;$ see (410).
    i. $k = 1/2;$ see (369).
    ii. $p = n,$ an integer. The solutions are Gegenbauer or ultraspherical polynomials, identical with Legendre polynomials, when $k = 1/2;$ see also (366).

b. Linearly independent solutions in the general case are

$$C_p{}^k(x) = \frac{\Gamma(p+2k)}{\Gamma(1+p)\Gamma(2k)} {}_2F_1\left(2k+p,\ -p,\ \frac{2k+1}{2};\ \frac{1-x}{2}\right)$$

$$= 2^{k-1/2}\frac{\Gamma(p+2k)\Gamma(k+1/2)}{\Gamma(1+p)\Gamma(2k)}$$

$$\times (x^2-1)^{1/4-1/2k}P_{p+k-1/2}{}^{1/2-k}(x)$$

$$D_p{}^k(x) = 2^{-1-p}\frac{\Gamma(k)\Gamma(p+2k)}{\Gamma(1+k+p)}x^{-p-2k}{}_2F_1$$

$$\times \left(\frac{2k+p}{2},\ \frac{2k+p+1}{2},\ 1+k+p;\ x^2\right)$$

See (410) for the meaning of $_2F_1$ and (555) for $P_\beta{}^\alpha(x)$.

c. For the Gegenbauer polynomials, $p = n$ and they can be defined by means of a generating function

$$(1-2xt+t^2)^{-k} = \sum_{n=0}^{\infty} C_n{}^k(x)t^n$$

The following relations are also useful.

$$C_n{}^k(x) = \frac{(-2)^n k(k+1)...(k+n-1)(1-x^2)^{1/2-k}}{n!(2n+2k-1)(2n+2k-2)...(n+2k)}$$

$$\times \frac{d^n}{dx^n}[(1-x^2)^{n+k-1/2}]$$

$$C_{n-m}{}^{m+1/2}(x) = \frac{1}{(2m-1)(2m-3)...3\cdot 1}\ \frac{d^m}{dx^m}P_n(x)$$

$$= \frac{(x^2-1)^{-m/2}}{(2m-1)(2m-3)...3\cdot 1}P_n{}^m(x)$$

See (366) for a definition of $P_\alpha(x)$ and (555) for $P_\beta{}^\alpha(x)$.
Recurrence formulas for the polynomials include

$$xC_{n-1}{}^{k+1}(x) - C_{n-2}{}^{k+1}(x) = \frac{n}{2k}C_n{}^k(x)$$

$$C_n{}^{k+1}(x) - xC_{n-1}{}^{k+1}(x) = \frac{(n+2k)}{2k}C_n{}^k(x)$$

$$\frac{dC_n{}^k(x)}{dx} = 2kC_{n-1}{}^{k+1}(x)$$

$$nC_n{}^k(x) = (n-1+2k)xC_{n-1}{}^k(x) - 2k(1-x^2)C_{n-2}{}^{k-1}(x)$$

378    $(1-x^2)y'' - 2(1+k)xy' + p(1+p+2k)y = 0$ **9-3**
This is called the Gegenbauer equation by some writers; see (377).
In terms of associated Legendre functions, see (555), its
solutions are

$$y_1 = C_p{}^k(x) = (x^2-1)^{-k/2}P_{p+k}{}^k(x)$$

$$y_2 = D_p{}^k(x) = (x^2-1)^{-k/2}Q_{p+k}{}^k(x).$$

379    $(1-x^2)y'' - 2(1+k)xy' - (k-p)(1+k+p)y = 0$ **4-2**
   i. $y(x) = u(z);$ $2z = 1-x;$ $z(1-z)u''$
      $+ (1+k)(1-2z)u' - (k-p)(1+k+p)u = 0;$ see
      (410). A solution is
         $y_1 = {}_2F_1(k-p,\ 1+k+p,\ 1+k;\ z)$
  ii. $y(x) = u(z);$ $z = x^2;$ $4z(1-z)u''$
      $+ 2[1-(2k+3)z]u' - (k-p)(1+k+p)u = 0;$ see
      (410) and (470).

380    $(1-x^2)y'' - 2axy' + a(1-a)y = 0$ **6**
$[(1-x)D-a][(1+x)D-1+a]y = 0,$ where $D = d/dx,$
$y = C_1(1+x)^{1-a} + C_2(1-x)^{1-a}.$

381    $(1+x^2)y'' + axy' - (2-a)y = 0$ **5-1**
A first integral is $(1+x^2)y' = C_1 + (2-a)xy;$ see **A1-2**.

382    $(1-x^2)y'' + axy' + by = 0$ **4-1**
$y = (1-x^2)^k u(x);$ $k = 1+a/2;$ $(1-x^2)u'' - (4+a)xu'$
$- (2+a-b)u = 0;$ see (384).

383    $(1-x^2)y'' + axy' + (a_0 + b_0x + c_0x^2)y = 0$ **9-3**
There are regular singular points at $x = \pm 1$ and an irregular
singular point at $x = \infty$. A series solution around the ordinary
point $x = 0$ could be found by **8-1**.

384    $(1-x^2)y'' + (a+bx)y' + cy = 0$ **4-2**
$y(x) = u(z);$ $2z = 1+x;$ $z(1-z)u'' + [(a-b)/2+bz]u' + cu = 0;$
see (410). For some special cases, see (356), (369), and (370).

385    $(a^2-x^2)y'' - xy' + (b^2+c^2x^2)y = 0$ **9-6**
$y(x) = u(z);$ $x = a\cosh z;$ $u''(z) + (b^2 - a^2c^2\cosh^2 z)u = 0;$ see
(56).

386 $(a^2 - x^2)y'' - 8xy' - 12y = 0$ **6**
$[(a-x)D-4][(a+x)D+3]y = 0$, where $D = d/dx$; see (380).
$$y = C_1(a+x)^{-3} + C_2(a-x)^{-3}$$

387 $x(1-x)y'' + 2y' + y = 0$ **5-1**
A first integral is $x(1-x)y' + (1+2x)y = C_1$; see (1-317).
$$xy = C_1 + C_2(1-x)^3$$

388 $x(1-x)y'' - 2y' + 2y = 0$ **8-2-3**
$y_1 = 1+x+x^2$; $y_2 = x^3(1+x+x^2+...)$.
$$y = C_1 y_1 + C_2 y_2$$

389 $x(1-x)y'' + 2y' + 6y = 0$ **4-1-1**
$y_1 = (1-x)^3$;   see also (410).

390 $x(1-x)y'' - 2y' + 6y = 0$ **4-1-1**
$y_1 = x^3$;   see also (410).

391 $x(1-x)y'' + 3y' + 2y = 0$ **4-1-1**
$y_1 = 6 - 4x + x^2$.
$$x^2 y = C_1 x^2 y_1 + C_2(1-4x)$$

392 $x(1-x)y'' - 3y' + 2y = 0$ **5-1**
A first integral is $x(1-x)y' = C_1 + 2(2-x)y$;   see (1-318).
$$12(1-x)^2 y = C_1(4x-3) + C_2 x^4$$

393 $x(1-x)y'' - 3y' + 2y = x(1+3x^3)$ **12-3**
See (392); $F(x) = -x^2/4 - 3x^4/10$.

394 $x(1-x)y'' - ay' + 2y = 0$ **5-1**
A first integral is $x(1-x)y' = C_1 + (1+a-2x)y$;   see **A1-2**.

395 $x(1+x)y'' + (1-x)y' + y = 0$ **4-1-1**
$y_1 = 1-x$.
$$y = C_1(1-x) + C_2[(1-x)\ln x + 4x]$$

396 $x(1-x)y'' - (1+x)y' + y = 0$ **4-1-1**
$y_1 = 1+x$.
$$(1-x)y = C_1 + C_2(1-x^2)$$

397 $x(1-x)y'' - (4+x)y' + 4y = 0$ **4-1-1**
$y_1 = 1 + x + x^2/2$.

398 $x(1-x)y'' + 2xy' - 2y = 0$ **4-1-1**
$y_1 = x$.
$$y = C_1 x + C_2(1 - x^2 + 2x \ln x)$$

399 $x(1-x)y'' + (1-2x)y' + 6y = 0$ **4-1-1**
$y_1 = 1 - 6x + 6x^2$; $y_2 = 3(2x-1) + y_1 \ln(1-1/x)$.
$$y = C_1 y_1 + C_2 y_2$$

400     $x(1-x)y'' + (1-2x)y' + p(p+1)y = 0$ **9-3**
See (407) and (410). A solution is $y_1 = {}_2F_1(1+p, -p, 1; x)$.

401     $x(1-x)y'' + 2(1-x)y' + 2y = 0$ **4-1-1**
$y_1 = 1-x$.

402     $x(1-x)y'' - 3xy' - y = 0$ **5-1**
A first integral is $x(1-x)y' = C_1 + (1+x)y$; see (1-313).
$$(1-x)^2 y = C_1 x + C_2(1 + x \ln x)$$

403     $x(1+x)y'' + (2+3x)y' + y = 0$ **4-2**
$y(x) = u(z)$; $z = -x$; $z(1-z)u'' + (2-3z)u' - u = 0$;   see
(410); $y_1 = {}_2F_1(1, 1, 2; -x) = (1/x) \ln x$.

404     $x(1-x)y'' + (1-4x)y' - 2y = 0$ **8-2**
See (410); $a = 1, b = 1, c = 2$. The resulting hypergeometric
series can be summed to get the general solution
$$(1-x)^2 y = C_1 + C_2(x - \ln x)$$

405     $x(1-x)y'' - 2(1+2x)y' - 2y = 0$ **5-1**
A first integral is $x(1-x)y' = C_1 + 3y$; see **A1-2**.
$$(1-x)^5 y = C_1 x^3 + C_2(x^4 - 6x^2 + 2x - 1/3 - 4x^3 \ln x)$$

406     $x(1-x)y'' - 2(1-2x)y' - 6y = 0$ **4-1-1**
$y_1 = x^3$.
$$y = C_1 x^3 + C_2(1-x)^3$$

407     $x(1-x)y'' + (1+k)(1-2x)y' + (p-k)(1+p+k)y = 0$ **9-3**
See (410); $a = k-p$; $b = 1+k+p$; $c = 1+k$. A solution is
$y_1 = {}_2F_1(k-p, 1+k+p, 1+k; x)$.

408     $x(1-x)y'' + [c - (1+a)x]y' + n(n+a)y = 0$ **9-3**
The equation of Jacobi polynomials, a special case of the Gauss
hypergeometric equation, see (410), but see also (376).
      a.   For a, c real; $c > 0$, $a > (c-1)$, a solution, defin-
ing the Jacobi polynomials is

$$y_1 = Y_n(a, c; x) = {}_2F_1(-n, a+n, c; x)$$

$$= \sum_{k=0}^{n} (-1)^k \binom{n}{k} \frac{(a+n)(a+n+1)...(a+n+k-1)}{c(c+1)...(c+k-1)} x^k$$

$$= \frac{x^{1-c}(1-x)^{c-a}}{c(c+1)...(c+k-1)} D^n[x^{c+n-1}(1-x)^{a+n-c}]$$

where $D = d/dx$; $Y_0(a, c; x) = 1$.
      The second solution is an infinite series. It can be found
from (410). See also that equation if n is not an integer or if
other exceptional cases occur.

b. Other polynomials are often given in terms of the Jacobi polynomials.

i. Legendre polynomials; see (369).
$$P_n(x) = Y_n(1, 1; z); \quad 2z = 1-x$$

ii. Tchebichef polynomials; see (356).
$$T_n(x) = Y_n(0, 1/2; z); \quad 2z = 1-x$$

iii. Gegenbauer polynomials; see (377).
$$C_n{}^k(x) = (-1)^n \frac{\Gamma(2k+n)}{\Gamma(2k)} Y_n\left(2k, \frac{2k+1}{2}; z\right); \quad 2z = 1+x$$

409    $x(1+x)y'' + (a+bx)y' + cy = 0$ 4-2
$y(x) = u(z);\quad z = -x;\quad z(1-z)u'' + (a-bz)u' - cu = 0;\quad$ see
(410) and (427).

410    $x(1-x)y'' + [c - (1+a+b)x]y' - aby = 0$ 9-3
The Gauss hypergeometric equation. There are regular singular points at $x = 0, 1, \infty$ with exponents $0, 1-c;\ 0, c-a-b;\ a, b$, respectively. Two analytic solutions, called hypergeometric series, can be found for each singular point by the methods of **8-2**, provided that the exceptional cases of **8-2-2** and **8-2-3** do not occur. Moreover, the form of the equation remains the same, although the constants are different, in the six variables

$$x^{\pm 1},\ (1-x)^{\pm 1},\ \left(\frac{x-1}{x}\right)^{\pm 1}.$$

There are four possible series solutions for each of these variables; hence there are 24 solutions in terms of hypergeometric series. Of course, there are only two linearly independent solutions so there are many relations between these special solutions. Here, we give only the general solution at the three regular singular points and some of the exceptional cases. Integral solutions of the hypergeometric equation can also be found by the methods of **10**. There is a very large literature on the Gauss equation.

a. If $c \neq \pm n$, where n is zero or an integer, the general solution is
$$y = C_1 y_1 + C_2 y_2;\quad y_1 = {}_2F_1(a, b, c; x);$$
$$y_2 = x^{1-c}\, {}_2F_1(1+a-c,\ 1+b-c,\ 2-c;\ x)$$

where
$${}_2F_1(a, b, c; x) = 1 + \frac{ab}{c}x + \frac{a(a+1)b(b+1)}{2!\,c(c+1)}x^2 + \ldots$$

The notation for this series indicates that there are two factorial-like terms in the numerator and one in the denominator. In another notation, define $(a)_k = a(a+1) \ldots (a+k-1) = \Gamma(a+k)/\Gamma(a)$; $(a)_0 = 1$. Then, if A_k is the coefficient of x^k in y_1

$$A_k = \frac{(a)_k(b)_k}{k!(c)_k} = \frac{\Gamma(c)\Gamma(a+k)\Gamma(b+k)}{k!\Gamma(a)\Gamma(b)\Gamma(c+k)}$$

Both of the series y_1 and y_2 converge absolutely for $-1 < x < 1$, but see the following cases.

    i.   Both solutions of the equation are distinct, provided that the difference of the exponents $\Delta \neq n$, an integer or zero. However, if a or b is a negative integer, y_1 reduces to a polynomial.

    ii. $c = n \geqslant 1$, $\Delta = n-1$. When $c = 1$, $y_1 = y_2$, see **8-2-2**, and the second solution involves a logarithm. When $c > 1$, $\Delta = m \geqslant 1$ and **8-2-3** occurs which may or may not give a logarithmic factor. In either case y_1 is still an integral but y_2 becomes meaningless because of zero factors in the denominator. The zero factors are avoided if a or b equals unity, because in that case y_2 reduces to a polynomial. If a or b equals one of the positive integers 2, 3, ..., m, the nonlogarithmic case of **8-2-3** occurs and y_2 is an infinite series. Zeros in both its numerator and denominator vanish and can be canceled out beginning with the coefficient A_m.

If none of these special cases arise, the methods of **8-2-3** show that the general solution is $y = C_1y_1 + C_2y_2$,

$$y_1 = {}_2F_1(a, b, n; x)$$

$$y_2 = y_1 \ln x + Y(a, b, n; x)$$

$$Y(a, b, n; x) = Y_1(x) + Y_2(x)$$

$$Y_1(x) = x^{1-n} \sum_{k=0}^{n-2} A_k x^k$$

$$A_k = \frac{(-1)^n(n-1)!(n-k-2)!}{k!(a-1)\ldots(a+k+1-n)(b-1) \ldots (b+k+1-n)}$$

$$Y_2(x) = \sum_{k=1}^{\infty} B_k x^k$$

$$B_k = \frac{(a)_k(b)_k}{(c)_k k!}\left[\frac{1}{a} + \frac{1}{a+1} + \ldots \frac{1}{a+k-1} + \frac{1}{b} + \ldots\right]$$

$$+\frac{1}{b+k-1}-\frac{1}{1}-\frac{1}{2}-\dots-\frac{1}{k}$$

$$-\frac{1}{n}-\frac{1}{n+1}-\dots-\frac{1}{n+k-1}\Big]$$

iii. $c = -n$, where n is a positive integer or zero. Polynomial or nonlogarithmic cases will occur as in ii, for special values of a or b. In the general case,

$$y_1 = x^{1+n}{}_2F_1(1+a+n, 1+b+n, 2+n; x)$$
$$y_2 = y_1 \ln x + x^{1+n} Y(1+a+n, 1+b+n, 2+n; x)$$

b. The general solution around the singular point $x = 1$ is $y = C_1 y_1 + C_2 y_2$, with $z = 1-x$,

$$y_1 = {}_2F_1(a, b, 1+a+b-c; z)$$
$$y_2 = z^{c-a-b}{}_2F_1(c-a, c-b, 1-a-b+c; z)$$

Both series converge for $-1 < (1-x) < 1$; that is, for $0 < x < 2$.

Ignoring polynomial and nonlogarithmic cases, logarithmic integrals occur as follows

i. $(c-a-b) = n \geqslant 1$; $y_1 = z^n {}_2F_1(c-a, c-b, 1+n; z)$; $y_2 = y_1 \ln z + z^n Y(c-a, c-b, 1+n; z)$.

ii. $(c-a-b) = -n$; $n = 0, 1, 2, \dots$; $y = {}_2F_1(a, b, 1+n; z)$　$y_2 = y_1 \ln z + Y(a, b, 1+n; z)$.

c. Around the singular point at $x = \infty$, let $x = 1/z$ and the two linearly independent solutions are

$$y_1 = z^a {}_2F_1(a, 1+a-c, 1+a-b; z)$$
$$y_2 = z^b {}_2F_1(b, 1+b-c, 1-a+b; z)$$

Both converge for $-1 < z < 1$; hence the range consists of two parts $-\infty < x < -1$ and $1 < x < \infty$.

The exceptional cases follow; polynomial or nonlogarithmic cases are not included.

i. $(a-b) = n \geqslant 1$;　$y_1 = z^a {}_2F_1(a, 1+a-c, 1+n; z)$; $y_2 = y_1 \ln z + z^a Y(a, 1+a-c, 1+n; z)$.

ii. $(a-b) = -n$;　$y_1 = z^b {}_2F_1(b, 1+b-c, 1+n; z)$; $y_2 = y_1 \ln z + z^b Y(b, 1+b-c, 1+n; z)$.

d. Sometimes, there is special interest in the cases where one or both of the solutions reduce to a polynomial. A few examples were noted in a, b, and c. More generally, suppose that a solution has the form

$$Y(x) = x^r (1-x)^s p_n(x)$$

where $p_n(x)$ is a polynomial of degree n, with $p_n(0) \neq 0$, $p_n(1) \neq 0$. Such a solution can occur only if one of the numbers a, b, $c-a$, $c-b$ is an integer. An equivalent statement is that at least one of the eight numbers $\pm(c-1) \pm (a-b) \pm (a+b-c)$ must be an odd integer. When these conditions are met and $c \neq \pm n$, one of the following four series will terminate and reduce to the form $Y(x)$

$$y_1 = {}_2F_1(a, b, c; x) = (1-x)^{c-a-b} {}_2F_1(c-a, c-b, c; x)$$

$$y_2 = x^{1-c} {}_2F_1(1+a-c, 1+b-c, 2-c; x)$$

$$= x^{1-c}(1-x)^{c-a-b} {}_2F_1(1-a, 1-b, 2-c; x)$$

Another procedure depends on the methods of **4-1-2**. When the Gauss equation is reduced to normal form, the result is

$$u''(x) + I(x)u = 0$$

with $v(x) = x^{(1-p)/2}(1-x)^{(1-r)/2}$; $\quad p = 1-c$; $\quad q = b-a$; $r = c-a-b$.

$$I(x) = \frac{1-p^2}{4x^2} + \frac{1-r^2}{4(1-x)^2} + \frac{1-p^2+q^2-r^2}{4x(1-x)}$$

Polynomial solutions will occur only for the values of p, q, r listed in Table 1.

TABLE 1. VALUES OF p, q, r FOR WHICH THE GAUSS HYPERGEOMETRIC EQUATION WILL HAVE POLYNOMIAL SOLUTIONS; $2m \leqslant n$.

p	q	r
1/2	1/2	m/n
1/2	1/3	1/3
2/3	1/3	1/3
1/2	1/3	1/4
2/3	1/4	1/4
1/2	1/3	1/5
2/5	1/3	1/3
2/3	1/5	1/5
1/2	2/5	1/5
3/5	1/3	1/5
2/5	2/5	2/5
2/3	1/3	1/5
4/5	1/5	1/5
1/2	2/5	1/3
3/5	2/5	1/3

e. Many well-known functions can be expressed in terms of the hypergeometric series. Typical examples are

$$(1+x)^k = {}_2F_1(-k, b, b; -x)$$

$$\sin^{-1}x = x{}_2F_1(1/2, 1/2, 3/2; x^2)$$

$$\tan^{-1}x = x{}_2F_1(1/2, 1, 3/2, -x^2)$$

$$\ln(1+x) = x{}_2F_1(1, 1, 2; -x)$$

$$\ln\left(\frac{1+x}{1-x}\right) = 2x{}_2F_1(1/2, 1, 3/2; x^2)$$

There are a number of further cases, where the series is the solution of a familiar differential equation or where it can be used to represent known functions. Examples are the incomplete beta function $(c-a = 1)$; complete elliptic integrals $(a = \pm 1/2, \; b = 1/2, \; c = 1, \; z = x^2)$; Legendre functions, see (369); Gegenbauer polynomials, see (378); Jacobi polynomials, see (408).

411 $x(1+x)y'' - [a-(2-a)x]y' - ay = 0$ **4-1-1**
$y_1 = 1/(1+x)$.
$\qquad\qquad (1+x)y = C_1 + C_2 x^{1+a}$

412 $x(1+x)y'' - [a-(2-a)x]y' - ay = x^{a+1}$ **12-3**
See (411); $F(x) = x^{2+a}/(2+a)(1+x)$.

413 $x(1-x)y'' + (a+bx)y' + cy = 0$ **9-3**
See (410).

414 $x(1-x)y'' + a(1-2x)y' + (a_0 + a_1 x + \ldots + a_n x^n)y = 0$ **9-3**
The oblate or spheroidal wave equation.

415 $(2-x-x^2)y'' + x(1-x)y' + x(7+6x)y = 0$ **6**
$[(2+x)D + 4 + 3x][(1-x)D - 1 + 2x]y = 0$; $D = d/dx$. A first integral is $(1-x)y' = C_1(2+x)^2 e^{-3x} + (1-2x)y$; see **A1-2**.

416 $x(2-x)y'' + 2(1-x)y' + 2y = 0$ **4-1-1**
$y_1 = 1-x$.

417 $x(2-x)y'' - (2-x^2)y' + 2(1-x)y = 0$ **4-1-1**
$y_1 = x^2$.
$\qquad\qquad y = C_1 x^2 + C_2 e^x$

418 $(1-x)^2 y'' - 4(1-x)y' + 2y = 0$ **3-2**
$\qquad\qquad (1-x)^2 y = C_1 + C_2 x$

419 $(1-x)^2 y'' - 4(1-x)y' + 2y = \cos x$ **12-2**
See (418); $F(x) = -\cos x/(1-x)^2$.

420      $(1+x)^2y'' - 4(1+x)y' + 6y = 0$ **3-2**
$$y = (1+x)^2(C_1 + C_2x)$$

421      $(1+x)^2y'' - 4(1+x)y' + 6y = x$ **12-2**
See (420); $F(x) = x/2 + 1/3$.

422      $(1+x)^2y'' - (1-x-x^2)y' - (2+x)y = 0$ **4-1-1**
$y_1 = e^{-x}$.

423      $(1-x)^2y'' - 2(1-x)^2y' + (1-x)^2y = e^x$ **12-1**
See (61); $F(x) = -e^x \ln(1-x)$.
$$ye^{-x} = C_1 + C_2x - \ln(1-x)$$

424      $(4+3x+x^2)y'' + (1+x+x^2)y' - (3+2x)y = 0$ **4-1-1**
$y_1 = e^{-x}$.
$$y = C_1e^{-x} + C_2(3+x+x^2)$$

425      $(2+x)^2y'' - (2+x)y' + 2y = 0$ **3-2**
$$y = (2+x)[C_1 \cos \ln(2+x) + C_2 \sin \ln(2+x)]$$

426      $(2-x)^2y'' + (2-x)y' - 3y = 0$ **3-2**
$$y = C_1(2-x)^3 + C_2/(2-x)$$

427      $x(a_0+x)y'' + (a_1+b_1x)y' + a_2y = 0$ **4-2**
$y(x) = u(z)$; $a_0z = -x$; $z(1-z)u'' + (A-b_1z)u' - a_2u = 0$;
$A = a_1/a_0$;   see (409) and (410).

428      $(a+x)^2y'' - 4(a+x)y' + 6y = 0$ **3-2**
$$y = (a+x)^2[C_1 + C_2(a+x)]$$

429      $2x^2y'' - xy' + y = x^2$ **12-2**
See (311); $F(x) = x^2/3$.
$$y = C_1x + C_2\sqrt{x} + x^2/3$$

430      $2x^2y'' + xy' - 3y = 0$ **3-1**
$$xy = C_1 + C_2x^{5/2}$$

431      $2x^2y'' - x(7+2x)y' + 2(5+x)y = 0$ **4-1-1**
$y_1 = x^{5/2}e^x$.

432      $2x^2y'' - x(1-4x)y' - 2(1-3x)y = 0$ **4-1-1**
$y_1 = x^2e^{-x}$.

433      $2x^2y'' - x(1-4x)y' - 2(1-3x)y = x^3(1+x)$ **12-3**
See (432); $F(x) = 11x^2/252 + x^3/18$.

434      $(1+2x^2)y'' + 3xy' - 3y = 0$ **4-1-1**
$y_1 = x$.

435      $2(1-x^2)y'' - xy' + 2a^2y = 0$ **9-3**
See also (377).

436     $2x(1+x)y'' + y' - 4y = 0$ **4-1-1**
$y_1 = 1 + 4x + 8x^2/3$.

437     $2x(1-x)y'' + (1+x)y' - y = 0$ **4-1-1**
$y_1 = 1 + x$.
$$y = C_1(1+x) + C_2\sqrt{x}$$

438     $2x(1-x)y'' + (1-x)y' + y = 0$ **4-1-1**
$y_1 = 1 - x$.

439     $2x(1-x)y'' - (1-2x)y' - 2y = 0$ **4-1-1**
$y_1 = 1 - 2x$.

440     $2x(1-x)y'' + (1-2x)y' + 8y = 0$ **4-1-1**
$y_1 = 1 - 8x + 8x^2$.

441     $2x(1-x)y'' - (1-2x)y' + ay = 0$ **4-2**
$y(x) = u(z);\ x = \sin^2 z/2;\ u'' - 2u'\cot z + au/2 = 0;$ see (147),
(439), and (440).

442     $2x(1-x)y'' + (1-2x)y' + (a+bx)y = 0$ **4-2**
$y(x) = u(z);\ x = \cos^2 z;\ u'' + 2(a + b\cos^2 z)u = 0;$ see (43) and (50).

443     $2x(1-x)y'' - (1+3x)y' + 2a(1+a)y = 0$ **9-3**
A solution is $y_1 = {}_2F_1\left(-\dfrac{a}{2}, \dfrac{a+2}{2}, \dfrac{1}{2}; x\right);$ see (410).

444     $(1-x)(1-2x)y'' + 2(1-2x)y' + 4y = 0$ **4-2**
$y(x) = u(z);\ z = 2x - 1;\ z(1-z)u'' + 2zu' - 2u = 0;$ see (398)
and (410).

445     $(1-x)(1-2x)y'' + 2(3-4x)y' + 12y = 0$ **4-2**
$y(x) = u(z);\ z = 2x - 1;\ z(1-z)u'' - 2(1-2z)u' - 6u = 0;$ see
(406) and (410).

446     $2(1+x)^2 y'' - (1+x)y' + y = 0$ **3-2**
$$y = C_1(1+x) + C_2\sqrt{1+x}$$

447     $2(1+x)^2 y'' - (1+x)y' + y = x$ **12-2**
See (446); $F(x) = (1+x)\ln(1+x) - 1$.

448     $4x^2 y'' + y = 0$ **3-1**
$$y = \sqrt{x}(C_1 + C_2\ln x)$$

449     $4x^2 y'' + y = \sqrt{x}$ **12-2**
See (448); $F(x) = (1/8)\sqrt{x}(\ln x)^2$.

450     $4x^2 y'' + [(1 - 4p^2) + 4kx - x^2]y = 0$ **9-2**
Whittaker's equation; a confluent hypergeometric equation; the
normal form of the Kummer or Pochhammer–Barnes equations;
see (211). Provided that $2p \neq \pm n$, an integer (including zero),

two linearly independent solutions are Whittaker functions
$$M_{k,\pm p}(x) = x^{c/2}e^{-x/2}{}_1F_1(a, c; x)$$
$a = 1/2 - k \pm p;$ $c = 1 \pm 2p.$ When $2p = \pm n$, one solution can be taken as

$$W_{k,p}(x) = \frac{\Gamma(c-1)}{\Gamma(a-c+1)}M_{k,p}(x) + \frac{\Gamma(1-c)}{\Gamma(a)}M_{k,-p}(x)$$

The other solution is $W_{-k,p}(-x)$. Further special cases of the equation can be handled by methods given for (211).

451    $4x^2y'' + (1 + 4a^2x^2)y = 0$ **4-1-3**
$y = u\sqrt{x};$ $xu'' + u' + a^2xu = 0;$ see (199).

452    $4x^2y'' + 4xy' - (a^2 - x)y = 0$ **4-2-2**
$y(x) = u(z);$ $x = z^2;$ $z^2u'' + zu' - (a^2 - z^2)u = 0;$ see (274).

453    $4x^2y'' + 4xy' - (1 + 4x^2)y = 4e^xx^{3/2}$ **12-3**
See (455).
$$y\sqrt{x} = C_1e^x + C_2e^{-x} + xe^x/2$$

454    $4x^2y'' + 4xy' - [(1 + 2n)^2 - 4x^2]y = 0$ **9-2**
Bessel's equation of order $m = n + 1/2;$ m, n integers; see also (274). The general solution, also called spherical Bessel functions, is
$$y = C_1J_m(x) + C_2J_{-m}(x)$$
where
$$J_m(x) = \sqrt{2/\pi}x^m\left(-\frac{1}{x}\frac{d}{dx}\right)^n\frac{\sin x}{x}$$

The result of the differentiations is
$$J_m(x) = P_n(x)\cos x + Q_n(x)\sin x$$
where $P_n(x)$, $Q_n(x)$ are polynomials in $1/\sqrt{x}$.

455    $4x^2y'' + 4xy' - (1 \pm a^2x^2)y = 0$ **4-1-2**
$y\sqrt{x} = u(x);$ $4u''(x) \mp a^2u = 0;$ see (26) and also (454).

456    $4x^2y'' - 8xy' + 5y = 0$ **3-1**
$$y = \sqrt{x}(C_1 + C_2x^2)$$

457    $4x^2y'' - 2x(2 + x)y' + (3 + x)y = 0$ **4-1-1**
$y_1 = \sqrt{x}.$

458    $4x^2y'' + 4x(1 - 2x)y' - (1 + 4x - 4x^2)y = 0$ **4-1-2**
$ye^{-x}\sqrt{x} = u(x);$ $u''(x) = 0;$ see (1).
$$y\sqrt{x} = e^x(C_1 + C_2x)$$

459 $4x^2y'' + 4x^3y' - (3 - 2x^2)y = 0$ **4-1-3**

$y\sqrt{x} = u(x);$ $xu'' - (1 - x^2)u' = 0;$ see (219).

$\quad y\sqrt{x} = C_1 + C_2 e^{-x^2/2}$

460 $4x^2y'' + 4x^3y' + (1 + 2x^2 + x^4)y = 0$ **4-1-2**

$y = e^{-x^2/4}u(x);$ $4x^2u''(x) + u = 0;$ see **3-1**.

$\quad ye^{x^2/4} = \sqrt{x}(C_1 + C_2 \ln x)$

461 $4x^2y'' + 4x^3y' + (a + 2x^2 + x^4)y = 0$ **4-1-2**

$y = e^{-x^2/4}u(x);$ $4x^2u''(x) + au = 0;$ see **3-1**.

  i. If $a = 1$, see (460).

  ii. $ye^{x^2/4} = \sqrt{x}(C_1 x^r + C_2 x^s);$ $r,\ s = \pm\sqrt{1 - a}/2;$
   $a \neq 1$.

462 $4(1 - x^2)y'' - 8xy' - y = 0$ **9-3**
A special case of the Legendre equation; see (369). Solutions
are Legendre functions of half-integral order. They are also
called special ring, torus, or toroidal functions; see (578) and
(596).

  i. $y(x) = u(z);$ $x = \cosh z;$ $4zu'' + 4u' \coth z + u = 0;$
   see (241).

  ii. Linearly independent solutions are
   $y_1 = P_{-1/2}(\cosh z) = (2/\pi)\ \text{sech}\ (z/2)K(\tanh z/2)$
   $y_2 = Q_{-1/2}(\cosh z) = 2e^{-z/2}K(e^{-z})$

where $P_p(z)$, $Q_p(z)$ are Legendre functions and K is a complete
elliptic integral of the first kind.

463 $4(1 - x^2)y'' - 8xy' - (1 + 4p^2)y = 0$ **9-3**
A special case of the Legendre equation; see (369). Solutions are
Legendre functions of order $q = ip - 1/2$. They are also called
special conical functions; see (577). For real p, let $x = \cos z$.
A solution is

$$P_q(\cos z) = 1 + \frac{(1^2 + 4p^2)}{2^2}\sin^2\frac{z}{2}$$

$$+ \frac{(1^2 + 4p^2)(3^2 + 4p^2)}{2^2 \cdot 4^2}\sin^4\frac{z}{2} + \dots$$

  i. For $p = 0$, $\pi P_{-1/2}(\cos z) = 2K(\sin z/2)$,   where
K is a complete elliptic integral of the first kind.

  ii. $P_{ip-1/2}(x) = P_{-(ip+1/2)}(x)$.

464    $4(1+x^2)y'' = 4xy'+x^2$ **B2-1-2**
A first integral is $4(1+x^2)p' = 4xp+x^2$; $4y' = CR+RX-x$;
$R(x) = \sqrt{1+x^2}$; $X(x) = \ln(R+x)$; see (1-340) and **A1-1-1**.
$$16y = C_1+2C_2X+X^2+2xR(C_2+X)-3x^2$$

465    $4(1-x^2)y''+4axy'-a(2+a)y = 0$ **4-1-1**
$y_1 = (1\pm x)^{1+a/2}$; see also (378) and (382).

466    $4x(1-x)y''+2(1-x)y'+y = 0$ **4-1-1**
$y_1 = \sqrt{x}$.
$$y = C_1\sqrt{x}+C_2\sqrt{1-x}$$

467    $4x(1-x)y''+2(1-2x)y'+(a+bx)y = 0$ **9-3**
The Lindemann-Stieljes equation; the algebraic form of the
Mathieu equation.   Let $y(x) = u(z)$; $x = \sin^2z$; $u''(z)$
$+(a_0+b_0\cos 2z)u = 0$; $2a+b = 2a_0$; $b+2b_0 = 0$; see (43).

468    $4x(1-x)y''+2(1-2x)y'+(a+bx+cx^2)y = 0$ **9-3**
$y(x) = u(z)$; $x = \cos^2z$; $u''(z)+(a_0+b_0\cos 2z+k\cos 4z)u = 0$;
$a_0 = a+b/2+3c/8$; $2b_0 = b+c$; $k = c/8$; see (44).

469    $4x(1-x)y''+2(1-2x)y'+(a_0+a_1x+\ldots+a_nx^n)y = 0$ **9-3**
$y(x) = u(z)$; $x = \cos^2z$; $u''(z)+(a_0+a_1\cos^2z+\ldots$
$+a_n\cos^{2n}z)u = 0$; see (45).

470    $4x(1-x)y''+2[1-(3+2k)x]y'-(k-p)(1+k+p)y = 0$ **9-3**
A solution is $y_1 = {_2F_1}\left(\dfrac{1+k+p}{2},\dfrac{k-p}{2},\dfrac{1}{2};x\right)$ see (410).

471    $4x(1-x)y''+2(1+ax)y'+(b+k^2x)y = 0$ **9-3**
In the special case where $a = 2A-3$, let $y(x) = u(z)$, $x = \cos^2z$;
$u''+u'(1-2A)\cot z+(b+k^2\cos^2z)u = 0$; see (143).

472    $(1+2x)^2y''-2(1+2x)y'-12y = 0$ **3-2**
$$(1+2x)y = C_1+C_2(1+2x)^4$$

473    $(1+2x)^2y''-2(1+2x)y'-12y = 1+3x$ **12-2**
See (472); $F(x) = -3x/16-5/96$.

474    $(1-3x)^2y''-3(1-3x)y'-9y = 0$ **3-2**
$$(1-3x)y = C_1+C_2(1-3x)^2$$

475    $16x^2y''+(3+4x)y = 0$ **4-1-3**
$y = x^{1/4}u(x)$; $4xu''+2u'+u = 0$; see (239).
$$y = x^{1/4}(C_1\cos\sqrt{x}+C_2\sin\sqrt{x})$$

476    $16x^2y''+32xy'-(5+4x)y = 0$ **4-1-3**
$yx^{5/4} = u(x)$; $4xu''-2u'-u = 0$; see (240).
$$yx^{5/4} = C_1e^{\sqrt{x}}(\sqrt{x}-1)+C_2e^{-\sqrt{x}}(\sqrt{x}+1)$$

477 $(1 + ax^2)y'' + axy' \pm by^2 = 0$ **4-2-1**

$y(x) = u(z);$ $dx/dz = \sqrt{1 + ax^2};$ $u''(z) \pm b^2u = 0;$ see (26).

478 $(1 + ax^2)y'' + bxy' + cy = 0$ **4-2**

     i. $y(x) = u(z);$ $x\sqrt{a} = i(1 + 2z);$ $2az(1 - z)u''$
         $+ b(1 - 2z)u' - 2cu = 0;$ see (482) and (410).

     ii.   If m is an integer, the equation is integrable in
         finite terms provided that $b = (2m + 1)a;$
         $q = (2m + 1)^2a^2;$ or $q = [(2m + 1)a - b]^2,$ where
         $q = (a - b)^2 - 4ac.$

479 $(1 - a^2x^2)y'' - 2a^2xy' = 0$ **B2-1-2**

$$y = C_1 + C_2 \ln \frac{1 + ax}{1 - ax}$$

480 $(1 - a^2x^2)y'' - 2a^2xy' + 2a^2y = 0$ **4-1-1**

$y_1 = x.$

$$y = C_1x + C_2\left[ax \ln\frac{1 + ax}{1 - ax} - 2 \right]$$

481 $x(a + bx)y'' + 2ay' - 2by = 0$ **4-1-1**

$y_1 = 1/x.$

$$xy = C_1 + C_2(a + bx)^3$$

482 $(a_0 + b_0x + c_0x^2)y'' + (a_1 + b_1x)y' + a_2y = 0$ **4-2**

Calculate the roots of $a_0 + b_0r + c_0r^2 = 0.$ Let them be $r_1,$ $r_2;$
then there are simple poles at these values of $x = r_i.$ There
are two cases.

     i. $r_1 \neq r_2.$ Let $y(x) = u(z);$ $sz = x - r_1;$ $s = r_2 - r_1;$
$z(1 - z)u'' - (A_1 + B_1z)u' - A_2u = 0;$ $a_0sA_1 = a_1 + b_1r_1;$
$c_0B_1 = b_1;$ $c_0A_2 = a_2;$ see (410).

     ii. $r_1 = r_2 = r.$ Let $y(x) = z^ku(z);$ $x - r = 1/z;$
$c_0k^2 + (c_0 - b_1)k + a_2 = 0;$ $zu'' + (A + Bz)u' + kBu = 0;$ c_0A
$= 2c_0(k + 1) - b_1;$ $c_0B + a_1 + rb_1 = 0;$ see (215).

483 $(a + bx)^2y'' + a_1(a + bx)y' + a_2y = 0$ **3-2**

484 $x^3y'' = a + bx$ **B2-1-1; 12-1**

$$y = C_1 + C_2x + a/2x - b \ln x$$

485 $x^3y'' + xy' - y = 0$ **4-1-1**

$y_1 = x.$

$$y = x(C_1 + C_2e^{1/x})$$

486 $x^3y'' + xy' - 2y = 0$ **4-1-1**

$y_1 = e^{1/x}.$

487 $x^3y'' + 2xy' - y = 0$ **4-2-2**
$y(x) = u(z);$ $z = 1/x;$ $zu'' + 2(1-z)u' - u = 0;$ see (215).

488 $x^3y'' + a_1xy' + (a_2 + b_2x)y = 0$ **4-2-2**
$y(x) = u(z);$ $z = 1/x;$ $z^2u'' + z(2 - a_1z)u' + (b_2 + a_2z)u = 0;$
see (334).

489 $x^3y'' + x^2y' + (a + bx + cx^2)y = 0$ **9-2**
$y(x) = u(z);$ $kx = e^{2iz};$ $ak^2 = c;$ $u''(z) + (a_0 + b_0\cos 2z)u = 0;$
$a_0 + 4b = 0;$ $b_0 + 8\sqrt{ac} = 0;$ see (43).

490 $x^3y'' + 3x^2y' + xy = 0$ **3-1**
See also (294).
$$xy = C_1 + C_2\ln x$$

491 $x^3y'' + 3x^2y' + xy = 1$ **12-2**
See (490); $F(x) = (1/2x)\ln^2 x.$

492 $x^3y'' + ax^2y' + (b + cx)y = 0$ **4-3**
$y = x^{(1-a)/2}u(z);$ $xz^2 = 4b;$ $z^2u'' + zu' - (p^2 - z^2)u = 0;$
$p^2 + 4c = (1-a)^2;$ see (274).

493 $x^3y'' + (a_1 + b_1x^2)y' + a_2xy = 0$ **4-2-2**
$y(x) = u(z);$ $x = 1/z;$ $z^2u'' + z(A + Bz)u' + a_2u = 0;$ $A + b_1$
$= 2;$ $B + a_1 = 0;$ see (334).

494 $x^3y'' + x(a_1 + b_1x)y' + a_2y = 0$ **4-2-2**
$y(x) = u(z);$ $x = 1/z;$ $zu'' + (A + Bz)u' + a_2u = 0;$ $A + b_1 = 2;$
$B + a_1 = 0;$ see (215).

495 $x^3y'' + x(a_1 + b_1x)y' + (a_2 + b_2x)y = 0$ **4-1-3**
$y = x^ku(x);$ $a_1k + a_2 = 0;$ $x^2u'' + (a_1 + Ax)u' + Bu = 0;$
$A = b_1 + 2k;$ $B = k(k + b_1 - 1) + b_2;$ see (318).

496 $(1 - x^3)y'' + 6xy = 0$ **4-1-1**
$y_1 = 1 - x^3.$

497 $x(1 - x^2)y'' - y' = 0$ **B2-1-2**
$$y = C_1 + C_2\sqrt{x^2 - 1}$$

498 $x(1 - x^2)y'' - y' + x^3 = 0$ **12-3**
See (497); $F(x) = x^2/2.$

499 $x(1 - x^2)y'' - y' + ax^3y = 0$ **4-2**
$y(x) = u(z);$ $z = 1 - x^2;$ $4zu'' + 2u' + au = 0;$ see (233).

500 $x(1 - x^2)y'' - (7 + x^2)y' + 4xy = 0$ **4-1-1**
$y_1 = 1 + x^2/3.$

501 $x(1 + x^2)y'' - 2(1 + x^2)y' + 2xy = 0$ **4-1-1**
$y_1 = 1 + x^2.$
$$y = C_1(1 + x^2) + C_2[(1 + x^2)\tan^{-1}x - x]$$

502     $x(1+x^2)y'' - 2(1-x^2)y' - 2xy = 0$ **4-2**
$y(x) = u(z);$ $z = -x^2;$ $2z(1-z)u'' - (1+3z)u' + u = 0;$ see
(410) and (504).

503     $x(1-x^2)y'' - 2(1-x^2)y' - 2xy = 0$ **4-1-1**
$y_1 = (1-x^2).$

$$y = y_1\left[C_1 + C_2\left(\frac{2x}{1-x^2} + \ln\frac{1+x}{1-x}\right)\right]$$

504     $x(1+x^2)y'' + (a+bx^2)y' + cxy = 0$ **4-2**
$y(x) = u(z);$ $z = -x^2;$ $4z(1-z)u'' + 2(A-Bz)u' - cu = 0;$
$A = 1+a;$ $B = 1+b;$ see (410) and (511).

505     $x(1-x^2)y'' + (a+bx^2)y' + (a+b)(a-1)xy = 0$ **4-1-1**
$y_1 = x^{1-a};$ see also (508).

506     $x(1-x^2)y'' + (a+bx^2)y' + 2(1-b)xy = 0$ **4-1-1**
$y_1 = x^2 + \left(\dfrac{a+1}{b-1}\right);$ see also (508).

507     $x(1-x^2)y'' + [a-(1+a)x^2]y' + cxy = 0$ **4-2**
$y(x) = u(z);$ $x = \sin z;$ $u'' + au' \cot z + cu = 0;$ see (147).

508     $x(1-x^2)y'' + (a+bx^2)y' + cxy = 0$ **4-2**
$y(x) = u(z);$ $z = x^2;$ $4z(1-z)u'' + 2(A+Bz)u' + cu = 0;$
$A = 1+a;$ $B = b-1;$ see (410), (511).

509     $x(2+x^2)y'' - y' - 6xy = 0$ **4-2**
$y(x) = u(z);$ $2z = -x^2;$ $4z(1-z)u'' + (1-2z)u' + 6u = 0;$
see (410), (511).

510     $x(2-x^2)y'' - (2+2x-3x^2-x^3)y' - (2+4x+x^2)y = 0$ **4-1-1**
$y_1 = 1-x.$
$$y = C_1(1-x) + C_2x^2e^x$$

511     $x(a_0+x^2)y'' + (a_1+b_1x^2)y' + a_2xy = 0$ **4-2**
$y(x) = u(z);$ $a_0z = -x^2;$ $4z(1-z)u'' + 2(A-Bz)u' - a_2u = 0;$
$a_0A = a_0+a_1;$ $B = 1+b_1;$ see (410) and (504).

512     $x^2(1+x)y'' + xy' - (1+x)^3y = 0$ **4-1-1**
$y_1 = xe^x.$
$$y = C_1xe^x + C_2e^{-x}/x$$

513     $x^2(1-x)y'' - x(1+x)y' + y = 0$ **4-1-1**
$y_1 = x/(1-x).$
$$(1-x)y = x(C_1 + C_2 \ln x)$$

514     $x^2(1+x)y'' - x(1+2x)y' + (1+2x)y = 0$ **4-1-1**
$y_1 = x.$
$$y = x[C_1 + C_2(x + \ln x)]$$

515 $x^2(1-x)y'' + 2x(2-x)y' + 2(1+x)y = 0$ **4-1-3**
$xy = u(x);\quad x(1-x)u'' + 2u' + 2u = 0;\quad$ see (394).
$$x^2y = C_1 + C_2(1-x)^3$$

516 $x^2(1-x)y'' - x(4-5x)y' + (6-9x)y = 0$ **4-1-1**
$y_1 = x^3.$
$$y = y_1[C_1 + C_2(\ln x + 1/x)]$$

517 $x^2(1+x)y'' + 2x(2+3x)y' + 2(1+3x)y = 0$ **5-1**
A first integral is $x^2(1+x)y' + x(2+3x)y = C_1;$ see **A1-2**.
$$x^2(1+x)y = C_1 x + C_2$$

518 $x^2(1-x)y'' + x(a_1+b_1x)y' + (a_2+b_2x)y = 0$ **4-1-3**
$y = x^k u(x);\quad k^2 + k(a_1-1) + a_2 = 0;\quad x(1-x)u'' + (a-bx)u'$
$+ cu = 0;\quad a = 2k+a_1;\quad b = 2k-b_1;\quad c = b_2 + (1+b_1)k - k^2;$
see (410).

519 $x^2(a_0+x)y'' + x(a_1+b_1x)y' + (a_2+b_2x)y = 0$ **4-1-3**
$y = x^k u(x);\quad a_0k^2 + k(a_1-a_0) + a_2 = 0;\quad x(a_0+x)u''$
$+ (a+bx)u' + cu = 0;\quad a = 2ka_0+a_1;\quad b = 2k+b_1;$
$c = k^2 + k(b_1-1) + b_2;$ see (427).

520 $x(1-x)^2y'' - 2y = 0$ **4-1-1**
$y_1 = x/(1-x).$
$$y = C_1y_1 + C_2[(1+x) + 2y_1 \ln x]$$

521 $x(1+x)^2y'' + x(1+x)y' + y = 0$ **4-1-1**
$y_1 = x/(1+x).$
$$(1+x)y = C_1x + C_2(x \ln x - 1)$$

522 $x(2-x)^2y'' + 2(2-x)y' + 2y = 0$ **4-1-1**
$y_1 = 1 - x/2.$

523 $x(1-x)(a-x)y'' + [a_0a_2 - a_0 + a_1 - a_3 + 1 + (a_2+a_3)x$
$\qquad + (a_0+a_1+1)x^2]y' + a_0a_1(x-k)y = 0$ **9-4**

Heun's equation. There are regular singular points at $x = 0$, 1, a, ∞ with corresponding exponents 0, $1-a_2$; 0, $1-a_3$; 0, $1-a_4$; a_0, a_1; $1+a_0+a_1 = a_2+a_3+a_4$. A solution is
$$F(a, k;\quad a_0, a_1, a_2, a_3; x) = 1 + a_0a_1(A_1z + A_2z^2 + ...),$$
where $z = x/a$; $A_n = G_n(k)/[n!a_2(a_2+1) ... (a_2+n)]$; $G_1(k) = k$;
$G_2(k) = a_0a_1k^2 + [1+a_0+a_1-a_3+a(a_2+a_3)]k - a_0a_2$; $G_{n+1}(k)$
$= [n\{a_0+a_1-a_3+n\} + a(a_2+a_3+n-1)\} + a_0a_1k]G_n(k)$
$- (a_0+n-1)(a_1+n-1)(a_2+n-1)naG_{n-1}(k).$ There are 192 special solutions as powers of x, $1-x$, and $a-x$, each multiplied by functions of the type F. When k has certain characteristic values, the solutions are called Heun functions. In exceptional cases, the infinite series reduces to an algebraic Heun function or a Heun polynomial.

524 $\quad (a_1-x)(a_2-x)(a_3-x)y'' + (b_0+b_1x+b_2x^2)y' + (c_0+c_1x)y = 0 \quad$ **9-4**
An algebraic form of the Lamé equation; see also (58), (59), and (532).

525 $\quad (1-2x^3)y'' + 6x^2y' - 6xy = 0 \qquad\qquad\qquad$ **4-1-1**
$\qquad y_1 = x.$
$\qquad y = C_1x + C_2(1+x^3)$

526 $\quad 2x^2(1-x)y'' + x(3-5x)y' - (1+x)y = 0 \qquad\qquad$ **4-1-1**
$y_1 = 1/x.$

527 $\quad 2x^2(2-x)y'' - x(4-x)y' + (3-x)y = 0 \qquad\qquad$ **4-1-1**
$y_1 = \sqrt{x}.$
$\qquad y = \sqrt{x}(C_1 + C_2\sqrt{x-2})$

528 $\quad x(1+3x^2)y'' + 2y' - 6xy = 0 \qquad\qquad\qquad$ **4-1-1**
$y_1 = 1+x^2.$
$\qquad xy = C_1 + C_2x(1+x^2)$

529 $\quad 4x^2(1+x)y'' - 4x^2y' + (1+3x)y = 0 \qquad\qquad$ **4-1-1**
$y_1 = \sqrt{x}.$
$\qquad y = \sqrt{x}[C_1 + C_2(x+\ln x)]$

530 $\quad x^2(a+bx)y'' - 2x(2a+bx)y' + 2(3a+bx)y = 0 \qquad\qquad$ **6**
$(xD-3)[x(a+bx)D - (2a+bx)]y = 0; \quad D = d/dx; \quad$ see **A1-1-1**.
$\qquad y(a+bx) = x^2(C_1 + C_2x)$

531 $\quad 4x(1-x)^2y'' + 2(1-x)(1-3x)y' + (a+bx)y = 0 \qquad$ **9-3**
$y(x) = u(z); \quad x = z^2; \quad (1-z^2)^2u'' - 2z(1-z^2)u' + (a+bz^2)u = 0;$
see (555).

532 $\quad 4x(1-x)(1-ax)y'' + (a_0+a_1x+a_2x^2)y' + (b_0+b_1x^2)y = 0 \qquad$ **9-4**
An algebraic form of the Lamé equation; see also (524).

533 $\quad x^4y'' + a^2y = 0 \qquad\qquad\qquad\qquad\qquad$ **4-2**
$y(x) = xu(z); \quad z = 1/x; \quad u''(z) + a^2u = 0; \quad$ see (26) and (41).

534 $\quad x^4y'' + (1-2x^2)y = 0 \qquad\qquad\qquad\qquad$ **4-2**
$y(x) = xu(z); \quad z = 1/x; \quad z^2u'' - (2-z^2)u = 0 \quad$ see (252).
$\qquad y = x[C_1(x\cos z + \sin z) + C_2(x\sin z - \cos z)]$

535 $\quad x^4y'' - (1+2x^2)y = 0 \qquad\qquad\qquad\qquad$ **4-2**
$y(x) = xu(z); \quad z = 1/x; \quad z^2u'' - (2+z^2)u = 0; \quad$ see (254).
$\qquad y = x[C_1(x-1)e^z + C_2(x+1)e^{-z}]$

536 $\quad x^4y'' + (e^{2/x} - a^2)y = 0 \qquad\qquad\qquad\qquad$ **4-2**
$y(x) = xu(z); \quad z = e^{1/x}; \quad z^2u'' + zu' - (a^2-z^2)u = 0; \quad$ see (274).

537 $\quad x^4y'' + xy' - 2y = 0 \qquad\qquad\qquad\qquad$ **4-1-1**
$y_1 = xe^{1/2x^2}.$

538     $x^4y'' - 2x^2y' + (1+2x)y = 0$ **4-1-1**
$y_1 = e^{-1/x}$
$$ye^{1/x} = C_1 + C_2x$$

539     $x^4y'' + x^3y' + y = 0$ **4-3**
$y(x) = u(z)$; $z = 1/x$; $zu'' - u' + zu = 0$;   see (199) and (202).

540     $x^4y'' + x^3y' - (1 \pm x)y = 0$ **4-2**
$y(x) = u(z)$; $z = 1/x$; $zu'' + u' - (z \pm 1)u = 0$;   see (184) and (216).

541     $x^4y'' + x^3y' + (a + bx^2 + cx^4)y = 0$ **9-2**
$y(x) = u(z)$; $kx = e^{iz}$; $ak^4 = c$; $u'' + (a_0 + b_0 \cos 2z)u = 0$;
$a_0 + b = 0$; $b_0 + 2\sqrt{ac} = 0$;   see (43).

542     $x^4y'' + x(1+x^2)y' + y = 0$ **4-2**
$y(x) = u(z)$; $2x^2 = 1/z$; $2zu'' + 2(1-z)u' + u = 0$;   see (211).

543     $x^4y'' - x(1-x^2)y' + (1-x^2)y = 0$ **4-1-1**
$y_1 = x$.
$$y = x(C_1 + C_2 e^{-1/2x^2})$$

544     $x^4y'' + 2x^3y' + a^2y = 0$ **4-2-1**
$y(x) = u(z)$; $z = 1/x$; $u''(z) + a^2u = 0$;   see (26).
$$y = C_1 \cos a/x + C_2 \sin a/x$$

545     $x^4y'' + x(1+2x^2)y' - y = 0$ **4-1-1**
$y_1 = e^{1/2x^2}$.

546     $x^4y'' + 2x^2(a+x)y' + by = 0$ **4-2-1**
$y(x) = u(z)$; $z = 1/x$; $u'' - 2au' + bu = 0$;   see (102).

547     $x(1+x^3)y'' - (1-x^3)y' - x^2y = 0$ **4-2**
$y(x) = u(z)$; $z = x^3$; $9z(1+z)u'' + 3(1+3z)u' - u = 0$;   see (409).

548     $x^2(1-x^2)y'' - x^3y' - 2y = 0$ **4-1-1**
$xy_1 = \sqrt{1-x^2}$.
$$y = C_1 + y_1(C_2 - C_1 \sin^{-1}x)$$

549     $x^2(1-x^2)y'' - x(2-x^2)y' + (2-x^2)y = 0$ **4-1-1**
$y_1 = x$.
$$y = x[C_1 + C_2 \ln(x + \sqrt{x^2-1})]$$

550     $x^2(1-x^2)y'' - 2x^3y' + a(1+a)y = 0$ **4-2**
$y(x) = u(z)$; $z = 1/x$; $(1-z^2)u'' - 2zu' - a(1+a)u = 0$;   see (369).

551     $(1+x^2)^2y'' + 2x(1+x^2)y' + y = 0$ **4-2-1**
$y(x) = u(z)$; $x = \tan z$; $u''(z) + u = 0$;   see (6).
$$y\sqrt{1+x^2} = C_1 + C_2x$$

552    $(1+x^2)^2 y'' + 2x(1+x^2)y' + 4y = 0$ **4-2-1**
$y(x) = u(z);\quad x = \tan z/2;\quad u''(z) + u = 0;\quad$ see (6).
$$y(1+x^2) = C_1(1-x^2) + C_2 x$$

553    $(1-x^2)^2 y'' - 2x(1-x^2)y' - a^2 y = 0$ **4-2-1**
$y(x) = u(z);\quad x = \tanh z/a;\quad u''(z) = u;\quad$ see (7).
$$y = C_1\left(\frac{1+x}{1-x}\right)^{a/2} + C_2\left(\frac{1-x}{1+x}\right)^{a/2}$$

554    $(1-x^2)^2 y'' - 2x(1-x^2)y' - [m^2 - n(n+1)(1-x^2)]y = 0$ **9-3**
A special case of the associated Legendre differential equation;
see (555). Both m and n are integers and the solutions are
associated Legendre polynomials or spherical harmonics.
Two linearly independent solutions are $P_n{}^m(x)$ and $Q_n{}^m(x)$. See
(555) for the second solution. If $x = \cos\theta$ is real; $-1 < x < 1$;
$m \leqslant n$,

$$y_1 = P_n{}^m(x) = \frac{(-1)^m(m+n)!}{2^m m!(n-m)!}(1-x^2)^{m/2}\Bigg[1$$

$$-\frac{(n-m)(1+m+n)}{1!(1+m)}\frac{(1-x)}{2}$$

$$+\frac{(n-m)(n-m+1)(m+n+1)(m+n+2)}{2!(1+m)(2+m)}\frac{(1-x)^2}{4}\mp\cdots\Bigg]$$

$$= \frac{(-1)^m(2n)!}{2^n n!(n-m)!}(1-x^2)^{m/2}\Bigg[x^{n-m} - \frac{(n-m)(n-m-1)}{2(2n-1)}x^{n-m-2}$$

$$+\frac{(n-m)(n-m-1)(n-m-2)(n-m-3)}{2\cdot 4(2n-1)(2n-3)}x^{n-m-4}\mp\cdots\Bigg]$$

Further relations, which are often useful, follow.

i. $P_n{}^m(x) = (1-x^2)^{m/2}\dfrac{d^m}{dx^m}P_n(x).$

$Q_n{}^m(x) = (1-x^2)^{m/2}\dfrac{d^m}{dx^m}Q_n(x).$

ii. $P_n{}^m(x) = \dfrac{1}{2^n n!}(x^2-1)^{m/2}\dfrac{d^{m+n}}{dx^{m+n}}(x^2-1).$

iii. $P_n{}^{-m}(x) = \dfrac{\Gamma(n-m+1)}{\Gamma(n+m+1)}P_n{}^m(x).$

$$Q_n{}^{-m}(x) = \frac{\Gamma(n-m+1)}{\Gamma(n+m+1)} Q_n{}^m(x).$$

iv. $\quad (2m)!(1-x^2)^{m/2} t^m =$

$$2^m m! (1-2xt+t^2)^{m+1/2} \sum_{n=m}^{\infty} P_n{}^m(x) t^n.$$

555 $\quad (1-x^2)^2 y'' - 2x(1-x^2)y' - [k^2 - p(p+1)(1-x^2)]y = 0$ $\qquad$ **9-3**
The associated Legendre differential equation. If $k = 0$, see
(369); if both k and p are integers, see (554).

a. The equation can be converted into the Gauss
hypergeometric equation as follows.

i. $\quad y(x) = (x^2-1)^{k/2} u(z); \qquad 2z = 1-x; \qquad z(1-z)u''$
$+ (1+k)(1-2z)u' + (p-k)(1+p+k)u = 0; \quad$ see (407).

ii. $\quad y(x) = (x^2-1)^{k/2} u(z); \qquad x^2 = z; \qquad 4z(1-z)u''$
$+ 2[1-(2k+3)z]u' + (p-k)(1+p+k)u = 0; \quad$ see (470).
The hypergeometric series in i and ii are two linearly independent solutions of the differential equation. These series can be
transformed into 72 particular solutions of the equation.

b. The general solution of the equation is usually given in
terms of $P_p{}^k(x)$, a Legendre function of the first kind, of order
k, and of degree p; $Q_p{}^k(x)$, a Legendre function of the second
kind. The following results refer to real $x = \cos \theta, -1 < x < 1$.
They can be generalized for a complex variable.

$$y_1 = P_p{}^k(x) = \frac{1}{\Gamma(1-k)} \left(\frac{x+1}{x-1}\right)^{k/2} {}_2F_1(-p, 1+p, 1-k; z);$$

$2z = 1-x; \quad$ see (410).

$$y_2 = Q_p{}^k(x) = \frac{\pi}{2}\csc k\pi \left[P_p{}^k(x)\cos k\pi - \frac{\Gamma(1+k+p)}{\Gamma(1-k+p)} P_p{}^{-k}(x)\right]$$

Definitions with different constant factors are often given.

c. Provided that $(p \pm k) \neq \pm n$, solutions of the equation
are $P_p{}^{\pm k}(\pm x)$, $Q_p{}^{\pm k}(\pm x)$, $P_q{}^{\pm k}(\pm x)$, $Q_q{}^{\pm k}(\pm x)$; $q = -(1+p)$.
Linearly independent solutions can be taken in the following
ways.

i. $\quad y_1 = P_p{}^k(x); \quad y_2 = Q_p{}^k(x); \quad (p \pm k) \neq \pm n.$

ii. $\quad y_1 = P_p{}^k(x); \quad y_2 = P_p{}^{-k}(x); \quad (p \pm k) = \pm n; \; k \neq \pm m.$

iii. $\quad k = \pm m, \; p \neq n;$

$$y_1 = P_p{}^m(x) = (-1)^m(1-x^2)^{m/2}\frac{d^m}{dx^m}P_p(x); \quad y_2 = Q_p{}^m(x)$$

$$= (-1)^m(1-x^2)^{m/2}\frac{d^m}{dx^m}Q_p(x).$$

556 $(1-x^2)^2y'' - 2x(1-x^2)y' - [a^2 - k(1-x^2)]y = 0$ **4-1**

    i. $y = (1-x^2)^{a/2}u(x);$ $(1-x^2)u'' - 2x(1+a)u'$
        $-[a(1+a) - k]u = 0;$ see (382).

    ii. The integral is in closed form if $k = n(1-n)$ or if
        $a + 1/2 = n$, where n is an integer; see (478).

    iii. See also (555) and (578).

557 $(1-x^2)^2y'' - 2x(1-x^2)y' + (a_0 + a_2x^2 + a_4x^4)y = 0$ **9-3, 9-6**

    i. A special case is that of spheroidal wave functions;
        $a_0 = a + 4b - k^2;$ $a_2 + a + 8b = 0;$ $a_4 = 4b.$

    ii. $y(x) = u(z);$ $x = \cos z;$ $u''(z) + u' \cot z$
        $+ (a + 4b \sin^2 z - k^2 \csc^2 z)u = 0.$ This is the trigono-
        metric form of the spheroidal wave equation;
        see (140).

558 $(1-x^2)^2y'' - 2x(1-x^2)y' + (a_0 + a_1x + \ldots + a_nx^n)y = 0$ **9-3**

559 $(1+x^2)^2y'' + ax(1+x^2)y' + by = 0$ **4-2**

$y(x) = u(z);$ $z\sqrt{1+x^2} = x;$ $(1-z^2)u'' + (a-3)zu' + bu = 0;$
see (382).

560 $(1-x^2)^2y'' + a_1x(1-x^2)y' + (a_2 + b_2x + c_2x^2)y = 0$ **4-3**

$y(x) = (1+x)^r(1-x)^s u(z);$ $2z = 1+x;$ $a_2 - b_2 + c_2 - 2a_1r$
$+ 4r(r-1) = 0;$ $b_2 = (r-s)[2(r+s-1) - a_1];$ $2z(1-z)u''$
$+ (a+bz)u' + 2cu;$ $a = 4r - a_1;$ $b = 2a_1 - 2s - 4r;$ $c = r(r-1)$
$+ s(s-1) + 2rs + c_2 - a_1(r+s);$ see (410).

561 $x^2(a^2 + x^2)y'' + x(a^2 + 2x^2)y' \pm b^2y = 0$ **4-2**

    i. $y(x) = u(z); \, x = 1/z; \, (1 + a^2z^2)u'' + a^2zu' \pm b^2u = 0;$
see (480).

    ii. $x = -a \operatorname{csch} az;$ $u''(z) \pm b^2u = 0;$ see (26).

562 $(a^2 + x^2)^2y'' + 2x(a^2 + x^2)y' - (a_0 + a_2x^2 + a_4x^4)y = 0$ **9-6**

$y(x) = u(z);$ $x = iaz;$ $(1 - z^2)^2u'' - 2z(1 - z^2)u'$
$- (A_0 + A_2z^2 + A_4z^4)u = 0;$ $A_0a^2 = a_0;$ $A_2 + a_2 = 0;$
$A_4 = a^2a_4;$ see (557).

563 $(a^2 - x^2)^2y'' - 2x(a^2 - x^2)y' + (a_0 + a_2x^2 + a_4x^4)y = 0$ **9-6**

$y(x) = u(z);$ $x = az;$ $(1 - z^2)^2u'' - 2z(1 - z^2)u'$
$+ (A_0 + A_2z^2 + A_4z^4)u = 0;$ $A_0a^2 = a_0;$ $A_2 = a_2;$
$A_4 = a^2a_4;$ see (557).

564 $(a^2 \pm x^2)(b^2 \pm x^2)y'' + x(a_0 + b_0 x^2)y' + (a_1 + b_1 x^2)y = 0$ **9-6**
Use **8-1** to get series solutions about the ordinary point $x = 0$
or **8-2**, for solutions at the regular singular points $x = \pm a$,
$\pm ia$, $\pm b$, $\pm ib$, ∞.

565 $(a^2 - x^2)(b^2 - x^2)y'' + x(a_0 + b_0 x^2)y' + (a_1 + b_1 x^2 + c_1 x^4)y = 0$ **9-6**
Proceed as for (564). There is an ordinary point at $x = 0$ and
regular singular points at $x = \pm a$, $\pm b$, ∞.

566 $x(1-x)(1+x)^2 y'' + 2x(1+x)(3-x)y' - 2(1-x)y = 0$ **4-1**
$u(x) = y(1+x)^2$; $x(1-x)u'' + 2xu' - 2u = 0$;   see (398).
$$y(1+x)^2 = C_1 x + C_2(1 - x^2 + 2x \ln x)$$

567 $x^2(1-x)^2 y'' + (a + bx + cx^2)y = 0$ **4-1**
$y = x^r(1-x)^2 u(x)$; $x(1-x)u'' + (a_1 + b_1 x)u' + c_1 u = 0$;
$a_1 = 2r$; $b_1 + 2(r+s) = 0$; $c_1 = 2a + b - 2rs$; $a + r(r-1) = 0$;
$2rs = b + 2a$;   see (410).

568 $x^2(1-x)^2 y'' + x(1-x)(1-2x)y' - y = 0$ **4-1-1**
$y_1 = x/(1-x)$; $y_2 = (1-x)/x$.
$$y = C_1 y_1 + C_2 y_2$$

569 $x^2(1-x)^2 y'' + x(1-x)(a_1 + b_1 x)y' + (a_2 + b_2 x + c_2 x^2)y = 0$ **9-3**
See (588).

570 $x^2(1-x)^2 y'' + x(1-x)(1-2x)y' + (a_0 + a_1 x + \ldots + a_n x^n)y = 0$ **9-3**
Use the methods of **8-2** to get series solutions at the regular
singular points $x = 0, 1$.

571 $x^2(a-x)^2 y'' + by = 0$ **4-1-1**
$y_1 = x^r(a-x)^s$; $s = 1 - r$; $r(r-1)a^2 + b = 0$.
$$y = C_1 x^r(a-x)^{1-r} + C_2 x^{1-r}(a-x)^r$$

572 $(a-x)^2(b-x)^2 y'' = k^2 y$ **4-1-1**
$y_1 = (a-x)^r(b-x)^s$; $a^2 s(s-1) + 2abrs + b^2 r(r-1) = k^2$;
$s = 1 - r$; $c^2 = 1 + 4k^2/(a-b)^2$; $2r = 1 + c$; $2s = 1 - c$.
$$y = [(a-x)(b-x)]^{1/2}\left[C_1\left(\frac{a-x}{b-x}\right)^{c/2} + C_2\left(\frac{b-x}{a-x}\right)^{c/2} \right]$$

573 $(a-x)^2(b-x)^2 y'' + (a-x)(b-x)(A + 2x)y' + By = 0$ **9-2**
If $x = a, b$ are to be regular singular points, it is necessary that
$A = b(\alpha + \beta - 1) - a(\alpha + \beta + 1)$; $B = \alpha\beta(a-b)^2$, where α, β are
the exponents at $x = a$ and $-\alpha$, $-\beta$ are the exponents at $x = b$.
The term $2x$ is required to prevent a singular point at $x = \infty$.
Let $y(x) = u(x)$; $z = (a-x)/(b-x)$. The result is an Euler
equation; see **3-1**.
     i. $\alpha \neq \beta$; $u(z) = C_1 z^\alpha + C_2 z^\beta$.
     ii. $\alpha = \beta$; $u(z) = z^\alpha(C_1 + C_2 \ln z)$.

574 $(a-x)^4y'' - 2(a-x)^3y' - y = 0$ **9-1**
$y(x) = u(z)$; $z = 1/(a-x)$; $u''(z) = u$;   see (7).
$$y = C_1e^{1/(a-x)} + C_2e^{1/(x-a)}$$

575 $x^2(1-x)(1-2x)y'' + 2x(2-3x)y' + 2(1+3x)y = 0$ **4-1**
$x^2y = u(x)$; $(1-x)(1-2x)u'' + 2(3-4x)u' + 12u = 0$;   see (445).
$$x^2y = C_1(1-2x)^3 + C_2(1-x)^3$$

576 $x^2(1-x)(1-2x)y'' + 2x(2-x)(1-2x)y' + 2(1-x)y = 0$ **4-1**
$x^2y = u(x)$; $(1-x)(1-2x)u'' + 2(1-2x)u' + 4u = 0$;   see (444).

577 $4(1-x^2)^2y'' - 8x(1-x^2)y' - [4k^2 + (1+4p^2)(1-x^2)]y = 0$ **9-3**
A special case of the associated Legendre equation; see (555).

> i. $k = 0$;   see (463).
>
> ii. $k \neq 0$; $q = ip - 1/2$
> $$y = C_1P_q{}^k(x) + C_2Q_q{}^k(x).$$

These solutions are special spherical harmonics or conical functions.

578 $4(1-x^2)^2y'' - 8x(1-x^2)y' - [4k^2 + (1-4p^2)(1-x^2)]y = 0$ **9-3**
A special case of the associated Legendre equation; see (555) and (577).

> i. $k = p = 0$;   see (369).
>
> ii. $k \neq 0$; $q = p - 1/2$
> $$y = C_1P_q{}^k(x) + C_2Q_q{}^k(x).$$

The solutions are special spherical harmonics and are also called ring, torus, or toroidal functions.

> iii. $y(x) = u(z)$; $x = \cosh z$; $4u'' \sinh^2 z$
> $+ 4u' \cosh z \sinh z - [4k^2 - (1-4p^2)\sinh^2 z]u = 0$;
> see (596).

579 $4x^2(1-x)^2y'' + 2x(1-x)(1-3x)y' - [a(1+a)(1-x)$
               $+ b^2x]y = 0$ **4-2-2**
$y(x) = u(z)$; $x = 1/z^2$; $(1-z^2)^2u'' - 2z(1-z^2)u'$
$- [b^2 - a(1+a)(1-z^2)]u = 0$;   see (556).

580 $(a+bx)^4y'' + y = 0$ **4-2**
$y(x) = u(z)$; $z = a+bx$; $a^2z^4u'' + u = 0$;   see (41).

581 $(a+bx+cx^2)^2y'' + Ay = 0$ **4-3**
$y = (a+bx+cx^2)^{1/2}u(z)$; $dx/dz = a+bx+cx^2$;
$u'' + (A+ac-b^2/4)u = 0$;   see (26).

582 $x^5y'' + xy' - y = 0$ **4-1-1**
$y_1 = x$.

583 $x^5y'' - x(1 - 2x^3)y' + (1 - 2x^3)y = 0$ **5-2**
$I(x) = 1/x^2$. A first integral is $x^4y' - (1 + x^3)y = Cx$; see **A1-2**.
$$y = x(C_1 + C_2 e^{-1/3x^3})$$

584 $x(a^2 - x^2)(b^2 - x^2)y'' + (a_0 + b_0 x^4)y' + x^3(a_1 + b_1 x^2 + c_1 x^4)y = 0$ **9-6**
There are regular singular points at $x = 0$, $\pm a$, $\pm b$. Use **8-2**
to get series solutions.

585 $x^6y'' - x^5y' + ay = 0$ **4-3**
$y = x^2 u(z)$; $z = 1/x^2$; $4u''(z) + au = 0$;   see (26).

586 $x^6y'' + 3x^5y' + y = 0$ **4-2-1**
$y(x) = u(z)$; $2x^2 = 1/z$; $u''(z) + u = 0$;   see (6).

587 $x^6y'' + x^3(a + 3x^2)y' + by = 0$ **4-1**
$y = e^{a/4x^2}u(x)$; $x^6u'' + 3x^5u' + (b - a^2/4)u = 0$;   see (591).

588 $(a - x)^2(b - x)^2(c - x)^2 y''$
$\qquad\qquad + (a - x)(b - x)(c - x)(a_1 + b_1 x + c_1 x^2)y'$
$\qquad\qquad + (a_2 + b_2 x + c_2 x^2)y = 0$ **9-3**

589 $4x^6y'' + 4x^3(1 + 2x^2)y' + (1 - 2x^2)y = 0$ **4-1-1**
$y_1 = e^{1/4x^2}$.
$$y = (C_1 + C_2/x)e^{1/4x^2}$$

590 $4x^6y'' - 4x^3(1 + 2x^2)y' + (1 + 10x^2 + 8x^4)y = 0$ **4-1-1**
$y_1 = xe^{-1/4x^2}$.
$$y = y_1(C_1 + C_2 x).$$

591 $4x^6y'' + 12x^5y' + (4b - a^2)y = 0$ **4-2**
$y(x) = u(z)$; $z = x^2$; $16z^4u'' + 32z^3u' + (4b - a^2)u = 0$; see (544).

592 $x^{2a}y'' + ax^{2a-1}y' + (1 - a)^2 y = 0$ **4-2-1**
$z = x^{1-a}$; $u''(z) + u = 0$;   see (6).
$$y = C_1 \cos z + C_2 \sin z$$

593 $x^{a+1}y'' + (1 - 2a)x^a y' + a^2 x^{a-1}y = 0$ **4-2-1**
$z = a \ln x$; $u''(z) - 2u' + u = 0$;   see (102).
$$y = x^a(C_1 + C_2 \ln x)$$

594 $x^2(a_0 + b_0 x^k)y'' + x(a_1 + b_1 x^k)y' + (a_2 + b_2 x^k)y = 0$ **4**
Pfaff's equation. Calculate the roots of the two quadratic
equations
$b_0 k^2 \alpha^2 - 2k\alpha[b_0(1 + 2k) - b_1] + 4[b_0 k(1 + k) - b_1 k + b_2] = 0$;
$a_0 k^2 \beta^2 - 2k\beta(a_0 + a_1) + 4a_2 = 0$. Call them α_1, α_2, β_1, β_2. The
equation is integrable in finite terms in the following cases:
$\qquad$ i. $\alpha_i - \beta_j$ is even; $i = 1, 2$; $j = 1, 2$; four cases.

ii.   Any pair of the following is an odd integer: $\Delta\alpha = \alpha_1 - \alpha_2$; $\Delta\beta = \beta_1 - \beta_2$; $(\alpha_1 + \alpha_2) - (\beta_1 + \beta_2)$. For a symbolic method of completing the solution, see Boole.

595        $(1 - a^2 \cos^2 x)y'' + a^2 y' \cos x \sin x + (a_0 + a_1 \cos^2 x)y = 0$ **9-4**
A trigonometric form of the Lamé equation; see also (58), (59).

596        $4y'' \sinh^2 x + 4y' \cosh x \sinh x - [4k^2 - (1 - p^2)\sinh^2 x]y = 0$ **4-2-2**
See (578).

4. THE NONLINEAR EQUATION OF SECOND ORDER

The most general equation in this section will contain a sum of terms $X_i(x, y, y', y'')$. To search for a given equation, determine the member with highest rank, continue with the one of next lower rank, etc. See 1 for rules to arrange equations of first order. They are readily generalized for this case. Thus, y'' is of higher rank than y'; $f(x)y''$ is of lower rank than $f(y)y''$; $f(x, y)y''$ is of lower rank than $g(x, y)y''y'$.

Integration constants in the general solution are C_1 and C_2. Often only a first integral can be given explicitly and, in those cases, the single integration constant may be called either C_1 or C. A singular first integral or a singular solution may contain a constant C or C_0 but there should be no confusion between such a case and a more general solution. The symbol p has been used here to mean dy/dx.

For further information about notation, see Part I, Introduction–4 and **B2** or Part II–3. The Weierstrassian elliptic function $\mathscr{P}(x; a, b)$ often appears as a solution of nonlinear second-order equations.

1     $y'' = 0$ **2-1, 8-1**
$$y = C_1 x + C_2$$
See also (3-1).

2     $y'' = a^2 y$ **2-1**
$p^2 = a^2 y^2 + C$;   see **A1-1-3**.
$$a(x + C_2) = \ln[ay + \sqrt{C_1 + a^2 y^2}]$$

3     $y'' = 6y^2$ **2-1, 8-1**
$p^2 = 4y^3 + C$;   see **A1-1-3** and (5).
$$y = \mathscr{P}(C_2 + x; 0, C_1)$$

4     $y'' = x + 6y^2$ **8-1**
See (5) and **9**.

5     $y'' = a + bx + cy^2$ **5**
$$y(x) = ku(z); \quad z = r(s + x); \quad u''(z) = a_1 + b_1 z + c_1 z^2;$$

$kr^2a_1 = a - bs$; $kr^3b_1 = b$; $r^2c_1 = ck$. Choose k, r, and s to get standard forms:

    i. $a = b = 0$; $u'' = 6u^2$;   see (3).
    ii. $a \neq 0$, $b = 0$; $2u'' = 1 + 12u^2$;   see (73).
    iii. $b \neq 0$; $u'' = z + 6u^2$;   see (4).

6    $y'' = 2y^3$ **2-1, 8-1**
$p^2 = y^4 + C$;   see **A1-1-3** and (11).

7    $y'' = a + by + 2y^3$ **2-1, 8-1**
$p^2 = 2ay + by^2 + y^4$;   see **A1-1-3** and (11).

8    $y'' = a + xy + 2y^3$ **8-1**
See **9**.

9    $y'' = f(x) + g(x)y + 2y^3$ **8-1**

10    $y'' = a - 2abxy + 2b^2y^3$ **8-1**
A first integral is any solution of $y' = ax - by^2$; see **A1-3-2**.

11    $y'' = a_0 + a_1xy + a_2y + a_3y^3$ **5**
$y = ku(z)$; $z = r(s + tx)$; $u''(z) = b_0 + b_1zu + b_2u + b_3u^3$;
$a_0 = kr^2t^2b_0$; $a_1 = r^3t^3b_1$; $a_2t - a_1s = r^2t^3b_2$; $a_3k^2 = r^2t^2b_3$.
Choose k, r, s, t to get standard forms.

    i. $a_0 = a_1 = a_2 = 0$; $u''(z) = 2u^3$;   see (6).
    ii. $a_1 = 0$; $u''(z) = b_0 + b_2u + 2u^3$;   see (7).
    iii. $a_2t = a_1s$; $u''(z) = b_0 + b_1zu + 2u^3$;   see (8).

12    $y'' = a_0 + a_1y + a_2y^2 + a_3y^3$ **2-1**
$p^2 = 2a_0y + a_1y^2 + 2a_2y^3/2 + a_3y^4/2 + C$;   see **A1-1-3**.

13    $y'' + ax^ry^s = 0$ **5**
    i. $y(x) = u(z)$; $x = 1/z$; $zu'' + 2u' + az^{-3-r}u^s = 0$;
see (78).
    ii.   A special solution is $y_1 = Ax^k$; $(1 - s)k = 2 + r$;
$a(1 - s)^2A + (2 + r)(1 + r + s) = 0$.
    iii.   See (117) for a special case.

14    $y'' + a \sin y = 0$ **2-1**
$p^2 = C + 2a \cos y$;   see (1-131).

15    $y'' + ae^y = 0$ **2-1**
$p^2 + ae^y = 0$;   see **A1-1-3**.

16    $y'' = f(y)$ **2-1**

17    $y'' + 3f(x)y' + (f' + 2f^2)y = 2y^3$ **8-1**
$y(x) = u(z)v(x)$; $\ln v + \int f(x)dx = 0$; $z = \int v dx$; $u''(z) = 2u^3$;
see (6).

18     $y'' + yy' = 0$ 2-3
$p(p' + y) = 0$;   see **A1-1-3**.

$$\ln\frac{C_1 + y}{C_1 - y} = C_1(x + C_2); \quad y = C$$

19     $y'' + yy' = y^3$ 2-3
$pp'(y) + yp - y^3 = 0$; $u = C_1 x + C_2$.

$$y = C_1 e^{-ax}\frac{\mathscr{P}'(u;\, 0,\, 1)}{\mathscr{P}(u;\, 0,\, 1)}$$

20     $y'' + yy' + ay = y^3$ 2-3
$pp'(y) + yp + ay - y^3 = 0$; $u = (x/2)\sqrt{a/3} + C_2$.

$$2y = \sqrt{a/3}\frac{\mathscr{P}'(u;\, 12,\, C_1)}{\mathscr{P}(u;\, 12,\, C_1) - 1}$$

21     $y'' + yy' = 12f'(x) - 12f(x)y + y^3$ 8-1
     i. $f(x) = 0$;   see (19).
    ii. $f(x) = a$;   see (20).
   iii. $f(x)$ is a solution of $f''(x) = 6f^2$;   see (3).
   iv. $f(x)$ is a solution of $f''(x) = 1 + 6f^2$;   see (5).
    v. $f(x)$ is a solution of $f''(x) = x + 6f^2$;   see (4).
If $u(x) \neq f(x)$ is a solution of $u''(x) = x + 6u^2$, then
$y[u(x) - f(x)] = u' - f'$.

22     $y'' + (3a + y)y' + 2a^2 y + ay^2 = y^3$ 2-3
     i.   If $a = 0$, see (19).
    ii. $a \neq 0$; $au = C_1 e^{-ax} + C_2$

$$y = C_1 e^{-ax}\frac{\mathscr{P}'(u;\, 0,\, 1)}{\mathscr{P}(u;\, 0,\, 1)}$$

23     $y'' = (3f - y)y' + (f' - 2f^2)y + fy^2 + y^3$ 8-1
    i. $y(x) = u(z)v(x)$; $v(x) = \dfrac{dz}{dx}$; $v'(x) = fv$;

        $u''(z) + uu' = u^3$;   see (19).

    ii. $yv = v'(x)$; $fu = u'(x)$; $\dfrac{d}{dx}(U_1 - U_2) = 0$;

$$U_1 = \frac{v''}{u^2 v^2}; \quad U_2 = \frac{u'v'}{u^3 v^2}; \quad U_1 - U_2 = \frac{3}{2}C_1;$$

$$\frac{d}{dx}(v'^2/u^2) = 3C_1 v^2 v'; \quad v'^2 = u^2(C_1 v^3 + C_2); \text{ see } \textbf{A1-1-2.}$$

24    $y'' = (3f_1 - y)y' + f_2 + f_3y + f_1y^2 + y^3$ 8-1

There are five special cases, each of which can be converted into the standard form (21); see **8-1d** for details.

25    $y'' = (f_0y + f_1)y' + g_0y^3 + g_1y^2 + g_2y + g_3$ 8-1

The coefficients are constants or functions of x only. To prevent movable critical points further restrictions are necessary.

26    $y'' = (f - 2y)y' + f'y$ 8-1, 5

$y = u + f/2$; $g(x) = f^2/4 - f'/2$; $u''(x) + 2uu' = g'(x)$. A first integral, see **A1-3-1**, is $u'(x) + u^2 = g(x) + C$.

27    $y'' = (f - 2y)y' + g(x) + f(x)y^2$ 8-1

A first integral is $y' = u - y^2$; see **A1-3-1**; where $u'(x) = g(x) + f(x)u$; see **A1-2**. See also (26), which has the same first integral but which is more convenient as the standard form.

28    $y'' = (f_1 - 2y)y' + f_2y^2 + f_3$ 8-1

To prevent movable critical points, it is necessary that $f_1(x) = f_2(x)$; see also (27).

29    $y'' = (f_1 - 2y)y' + f_2y^2 + f_3y + f_4$ 8-1

The term in y can be removed. Let $y(x) = u(x) + w(x)$; $2w' = 2f_2w + f_3$; $u'' = (F_1 - 2u)u' + F_2u^2 + F_3$; see (28). For the relations between $f_i(x)$ and $F_i(x)$, see **8-1b**.

30    $y'' = 3yy' + a + 4b^2y + 3by^2$ 2-3

$pp'(y) = 3yp + a + 4b^2y + 3by^2$; see **A1-4-2**.

31    $y'' + 3yy' = f(x) + g(x)y - y^3$ 5

$uy = u'(x)$; $u'''(x) = gu' + fu$; see **C1**.

32    $y'' = (f - 3y)y' + fy^2 - y^3$ 8-1

$uy = u'(x)$; $u'''(x) = f(x)u''$; see **C1**.

33    $y'' = a(1 + 2yy')$ 2-3

$pp'(y) = a(1 + 2yp)$; see **A1-4-2**.

34    $y'' + a(y^2 - 1)y' + by = 0$ 6

The van der Pol equation. It occurs in the study of electric circuits containing vacuum tubes. It is not one of the types in **7, 8, 9, 10** and no simple solution of it is known. The equation has been investigated extensively. For further details, see Andronow and Chaikin.

35 $y'' + f(x, y)y' + g(x, y) = 0$ 6
If $g_y - f_x = fX - X^2 - X'$, where $X(x)$ is a function of x alone,
calculate $F(x) = \exp \int X(x)dx$; $G_x = gF$; $G_y = (f-X)F$.
Then, solve $F(x)y' + G(x, y) = 0$; see **A1**.

36 $y'' = 2x + (x^2 - y')^2$ 1-2
$p'(x) = 2x + (x^2 - p)^2$; $(C-x)p = 1 + x^2(C-x)$;   see (1-47)
and **A1-1-1**.
$$3y = x^3 - 3 \ln (C_1 - x) + C_2$$

37 $y'' + 2y'^2 \tan y + 2y' \cot x = 0$ 4-1
$I = 1/y'$; see also (47)
$$\tan y = C_1 \cot x + C_2$$

38 $y'' = ay'^2$ 2-2
$p' = ap^2$.
$$ay + \ln(x + C_1) = C_2$$

39 $y'' = a^2 + b^2 y'^2$ 2-2
$p' = a^2 + b^2 p^2$.
$$ab^2 y = \ln \sec ab(x - C_1) + C_2$$

40 $y'' + ay'^2 + by = 0$ 2-3
$pp'(y) + ap^2 + by = 0$; see (1-427).
$$2a^2 p^2 = C_1 e^{-2ay} + b(1 - 2ax)$$

41 $y'' + ay'^2 + b \sin y = 0$ 2-3
$pp'(y) + ap^2 + b \sin y = 0$; see (1-428).
$$(4a^2 + 1)p^2 = Ce^{-2ay} + 2b(\cos y - 2a \sin y)$$

42 $y'' + ay'^2 + by' + cy = 0$ 2-3
$pp'(y) + ap^2 + bp + cy = 0$; see **A1-4-2**.

43 $y'' = e^x y'^2$ 1-2
$p' = e^x p^2$.
$$C_1 y + x = C_2 + \ln(C_1 + e^x)$$

44 $y'' + f(x)y' + g(x)y'^2 = 0$ 1-2
$p'(x) + f(x)p + g(x)p^2 = 0$; see **A1-5**.
$$y + C_2 = \int X(x)e^{-\phi}dx; \phi(x) = \int f(x)dx$$
$X(x) = [C_1 + \int e^{-\phi}g(x)dx]^{-1}$.

45 $y'' + ayy'^2 + by = 0$ 2-3
$pp'(y) + ayp^2 + by = 0$; see (1-430).

46 $y'' + f(y)y'^2 + g(y) = 0$ 2-3
$pp'(y) + f(y)p^2 + g(y) = 0$; see **A1-5**.
$$p^2 e^{2\phi} = C - 2\int g(y)e^{2\phi}dy; \phi(y) = \int f(y)dy$$

47 $y'' + g(y)y'^2 + f(x)y' = 0$ 4-1
Liouville's equation.
   i. $I = 1/y';$ $\ln p + X(x) + Y(y) = C_1;$
      $\int e^Y dy = C_1 \int e^{-X} dx + C_2;$ $X(x) = \int f(x)dx;$
      $Y(y) = \int g(y)dy.$
   ii. $y = C$ is also a solution.

48 $y'' + g(y)y'^2 + f(y)y' = 0$ 5, 2-3
Interchange the dependent and independent variables; see (44).

49 $y'' + g(y)y'^2 + f(y)y' + h(y) = 0$ 2-3
$pp'(y) + fp + gp^2 + h = 0;$ see **A1-4-2**.
   i. If $f(y) = 0;$ see **A1-5**.
   ii. If $h(y) = 0;$ see **A1-2**.

50 $y'' + y' + y'^3 = 0$ 2-2
$p'(x) + p(1 + p^2) = 0;$ see **A1-1-3**.
   $C_1 e^{-x} = \sin(C_2 - y)$

51 $y'' = (a - x)y'^3$ 1-2
$p' = (a - x)p^3;$ $p^2(x^2 - 2ax + 2C) = 1;$ see **A1-1-2**.
   $(a - x) = C_1 \cosh y + C_2 \sinh y$

52 $y'' + (x + e^{2y})y'^3 = 0$ 5
Interchange the dependent and independent variables;
$x''(y) - x = e^{2y};$ see **B1-12-1**.
   $3x = C_1 e^y + C_2 e^{-y} + e^{2y}$

53 $y'' + 2y' + 4y'^3 = 0$ 2-2
$p'(x) + 2p(1 + 2p^2) = 0;$ see **A1-1-3**.
   $\sin(C_2 - 2y\sqrt{2}) = C_1 e^{-2x}$

54 $y'' + ay'^3 = 0$ 2-2
$p'(x) + ap^3 = 0;$ see **A1-1-3**.
   $a(y - C_2)^2 = 2(x - C_1);$ $y = C$

55 $y'' = xy'^3$ 1-2
$p' = xp^3;$ see **A1-1-2**.
   $x = C_1 \sin(C_2 + y);$ $y = C$

56 $y'' + (ax + by)y'^3 = 0$ 5
Interchange x and y; $x''(y) = ax + by;$ see **B1-12-1** and (3-28).

57 $y'' + ay(1 + y'^2)^2 = 0$ 2-3
$pp'(y) + ay(1 + p^2)^2 = 0;$ see **A1-1-2**.
   $p^2(C + ay^2) = 1 - ay^2 - C$

58 $\quad y'' = a(xy'-y)^k$ $\qquad\qquad$ **5**

$y = xu(x);\quad xu''+2u' = ax^{2k}u'^k;\quad$ see **1-2**

    i. $\quad k=1;\quad$ see (82).

    ii. $\quad k \neq 1;\quad$ see (91).

59 $\quad y''+f(x)y'^k+g(x)y' = 0$ $\qquad\qquad$ **1-2**

$p'+p^k f+pg = 0;\quad$ s⌃e **A1-5**.

60 $\quad y'' = Ax^a y^b y'^c$ $\qquad\qquad$ **3-4**

$(b+c) \neq 1;\quad y = x^n u(z);\quad z = \ln x;\quad (1-b-c)n = 2+a-c;$

$(1-b-c)k = a+2b+c;\quad u''(z)+(2n-1)u'+n(n-1)u$

$= Au^b(nu+u')^c;\quad$ see **2-3**.

61 $\quad y'' = a\sqrt{1+y'^2}$ $\qquad\qquad$ **2-2**

$p = \sinh(ax+C);\quad$ see **A1-1-1**.

$\qquad ay = \cosh(ax+C_1)+C_2$

62 $\quad y'' = a\sqrt{by^2+y'^2}$ $\qquad\qquad$ **2-3, 3-1**

$pp'(y) = a\sqrt{b^2y^2+p^2};\quad$ see **A1-8-1**.

63 $\quad y'' = a(1+y'^2)^{3/2}$ $\qquad\qquad$ **2-2**

$\qquad (x-C_1)^2+(y-C_2)^2 = 1/a^2$

64 $\quad y'' = ax(1+y'^2)^{3/2}$ $\qquad\qquad$ **1-2**

$p'(x) = ax(1+p^2)^{3/2};\quad$ see **A1-1-2**.

$\qquad 2p/\sqrt{1+p^2} = ax^2+C$

65 $\quad y'' = ay(1+y'^2)^{3/2}$ $\qquad\qquad$ **2-3**

$pp'(y) = ay(1+p^2)^{3/2};\quad$ see **A1-1-2**.

$\qquad p(C-ay^2) = \pm\sqrt{4-(C-ay^2)^2}$

66 $\quad y'' = ay[1+(b-y')^2]^{3/2}$ $\qquad\qquad$ **2-3**

$pp'(y) = ay[1+(b-p)^2]^{3/2};\quad$ see **A1-1-2**.

67 $\quad y'' = a(b+cx+y)(1+y'^2)^{3/2}$ $\qquad\qquad$ **5**

$u(x) = b+cx+y;\quad u'' = au[1+(u'-c)^2]^{3/2};\quad$ see (66).

$\qquad 2[cu'-(1+c^2)] = (C+au^2)\sqrt{(u'-c)^2+1}$

68 $\quad y''+y^3y' = yy'\sqrt{y^4+4y'}$ $\qquad\qquad$ **2-3**

$p[p'(y)+y^3-y\sqrt{y^4+4p}] = 0;\quad$ see (1-102);$\quad 4p = C(C+2y^2);$

see **A1-1-3**.

$\qquad y = C_1\tan(C_1^3x+C_2)$

A singular integral, see **11**, is $4p+y^4 = 0$. Singular solutions

are $3(C-x)y^3 = 4$ and $y = C$.

69 $\quad y'' = f(y')$ $\qquad\qquad$ **2-2**

70 $\quad y'' = f(ax+by, y')$ $\qquad\qquad$ **5**

$u(x) = ax+by;\quad u'' = [u, (u'-a)/b];\quad$ see **2-3**.

71     $y'' = yf(x, y'/y)$ **3-1**
     $y' = yu(x)$; $u' + u^2 = f(x, u)$;   see **A1**.

72     $y'' = x^{n-2}f(y/x^n, y'/x^{n-1})$ **3-4**
     $y = x^n u(z)$; $z = \ln x$; $u''(z) + (2n-1)u' + n(n-1)u$
     $= f(u, u' + nu)$;   see **2-3**.

73      $2y'' = 1 + 12y^2$ **2-1, 8-1**
     $p^2 = 4y^3 + y + C$;   see **A1-1-3** and **(5)**.
           $y = \mathscr{P}(x + C_2; \; 1, C_1)$

74      $2y'' = y(a - y^2)$ **2-1**
        $y' = \sqrt{C + ay^2/2 - y^4/4}$

75     $8y'' + 9y'^4 = 0$ **2-2**
    $27p^3(x + C) = 8$;   see **A1-1-1**.
      $(x + C_1)^2 = (y + C_2)^3$

76     $xy'' + y' + axe^y = 0$ **5**
        i. $xy'(x) = u(z)$; $x^2e^y = z$; $z(2 + u)u' + az = 0$; see **(1-524)**.
A first integral is
       $u^2(z) + 4u + 2az + 4C = 0$
       ii.   Combine the first integral in i with the original
equation   and   get $2x^2p'(x) = x^2p^2 + 2xp + 4C$; $y'(x) = p$;
see **A1-3**.
       iii.   Use the equation of ii and $pv(x) = -2v'(x)$;
$x^2y'' - xv' + Cv = 0$;   see **B1-3-1**.

77     $xy'' + 2y' + xy^5 = 0$ **5**
The Lane-Emden equation of index 5; see also **(78)**. Let
$y\sqrt{x} = au(z)$; $z = -\ln x$; $a^4 = 1/4$; $4u''(z) = u(1 - u^4)$;
see **2-1**. A first integral is $p^2 = u^2(1 - u^4/3)/4 + C_1$. A solution
for $C_1 = 0$, which is an appropriate boundary condition for
certain physical problems is
      $y^2(x^2 + 3C^2) = 3C$

78     $xy'' + 2y' + xy^n = 0$ **5**
The Lane-Emden equation of index n.
        i. $n = 0$;   see **(3-189)**.
       ii. $n = 1$;   see **(3-191)**.
       iii. $n \neq 0$, 1, but not necessarily an integer. Let
$y(x) = x^k u(z)$; $(1-n)k = 2$; $z = -\ln x$; $u''(z) + au' + bu$
$+ u^n = 0$; $a(n-1) = 5 - n$; $b(n-1)^2 = 2(3-n)$;   see **2-3**.
For an integrable case, see **(77)**. The general cases are discussed
in detail by Sansone.

79    $xy'' + 2y' + x^m y^n = 0$ **5**

  i. A solution is $y_1 = Cx^k$; $(1-n)k = 1+m$; $C^{n-1} + k(k+1) = 0$.

  ii. $y(x) = u(z)$; $z = 1/x$; $z^{3+m}u''(z) + u^n = 0$; see (13).

  iii. $xy = u(x)$; $u''(x) + x^{m-n}u^n = 0$; see (13).

80    $xy'' + 2y' + ax^m y^n = 0$ **5**
$y(x) = Au(x)$; $A = a^{1/(n-1)}$; $n \neq 0, 1$; $xu''(x) + 2u' + x^m u^n = 0$; see (79). For $m = 1$, see (78).

81    $xy'' + ay' + bxe^y = 0$ **5**

  i. $a = 0$; see (15).

  ii. $a = 1$; see (76).

  iii. $b(a-1) > 0$; a solution is $y_1 = \ln\dfrac{2(a-1)}{bx^2}$.

  iv. $y(x) = u(z) + y_1$; $z = x^{1-a}$; $(1-a)z^2 u''(z) + 2(1-e^u) = 0$; see (94).

  v. $y(x) = u(z)$; $z = x\sqrt{b}$; $zu'' + au' + ze^u = 0$.

  vi. $y(x) = u(z) - 2z$; $z = \ln x$; $u'' + (a-1)u' + be^u = 2(a-1)$; see **2-3**.

  vii. $xy'(x) = u(z)$; $x^2 e^y = z$; $z(2+u)u' + (a-1)u + bz = 0$; see (1-527).

82    $xy'' + (2 - ax^2)y' = 0$ **1-2**
$xp' + (2 - ax^2)p = 0$; see (1-165).
  $x^2 p = Ce^{ax^2/2}$

83    $xy'' = (1-y)y'$ **3-2**
$y(x) = u(z)$; $z = \ln x$; $u''(z) - u'(2-u) = 0$; see **2-3**.

84    $xy'' + xy'^2 = y'$ **1-2**
$xp'(x) = p(1 - xp)$; see **A1-5**.
  $y = \ln(2C_1 + x^2) + C_2$

85    $xy'' = xy'^2 + y'$ **1-2**
$xp'(x) = p(xp - 1)$; see **A1-5**.
  $y + \ln(C_1 - \ln x) = C_2$

86    $xy'' + 3xy'^2 - 2y' = 0$ **1-2**
$xp'(x) = p(2 - 3xp)$; see **A1-5**.
  $3y = \ln(C_1 + x^3) + C_2$

87    $xy'' = x^2 y'^2 - 2y' - y^2$ **3-4**
$xy = u(z)$; $z = \ln x$; $p[p'(u) - 1 + 2u - p] = 0$; see (1-4).
  $p(u) = Ce^u + 1 + 2u$; $y = 0$

88    $xy'' + ax^2y'^2 + 2y' = b$ 1-2
$xp'(x) + ax^2p^2 + 2p = b$;   see (1-183).

89    $xy'' + (axy' - y)^2 = b$ 5
$y = xu(x)$; $x^2u'' + ax^4u'^2 + 2xu' = b$;   see (101).

90    $xy'' = y'^3 + y'$ 1-2
$xp'(x) = p(1 + p^2)$;   see (1-190); $p\sqrt{C - x^2} = x$.
$x^2 + (y + C_2)^2 = C_1$; $y = C_0$

91    $xy'' + 2y' = ax^{2k}y'^k$ 1-2
$xp'(x) + 2p = ax^{2k}p^k$;   see (1-194).
$2p^{1-k} = x^{2k}[C/x^2 + a(1 - k)]$

92    $2xy'' + y'^3 + y' = 0$ 1-2
$2xp'(x) + p(1 + p^2) = 0$; $p^2(x - C) = C$;   see (1-242).
$(y + C_1)^2 = C_2(2x - C_2)$; $y = C_0$

93    $x^2y'' + ay(1 - y^n) = 0$ 5
$y(x) = x^k u(z)$; $z = x^r$; $2k = 1 - r$; $r^2 = 1 - 4a$;
$r^2u''(z) = au^{n+1}z^m$; $r(m + 2) = kn$;   see (13).

94    $x^2y'' + a(e^y - 1) = 0$ 5
See (81).

95    $x^2y'' + (1 + a)xy' = x^k f(x^k y, xy' + ky)$ 5
$x^k y = u(z)$; $kz = x^k$; $u''(z) = f(u, u')$;   see 2-3.

96    $x^2y'' + y'^2 = 0$ 1-2
$x^2p' + p^2 = 0$; $p(Cx - 1) = x$;   see A1-1-2.
$C_1^2 y = C_1 x + \ln C_2(C_1 x - 1)$

97    $x^2y'' = (3x - 2y')y'$ 1-2
$x^2p' = (3x - p)p$; $p(C + x^2) = x^3$;   see (1-264).
$2y + C_1 \ln (C_1 + x^2) = x^2 + C_2$

98    $x^2y'' + x^2y'^2 + 4xy' + 2 = 0$ 5, 1-2
$xy'(x) = u(z)$; $z = \ln x$; $u'(z) + 2 + 3u + u^2 = 0$;
$x(x - C)y' = 2C - x$;   see A1-1-3 and A1-1-1.
$$y = C_2 + \ln\left(\frac{x - C_1}{x^2}\right)$$

99    $x^2y'' = x^4y'^2 + 6y - 4x^2y^2$ 3-4
$x^2y(x) = u(z)$; $z = \ln x$; $p[p'(u) - 5 + 4u - p] = 0$;   see (1-4).
$p(u) = Ce^u - 1 + 4u$

100   $x^2y'' + a(xy' - y)^2 = bx^2$ 5
$y = xu(x)$; $xu'' + ax^2u'^2 + 2u' = b$;   see (88).

101   $x^2y'' + ax^4y'^2 + 2xy' = b$ 1-2
$x^2p'(x) + ax^4p^2 + 2xp = b$;   see (1-272).

102    $x^2y'' + ayy'^2 + bx = 0$ **3-3, 3-4**

$y = xu(z);$ $z = \ln x;$ $pp'(u) + au(p+u)^2 + p + b = 0;$ see

A1-4-2.

103    $x^2y'' = \sqrt{ax^2y'^2 + by^2}$ **3-3, 3-4**

$y(x) = xu(z);$ $z = \ln x;$ $p(p'+1) = \sqrt{a(p+u)^2 + bu^2};$ see

A1-1-2.

104    $x^2y'' = yf\left(\dfrac{xy'}{y}\right)$ **3-5**

105    $(1+x^2)y'' + y'^2 + 1 = 0$ **1-2, 11**

$(1+x^2)p' + 1 + p^2 = 0;$ $(1+Cx)p = C - x;$ see **A1-1-2.**

$C_1^2y = (1+C_1^2)\ln(1+C_1x) - C_1x + C_2;$ $2y + x^2 = C_0.$

106    $9x^2y'' + ay^3 + 2y = 0$ **5, 3-2**

$y = zu(z);$ $z^3 = x;$ $u''(z) + au^3 = 0;$ see (11).

107    $x^3y'' - x^2y' = 3 - x^2$ **1-2**

$x^3p' - x^2p = 3 - x^2;$ see (1-347); $px^2 = Cx^3 - 1.$

$xy = 1 + C_1x + x^2 + C_2x^3$

108    $x^3(y'' + yy' - y^3) + 12xy + 24 = 0$ **8-1**

See (122). A solution is $x(x^2u-1)y = x^3u' + 2$, where $u(x)$ is a

solution of $u''(x) = 6u^2;$ see (3).

109    $x^3y'' = a(xy' - y)^2$ **3-4, 3-3**

$p[p'(u) + 1 - ap] = 0;$ $ap = Ce^{au} - 1;$ see **A1-1-3.**

$$ay = x \ln \frac{x}{C_1x + C_2};   y = C_0x$$

110    $2x^3y'' + x^2(9 + 2xy)y' - 6 + xy(12 + 3xy - 2x^2y^2) = 0$ **5**

$y(x) = v(x)u(z);$ $v(x) = dz/dx;$ $z\sqrt{x} + 2 = 0;$

$z^3(u'' + uu' - u^3) + 12zu + 24 = 0;$ see (108).

111    $x^4y'' = x(x^2 + 2y)y' - 4y^2$ **3-4**

$y(x) = x^2u(z);$ $z = \ln x;$ $p[p'(u) + 2 - 2u] = 0;$

$p = C + (u-1)^2;$ see **A1-1-1.**

$(x-y)^2 = C_1x^2 \tan(C_1 \ln x + C_2);$ $y = C_0x^2$

112    $x^4y'' = x^2(x + y')y' - 4y^2$ **3-4**

$y(x) = x^2u(z);$ $z = \ln x;$ $p[p'(u) + 2 - p - 4u] = 0;$ see (1-4).

$p = Ce^u - 2(1 + 2u);$ $y = C_0x^2$

113    $x^4y'' + (xy' - y)^3 = 0$ **3-4**

$y(x) = xu(z);$ $z = \ln x;$ $p[p'(u) + 1 + p^2] = 0;$ $p = \tan(C - u);$

see **A1-1-3.**

$$y = x(C_1 - \sin^{-1}C_2/x);   y = C_0x$$

114 $x^a y'' + y^b = 0$ **3-4**
$y(x) = x^n u(z);\quad z = \ln x;\quad (1-b)n = 2-a;\quad pp'(u) + (2n-1)p$
$+ n(n-1)u + u^b = 0;\quad$ see **A1-4-2**.

115 $2x(1-4x^2)(y'' + yy' - y^3) + (1-12x^2)(3y' + y^2) - 48xy + 24 = 0$ **5**
$y(u' - x) = u' - 1$
$\qquad x(4x^2 - 1)u'^2 = 4u^3 - u + C$

116 $2(x^k - 4x^3)(y'' + yy' - y^3) - (kx^{k-1} - 12x^2)(3y' + y^2)$
$\qquad + axy + b = 0$ **8-1**
See also (115); $y(x) = v(x)u(z);\quad v = dz/dx = (x^k - 4x^3)^{-1/2};$
$2(u'' + uu' - u^3) + [(24-a)x + k(k-1)x^{k-2}]u + b\sqrt{x^k - 4x^3} = 0$

117 $y''\sqrt{x} = y^{3/2}$ **3-4**
The Thomas–Fermi equation; see Sansone for details about the
equation and its solutions.
     i. A solution is $x^3 y_1 = 144$.
     ii. In atomic theory, it is necessary that the boundary
conditions $y(0) = 1, y(\infty) = 0$ be satisfied. Such solutions must
be found by numerical methods.

118 $x^{3/2}y'' = f(y/\sqrt{x})$ **3-4**
$y(x) = u(z)\sqrt{x};\quad z = \ln x;\quad 4pp'(u) = 4f(u) - u;\quad$ see **A1-1-2**.

119 $X^3(x)y'' = f(y/X);\; X(x) = \sqrt{a + 2bx + cx^2}$ **5**
$y = X(x)u(x);\quad X^4 u'' + 2X^3 X' u' = (ac - b^2)u + f(u);$
$d(X^4 u'^2) = 2[(ac - b^2)u + f(u)]du;\; X^4 u'^2 = (ac - b^2)u^2 + 2\int f(u)du;$
see **A1-1-2**.

120 $f^2(x)y'' + ff'y' = g(y, fy')$ **5**
$y(x) = u(z);\quad fz'(x) = 1;\quad u''(z) = g(u, u');\quad$ see **2-3**

121 $f^2(x)y'' = (3f^3 + 3ff' - f^2y)y' - 24f^5$ **8-1**
$\qquad + (ff'' - 3f'^2 - 3f^2f' - 14f^4)y + (ff' + f^3)y^2 + f^2y^3$
A solution is $y(x) = f(x)(z^3 u' + 2)/(z^3 u - 1)$, where $z = \exp\int f(x)dx$
and $u(z)$ is a solution of $u''(z) = 6u^2$; see (3) and (122).

122 $f^2(x)y'' = (3f^3 + 3ff' - f^2y)y' - af^5$ **8-1**
$\qquad + (ff'' - 3f'^2 - 3f^2f' - bf^4)y + (ff' + f^3)y^2 + f^2y^3$
$y(x) = z'u(z);\quad z = \exp\int f(x)dx.$
$\qquad z^3(u'' + uu' - u^3) + (b-2)zu + a = 0$

123 $2f^2(x)y'' = f(3f' - 2fy)y' + (ff'' - 2f'^2 - 2f^3)y + ff'y^2 + 2f^2y^3$ **8-1**
$\qquad$ i. $y = u(z)v(x);\quad v = dz/dx;\quad 12v^2 = f(x);$
$u''(z) + uu' + 12u = u^3;\quad$ see (20).

ii. $y(u-1) = u'(x)$; $v(x) = 2u'' - u'f'/f - (u^2-1)f$;
$v'/v - f'/f = 2u'/(u-1)$; $v = C(u-1)^2 f$; $2u'u''/f - u'^2 f'/f^2$
$= [C(u-1)^2 + u^2 - 1]u'$; $u'^2 = f[C_1(u-1)^3 + (u-1)^2 + C_2]$;
see **A1-1-3**.

124 $yy'' = a$ **2-1**
       $p^2 = 2a \ln y + C$;   see **A1-1-3**.

125 $yy'' = y'^2$ **2-3, 4, 8-2**
       $p[yp'(y) - p] = 0$; $p = Cy$;   see **A1-1-2** and (153).
           $\ln y = C_1 + C_2 x$

126 $yy'' + y'^2 = 0$ **2-3, 4**
       $p[yp'(y) + p] = 0$; $py = C$;   see **A1-1-2** and (153).
           $y^2 = C_1 + C_2 x$

127 $yy'' = y'^2 - a^2$ **2-3**
       $ypp'(y) = p^2 - a^2$; $p^2 = C^2 y^2 - a^2$;   see **A1-1-2**.
        i. $C_1 y = a \cos (C_1 x + C_2)$; $a^2 > 0$.
        ii. $a^2 < 0$;   replace $\cos(C_1 x + C_2)$ by $\cosh (C_1 x + C_2)$.

128 $yy'' + y'^2 = a^2$ **2-3**
       $ypp'(y) = a^2 - p^2$; $C^2 y^2 (a^2 - p^2) = 1$;   see **A1-1-2**.
           $y^2 = C_1 + C_2 x + a^2 x^2$

129 $yy'' + y'^2 + y^2 = 0$ **2-3**
       $ypp'(y) + p^2 + y^2 = 0$; $y^2(2p^2 + y^2) = C$;   see (1-516) and (46).
           $y^2 = C_1 \sin(x\sqrt{2} + C_2)$

130 $yy'' + y'^2 + 2a^2 y^2 = 0$ **2-3**
       $ypp'(y) + p^2 + 2a^2 y^2 = 0$; $y^2(p^2 + a^2 y^2) = C$;   see (1-516) and (46).
           $y^2 = C_1 \cos 2ax + C_2 \sin 2ax$

131 $yy'' = y'^2 + a_0 + a_1 y + (a_2 + a_3 y)y^3$ **2-3, 8-2**
           $y'^2 = Cy^2 - a_0 - 2a_1 y + (2a_2 + a_3 y)y^3$
    See also (46).

132 $yy'' = y'^2 + a_0 + a_1 y + a_2 y^2 + a_3 y^3 + a_4 y^4$ **2-3**
       $ypp'(y) = p^2 + a_0 + a_1 y + a_2 y^2 + a_3 y^3 + a_4 y^4$;   see **A1-5**.
          $y'^2 = Cy^2 - a_0 - 2a_1 y + 2a_2 y^2 \ln y + 2a_3 y^3 + a_4 y^4$

133 $yy'' = y'^2 + yy'$ **2-3**
       $ypp'(y) = p^2 + yp$; $p = y \ln Cy$;   see (1-157).
          $y = C_1 \exp(C_2 e^x)$

134 $yy'' = y'^2 + e^x y(a_0 + a_1 y^2) + e^{2x}(a_2 + a_3 y^4)$ **5**
       $y(x) = u(z)$; $\ln z = x$; $z(uu'' - u'^2) + uu' = u(a_0 + a_1 u^2)$
       $+ z(a_2 + a_3 u^4)$;   see (202) and **9**.

135    $yy'' = y'^2 + y^2 \ln y$ **5, 2-3**
    $u(x) = \ln y;\ \ u''(x) - u = 0;\ \ \text{see (3-7)}.$
        $\ln y = C_1 \sinh(C_2 + x)$

136    $yy'' = y'^2 + y^2 \ln y - x^2 y^2$ **5**
    $\ln y = y(x);\ \ y^2(u'' - u + x^2) = 0;\ \ \text{see (3-7) and } \mathbf{B1\text{-}12\text{-}1}.$
        $\ln y = C_1 e^x + C_2 e^{-x} + 2 + x^2;\ \ y = 0$

137    $yy'' + y'^2 = y'$ **2-3**
    $p(yp' + p - 1) = 0;\ \ yp = C + y;\ \ \text{see } \mathbf{A1\text{-}1\text{-}2}.$
        $y = x + C_1 \ln(y + C_1) + C_2;\ \ y = C_0$

138    $yy'' = y'^2 - y'$ **2-3**
    $p(yp' - p + 1) = 0;\ \ p = 1 + Cy;\ \ \text{see } \mathbf{A1\text{-}1\text{-}2}.$
        $y + C_2 = C_1 e^{x/C_2}$

139    $yy'' = y'^2 + y' + y^2(fy + g')$ **8-2**
    $f = f(x);\ g(x) = -f'/f.\ \ \text{A first integral is}$
        $(y' - gy + 1)^2 = 2y^2(fy + \int f dx + C)$

140    $yy'' = y'^2 - 2y'$ **2-3**
    $p(yp' + 2 - p) = 0;\ \ p = Cy + 2;\ \ \text{see } \mathbf{A1\text{-}1\text{-}2}.$
        $C_1 y + C_2 e^{C_1 x} + 2 = 0;\ \ y = C_0$

141    $yy'' + y'^2 - xy' + y = 0$ **3-4**
    $y = x^2 u(z);\ z = \ln x;\ \ u'(z) = p;\ \ upp'(u) + p^2 + (7u - 1)p$
    $+ u(6u - 1) = 0;\ \ \text{see } \mathbf{A1\text{-}4\text{-}2}.$

142    $yy'' + y'^2 + axy' = 0$ **3-4**
    $y = x^2 u(z);\ \ z = \ln x;\ \ u'(z) = p;\ \ upp'(u) + p^2 + (a + 7u)p$
    $+ 2u(a + 3u) = 0;\ \ \text{see } \mathbf{A1\text{-}4\text{-}2}.$

143    $yy'' = y'^2 + f(x)y' - f'(x)y + y^3$ **8-2**
    A first integral is
        $(y' + f)^2 = 2y^2(y + \int f dx + C)$

144    $yy'' = y'^2 - f'y' + f''y - fy^3 + y^4$ **8-2**
    A first integral is
        $(y' - f')^2 = y^2[(y - f)^2 + C]$

145    $yy'' = y'^2 - ayy' - by^2$ **3-1, 2-3**
    $y' = yu(x);\ \ u'(x) + au + b = 0;\ \ \text{see } \mathbf{A1\text{-}1\text{-}3}.$
        $a \ln C_2 y = C_1 e^{-ax} - bx$

146    $yy'' = y'^2 + ayy' + by^2 \pm y^3$ **2-3**
    $ypp'(y) = p^2 + ayp + by^2 \pm y^3;\ \ \text{see } \mathbf{A1\text{-}4\text{-}2}.$

147    $yy'' = y'^2 + y^2 y'$ **2-3**
    $p(yp' - p - y^2) = 0;\ \ p = y(y + C);\ \ \text{see } \mathbf{A1\text{-}2}.$
        $y = C_2 e^{C_1 x}(y + C_1);\ \ y = C_0$

148    $yy'' = y'^2 + f(x)yy' + g(x)y^2$ **3-1**
      $y' = yu(x)$; $u'(x) = g + fu$;   see **A1-2**.

149    $yy'' = y'^2 + (f + gy^2)y' - y(f' - g'y^2)$ **8-2**
      A first integral, see **A1-3**, is $y' = y(C + gy) - f$

150    $yy'' = 2y'^2 + y^2$ **3-1, 2-3**
      $y' = yu(x)$; $u' = 1 + u^2$; $u = \tan(C + x)$;   see (1-55).
         $y = C_1 \csc(C_2 + x)$

151    $yy'' = 2(y'^2 - y^3)$ **2-3, 5**
      $ypp'(y) = 2(p^2 - y^3)$; $p^2 = y^3(Cy + 4)$;   see (1-516) and (158).
         $(C_1 + C_2x + x^2)y = 1$

152    $yy'' = 3y'^2 - 3yy' + y^2$ **3-1, 2-3**
      $y' = yu(x)$; $u' = 2u^2 - 3u + 1$; $(1 - 2Ce^x)u = 1 - Ce^x$;
      see (1-60).
         $y^2(2e^x - C_1) = C_2 e^{2x}$

153    $yy'' = ay'^2$ **4-1, 2-3, 3-1**
         i. $a = 1$;   see (125).
         ii. $a \neq 1$; $I = 1/yy'$; $y' = Cy^a$; $y^{1-a} = C_1x + C_2$.

154    $yy'' = ay'^2 + b$ **2-3**
         i. $a = 0$;   see (124).
         ii. $b = 0$;   see (153).
         iii. $a \neq 0$, $b \neq 0$; $ypp'(y) = ap^2 + b$;
             $(b + ap^2) = Cy^{2a}$;   see (1-515).
         iv.   For some other special cases, see (125), (126),
            (127), (128).

155    $yy'' = ay'^2 + by^3$ **2-3**
      $ypp'(y) = ap^2 + by^3$; $(3 - 2a)p^2 = Cy^{2a} + 2by^3$;   see (1-516).

156    $yy'' = ay'^2 + a_0 + a_1y + a_2y^2 + a_3y^3 + a_4y^4$ **2-3**
         i. $ypp'(y) = ap^2 + a_0 + a_1y + a_2y^2 + a_3y^3 + a_4y^4$;
            see **A1-5**.
         ii. $a = 1$;   see (132).

157    $yy'' = ay'^2 + byy' + cy^2$ **3-1, 2-3**
         i. $a = 1$;   see (145).
         ii. $y' = yu(x)$; $u' = (a - 1)u^2 + bu + c$. Let u_1, u_2 be
            the roots of $f(u) = (a - 1)u^2 + bu + c = 0$ and see
            (1-60). There are three cases.
         iii. $u_1 = u_2$; $y = e^{u_1 x}(C_1 + C_2x)^{1/(1-a)}$
         iv. $u_1 \neq u_2$, real; $y = (C_1 e^{u_1(1-a)x} + C_2 e^{u_2(1-a)x})^{1/(1-a)}$.
         v. $u_1 = h + ik$; $u_2 = h - ik$; h, k real;
      $y = C_1 e^{hx}[\cos k(a - 1)(x - C_2)]^{1/(1-a)}$.

158 $\quad yy'' = ay'^2 + a_1yy' + a_2y^2 + a_3y^{a+1}$ **5, 2-3**
$\qquad$ i. $\;\; a \neq 1; \;\; y = u^k(x); \;\; k = 1/(1-a);$
$ku'' - ka_1u' - a_2u = a_3;$ see **B1-12-1**.
$\qquad$ ii. $\;\; a = 1;$ see (145).

159 $\quad yy'' + ay'^2 + f(x)yy' + g(x)y^2 = 0$ **5, 2-3**
$y = u^{1/(a+1)}; \;\; u'' + fu' + (1+a)gu = 0; \;\;$ see **B1**.

160 $\quad yy'' + y'^3 = 0$ **2-3**
$p(yp' + p^2) = 0; \;\; \ln y = C + 1/p; \;\;$ see **A1-1-2**.
$\qquad x = C_1 + y \ln C_2y$

161 $\quad yy'' + y'^3 - y'^2 = 0$ **2-3**
$p[yp'(y) - p(1-p)] = 0; \;\; p(1+Cy) = Cy; \;\;$ see **A1-1-2**.
$\qquad y + C_1 \ln y = x + C_2$

162 $\quad yy'' = y'^2(1 - y' \sin y - yy' \cos y)$ **2-3**
$p[yp'(y) - p(1 - p \sin y - yp \cos y)] = 0; \quad 1/p = C/y + \sin y;$
see **A1-5**.
$\qquad x + C_1 = C_2 \ln y - \cos y$

163 $\quad (1-y)y'' + 2y'^2 = 0$ **2-3**
$p[(1-y)p'(y) + 2p] = 0; \;\; p = C(1-y)^2; \;\;$ see **A1-1-2**.
$\qquad y(C_1 + x) = C_2 + x$

164 $\quad (a+y)y'' = y'^2$ **2-3**
$p[(a+y)p'(y) - p] = 0; \;\; p = C(a+y); \;\;$ see **A1-1-2**.
$\qquad a + y = C_1e^{C_2x}$

165 $\quad (a+y)y'' + y'^2 = b$ **4**
A first integral is $(a+y)y' = bx + C_1;$ see **A1-1-2**.
$\qquad y(2a+y) = x(2C_1 + bx) + C_2$

166 $\quad (a+y)y'' + by'^2 = 0$ **2-3**
$\qquad$ i. $\;\; b = 1;$ see (164).
$\qquad$ ii. $\;\; b \neq -1; \;\; p[(a+y)p'(y) + bp] = 0;$
$p(a+y)^b = C;$ see **A1-1-2**.
$\qquad (a+y)^{b+1} = C_1x + C_2$

167 $\quad (x+y)y'' + y'^2 - y' = 0$ **4**
$\qquad (x+y)y' = C + 2y$

168 $\quad (x-y)y'' + 2y'(1+y') = 0$ **5, 3-3**
$\qquad$ i. A first integral is $\;\; (x-y)\sqrt{p} = C(1+p);$
see (170) and (2-374).
$\qquad (y - C_1)(x - C_1) = C_2$

169 $\quad (x-y)y'' = (1+y')(1+y'^2)$ **5**
$\qquad$ i. A first integral is $\;\; (x-y)^2(1+p^2) = C^2(1+p^2);$
see (170). A special solution is $(x+y) = C.$

ii. From (2-243), the general solution is
$$(x - C_2)^2 + (y - C_2)^2 = C_1^2$$

170    $(x - y)y'' = f(y')$ **5**

     i. $y' = u(x); \quad F(u) = e^\phi; \quad \phi(u) = \displaystyle\int \frac{(u-1)}{f(u)} du.$

A first integral is $(x - y)F(u) = C.$

     ii.   Special solutions are $y_i = C + a_i x$, where a_i is a root of $f(a) = 0.$

171    $2yy'' = y'^2$ **2-3**
$p(2yp' - p) = 0; \quad p^2 = Cy; \quad$ see **A1-1-2**.
     $y = (C_1 + C_2 x)^2$

172    $2yy'' + y'^2 + 1 = 0$ **2-3**
$2ypp'(y) + 1 + p^2 = 0; \quad y(1 + p^2) = C; \quad$ see (1-515) and (2-206);
$p = \cot u.$
     $x = C_1(u - \cos u \sin u) + C_2; \quad y = C_1 \sin^2 u$

173    $2yy'' = a + y'^2$ **2-3, 8-3**
$2ypp'(y) = p^2 + a; \quad$ see (1-515).
     $y'^2 + a = Cy$

174    $2yy'' = 8y^3 + y'^2$ **2-3, 8-3**
$2ypp'(y) = 8y^3 + p^2; \quad$ see (1-516).
     $y'^2 = y(C + 4y^2)$

175    $2yy'' = y'^2 + 4y^2 + 8y^3$ **2-3, 8-3**
$2ypp'(y) = p^2 + 4y^2 + 8y^3; \quad$ see (1-547).
     $y'^2 = y(C + 4y + 4y^2)$

176    $2yy'' = y'^2 + 4(x + 2y)y^2$ **5**
$y = \pm u^2(x); \quad u'' \mp 2u^3 - xu = 0; \quad$ see (11) and (8).

177    $2yy'' = y'^2 + (a + by)y^2$ **5**
$y = u^2(x); \quad 4u'' + au + bu^3 = 0; \quad$ see (12).

178    $2yy'' = y'^2 - 1 - 2xy^2 + ay^3$ **5, 8-3**
$a \neq 0; \quad y' = 2yu(x) - 1; \quad ay + 4u' + 4u^2 + 2x = 0;$
$4u'' - 4xu - 8u^3 = a - 2; \quad$ see (8).

179    $2yy'' = y'^2 + (ax + by)y^2$ **5**
$y = u^2(x); \quad 4u'' = u(ax + bu^2); \quad$ see (11).

180    $2yy'' = y'^2 + 3y^4$ **2-3, 8-3**
$2ypp'(y) = p^2 + 3y^4; \quad$ see (1-516).
     $y'^2 = y(C + y^3)$

181    $2yy'' = y'^2 - a^2 - 4(b - x^2)y^2 + 8xy^3 + 3y^4$ **8-3**
See **9**.

182     $2yy'' = y'^2 - 3fyy' - 2(f' + f^2)y^2 + 8y^3$ 5
A first integral is $(y' + fy)^2 = 4y(y^2 + Ce^{-2u})$; $u = \int f(x)dx$.

183     $2yy'' = y'^2 - 4y^2y' - 1 + 2f(x)y^2 - y^4$ 5, 8-3
$yu(x) = u'$; $u^2(2u'u''' - u''^2 - 2fu'^2 + u^2) = 0$.   Differentiate to
get $2u'(u^{iv} - f'u' - 2fu'' + u) = 0$; see **C1-2**. This is a special
case of **8-3** [27].

184     $2yy'' = 3y'^2$ 2-3
$p[2yp'(y) - 3p] = 0$; $p^2 = Cy^3$; see **A1-1-2**.
$\qquad (x + C_2)^2y = C_1$

185     $2yy'' = 3y'^2 + 4y^2$ 2-3
$2ypp'(y) = 3p^2 + 4y^2$; $p^2 = y^2(Cy - 4)$;   see (1-516).
$\qquad y = C_1 \sec^2(C_2 + x)$

186     $2yy'' = 3y'^2 + f(x)y^2$ 5
$yu^2(x) = 1$; $4u''(x) + fu = 0$; see **B1-2**.

187     $2yy'' = 6y'^2 + (1 - 3y^2)y^2$ 5, 2-3
$y\sqrt{u} = 1$; $2u'' + u + 6 = 0$; see **B1-12-1** and (158).
$\qquad y(3 + C_1 \cos x + C_2 \sin x)^{1/2} = 1$

188     $2yy'' = 6y'^2 - (1 + ay^3)y^2$ 2-3
$2ypp'(y) = 6p^2 - (1 + ay^3)y^2$;   see (1-548).
$\qquad 4y'^2 = (1 + 4ay^3 + Cy^4)y^2$

189     $2yy'' = y'^2(1 + y'^2)$ 2-3
$2ypp'(y) = p^2(1 + p^2)$; $p^2(1 - Cy) = Cy$; $p = \tan u$; see (2-211)
and (1-241).
$\qquad x = u + \cos u \sin u + C_2$; $C_1y = \sin^2 u$

190     $3yy'' = 2y'^2 + 36y^2$ 3-1, 2-3
$y' = yu$; $3u' = 36 - u^2$; see also (157).
$\qquad y = (C_1e^{2x} + C_2e^{-2x})^3$

191     $3yy'' = 5y'^2$ 2-3, 3-1
$p(3yp' - 5p) = 0$; $p^3 = Cy^5$; see **A1-1-2**.
$\qquad (C_1 + C_2x)^3y^2 = 1$

192     $4yy'' = 3y'^2 - 4y$ 5, 2-3, 8-3
$y = \pm u^2(x)$; $2uu'' - u'^2 + 1 = 0$; see (173).
$\qquad u'^2(x) = Cu \pm 1$

193     $4yy'' = 3y'^2 + 12y^3$ 5, 2-3, 8-3
$y = \pm u^2(x)$; $2uu'' = u'^2 \pm 3u^4$; see (180).
$\qquad u'^2(x) = u(C \pm u^3)$

194     $4yy'' = 3y'^2 + ay + by^2 + cy^3$ 5, 2-3, 8-3
$y = \pm u^2(x)$; $8uu'' - 4u'^2 \pm (a \pm bu^2 + cu^4) = 0$; see (156).

195 $\quad 5yy'' = y'^2$ $\qquad\qquad$ 2-3
$p(5yp'-p) = 0$; $\quad p^5 = Cy$; $\quad$ see **A1-1-2**.
$$C_1 y^4 = (C_2+x)^5$$

196 $\quad 12yy'' = 15y'^2 - 8y^3$ $\qquad\qquad$ 2-3
$12pp'(y) = 15p^2 - 8y^3$; $\quad 3p^2 = Cy^{5/2} - 8y^3$; $\quad$ see (1-516).
$$y[(C_1+x)^2 + C_2]^2 = 6C_2$$

197 $\quad ayy'' = (a-1)y'^2$ $\qquad\qquad$ 2-3, 8-3
$p[ayp' - (a-1)p] = 0$; $\quad$ see **A1-1-2**.
$$y = (C_1 x + C_2)^a$$

198 $\quad a(a+2)^2 yy'' = (a-1)(a+2)^2 y'^2 + a(a+2)^2 f(x) y^2 y'$
$\qquad\qquad + a^2(a+2)f'y^3 - a^2 f^2 y^4$ $\qquad\qquad$ 5, 8-3
$u(x) = ye^\phi$; $\quad \phi(x) = -a/(a+2)\int yf(x)dx$; $\quad auu''(x) = (a-1)u'^2$;
see (197). Let $y = 1/w(x)$; $\quad w'(x) + u'u/w + af/(a+2) = 0$; $\quad$ see
A1-2.
$$y[aX(x) + C_2] + (a+2)(x+C_1)^a = 0$$
$$X(x) = \int (x+C_1)^a f(x)dx$$

199 $\quad xyy'' + xy'^2 + yy' = 0$ $\qquad\qquad$ 4
$xyy' = C$; $\quad$ see **A1-1-2**.
$$y^2 = C_1 \ln x + C_2$$

200 $\quad xyy'' + xy'^2 = yy'$ $\qquad\qquad$ 4
$xyy' = C + y^2$; $\quad$ see **A1-1-2**.
$$y^2 = C_1 x^2 + C_2$$

201 $\quad xyy'' = xy'^2 - yy'$ $\qquad\qquad$ 3-1
$y' = yu(x)$; $\quad xu' + u = 0$; $\quad ux = C$; $\quad$ see **A1-1-2**.
$$y = C_2 x^{C_1}$$

202 $\quad xyy'' = xy'^2 - yy' + x(a_0 + a_1 y^4) + y(a_2 + a_3 y^2)$ $\qquad\qquad$ 5, 8-2
$y(x) = u(z)$; $\quad z = \ln x$; $\quad uu''(z) = u'^2 + e^{2z}(a_0 + a_1 u^4)$
$+ e^z u(a_2 + a_3 u^2)$; $\quad$ see (134) and **9**.

203 $\quad xyy'' + xy'^2 + 2yy' = 0$ $\qquad\qquad$ 4
$2xyy' + y^2 = C$; $\quad$ see (1-543).
$$x(C_1 + y^2) = C_2$$

204 $\quad xyy'' + xy'^2 = 3yy'$ $\qquad\qquad$ 3-2, 3-1
$y(x) = u(z)$; $\quad z = \ln x$; $\quad p[up'(u) + p - 4u] = 0$; $\quad p = 2u + C/u$;
see (1-157).
$$y^2 = C_1 + C_2 x^4$$

205 $\quad xyy'' + xy'^2 + ayy' + f(x) = 0$ $\qquad\qquad$ 5
$y^2 + u(x)$; $\quad xu'' + au' + 2f(x) = 0$; $\quad$ see **1-2**.

206 $\quad xyy'' = xy'^2 + ayy' \pm xy^3$ $\hspace{3cm}$ **5**
$\qquad$ i. A solution is $x^2 y = \pm 2(1+a)$.
$\qquad$ ii. $x^2 y = u(z);\quad z = \ln x;\quad uu''(z) = u'^2 + (1-a)uu'$
$-2(1+a)u^2 \pm u^3;\quad$ see (146).

207 $\quad xyy'' = xy'^2 + ayy' \pm b^2 xy^3$ $\hspace{2.5cm}$ **5**
$\qquad$ i. $u(x) = \ln y;\quad xu'' = au' + b^2 xe^u;\quad$ see (81).
$\qquad$ ii. $y(x) = u(z);\quad z = bx;\quad zuu'' = zu'^2 + auu' \pm zu^3;$
$\qquad$ see (206).

208 $\quad xyy'' + 2xy'^2 + yy' = 0$ $\hspace{4cm}$ **3-1**
$y' = yu(x);\quad xu' + 3xu^2 + u = 0;\quad xu(C + 3\ln x) = 1;\quad$ see
(1-185).
$\qquad\qquad y^3 = C_1 + C_2 \ln x$

209 $\quad xyy'' - 2xy'^2 + yy' = 0$ $\hspace{4cm}$ **3-1**
$y' = yu(x);\quad xu' + u - xu^2 = 0;\quad xu(C - \ln x) = 1;\quad$ see (1-175).
$\qquad\qquad 1/y = C_1 + C_2 \ln x$

210 $\quad xyy'' - 2xy'^2 - yy' = 0$ $\hspace{4cm}$ **3-1**
$y' = yu(x);\quad xu' - u - xu^2 = 0;\quad u(C - x^2) = 2x;\quad$ see (1-177).
$\qquad\qquad y(C_1 - x^2) = C_2$

211 $\quad xyy'' = 2xy'^2 - (1+y)y'$ $\hspace{3cm}$ **3-2**
$y(x) = u(z);\quad z = \ln x;\quad p[up'(u) + 1 - 2p] = 0;\quad$ see **A1-1-2**;
$C(1+2p) + u^2 = 0;\quad 2C_1 u(z) = \tan(C_2 - C_1 z).$

212 $\quad xyy'' + 2xy'^2 + ayy' = 0$ $\hspace{3cm}$ **3-1**
$\qquad$ i. $a = 1;\quad$ see (208).
$\qquad$ ii. $a \neq 1;\quad y' = yu(x);\quad xu' + au + 3xu^2 = 0;$
$u(Cx^a + 3x) = 1 - a;\quad$ see (1-185).
$\qquad\qquad y^3 = C_1 + C_2 x^{1-a}$

213 $\quad xyy'' - 2xy'^2 + ayy' = 0$ $\hspace{3cm}$ **3-1**
$\qquad$ i. $a = 1;\quad$ see (209).
$\qquad$ ii. $a \neq 1;\quad y' = yu(x);\ xu' + au - xu^2 = 0;$
$u(Cx^a - x) = 1 - a;\quad$ see (1-185).
$\qquad\qquad 1/y = C_1 + C_2 x^{1-a}$

214 $\quad xyy'' - 4xy'^2 + 4yy' = 0$ $\hspace{3cm}$ **3-1**
$y' = yu(x);\quad xu' + 4u - 3xu^2 = 0;\ ux(3 + Cx^3) = 3;\quad$ see (1-185).
$\qquad\qquad y^3(C_1 + C_2 x^3) = x^3$

215 $\quad xyy'' + ay'(xy' - y) = 0$ $\hspace{3cm}$ **3-1**
$\qquad$ i. $(a+1) = 0;\quad$ see (201).
$\qquad$ ii. $(a+1) \neq 0;\quad y' = yu(x);\quad xu' - au + (1+a)xu^2 = 0;$
$\qquad u(x + Cx^{-a}) = 0;\quad$ see (1-185).
$\qquad y^{1+a} = C_1 + C_2 x^{1+a}$

216   $x(x+y)y''+xy'^2+(x-y)y' = y$ **3-4, 3-3**
$y = xu(z);\quad z = \ln x;\quad p[(1+u)p'+2(1+u)+p] = 0;$
$(1+u)p = C-u(2+u);$ see **A1-2**.
$$(x+y)^2 = C_1+C_2x^2$$

217   $2xyy'' = xy'^2-yy'$ **3-1**
$y' = yu(x);\quad 2xu'+u(1+xu) = 0;\quad u(C\sqrt{x}+x) = 1;\quad$ see
(1-185) and (215).
$$y = C_1(C_2+\sqrt{x})^2$$

218   $x(x+2y)y''+2xy'^2+4(x+y)y'+x^2+2y = 0$ **4**
A first integral is $x(x+2y)y'+x^3/3+2xy+y^2 = C;$ see (1-560).
$$12xy(x+y) = C_1+C_2x-x^4$$

219   $x^2yy''+(xy'-y)^2 = 0$ **5**
    i. $y = ux;\quad xuu''+2uu'+xu'^2 = 0;\quad$ see (203).
        $$y^2 = x(C_1+C_2x).$$
    ii. $y^2 = u(x);\quad x^2u''-2xu'+2u = 0;\quad$ see **B1-3-1**.

220   $x^2yy''+(xy'-y)^2 = 3y^2$ **5, 4**
$y^2 = u(x);\quad x^2u''-2xu'-4u = 0;\quad$ see **B1-3-1**.
$$xy^2 = C_1+C_2x^5$$

221   $x^2yy'' = 2x^2y'^2+axyy'+ay^2$ **3-1**
$y' = yu(x);\quad x^2u' = a+xu(a+xu);\quad$ see (1-271); $\quad xu(Cx^{a-1}-1)$
$= 1-aCx^{a-1}.$
$$y(C_1x+C_2x^a) = 1$$

222   $x^2yy''+ax^2y'^2+bxyy'+cy^2 = 0$ **3-1**
$y' = yu(x);\quad x^2u'+c+bxu+(1+a)x^2u^2 = 0;\quad$ see (1-271).

223   $x^2(1-y)y''+2x^2y'^2-2x(1-y)y'+2y(1-y)^2 = 0$ **5, 3-2**
$(1-y)u(x) = 1;\quad x^2u''-2xu'+2u = 2;\quad$ see **B1-12-2**.
$$y(1+C_1x+C_2x^2) = x(C_1+C_2x)$$

224   $x^2(x+y)y'' = (xy'-y)^2$ **3-4, 3-3**
$y = xu(z);\quad z = \ln x;\quad p[(1+u)p'+1+u-p] = 0$
$p = (1+u)[C-\ln(1+u)];$ see **A1-2**.
$$C_1(x+y) = xe^{C_2/x}$$

225   $x^2(x-y)y''+(xy'-y)^2 = 0$ **3-4, 3-3**
$y = xu(z);\quad z = \ln x;\quad p[(1-u)p'+1-u+p] = 0;$
$p = (u-1)[C-\ln(u-1)];$ see **A1-2**.
$$C_1(x-y) = xe^{C_2/x}$$

226   $x^2(x-y)y'' = a(xy'-y)^2$ **3-4, 3-3**
    i. $(a+1) = 0;\quad$ see (225).

ii. $(a+1) \neq 0$; $y = xu(z)$; $z = \ln x$;
$p[(1-u)p' + 1 - u - ap] = 0$;
$(a+1)p = C(1-u)^{-a} + 1 - u$; see **A1-2**.
$(x-y)^{a+1} = x^a(C_1 + C_2 x)$

227    $2x^2yy'' = x^2y'^2 - y^2$ **3-4, 3-3**
$y = xu(z)$; $z = \ln x$; $p(2up' - p) = 0$; $p^2 = Cu$; see **A1-1-2**.
$y = x(C_1 + C_2 \ln x)^2$

228    $2x^2yy'' = x^2y'^2 + 2xyy' - 4y^2$ **5**
$y = u^2(x)$; $x^2u'' - xu' + u = 0$; see **B1-3-1**.
$y = x^2(C_1 + C_2 \ln x)^2$

229    $x^3yy'' + x^3y'^2 + 6x^2yy' + 3xy^2 = a$ **4**
A first integral is $x^3yy' + 3x^2y^2/2 = ax + C_1$; see **A1-7-1**.
$x^3y^2 = ax^2 + C_1x + C_2$

230    $x(1+x)^2yy'' = x(1+x)^2y'^2 - 2(1+x^2)yy' + a(2+x)y^2$ **3-1**
$y' = yu(x)$; $x(1+x)^2u' + 2(1+x)^2u - a(2+x) = 0$; see **A1-2**.
$y = C_1(1+x)^a e^{C_2/x}$

231    $8(1-x^3)yy'' + 4(1-x^3)y'^2 - 12x^2yy' + 3xy^2 = 0$ **5**
$y = u^2(z)$; $z = x^3$; $48z(1-z)u'' + 8(4-7z)u' + u = 0$;
see (3-410).

232    $\sqrt{a^2+x^2}(yy'' + by'^2) = yy'$ **3-1**
$y' = yu(x)$; $\sqrt{a^2+x^2}[u' + (1+b)u^2] = u$; see **A1-5**.

233    $\sqrt{a^2-x^2}(xyy'' - xy'^2 - yy') = bxy'^2$ **3-1**
$y' = yu(x)$; $\sqrt{a^2-x^2}(xu' - u) = bxu^2$; see **A1-5**.

234    $f_0(x)yy'' + f_1(x)y'^2 + f_2(x)yy' + f_3(x)y^2 = 0$ **3-1**
$y' = yu(x)$; $f_0u' + (f_0 + f_1)u^2 + f_2u + f_3 = 0$; see **A1-3**.

235    $4f(x)yy'' = 3fy'^2 + (2f' - 6fy^2)y' + 4f^2y + 4fgy^2 + 2f'y^3 - fy^4$ **8-3**
$y\phi(x) = f(x)$; $\phi(x) = 2u' + u^2 - f'u/f - g$; $vu = v'$; $v(x)$ is the
general solution of

$$v'''(x) = \frac{3f'}{2f}v'' + \left(g + \frac{f''}{f} - \frac{f'^2}{f^2}\right)v' + \frac{1}{2}\left(g' + f - \frac{f'g}{f}\right)v; \text{ see } \textbf{C1-2}.$$

236    $y^2y'' = a$ **2-1**
$p^2 = C - 2a/y$; $y = (Cy - 2a)x'^2(y)$.

237    $y^2y'' + yy'^2 + ax = 0$ **5**
$yu'(x) = 1$; $u'u''' = 3u''^2 + axu'^5$; see (6-13).

238    $y^2y'' + yy'^2 = a + bx$ **5**
i. $a = 0$; see (237).
ii. $a \neq 0$; $y^2 = u(x)$; $u''\sqrt{\bar{u}} = 2(a+bx)$; see (273).

239     $(1+y^2)y'' + (1-2y)y'^2 = 0$ **2-3, 4-1**
        i. $p[(1+y^2)p' + (1-2y)p] = 0$;   see **A1-1-2**.
      $y = \tan \ln(C_1 + C_2 x)$
       ii. $I(y) = 1/(1+y^2)$.

240     $(1+y^2)y'' = 3yy'^2$ **2-3**
    $p[(1+y^2)p'(y) - 3yp] = 0$; $p = C(1+y^2)^{3/2}$;   see **A1-1-2**.
      $y^2 = (1+y^2)(C_1 + C_2 x)^2$

241     $(1+y^2)y'' = (a+3y)y'^2$ **2-3**
    $p[(1+y^2)p' - (a+3y)p] = 0$;   see (1-297).
      $x = C_1 e^{-at}(\sin t - a \cos t) + C_2$; $y = \tan t$

242     $(1+y^2)y'' + y'(1+y'^2) = 0$ **2-3**
    $p[(1+y^2)p' + 1 + p^2] = 0$; $p(1+Cy) = C - y$;   see **A1-1-2**.
      $x = C_1 + C_2 y - (1+C_2^2)\ln(C_2 + y)$

243     $(x+y^2)y'' + 2yy'^2 + 2y' = a$ **4**
    A first integral is $(x+y^2)y' + y = ax + C_1$;   see (1-599).
      $2y(3x+y^2) = ax^2 + C_1 x + C_2$

244     $(x+y^2)y'' = 2(x-y^2)y'^3 - y'(1+4yy')$ **5**
    $y(x) = u(z)$; $z = x+y^2$; $zu'' + u' = 0$; $zu' = C$;   see **1-2**.
      $y = C_1 + C_2 \ln(x+y^2)$

245     $(x^2+y^2)y'' = (1+y'^2)(xy'-y)$ **5, 3-3**
    $x = r \cos\theta$, $y = r \sin\theta$, $rr''(\theta) = r'^2$;   see (125).
      $\ln r = C_1 + C_2\theta$

246     $(x^2+y^2)y'' = 2(1+y'^2)(xy'-y)$ **5, 3-3**
    $x = r \cos\theta$, $y = r \sin\theta$, $r''(\theta) + r = 0$;   see (3-6).
      $x^2 + y^2 + C_1 x + C_2 y = 0$

247     $2y(1-y)y'' = (1-2y)y'^2$ **1-2**
    $2y(1-y)p' = (1-2y)p^2$;   see **A1-1-2**.
      $p^2 = Cy(1-y)$

248     $2y(1-y)y'' = (1-2y)y'^2 + y(1-y)y'f(x)$ **5**
        i. $f(x) = 0$;   see (247).
       ii. $f(x) \neq 0$;   use the first integral from (247) but
           regard C as a variable parameter. The result is
      $y'^2 = Cy(1-y)e^{\phi}$; $\phi(x) = \int f(x)dx$

249     $2y(1-y)y'' = (1-3y)y'^2$ **2-3, 8-4**
    $p[2y(1-y)p' - (1-3y)p] = 0$; $p^2 = 4C^2 y(1-y)^2$;   see **A1-1-2**.
      $y = \tanh^2(C_1 + C_2 x)$

250     $2y(1-y)y'' = (1-3y)y'^2 + 4y(f+gy)y'$
          $+ 4(1-y)y^2(f^2 - f' - g^2 - g') = 0$ **5**

Use the first integral of (249), regarding C as a variable parameter. The result is

$$[p - 2(f+g)y]^2 = Cy(1-y)^2 e^{2\phi}; \quad \phi(x) = \int(f-g)dx$$

251    $2y(1-y)y'' = (1-3y)y'^2 - 4y(f+gy)y'$ **8-4**
$\qquad\qquad - (1-y)^3(F^2 - G^2 y^2) - 4(1-y)y^2(f^2 + f' - g^2 + g') = 0$
$G' = 2gG(x); \ f' + 2fF(x) = 0; \ y' + 2(f+g) = (1-y)(2u+yG);$
$u' = (2v + F^2)/4 + (G-2f)u - u^2; \ v' = 2(g-f)v; \ $ see **A1-3**.
Provided that $F(x) \neq 0, \ G(x) \neq 0; \ v'/v = F'/F + G'/G;$
$v = CF(x)G(x).$

252    $3y(1-y)y'' = 2(1-2y)y'^2$ **2-3**
$\quad\ p[3y(1-y)p' - 2(1-2y)p] = 0; \ $ see **A1-1-2** and (2-274).
$\qquad\ p^3 = Cy^2(1-y)^2$

253    $4y(1-y)y'' = 3(1-2y)y'^2$ **2-3, 8-6**
$\quad\ p[4y(1-y)p' - 3(1-2y)p] = 0; \qquad p^4 = 256 C^4 y^3 (1-y)^3; \quad$ see
A1-1-2.
$\qquad (y-1) = y\mathscr{P}^2(C_1 + C_2 x; \ 4, \ 0)$

254    $xy^2 y'' = a$ **5**
$\quad\ y = xu(x); \ u^2(x^4 u'' + 2x^3 u') = a; \ $ see (119), with $X(x) = x;$
$\quad\ a = b = 0; \ c = 1.$
$\qquad\ x^4 u'(x) + a/u^2 = C$

255    $xy^2 y'' = xyy'^2 + (a - y^2)y'$ **3-2**
$\quad\ p(u^2 p' - up - a) = 0; \ 2pu = Cu^2 - a; \ $ see (1-253).
$\qquad\ C_1 y^2 = a + C_2 x^{C_1}$

256    $x^2 y^2 y'' = (x^2 + y^2)(xy' - y)$ **3-3, 3-4**
$\quad\ y = xu(z); \ z = \ln x; \ p(u^2 p' - 1) = 0; \ p = C - 1/u; \ $ see **A1-1-1**.
$\qquad\ \ln x = C_1 y/x + C_1^2 \ln(y - C_1 x) - C_1^2 \ln x + C_2$

257    $(a^2 - x^2)(a^2 - y^2)y'' + (a^2 - x^2)yy'^2 = x(a^2 - y^2)y'$ **5**
$\quad\ y' = u(x)\sqrt{a^2 - y^2}; \quad (a^2 - x^2)u' = ux; \quad u^2(a^2 - x^2) = C;$
$\quad\ (a^2 - x^2)y'^2 = C(a^2 - y^2); \ $ see **A1-1-2** and **A2-2-1**.

$$\sin^{-1}\frac{y}{a} = C_1 + C_2 \sin^{-1}\frac{x}{a}$$

258    $2x^2 y(1-y)y'' - x^2(1-3y)y'^2 + 2xy(1-y)y'$
$\qquad\qquad + (a_0 + a_1 y^2)(1-y)^3 + a_2 xy^2(1-y) + a_3 x^2 y^2(1+y) = 0$ **8-4**
$\quad\ $ See **9**.

259    $x^3 y^2 y'' + (x+y)(xy' - y)^3 = 0$ **3-3, 3-4**
$\quad\ y = xu(z); \ z = \ln x; \ p[u^2 p' + u^2 + (1+u)p^2] = 0; \ $ see **A1-3**.

260     $y^3 y'' = a^2$ **2-1**

$y^2 p^2 = C y^2 - a^2$; see **A2-1-2-1**.

$$C_1 y^2 + a^2 + (C_1 x + C_2)^2 = 0; \quad y^2 = 2aix + C_0$$

261     $y(1 + y^2)y'' + (1 - 3y^2)y'^2 = 0$ **2-3**

$p[y(1 + y^2)p' + (1 - 3y^2)p] = 0$; $yp = C(1 + y^2)^2$;   see **A1-1-2**.

$$(C_1 x + C_2)(1 + y^2) = 1$$

262     $2y^3 y'' + y^2 y'^2 = 2$ **2-3**

$2y^3 pp' + y^2 p^2 = 2$; $y^2 p^2 = Cy - 2$;   see **A1-5**.

$$4(C_1 y - 2)(C_1 y + 4)^2 = 9C_1^4 (x + C_2)^2$$

263     $2y(1 - y)(a - y)y'' + [y(1 - y) + y(a - y) - (1 - y)(a - y)]y'^2$

$\qquad\qquad = [a_0 y^2 (1 - y)^2 (a - y)^2 + a_1 y^2 (1 - y)^2 + a_2 y^2 (a - y)^2$

$\qquad\qquad + a_3 (1 - y)^2 (a - y)^2]$ **8-8**

$y'^2 = [(a_0 + C)y(1 - y)(a - y) + a_1 y(1 - y)$

$\qquad + a_2 y(a - y) - a_3 (1 - y)(a - y)].$

264     $2(a - y)(b - y)(c - y)y'' + [(a - y)(b - y) + (a - y)(c - y)$

$\qquad\qquad + (b - y)(c - y)]y'^2 = [a_0 (a - y)^2 (b - y)^2 (c - y)^2$

$\qquad\qquad + a_1 (b - y)^2 (c - y)^2 + a_2 (a - y)^2 (c - y)^2$

$\qquad\qquad + a_3 (a - y)^2 (b - y)^2]$ **5**

$(b - c)(c - y)u(x) = (a - c)(b - y);$ $2u(1 - u)(\alpha - u)u''$

$+ [u(1 - u) + u(\alpha - u) - (1 - u)(\alpha - u)]u'^2 = [\beta_0 u^2 (1 - u)^2 (a - u)^2$

$+ \beta_1 u^2 (1 - u)^2 + \beta_2 u^2 (\alpha - u)^2 + \beta_3 (1 - u)^2 (\alpha - u)^2]$; see (263). The constants α, β_i are functions of a, b, c.

265     $2xy(1 - x)(1 - y)(x - y)y'' = x(1 - x)(x - 2xy - 2y + 3y^2)y'^2$

$\qquad\qquad + 2y(1 - y)(x^2 + y - 2xy)y' - y^2 (1 - y^2)$ **5**

A special case of **8-8** [50]; see (266) and (267). The solution is $y = \phi(C_1 w_1 + C_2 w_2; x)$, where $\phi(u, x)$ is the elliptic function defined by

$$u = \int_0^\phi \frac{dy}{\sqrt{y(1 - y)(x - y)}}$$

with periods $2w_1(x)$, $2w_2(x)$.

266     $2xy(1 - x)(1 - y)(x - y)y'' = x(1 - x)(x - 2xy - 2y + 3y^2)y'^2$

$\qquad\qquad + 2y(1 - y)(x^2 + y - 2xy)y' - y^2 (1 - y^2)$

$\qquad\qquad + f(x)[y(1 - y)(x - y)]^{3/2}$ **5**

    i. $f(x) = 0$;   see (265).

   ii. $f(x) \neq 0$;   find any solution of

$\qquad\qquad 4x(1 - x)u'' - 4(1 - 2x)u' - u = f(x)$;   see **B1-12-3**.

$\qquad\qquad$ Then, $y = \phi(u + C_1 w_1 + C_2 w_2; x)$ where $\phi(u, x)$ is the elliptic function defined in (265).

267    $2x^2y(1-x)^2(1-y)(x-y)y' = x^2(1-x)^2(x-2xy-2y+3y^2)y'^2$
$+2xy(1-x)(1-y)(x^2-2xy+y)y'$
$+a_0x(1-y)^2(x-y)^2+a_1(1-x)y^2(x-y)^2$
$+(a_2-1)xy^2(1-x)(1-y)^2+a_3y^2(x-y)^2(1-y)^2$ **8-8**

    i. If all $a_i = 0$; see (265).
    ii. At least one $a_i \neq 0$; see **9**.

268    $(1-y^2)(1-a^2y^2)y'' + b\sqrt{(1-y^2)(1-a^2y^2)}y'^2$
$+(1+a^2-2a^2y^2)y = 0$ **5**
$a, b \neq 0$ and, in terms of the Jacobi elliptic function,
    $y = \mathrm{sn}[1/b \ln(C_1x-C_2); a]$

269    $(x^2+y^2)^2y'' + a^2y = 0$ **4-1**
$I(x, y) = 2x(xy'-y)/r^4$; $r^2 = x^2+y^2$; $dF_2 = (a^2x^2+r^4)y'$
$-a^2xy = 0$; $F_2 = y^2-C-a^2x^2/r^2$; see (1-711). A first integral
is
    $(xy'-y)^2 = C+a^2x^2/r^2$

270    $(X+y^2)^2y'' + Ay = 0$; $X(x) = a+2bx+cx^2$ **4-1, 5**
    i. $I(x, y)(X+y^2)^2 = Xy'-X'y/2$. A first integral is
        $(X+y^2)(Xy'^2-X'yy'+cy^2+C) = Ay^2$
    ii. $y(x) = u(x)\sqrt{X}$. The same first integral results.

271    $f_0(y)y'' + f_1(y)y'^2 + f_2(y)y' + f_3(y) = 0$ **6**
The coefficients are polynomials in y, not necessarily all of the
same degree. The coefficients of y in $f_k(y)$ are functions of x;
perhaps constants. Special cases are treated in **7, 8, 9, 10**.

272    $y''\sqrt{y} = a$ **2-1**
$pp'\sqrt{y} = a$; $p^2 = 4a\sqrt{y}+C$; see **A1-1-2**.
    $3x\sqrt{a} = (\sqrt{y}-2C_1)(\sqrt{y}+C_1)^{1/2}+C_2$

273    $y''\sqrt{y} = 2(a+bx)$ **4-1**
$I(x, y) = y'^2/\sqrt{y}-4(a+bx)$; $F_1 = p^3/3-4(a+bx)p\sqrt{y}$;
$F_2 = 8[by^{3/2}+(a+bx)^3/b]/3-C$; $y'^3-12y'(a+bx)\sqrt{y}$
$+8by^{3/2}+8(a+bx^3)/b = C$; see also (238).

274    $X^3(x, y)y'' = 1$ **5**
$X^2(x, y) = a_0+2a_1x+a_2x^2+2a_3y+2a_4xy+a_5y^2$.   Let a_5X^2
$=u^2+X_1^2$; $u = a_3+a_4x+a_5y$; $X_1^2 = b_0+2b_1x+b_2x^2$. where the
b_i are functions of the a_i. Then, $u''(x) = a_5^{5/2}(u^2+X_1^2)^{-3/2}$;
$X_1^3u''(x) = a_5^{5/2}f(u/X_1)$, where $f(u/X_1) = (u/X_1+1)^{-3/2}$; see (119).

275    $(a_0+a_1\sin^2y)y'' + a_1y'^2\cos y \sin y + a_2y(a_3+a_1\sin^2y) = 0$ **5**
$y'^2 = u(y)$; $(a_0+a_1\sin^2y)u'(y) + 2a_2y(a_3+a_1\sin^2y)$
$+a_1u\sin 2y = 0$; see (1-417).

276 $\quad y(1-\ln y)y'' + (1+\ln y)y'^2 = 0$ $\qquad\qquad$ 5

$\quad u(x) = \ln y;\quad (1-u)u'' + 2u'^2 = 0;\quad$ see (166).

$\qquad (x+C_2)\ln y = x+C_1$

277 $\quad f(y)y'' = f'(y)y'^2 - g(x)f(y)y' - h(x)f^2(y)$ $\qquad$ 5

$\quad y(x) = u(z)$, where z is a solution of $z''(x) + g(x)z' + h(x) = 0$;

see **B1-2**;$\quad z'^2 f(u)u''(z) = z'^2 f'(u)u'^2 + h(x)f(u)(u'-f)$. $\quad$ **A**

solution of the last equation is $u'(z) = f(u)$.

278 $\quad f(y)y'' = f'(y)y'^2 + f^2(y)F(x, y'/f)$ $\qquad\qquad$ 5

$\quad f(y)u(x) = y';\quad u' = F(x, u);$ see **A1**.

279 $\quad f(y)y'' + af'(y)y'^2 + g(y) = 0$ $\qquad\qquad$ 5, 4-1

$\qquad$ i.$\quad$ Divide by $f(y)$ and see (49).

$\qquad$ ii.$\quad I(x, y) = \pm 2|f|^{2a-1}y'$, using the $(\pm)$ sign for

$f(y) \gtrless 0$. The sum of the first two terms is the derivative of

$|f|^{2a}y'^2$; a first integral is

$$|f|^{2a}y'^2 \pm 2\int |f|^{2a-1}g(y)dy = C$$

280 $\quad y'y'' = a^2 x$ $\qquad\qquad$ 1-2

$\quad p^2 = C + a^2 x^2.$

$\qquad 2y = a[x\sqrt{x^2+C_1^2} + C_1^2 \ln(x+\sqrt{x^2+C_1^2})] + C_2$

281 $\quad y'y'' = x^2 yy' + xy^2$ $\qquad\qquad$ 4

$\qquad y'^2 = C + x^2 y^2$

282 $\quad (y^2 + 2x^2 y')y'' + 2(x+y)y'^2 + xy' + y = 0$ $\qquad$ 4

$\qquad (y^2 + x^2 y')y' + xy = C$

283 $\quad x^3 y'y'' + ay^2 = 0$ $\qquad\qquad$ 3-1

$\quad yu(x) = y';\quad x^3 u(u' + u^2) + a = 0;$ see **A1-4-2**.

284 $\quad f_1 y'y'' + f_2 yy'' + f_3 y'^2 + f_4 yy' + f_5 y^2 = 0$ $\qquad$ 3-1

$\quad f_i = f_i(x);\quad f_1(x) \neq 0;\quad yu(x) = y';\quad (f_2 + f_1 u)u' + f_5$

$\quad + f_4 u + (f_2 + f_3)u^2 + f_1 u^3 = 0;\quad$ see **A1-4-2**.

285 $\quad 3yy'y'' = y'^3 - 1$ $\qquad\qquad$ 2-3

$\quad 3yp^2 p'(y) = p^3 - 1;\quad p^3 = Cy + 1;\quad$ see **A1-1-2**.

$\qquad 27C_1(y+C)^2 = 8(x+C_2)^3$

286 $\quad (x^2 + 2y^2 y')y'' + 2yy'^3 + 3xy' + y = 0$ $\qquad$ 4

$\qquad (x^2 + y^2 y')y' + xy = C$

287 $\quad (x - y'^2)y'' = x^2 - y'$ $\qquad\qquad$ 1-2

$\quad (x - p^2)p' = x^2 - p;\quad$ see (1-600).

$\qquad p^3 - 3px + x^3 = C$

288 $\quad (y^2 + y'^2)y'' + y^3 = 0$ $\qquad\qquad$ 2-3

$\quad y' = yu(x);\quad (1+u^2)u' + 1 + u^2 + u^4 = 0;\quad$ see **A1-1-3**.

$\qquad u\sqrt{3} = (1-u^2)\tan(C - x\sqrt{3})$

289    $[y'^2 + a(xy' - y)]y'' = b$ **5**
Differentiate with respect to x and eliminate $(xy' - y)$ with the
given differential equation. The result, with $y'(x) = p$, see
(56), is
$$bp'' + (2p + ax)p'^3 = 0$$

290    $4yy'^2 y'' = y'^4 + 3$ **2-3**
$4y^3 pp'(y) = p^4 + 3;$ $p^4 = Cy - 3;$ see **A1-1-2**.
$$256C_1(y - C_1)^3 = 243(x - C_2)^4$$

291    $f(y')y'' + g(y)y' + h(x) = 0$ **5**
$y' = p(x);$ $f(p)dp + g(y)dy + h(x)dx = 0.$ A first integral is
$$\int f(p)dp + \int g(y)dy + \int h(x)dx = C$$

292    $y''^2 = a + by$ **2-1**
$$3by'^2 = 4(a + by)^{3/2} + C$$

293    $y''^2 = a + by'^2$ **2-2**
$$by = \sqrt{a}\,\cosh(C_1 + x\sqrt{b}) + C_2$$

294    $y''^2 - xy'' + y' = 0$ **1-2**
$p'^2 - xp' + p = 0;$ see (2-35).
$$2y = C_1 x^2 - 2C_1^2 x + C_2; \quad 12y = C_0 + x^3$$

295    $a^2 y''^2 = (1 + y'^2)^3$ **2-2**
$a^2 p'^2 = (1 + p^2)^3;$ see **A1-1-3**.
$$(x + C_1)^2 + (y + C_2)^2 = a^2$$

296    $xy''^2 - 2y'y'' + ax = 0$ **1-2**
$xp'^2 - 2pp' + ax = 0;$ $2Cp = a + C^2 x^2;$ see (2-120).
$$2C_1 y = C_1^2 x^3/3 + ax + C_2; \quad 2y = C_0 + x^2$$

297    $(xy'' - y')^2 = 1 + y'^2$ **1-2**
$(1 - x^2)p'^2 + 2xpp' + 1 - p^2 = 0;$ $(p - Cx)^2 = 1 + C^2;$ see (2-175).
$$2y = C_1 x^2 + 2x\sqrt{1 + C_1^2} + C_2;$$
$$2y = x\sqrt{1 - x^2} + \sin^{-1}x + C_0$$

298    $2(1 + x^2)y''^2 - xy''(x + 4y') + 2(x + y')y' = 2\zeta$ **5, 11**
    i.   Differentiate and get
$$y'''[4(1 + x^2)y'' - 4xy' - x^2] = 0$$
The third-order equation, see (5-1), gives the general solution
$$y = C_1(x^2 + 4C_1) + C_2(x + C_2)$$
The second factor gives a singular solution, see (3-464),
$$16y = (C_0 + X)^2 + 2x(C_0 + X)\sqrt{1 + x^2} - 3x^2;$$
$$X(x) = \ln(x + \sqrt{1 + x^2}).$$
    ii.   Two independent first integrals are
$$p^2 + x(1 - 4A)(p - x) + 4A^2 = y$$
$$2(B - p)^2 + x^3(B + p) + 2B^2 x^2 = 2x^2 y$$

where A, B are arbitrary constants.   Either will give the singular integral $8p(2p+2x+x^3) = x^4+16(1+x^2)y$. The solution of this first-order equation is a singular solution of (298), agreeing with that in i.   A singular solution of the first-order equation is $16y = x^2(x^2-4)$. It does not satisfy (298).

299 $3x^2y''^2 - 2(3xy'+y)y'' + 4y'^2 = 0$ **5, 11**
Differentiate to get
$$y'''(3x^2y'' - 3xy' - y) = 0$$
The first factor, see (5-1) gives the general solution
$$y = C_1x(C_2+C_1x)+C_2^2$$
The second factor, see **B1-3-1**, gives singular solutions
$$y = C_0x^r;\quad r = 1\pm 2/\sqrt{3}$$

300 $x^2(2-9x)y''^2 - 6x(1-6x)y'y'' + 6yy'' = 36xy'^2$ **5, 11**
$$y = C_1x(C_2+C_1x^2)+C_2^2$$
See (301) and (284).
    Singular solutions come from the second-order equation
$$(9x^3-2x^2)y'' - 3x(6x-1)y' - 3y = 0$$
$$y_i = CX^{\pm 1}(x)x\sqrt{4x-1}$$

$$X(x) = \exp\left[2\int \frac{\sqrt{9x^2-2x}}{4x^2-x}dx\right]$$

301 $f_0y''^2 + f_1y'y'' + f_2yy'' + g_0y'^2 + g_1yy' + hy^2 = 0$ **5, 11**
$f_i = f_i(x)$; $g_i = g_i(x)$; $h = h(x)$;   see (284) and (300).   Under appropriate conditions, the general solution is
$$y = C_1^2u_1 + C_1C_2u_2 + C_2u_3$$
where the $u_i(x)$ are solutions of a third-order equation.   There are singular solutions, resulting from the second-order equation. For the details, see P. Appell, *J. Math.* (4), 5, 410 (1889).

302 $yy'' - y'^2 + 4yy'^3 = 0$ **3-1**
$y' = yu(x)$; $u'^2 = 4u^3$; $(x+C)^2u = 1$; see **A1-1-3**.
$$y = C_1\exp(1/C_2-x)$$

303 $(1+y'^2+yy'')^2 = (1+y'^2)^3$ **2-3**
$ypp'(y) = (1+p^2)(\sqrt{1+p^2}-1)$; $(C-y)^2p^2 = y(2C-y)$;
see **A1-1-2**.
$$(x-C_1)^2+(y-C_2)^2 = C_2^2$$

304 $(a^2-b^2y^2)y''^2 + 2b^2yy'^2y'' + (1-b^2y'^2)y'^2 = 0$ **5**
$y'(x) = p(y)$;   differentiate with respect to y and get
$$p''(y)[(a^2-b^2y^2)p' + b^2yp] = 0.$$

The first term gives $p(y) = A + By$, where A, B are constants; see (3-1). Another quadrature produces the general solution
$$y = C_1 e^{cx} + C_2; \quad b^2 c^2 C_2^2 = 1 + a^2 c^2$$
There is a singular solution, resulting from the first-order equation, see **A1-1-2**,
$$by = \pm a \sin(C_0 + x/a)$$

305 $(y^2 - x^2 y'^2 + x^2 yy'')^2 = 4xy(xy' - y)^3$ **5, 3-1**
$y = xu(x); \quad uu'' - u'^2 = 4uu'^3; \quad$ see (302).
$$y = C_1 x \exp(1/C_2 - x)$$

306 $y''^3 = 12y'(xy'' - 2y')$ **1-2**
$p'^3 - 12xpp' + 24p^2 = 0; \quad$ see (2-290).
$$y = C_1(x - C_1)^3 + C_2; \quad 9y = x^4 + C_0$$

307 $(2yy'' - y'^2)^3 + 32y''(xy'' - y')^3 = 0$ **5, 11**
Differentiate with respect to x and get $2y'''(x)f(x, y, y', y'') = 0$. The solution of the third-order equation, see (5-1), is $y = a + bx + cx^2$. It satisfies the original second-order equation if $a = (1 + 2C_2^2)/C_1C_2^3; \quad b = 2C_1/C_2^3; \quad c = (C_1/C_2)^3;$ hence
$$C_1 C_2^3 y = (1 + C_1^2 x)^2 + 2C_2^2$$
There is a singular solution, $y^2 = 8x$, which comes from the second-order factor.

308 $f(y'') + xy'' = y'$ **1-2**
$p = xp' + f(p'); \quad$ see **A2-4-1**; $\quad p = C_1 x + f(C_1)$.
$$2y = C_1 x^2 + 2xf(C_1) + C_2$$

309 $y'f(y''/y') = y'^2 - yy''$ **2-3**
$p[p - yp'(y) - f(p')] = 0; \quad p = C_1 y + f(C_1); \quad$ see **A2-4-1**.
$$C_1 x = \ln[C_1 y + f(C_1)] + C_2$$

310 $f(y'', \ y' - xy'', \ y - xy' + x^2 y''/2) = 0$ **5, 3-2**
Differentiate with respect to x and get $y'''(f_1 - xf_2 + x^2 f_3/2) = 0$, where the f_i are the partial derivatives with respect to the i-th argument in the given equation. The third-order equation, see (5-1), gives the general solution
$$y = C_1 + C_2 x + C_3 x^2/2$$
provided that $f(C_3, C_2, C_1) = 0$.

311 $f(x, y'') = 0$ **1-1**

312 $f(y, y'') = 0$ **2-1**

313 $f(y', y'') = 0$ **2-2**

314 $f(x, y', y'') = 0$ **1-2**

315 $f(y, y', y'') = 0$ **2-3**

5. THE EQUATION IS LINEAR AND OF ORDER GREATER THAN TWO

This section contains equations of the general form
$$A_0(x)y^{(n)} + A_1(x)y^{(n-1)} + \ldots + A_n(x)y = f(x)$$
They are arranged in order of increasing rank, as explained in 1 and 3, beginning with the coefficient of the highest derivative. See also Part I, Introduction–4 and **C1** for further information about such equations.

The arbitrary integration constants, n in number, are called C_1, C_2, ... , C_n in the general solution. It is not always possible to present the general solution in explicit form. In such cases, a first integral, a second integral, etc., will contain fewer than n integration constants. The letter p is never used here to mean dy/dx but is always a constant.

1    $y''' = 0$ **1; C2-1-1**
$$y = C_1 + C_2 x + C_3 x^2$$

2    $y''' = 1 + \cos x$ **9-1**
See (1); $F(x) = x^3/6 - \sin x$.

3    $y''' + \sin x = 0$ **9-1**
See (1); $F(x) = -\cos x$.

4    $y''' = \sin^3 x$ **9-1**
See (1); $F(x) = (1/27) \cos x \, (21 - \cos^2 x)$.

5    $y''' = y$ **1; C2-2-4**

$$y = C_1 e^x + e^{-x/2}\left(C_2 \cos\frac{x\sqrt{3}}{2} + C_3 \sin\frac{x\sqrt{3}}{2}\right)$$

6    $y''' = x^2 + y$ **9-1**
See (5); $F(x) = -x^2$.

7    $y''' = xe^x + \cos^2 x + y$ **9-1**

See (5); $F(x) = \dfrac{1}{6}xe^x(x-2) - \dfrac{1}{2} - \dfrac{1}{130}(\cos 2x + 8 \sin 2x)$.

8   $y''' + ay = 0$ 1
    i. $a = 0$; see (1).
    ii. $a = -1$; see (5).
    iii. $a \neq 0$; $y = C_1 e^{-kx} + e^{kx/2}(C_2 \cos kx\sqrt{3}/2$
       $+ C_3 \sin kx\sqrt{3}/2)$, where k is the real root of $a = k^3$.

9   $y''' = xy$ 6-1

$$y = C_1 y_1 + C_2 y_2 + C_3 y_3; \quad y_1 = 1 + \frac{x^4}{2 \cdot 3 \cdot 4}$$

$$+ \frac{x^8}{2 \cdot 3 \cdot 4 \cdot 6 \cdot 7 \cdot 8} + \ldots; \quad y_2 = x\left(1 + \frac{x^4}{3 \cdot 4 \cdot 5} + \ldots\right);$$

$$y_3 = x^2\left(1 + \frac{x^4}{4 \cdot 5 \cdot 6} + \ldots\right).$$

10 $y''' + y' = 0$ 1; C2-2-2
    $y = C_1 + C_2 \cos x + C_3 \sin x$

11 $y''' = y'$ 1; C2-2-2
    $y = C_1 + C_2 e^x + C_3 e^{-x}$

12 $y''' + y' = x^3 + \cos x$ 9-1
  See (10); $F(x) = (1/4)x^2(x^2 - 12) - (1/2)x \cos x$.

13 $y''' - 2y' + 4y = 0$ 1
    $y = C_1 e^{-2x} + e^x(C_2 \cos x + C_3 \sin x)$

14 $y''' - 2y' + 4y = e^x \cos x$ 9-1

  See (13); $F(x) = \dfrac{xe^x}{20}(3 \sin x - \cos x)$.

15 $y''' - 3y' + 2y = 0$ 1
    $y = C_1 e^{-2x} + e^x(C_2 + C_3 x)$

16 $y''' - 3y' + 2y = 3e^x$ 9-1
  See (15); $F(x) = x^2 e^x / 2$.

17 $y''' - 3y' + 2y = x^2 e^x$ 9-1

  See (15); $F(x) = x^2 e^x \left(\dfrac{1}{27} - \dfrac{x}{27} + \dfrac{x^2}{36}\right)$

18 $y''' - 4y' = x^2 - 3e^{2x}$ 9-1

  See (20); $F(x) = -\dfrac{x}{8} - \dfrac{x^3}{12} - \dfrac{3}{8}xe^{2x}$.

19     $y''' - 7y' + 6y = 0$ **1**
           $y = C_1 e^x + C_2 e^{2x} + C_3 e^{-3x}$

20     $y''' = a^2 y'$ **1**
           $y = C_1 + C_2 e^{ax} + C_3 e^{-ax}$

21     $y''' + 2xy' + y = 0$ **6-1**
           $y = C_1 y_1 + C_2 y_2 + C_3 y_3$

$$y_1 = 1 - \frac{x^3}{3!} + \frac{1 \cdot 7}{6!} x^6 - \frac{1 \cdot 7 \cdot 13}{9!} x^9 \pm \dots;$$

$$y_2 = x\left(1 - \frac{3x^3}{4!} + \frac{3 \cdot 9}{7!} x^6 - \frac{3 \cdot 9 \cdot 15}{10!} x^9 \pm \dots\right);$$

$$y_3 = x^2\left(\frac{1}{2!} - \frac{5x^3}{5!} + \frac{5 \cdot 11}{8!} x^6 - \frac{5 \cdot 11 \cdot 17}{11!} x^9 \pm \dots\right).$$

22     $y''' + 2axy' + ay = 0$ **5-1**
         i. $a = 1$;   see (21).
         ii. $a \neq 1$; $y = C_1 y_1^2 + C_2 y_1 y_2 + C_3 y_2^2$, where y_1, y_2
are linearly independent solutions of $2y'' + axy = 0$;   see
(3-34) and (23).

23     $y''' + 2f(x)y' + f'(x)y = 0$ **5-1**
           $y = C_1 y_1^2 + C_2 y_1 y_2 + C_3 y_2^2$
where y_1, y_2 are linearly independent solutions of $2y''$
$+ f(x)y = 0$;   see **B1-2** and (66).

24     $y''' - y'' + y' = 0$ **1**
           $y = C_1 + e^{x/2}(C_2 \cos x\sqrt{3}/2 + C_3 \sin x\sqrt{3}/2)$

25     $y''' - y'' - y' + y = 0$ **1**
           $y = C_1 e^{-x} + e^x(C_2 + C_3 x)$

26     $y''' + y'' + y' - 3y = 0$ **1**
           $y = C_1 e^x + e^{-x}(C_2 \cos x\sqrt{2} + C_3 \sin x\sqrt{2})$

27     $y''' - y'' - 2y' = 0$ **1**
           $y = C_1 + C_2 e^{-x} + C_3 e^{2x}$

28     $y''' - y'' - 2y' = e^{-x}$ **9-1**
    See (27); $F(x) = xe^{-x}/3$.

29     $y''' + y'' + 4y' + 4y = 0$ **1**
           $y = C_1 e^{-x} + C_2 \cos 2x + C_3 \sin 2x$

30     $y''' + y'' + 4y' + 4y = \sin 2x$ **9-1**
    See (29); $F(x) = -(x/20)(\cos 2x + 2 \sin 2x)$.

31    $y''' + y'' - 7y' - 15y = 0$ 1
$$y = C_1 e^{3x} + e^{-2x}(C_2 \cos x + C_3 \sin x)$$

32    $y''' \pm 2y'' + y' = 0$ 1
$$y = C_1 + e^{\mp x}(C_2 + C_3 x)$$

33    $y''' + 2y'' + y' = x(x-1)$ 9-1
See (32); $F(x) = x(8 - 5x/2 + x^2/3)$.

34    $y''' - 2y'' + y' = e^x$ 9-1
See (32); $F(x) = x^2 e^x/2$.

35    $y''' - 2y'' - y' + 2y = \sinh x$ 9-1
See (40); $F(x) = -(1/2)e^x(1+x) - (1/36)e^{-x}(1+3x)$.

36    $y''' - 2y'' - 3y' = 0$ 1
$$y = C_1 + C_2 e^{-x} + C_3 e^{3x}$$

37    $y''' - 2y'' - 3y' = 3x^2 + \sin x$ 9-1
See (36); $F(x) = x(6x - 14)/9 + (2 \cos x + \sin x)/10$.

38    $y''' - 2y'' - 3y' = 3x^2 + e^{-x}$ 9-1

See (36); $F(x) = x\left(\dfrac{e^{-x}}{4} - \dfrac{14}{9} + \dfrac{2x}{3} - \dfrac{x^2}{3} \right)$.

39    $y''' - 2y'' + 3y' + 10y = 0$ 1
$$y = C_1 e^{-2x} + e^{2x}(C_2 \cos x + C_3 \sin x)$$

40    $y''' - 2y'' - a^2 y' + 2a^2 y = 0$ 1
$$y = C_1 e^{2x} + C_2 e^{ax} + C_3 e^{-ax}$$

41    $y''' - 2y'' - a^2 y' + 2a^2 y = \sinh x$ 9-1
     i. $a = 1$; see (35).
     ii. $a \neq 1$; see (40); $F(x) = (\cosh x + 2 \sinh x)/3(a^2 - 1)$.

42    $y''' - 3y'' + 4y = 0$ 1
$$y = C_1 e^{-x} + e^{2x}(C_2 + C_3 x)$$

43    $y''' \pm 3y'' - y' \mp 3y = 0$ 1
$$y = C_1 e^x + C_2 e^{-x} + C_3 e^{\mp 3x}$$

44    $y''' - 3y'' - y' + 3y = x^2$ 9-1
See (43); $F(x) = (20 + 6x + 9x^2)/27$.

45    $y''' + 3y'' - y' - 3y = \cosh x$ 9-1
See (43); $F(x) = x(3 \sinh x - \cosh x)/16$.

46    $y''' \pm 3y'' + 3y' \pm y = 0$ 1
$$y = e^{\mp x}(C_1 + C_2 x + C_3 x^2)$$

47    $y''' + 3y'' + 3y' + y = xe^{-x}$ 9-1
See (46); $F(x) = x^4 e^{-x}/24$.

48 $y''' - 3y'' + 3y' - y = x(1 - x^2 e^x)$ **9-1**
See (46); $F(x) = -(3 + x + x^6 e^x / 120)$.

49 $y''' + 3y'' + 3y' + y = e^{-x}(2 - x^2)$ **9-1**
See (46); $F(x) = x^3 e^{-x}(20 - x^2)/60$.

50 $y''' - 3y'' + 4y' - 2y = 0$ **1**
       $y = e^x(C_1 + C_2 \cos x + C_3 \sin x)$

51 $y''' - 3y'' + 4y' - 2y = e^x + \cos x$ **9-1**
See (50); $F(x) = (\cos x + 3 \sin x)/10 + x e^x$.

52 $y''' - 4y'' + 5y' - 2y = 0$ **1**
       $y = e^x(C_1 + C_2 x) + C_3 e^{2x}$

53 $y''' - 4y'' + 5y' - 2y = x$ **9-1**
See (52); $F(x) = -5/4 - x/2$.

54 $y''' - 4y'' + 6y' - 4y = 0$ **1**
       $y = C_1 e^{2x} + e^x(C_2 \cos x + C_3 \sin x)$

55 $y''' - 6y'' + 9y' = 0$ **1**
       $y = C_1 + e^{3x}(C_2 + C_3 x)$

56 $y''' - 6y'' + 12y' - 8y = x^2 e^{2x}$ **9-1**
See (57); $F(x) = x^5 e^{2x}/60$.

57 $y''' - 3ay'' + 3a^2 y' - a^3 y = 0$ **1**
       $y = e^{ax}(C_1 + C_2 x + C_3 x^2)$

58 $y''' - 3ay'' + 3a^2 y' - a^3 y = e^{ax}$ **9-1**
See (57); $F(x) = x^3 e^{ax}/6$.

59 $y''' = ay''$ **1**
       $y = C_1 + C_2 x + C_3 e^{ax}$

60 $y''' + a_1 y'' + a_2 y' + a_3 y = 0$ **1**

61 $y''' - 6xy'' - 2(1 - 2a - 4x^2)y' - 8axy = 0$ **5-1**
A special case of (66). If y_1, y_2 are linearly independent solutions of $y'' - 2xy' + ay = 0$, see (3-117), the general solution of (61) is
$$y = C_1 y_1{}^2 + C_2 y_1 y_2 + C_3 y_2{}^2$$

62 $y''' + 3axy'' + 3a^2 x^2 y' + a^3 x^3 y = 0$ **4-1-2**
$y = e^{-ax^2/2} u(x)$; $u''' - 3au' = 0$; see (20).
    i. $a < 0$; $y e^{ax^2/2} = C_1 + C_2 \cos X + C_3 \sin X$;
       $X(x) = x\sqrt{|3a|}$.
    ii. $a > 0$; replace cos (sin) by cosh (sinh).

63 $y''' - x^2 y'' + 2xy' - 2y = 0$ **4-1-1**
$y_1 = x$; $y = y_1 u(x)$; $xu''' + u''(3 - x^3)$; $u' = v(x)$; $y_1 u = y_2$;
$y_2 = x^2$; $xv'' + v'(3 - x^3) = 0$; $v' = w(x)$; $xw' + w(3 - x^3) = 0$.

The last equation is separable; see **A1-1-2**; and its solution is $x^3 w(x) = C e^{x^3/3}$. Solve successively the first-order equations in v' and u', which are also of type **A1-1-2**. The integrals must be evaluated by expanding the exponential factor. The general solution is

$$y = C_1 y_1 + C_2 y_2 + C_3 y_3$$

$$y_3 = 1 + \frac{2x^3}{1!3 \cdot 1 \cdot 2} + \frac{2x^6}{2!3^2 \cdot 4 \cdot 5} + \frac{2x^9}{3!3^3 \cdot 7 \cdot 8.} + \quad \cdots$$

64    $y''' + (2 \cot x + \csc x)y'' - y' = \cot x$ **5-1**
$I(x) = \sin x$; a first integral is
     $y'' \sin x + (1 + \cos x)y' = C + \sin x$;   see (3-150).
A second integral is
     $y' \sin x + y = C_1 + C_2 x - \cos x$

65    $y''' - y'' \sin x - 2y' \cos x + y \sin x = \ln x$ **5**
A first integral is
     $y'' - y' \sin x - y \cos x = C + x \ln x - x$;   see (3-155).
A second integral is
     $y' - y \sin x = C_1 + C_2 x + \frac{1}{2}x^2 \ln x - \frac{3}{4}x^2$

66    $y''' + 3f(x)y'' + (f' + 2f^2 + 4g)y' + 2(2fg + g')y = 0$ **5-1**
     $y = C_1 y_1^2 + C_2 y_1 y_2 + C_3 y_2^2$
where y_1, y_2 are linearly independent solutions of
$y'' + f(x))y' + g(x)y = 0$;   see **B1-2**.

67    $y''' + f(x)y'' + y' + f(x)y = 0$ **4-1**
$u(x) = y'' + y$; $u'(x) + f(x)u = 0$;   see **A1-1-2**.
     $y = C_1 \cos x + C_2 \sin x + C_3(X_1 \sin x - X_2 \cos x)$;
$X_1(x) = \int \phi \cos x dx$; $X_2(x) = \int \phi \sin x dx$; $\phi(x) = \exp(-\int f dx)$.

68    $4y''' - 3y' + y = 0$ **1**
     $y = e^{x/2}(C_1 + C_2 x) + C_3 e^{-x}$

69    $4y''' - 8y'' - 11y' - 3y = 0$ **1**
     $y = e^{-x/2}(C_1 + C_2 x) + C_3 e^{3x}$

70    $4y''' - 8y'' - 11y' - 3y + 18e^x = 0$ **9-1**
See (69); $F(x) = e^x$.

71    $xy''' = 2$ **C2-1-1**
See (1); $F(x) = x^2 \ln x$.

72    $xy''' + 3y' + xy = 0$ **4-2**
$u(x) = xy$; $u''' + u = 0$;   see (8).

73    $xy''' - y'' + xy' - y = 0$ **4-1**
$u(x) = y'' + y$; $xu' = u$; $u = C_1 x$; $y'' + y = C_1 x$;   see (3-8).
     $y = C_1 x + C_2 \cos x + C_3 \sin x$

74 $\quad xy''' - y'' - xy' + y = 0$ $\hfill$ **4-1-1**
$\quad y_1 = e^x; \;\; y_2 = e^{-x}; \;\; y_3 = x.$

75 $\quad xy''' - y'' - xy' + y = 1 - x^2$ $\hfill$ **9-3**
$\quad$ See (74); $\;\; F(x) = 3 + x^2.$

76 $\quad xy''' + 3y'' - x^2 y = 0$ $\hfill$ **4-2**
$\quad u(x) = xy; \;\; u'''(x) = xu; \;\;$ see (9).

77 $\quad xy''' - (3 - x^2)y'' + 4xy' + 2y = 0$ $\hfill$ **5**
$\quad$ A first integral is
$$xy'' - (4 - x^2)y' + 2xy = C_1; \quad \text{see (3-220)}.$$
$\quad$ A second integral is
$$xy' - (5 - x^2)y = C_1 x + C_2; \quad \text{see } \textbf{A1-2}.$$

78 $\quad (1 - 2x)y''' - (4 + x)y'' - 2y' = 0$ $\hfill$ **5**
$\quad$ A first integral is
$$(1 - 2x)y'' - (2 + x)y' - y = C_1; \quad \text{see (3-237)}.$$
$\quad$ A second integral is
$$(1 - 2x)y' - xy = C_1 x + C_2; \;\; \text{see } \textbf{A1-2}.$$

79 $\quad x^2 y''' - 6y' + ax^2 y = 0$ $\hfill$ **4-1**
$\quad y = x^2 u(x); \;\; x^3 u''' + 6x^2 u' - (12 - ax^3)u = 0; \;\;$ see (108).

80 $\quad x^2 y''' + 2xy'' = a$ $\hfill$ **5; C2-1-2**
$\quad$ A first integral is $x^2 y'' = ax + C_1;$ see (3-246).
$$y = ax \ln x - C_1 \ln x + C_2 x + C_3$$

81 $\quad x^2 y''' + 4xy'' + (2 + x^2)y' + 3xy = f(x)$ $\hfill$ **5-1**
$\quad I(x) = x.$ A first integral is
$$x^3 y'' + x^2 y' + x^3 y = \int xf(x)dx + C$$

82 $\quad x^2 y''' + 5xy'' + 4y' = \ln x$ $\hfill$ **5**
$\quad$ A first integral, see (3-296), is
$$x^2 y'' + 3xy' + y = C + x \ln x - x$$
$\quad$ The general solution is
$$4xy = C_1 + C_2 x + C_3 \ln x - 2x^2 + x^2 \ln x$$

83 $\quad x^2 y''' + 6xy'' + 6y' = 0$ $\hfill$ **C2-1-3**
$\quad y' = u(x); \;\; x^2 u'' + 6xu' + 6u = 0; \;\;$ see **B1-3-1**.
$$y = C_1/x + C_2/x^2 + C_3$$

84 $\quad x^2 y''' + 6xy'' + 6y' + ax^2 y = 0$ $\hfill$ **4-1**
$\quad u(x) = x^2 y; \;\; u''' + au = 0; \;\;$ see (8).

85 $\quad x^2 y''' - 2(1 + n)xy'' + 6ny' = 0$ $\hfill$ **C2-1-3**
$\quad y' = u(x); \;\; x^2 u'' - 2(1 + n)xu' + 6nu = 0; \;\;$ see **B1-3-1**.
$$y = C_1 x^4 + C_2 x^{2n+1} + C_3$$

86   $x^2 y''' + x(6 - x^3)y'' + (6 - 2x^3)y' + 2x^2 y = 0$ 4-1-1
$y_1 = 1/x^2$; $\quad y = y_1 u(x)$; $\quad u''' - x^2 u'' + 2xu' = 0$; $\quad u' = v(x)$;
$v'' - x^2 v' + 2xv = 0$; see (3-135).

87   $(1 + x^2)y''' + 8xy' + 10y' = 0$ 5
A first integral, see (3-381),
$$(1 + x^2)y'' + 6xy' + 4y = C_1$$
A second integral is
$$(1 + x^2)y' + 4xy = C_1 x + C_2$$

88   $(2 + x^2)y''' - 2xy'' + (2 + x^2)y' - 2xy = 0$ 4-1-1
$y_1 = x^2$; $\quad y_2 = \cos x$; $\quad y_3 = \sin x$.
$$y = C_1 y_1 + C_2 y_2 + C_3 y_3$$

89   $(2 - 2x + x^2)y''' - x^2 y'' + 2xy' - 2y = 0$ 4-1-1
$y_1 = x$; $\quad y = xu(x)$; $\quad x(2 - 2x + x^2)u''' + (6 - 6x + 3x^2 - x^3)u'' = 0$;
see (113).
$$y = C_1 e^x + C_2 x^2 + C_3 x$$

90   $(2 + x)^2 y''' + (2 + x)y'' + y' = 0$ 5
A first integral, see (3-425), is
$$(2 + x)^2 y'' - (2 + x)y' + 2y = C$$
The general solution is
$$y = (x + 2)[C_1 \cos \ln(x + 2) + C_2 \sin \ln(x + 2)] + C_3$$

91   $4x^2 y''' + 8xy'' + y' = 0$ 3-1
$$y = C_1 + \sqrt{x}(C_2 + C_3 \ln x)$$

92   $x(a_0 + b_0 x)y''' + (a_1 + b_1 x)y'' + xy' + y = f(x)$ 5
A first integral is
$$x(a_0 + b_0 x)y'' + [(a_1 - a_0) + (b_1 - 2b_0)x]y'$$
$$+ (2b_0 - b_1 + x)y = \int f(x)dx + C$$

93   $x^3 y''' = a$ 9-2; C2-1-1
See (1); $F(x) = (a/2) \ln x$.

94   $x^3 y''' + xy' - y = 0$ 3-1
$$y = x[C_1 + C_2 \ln x + C_3 (\ln x)^2]$$

95   $x^3 y''' + xy' - y = x \ln x$ 9-2
See (94); $F(x) = (1/24)x(\ln x)^4$.

96   $x^3 y''' - x^2 y'' + 2xy' - 2y = 0$ 3-1
$$y = C_1 x^2 + x(C_2 + C_3 \ln x)$$

97   $x^3 y''' - x^2 y'' + 2xy' - 2y = x(3 + x^2)$ 9-2
See (96); $F(x) = x^3/4 - (3/2)x(\ln x)^2$.

98   $x^3 y''' + x^2 y'' + 3xy' - 8y = 0$ 3-1
$$y = C_1 x^2 + C_2 \cos(C_3 + 2 \ln x)$$

99    $x^3y''' - x^2y'' + xy' = 0$ **3-1**
      $y = C_1 + x^2(C_2 + C_3 \ln x)$

100   $x^3y''' + 2x^2y'' + 2y = 0$ **3-1**
      $xy = C_1 + x^2(C_2 \cos \ln x + C_3 \sin \ln x)$

101   $x^3y''' + 2x^2y'' - xy' + y = 0$ **3-1**
      $xy = C_1 + x^2(C_2 + C_3 \ln x)$

102   $x^3y''' + 3x^2y'' = a$ **5; C2-1-2**
      A first integral is $x^3y'' = ax + C$;   see (3-484).   The general
      solution is
      $$2xy = C_1 + 2x(C_2 + C_3 x - a \ln x)$$

103   $x^3y''' + 3x^2y'' - 2xy' + 2y = 0$ **3-1**
      $x^2y = C_1 + x^3(C_2 + C_3 \ln x)$

104   $x^3y''' - 3x^2y'' + 7xy' - 8y = 0$ **3-1**
      $y = x^2[C_1 + C_2 \ln x + C_3(\ln x)^2]$

105   $x^3y''' + 3x^2y'' + (1 - a^2)xy' = 0$ **3-1**
      $y = C_1 + C_2 x^a + C_3 x^{-a}$

106   $x^3y''' + 4x^2y'' - 8xy' + 8y = 0$ **3-1**
      $x^4y = x^5(C_1 + C_2 x) + C_3$

107   $x^3y''' - 4x^2y'' + x(8 + x^2)y' - 2(4 + x^2)y = 0$ **4-1**
      $y = xu(x)$; $xu''' - u'' + xu' - u = 0$;   see (73).
      $y = C_1 x^2 + x(C_2 \cos x + C_3 \sin x)$

108   $x^3y''' + 6x^2y'' - (12 - ax^3)y = 0$ **4-2**
      Divide (84) by x^2, differentiate the result, and replace y' by y.
      The final equation is identical with (108). Thus, if $Y(x)$ is
      the general solution of (84), the general solution of (108) is

      $$y = \frac{d}{dx}\left(\frac{1}{x^2}Y\right).$$

109   $x^3y''' + x^2y'' \ln x + 2xy' - y = 2x^3$ **5-1**
      $I(x) = 1/x^2$; a first integral, see **B1-5**, is
      $xy'' - (1 - \ln x)y' + y/x = C$
      A second integral is
      $xy' - (2 - \ln x)y = x^3/3 + C_1 x + C_2$

110   $(1 + x^3)y''' + 9x^2y'' + 18xy' + 6y = 0$ **5**
      Successive integrals are exact; see **B1-5-1**, **A1-7-1**, and **A1-2**.
      $(1 + x^3)y'' + 6x^2y' + 6xy = C_0$; $(1 + x^3)y' + 3x^2y = C_0 x + C$;
      $(1 + x^3)y = C_1 x^2 + C_2 x + C_3$

111 $x(1+x^2)y''' + 3(1+2x^2)y'' - 12y = 0$ **5-1**

$I(x) = x$; $x^2(1+x^2)y'' + x(1+2x^2)y' - (1+6x^2)y = C_0$. This first integral is also exact, see **B1-5-1**, and the second integral is $x^2(1+x^2)y' - x(1+2x^2)y = C_0x + C$.   Use **A1-2**, to get the general solution

$$y = C_1(1+2x^2) + C_2xR + C_3\left(2x + \frac{2}{3x} - xR\ln\frac{R+1}{R-1}\right);$$

$R(x) = \sqrt{1+x^2}$.

112 $x(1-x^2)y''' + (3-8x^2)y'' - 14xy' - 4y = 0$ **5**

The first integral is also exact; use **A1-2** to get the general solution; $x(1-x^2)y'' + (2-5x^2)y' - 4xy = C_1$; $x(1-x^2)y' + (1-2x^2)y = C_1x + C_2$.

$$xy\sqrt{1-x^2} = C_1\sqrt{1-x^2} + C_2\sin^{-1}x + C_3$$

113 $x(2-2x+x^2)y''' + (6-6x+3x^2-x^3)y'' = 0$ **C2-1-2**

$y'' = u(x)$; $x^3u = C_1e^x(x^2-2x+2)$; $x^2y' = C_1e^x(x-1) + C_2x^2$; $xy = C_1e^x + C_2x^2 + C_3x$

114 $(1+x)^3y''' + (1+x)^2y'' + 3(1+x)y' - 8y = 0$ **3-2**

$y(x) = u(z)$; $z = \ln(1+x)$; $z^3u''' + z^2u'' + 3zu' - 8u = 0$;   see (98).

$$y = C_1(1+x)^2 + C_2\cos[C_3 + 2\ln(1+x)]$$

115 $x^2(3+y)y''' - 3x(2+x)y'' + 6(1+x)y' - 6y = 0$ **4-1-1, 5-1**

    i. $y_1 = x^2$; $y_2 = x^3$; $y_3 = 1+x$

       $y = C_1y_1 + C_2y_2 + C_3y_3$

    ii. $I(x) = 1/x^2$.

116 $4x^3y''' + xy' - y = 0$ **3-1**

$$y = x(C_1 + C_2x^{r_1} + C_3x^{r_2}); \quad r_{1,2} = \pm\sqrt{3}/2$$

117 $(1-2x)^3y''' + (1-2x)y' + 2y = 0$ **3-2**

$y(x) = u(z)$; $z = \ln(1-2x)$; $4z^3u''' + zu' - u = 0$;   see (116).

$$y = (1-2x)[C_1 + C_2(1-2x)^{r_1} + C_3(1-2x)^{r_2}];$$

$r_{1,2} = \pm\sqrt{3}/2$.

118 $x^4y''' + 2x^3y'' + 2xy = 10(1+x^2)$ **9-2**

See (100); $F(x) = 5x^2 + 2\ln x$.

119 $x^4y''' + 2x^3y'' - x^2y' + xy = 1$ **9-2**

See (101); $F(x) = (1/4x)\ln x$.

120 $x^2(1+x^2)y''' + 8x^3y'' + 10x^2y' = 2x^2\ln x - 1 + 3x^2$ **9-3**

See (87); $F(x) = (1+x^2)\ln x$

121    $x^3(1+x)y''' - 2x^2(1+2x)y'' + 2x(2+5x)y'$
$$- 4(1+3x)y = 0$$ **4-1-1, 6-2**

$y_1 = x^2.$
$$y = C_1 x^2 + C_2 x^2 \ln x + C_3 x[1 + x(\ln x)^2 + x^2]$$

122    $4x^4 y''' - 4x^3 y'' + 4x^2 y' = 1$ **9-2**

See (99); $F(x) = -1/36x.$

123    $x^3(1+x^2)y''' - 2x^2(1+2x^2)y'' + 2x(2+5x^2)y'$
$$- 4(1+3x^2)y = 0$$ **4-1-1, 6-2**

$y_1 = x^2.$
$$y = C_1 x^2 + C_2 x^2 \ln x + C_3 x(1 + x^2)$$

124    $(a-x)^3(b-x)^3 y''' = cy$ **4-2**

$$y = (b-x)^2 u(z); \quad z = \ln\frac{a-x}{b-x}; \quad a \neq b;$$

$$(a-b)^3(u''' - 3u'' + 2u') = cu; \quad \text{see } \mathbf{1}.$$

125    $(x+\sin x)y''' + 3(1+\cos x)y'' - 3y' \sin x$
$$- y \cos x + \sin x = 0$$ **4-1, 5**

$u(x) = (x+\sin x)y; \quad u''' + \sin x = 0; \quad \text{see (3)}.$
$$(x+\sin x)y = C_1 + C_2 x + C_3 x^2 - \cos x$$

126    $y^{\text{iv}} = 0$ **1, C2-1-1**
$$y = C_1 + C_2 x + C_3 x^2 + C_4 x^3$$

127    $y^{\text{iv}} = x \cos x$ **9-1**

See (126); $F(x) = x \cos x - 4 \sin x.$

128    $y^{\text{iv}} + 4e^{-x} \cos x = 0$ **9-1**

See (126); $F(x) = e^{-x} \cos x$

129    $y^{\text{iv}} = y + \cos x$ **9-1**

See (131); $F(x) = -(x/4) \sin x.$

130    $y^{\text{iv}} = y + e^x \cos x$ **9-1**

See (131); $F(x) = -(1/5) e^x \cos x.$

131    $y^{\text{iv}} + ay = 0$ **1**

    i. $a = 0$;   see (126).

    ii. $a = 4k^4 > 0$;   the characteristic roots are $k(1 \pm i)$,
        $-k(1 \pm i)$.
$$y = C_1 \cosh kx \cos kx + C_2 \cosh kx \sin kx$$
$$+ C_3 \sinh kx \cos kx + C_4 \sinh kx \sin kx.$$

    iii. $a = -k^4 < 0$; the characteristic roots are $\pm k, \pm ik$.
$$y = C_1 \cos kx + C_2 \cosh kx + C_3 \sin kx + C_4 \sinh kx$$

132    $y^{\text{iv}} = x^3 + a^4 y$ **9-1**

See (131); $F(x) = -x^3/a^4.$

133 $\quad y^{iv} + y'' + y = 0$ $\hfill$ 1
$$y = C_1 \cosh u_1 \cos u_2 + C_2 \cosh u_1 \sin u_2$$
$$+ C_3 \sinh u_1 \cos u_2 + C_4 \sinh u_1 \sin u_2$$
$u_1 = x/2; \quad u_2 = x\sqrt{3}/2.$

134 $\quad y^{iv} + 2y'' + y = 0$ $\hfill$ 1
$$y = (C_1 + C_2 x) \cos x + (C_3 + C_4 x) \sin x$$

135 $\quad y^{iv} - 2y'' + y = 0$ $\hfill$ 1
$$y = (C_1 + C_2 x) e^x + (C_3 + C_4 x) e^{-x}$$

136 $\quad y^{iv} + 2y'' + y = \cos x$ $\hfill$ 9-1
See (134); $F(x) = -(x^2/8) \cos x.$

137 $\quad y^{iv} - 2y'' + y = \cos x$ $\hfill$ 9-1
See (135); $\quad F(x) = (1/4) \cos x.$

138 $\quad y^{iv} + 2y'' + y = 24x \sin x$ $\hfill$ 9-1
See (134); $F(x) = -x^2(3 \cos x + x \sin x).$

139 $\quad y^{iv} - 2y'' + y = 4 + e^x$ $\hfill$ 9-1
See (135); $\quad F(x) = 4 + x^2 e^x/8.$

140 $\quad y^{iv} + 2y'' - 8y = 0$ $\hfill$ 1
$$y = C_1 e^{x\sqrt{2}} + C_2 e^{-x\sqrt{2}} + C_3 \cos 2x + C_4 \sin 2x$$

141 $\quad y^{iv} + 3y'' - 4y = 0$ $\hfill$ 1
$$y = C_1 e^x + C_2 e^{-x} + C_3 \cos 2x + C_4 \sin 2x$$

142 $\quad y^{iv} + 5y'' + 6y = 0$ $\hfill$ 1
$$y = C_1 \cos(C_2 + x\sqrt{2}) + C_3 \cos(C_4 + x\sqrt{3})$$

143 $\quad y^{iv} - 12y'' + 27y = 0$ $\hfill$ 1
$$y = C_1 e^{3x} + C_2 e^{-3x} + C_3 e^{x\sqrt{3}} + C_4 e^{-x\sqrt{3}}$$

144 $\quad y^{iv} + a^2 y'' = 0$ $\hfill$ C2-2-2
$\quad$ i. $a^2 = 0;$ see (126).
$\quad$ ii. $a^2 > 0;$ $\quad y'' = u(x);$ $\quad u'' = a^2 u;$ $\quad$ see (3-26) and
$\qquad$ (3-3).
$$y = C_1 + C_2 x + a^2(C_3 \cos ax + C_4 \sin ax)$$
$\quad$ iii. $a^2 < 0;$ see (3-26) and (3-5).
$$y = C_1 + C_2 x + a^2(C_3 e^{ax} + C_4 e^{-ax})$$

145 $\quad y^{iv} + 2a^2 y'' + a^4 y = 0$ $\hfill$ 1
$$y = (C_1 + C_2 x)\cos ax + (C_3 + C_4 x)\sin ax$$

146 $\quad y^{iv} + 2a^2 y'' + a^4 y = \cosh ax$ $\hfill$ 9-1
See (145); $\quad F(x) = (1/4a^4) \cosh ax.$

147 $\quad y^{iv} + (a^2 + b^2)y'' + a^2 b^2 y = 0$ $\hfill$ 1
$$y = C_1 \cos ax + C_2 \sin ax + C_3 \cos bx + C_4 \sin bx$$

148     $y^{iv} + 10f(x)y'' + 10f'y' + 3(f'' + 3f^2)y = 0$ **5-1**
$$y = C_1 y_1^3 + C_2 y_1^2 y_2 + C_3 y_1 y_2^2 + C_4 y_2^3$$
where y_1, y_2 are linearly independent solutions of $u'' + f(x)u = 0$;
see **B1-4-1-2**.

149     $y^{iv} - y''' - 3y'' + 5y' - 2y = 0$ **1**
$$y = e^x(C_1 + C_2 x + C_3 x^2) + C_4 e^{-2x}$$

150     $y^{iv} - y''' - 3y'' + 5y' - 2y = e^{3x}$ **9-1**
See (149); $F(x) = e^{3x}/40$.

151     $y^{iv} - 2y''' + y^2 = 0$ **1**
$$y = C_1 + C_2 x + e^x(C_3 + C_4 x)$$

152     $y^{iv} - 2y''' + y^2 = x^3$ **9-1**
See (151); $F(x) = 12x^2 + 3x^3 + x^4/2 + x^5/20$.

153     $y^{iv} + 2y''' - 2y' - y = 0$ **1**
$$y = C_1 e^x + e^{-x}(C_2 + C_3 x + C_4 x^2)$$

154     $y^{iv} - 2y''' + 2y'' - 2y' + y = 0$ **1**
$$y = C_1 \cos x + C_2 \sin x + e^x(C_3 + C_4 x)$$

155     $y^{iv} + 2y''' + 3y'' + 2y' + y = 0$ **1**
$$y = e^{-x/2}[(C_1 + C_2 x)\cos u + (C_3 + C_4 x)\sin u];$$
$u = x\sqrt{3}/2$.

156     $y^{iv} + 2y''' - 3y'' - 4y' + 4y = 0$ **1**
$$y = (C_1 + C_2 x)e^x + (C_3 + C_4 x)e^{-2x}$$

157     $y^{iv} - 3y''' + y'' - y' = 0$ **1**
$$y = C_1 + e^x(C_2 + C_3 x + C_4 x^2)$$

158     $y^{iv} - 4y''' + 6y'' - 4y' + y = 0$ **1**
$$y = e^x(C_1 + C_2 x + C_3 x^2 + C_4 x^3)$$

159     $y^{iv} - 4y''' + 12y'' - 16y' + 16y = 0$ **1**
$$y = e^x[(C_1 + C_2 x)\cos x\sqrt{3} + (C_3 + C_4 x)\sin x\sqrt{3}]$$

160     $y^{iv} + 4axy''' + 6a^2 x^2 y'' + 4a^3 x^3 y' + a^4 x^4 y = 0$ **4-1-1, C2-3-1**
$$y = C_1 y_1 + C_2 y_2 + C_3 y_3 + C_4 y_4$$
$y_i = \exp f_i(x)$; $f_i = x(r_i - ax/2)$; r_i is a root of $r^4 - 6ar^2 + 3a^2 = 0$.

161     $2[y^{iv} + (a^2 + b^2)y'' + a^2 b^2 y] = \cos ax + \cos bx$ **9-1**
See (147); $F(x) = \dfrac{x}{4(b^2 - a^2)}\left(\dfrac{\sin ax}{a} - \dfrac{\sin bx}{b}\right)$

162     $4y^{iv} - 12y''' + 11y'' - 3y' = 0$ **1**
$$y = C_1 + C_2 e^x + C_3 e^{x/2} + C_4 e^{3x/2}$$

163     $xy^{\mathrm{iv}} + 3y''' = 0$ C2-1-2
$y''' = u(x);$ $xu' + 3u = 0;$ $x^3u = C;$ see **A1-1-2** and (93).
$$y = C_1 + C_2x + C_3x^2 + C_4 \ln x$$

164     $xy^{\mathrm{iv}} + 5y''' = 0$ C2-1-2
$y''' = u(x);$ $xu' + 5u = 0;$ $x^5u = C;$ see **A1-1-2** and **C2-1-1**.
$$x^2y = C_1 + C_2x^2 + C_3x^3 + C_4x^4$$

165     $x^2y^{\mathrm{iv}} = 2y''$ C2-1-2
$y'' = u(x);$ $x^2u'' = 2u;$ see (3-247).
$$y = C_1 + C_2x + C_3x^4 + C_4(\ln x - 1)$$

166     $x^2y^{\mathrm{iv}} = ay''$ C2-1-2
i. $a = 2;$ see (165).
ii. $a \neq 2;$ $y'' = u(x);$ $x^2u'' = au;$ see (3-250).
$$y = C_1 + C_2x + C_3x^r + C_4x^s.$$
$2r = 5 + 2k;$ $2s = 5 - 2k;$ $2k = \sqrt{1 + 4a}.$

167     $x^2y^{\mathrm{iv}} + 4xy''' + 2y'' = 0$ 5, C2-1-3
A first integral is $x^2y''' + 2xy'' = C_1;$ see (80). A second integral
is $x^2y'' = C_1x + C_2;$ see (3-246).
$$y = C_1x \ln x + C_2 \ln x + C_3x + C_4$$

168     $x^2y^{\mathrm{iv}} + 6xy''' + 6y'' = 0$ 5-1
$I(x) = x;$ see (174).

169     $x^2y^{\mathrm{iv}} + 8xy''' + 12y'' = 0$ 5-1
$I(x) = x^2;$ see (178).

170     $x^2y^{\mathrm{iv}} + 8xy''' + 12y'' - a^2y = 0$ 4-2
$y(x) = u(z);$ $z = 2\sqrt{ax};$ see (172).
$$xy = C_1J_2(u) + C_2Y_2(u) + C_3J_2(iu) + C_4Y_2(iu)$$
See (3-274).

171     $(a + x)^2y^{\mathrm{iv}} = 1$ C2-1-1
$$y = C_1 + C_2x + C_3x^2 + C_4x^3 - (a + x)^2 \ln \sqrt{a + x}$$

172     $16x^2y^{\mathrm{iv}} + 32(2 + a - b)xy''' + 16(1 + a - b)(2 + a - b)y''$
$\qquad - c^4y = 0$ 4-2
$y(x) = u(z);$ $z = c\sqrt{x};$ see (180) and (3-274).
i. $y = x^k[C_1J_r(u) + C_2Y_r(u) + C_3J_r(iu) + C_4Y_r(iu)];$
$2k = b - a;$ $r = a - b.$
ii. If a is an integer $(a = n)$, set $a = 0$ in the general
solution of i and call this solution $y_b(x).$ The
general solution for $n \neq 0$ is $y_b^{(n)}(x).$

173     $x^3y^{\mathrm{iv}} + 2x^2y''' - xy'' - a^4x^3y = 0$ 4-2
See (180) and (3-274).
$$y = C_1J_0(ax) + C_2Y_0(ax) + C_3J_0(iax) + C_4Y_0(iax)$$

174 $x^3 y^{\mathrm{iv}} + 6x^2 y''' + 6xy'' = 0$ **5**

$(x^3 y'')'' = 0$; a first integral is $x^3 y''' + 3x^2 y'' = C_0$; see (102).
A second integral is $x^3 y'' = C_0 + Cx$; see (3-484).

$$xy = C_1 + C_2 x + C_3 x^2 + C_4 x \ln x$$

175 $x^3 y^{\mathrm{iv}} + (3 + a + b + c)x^2 y'''$

$$+ (1 + a + b + c + ab + ac + bc)xy'' - (x - abc)y' - ky = 0 \qquad \textbf{6-1}$$

See (3-410).

$$y_1 = {}_1F_3(k; a, b, c; x) = 1 + \frac{k}{abc} x$$
$$+ \frac{k(k+1)}{2!\,a(a+1)b(b+1)c(c+1)} x^2 + \ldots$$

176 $x^4 y^{\mathrm{iv}} + 6x^3 y''' + 4x^2 y'' - 2xy' - 4y = 0$ **3-1**

$$x^2 y = C_1 + C_2 x^4 + x^2(C_3 \cos \ln x + C_4 \sin \ln x)$$

177 $x^4 y^{\mathrm{iv}} + 6x^3 y''' + 9x^2 y'' + 3xy' + y = 0$ **3-1**

$$y = (C_1 + C_2 \ln x)\cos \ln x + (C_3 + C_4 \ln x) \sin \ln x$$

178 $x^4 y^{\mathrm{iv}} + 8x^3 y''' + 12x^2 y'' = 0$ **3-1, 5**

$(x^4 y'')'' = 0$.

$$x^2 y = C_1 + C_2 x + C_3 x^2 + C_4 x^3$$

179 $x^4 y^{\mathrm{iv}} + 8x^3 y''' + 12x^2 y'' + ay = 0$ **3-1**

$(x^4 y'')'' + ay = 0$; see (178).

     i. $a = 1$; $y = x^r(C_1 + C_2 \ln x) + x^s(C_3 + C_4 \ln x)$;
$r, s = \pm \frac{1}{2}(1 + \sqrt{5})$.

     ii. $a > 1$; $y\sqrt{x} = (C_1 x^r + C_2 x^{-r})\cos(s \ln x)$
$$+ (C_3 x^r + C_4 x^{-r})\sin(s \ln x); \quad r = \sqrt{k}\,\cos \phi/2;$$
$$s = \sqrt{k}\,\sin \phi/2; \quad k^2 = a + 9/16; \quad \sqrt{a-1} = k \sin \phi;$$
$$4k \cos \phi = 5.$$

     iii. $a < 1$; $y\sqrt{x} = C_1{}^{r_1} + C_2 x^{r_2} + C_3 x^{r_3} + C_4 x^{r_4}$;
$$r_i{}^2 = 5/4 \pm \sqrt{1-a}.$$

180 $x^4 y^{\mathrm{iv}} + A_1 x^3 y''' + A_2 x^2 y'' + A_3 xy' + A_4 y = 0$ **4-2**

$A_1 = 2(3 - 2a - 2c)$; $A_2 = 2(a^2 - k^2 c^2) + 4(a + c - 1)^2$
$+ 4(a-1)(c-1) - 1$; $A_3 = (2a + 2c - 1)[2(k^2 c^2 - a^2)$
$- (2a-1)(2c-1)]$; $A_4 = (a^2 - k^2 c^2)(a^2 + 4ac + 4c^2 - k^2 c^2) - b^4 c^4 x^{4c}$;
$y(x) = u(z)$; $z = bx^c$;   see (3-274).

$$y = x^a[C_1 J_k(z) + C_2 Y_k(z) + C_3 J_k(iz) + C_4 Y_k(iz)]$$

181 $16a^4 x^4 y^{\mathrm{iv}} - 32a^2 x^3(1 - 2a)y''' + 16a^2 x^2(1-a)(1-2a)y''$
$$- b^4 x^{2/a} y = 0 \qquad\qquad\qquad \textbf{4-2}$$

$y(x) = u(z)$; $z = bx^c$;   see (180) and (3-274).

$$y = \sqrt{x}[C_1 J_a(z) + C_2 Y_a(z) + C_3 J_a(iz) + C_4 Y_a(iz)]$$

182     $(2x + e^x)y^{iv} + 4(2 + e^x)y''' + 6e^xy'' + 4e^xy' + e^xy = 0$ **4-1**
$u(x) = (2x + e^x)y; \quad u^{iv} = 0; \quad$ see (126).
$$(2x + e^x)y = C_1 + C_2x + C_3x^2 + C_4x^3$$

183     $y^v - y''' - 2y'' + 2y' = 0$ **1**
$$y = C_1 + e^x(C_2 + C_3x) + e^{-x}(C_4 \cos x + C_5 \sin x)$$

184     $y^v + 2y''' + y' = 0$ **1**
$$y = C_1 + (C_2 + C_3x)\cos x + (C_4 + C_5x)\sin x$$

185     $y^v + 2y''' + y' = ax + b \cos x + c \sin x$ **9-1**
See (184); $\quad F(x) = x^2(4a + c \cos x - b \sin x)/8.$

186     $y^{vi} = 0$ **C2-1-1, 1**
$$y = C_1 + C_2x + C_3x^2 + C_4x^3 + C_5x^4 + C_6x^5$$

187     $y^{vi} + ay = 0$ **1**
    i. $a = 0;$ see (186).
    ii. $a = k^6 > 0;$ the characteristic roots are $\pm ik,$
     $k(1 \pm i\sqrt{3})/2, \; -k(1 \pm i\sqrt{3})/2.$
    $y = C_1 \cos kx + C_2 \sin kx + \cos (kx/2)(C_3 \cosh X + C_4 \sinh X)$
     $+ \sin (kx/2) (C_5 \cosh X + C_6 \sinh X); \quad X = kx\sqrt{3}/2.$
    iii $a = -k^6 < 0;$ the roots are $\pm k, \; k(1 \pm i\sqrt{3})/2,$
     $-k(1 \pm i\sqrt{3})/2.$
    $y = C_1 \cosh kx + C_2 \sinh kx + \cosh (kx/2)(C_3 \cos X$
     $+ C_4 \sin X) + \sinh (kx/2)(C_5 \cos X + C_6 \sin X);$
     $X = kx\sqrt{3}/2$

188     $y^{vi} + 2y''' + y = 0$ **1**
$$y = e^{-x}(C_1 + C_2x) + e^{x/2}[(C_3 + C_4x)\cos x\sqrt{3}/2$$
$$+ (C_5 + C_6x)\sin x\sqrt{3}/2]$$

189     $y^{viii} = y$ **1**
$$y = C_1 \cos x + C_2 \sin x + C_3 \cosh x + C_4 \sinh x$$
$$+ \cos kx(C_5 \cosh kx + C_6 \sinh kx) + \sin kx(C_7 \cosh kx$$
$$+ C_8 \sinh kx); \quad k = 1/\sqrt{2}.$$

190     $y^{viii} - 2y^{iv} + y = 0$ **1**
$$y = e^x(C_1 + C_2x) + e^{-x}(C_3 + C_4x)$$
$$+ \cos x(C_5 + C_6x) + \sin x(C_7 + C_8x)$$

191     $y^{(2n)} = a^{2n}y$ **1**
The characteristic roots are $\pm a, \; a[\cos(k\pi/n) \pm i \sin(k\pi/n)];$
$k = 1, 2, \dots, (n-1).$

$$y = C_1 e^{ax} + C_2 e^{-ax} + \sum_{k=1}^{n-1} e^{\phi_k}(A_k \cos \theta_k + B_k \sin \theta_k);$$

$$\phi_k = ax \cos\frac{k\pi}{n}; \quad \theta_k = ax \sin\frac{k\pi}{n}$$

192 $\quad x^n y^{(2n)} = y$ 4-2

The solution follows from the properties of Bessel functions; see Watson and (3-274). Let $a_0, a_1, \ldots, a_{n-1}$ be the roots of $a^n = 1$; $y(x) = u(z); \quad z_k = [2(-a_k x)]^{1/2}$

$$y = x^{n/2} \sum_{k=0}^{n-1} [A_k J_k(z_k) + B_k Y_k(z_k)]$$

193 $\quad x^{n+1/2} y^{(2n+1)} = y$ 4-2

See (192) and (3-274). The roots of $a^{2n+1} + i = 0$ are $a_0, a_1, \ldots,$ $a_{2n}; \quad y(x) = u(z); \quad z_k = 2a_k\sqrt{x}; \quad r = n+1/2;$

$$y = x^{(2n+1)/4} \sum_{k=0}^{2n} C_k[J_{-r}(z_k) + iJ_r(z_k)]$$

194 $\quad y^{(n)} = xe^x$ 9-1

$$y = C_1 + C_2 x + C_3 x^2 + \ldots + C_n x^{n-1} + (x-n)e^x$$

195 $\quad y^{(n)} + ax^m y' + amx^{m-1} y = 0$ 5

A first integral is $y^{(n-1)} + ax^m y = C.$

196 $\quad (a-x)^n (b-x)^n y^{(n)} = cy$ 4-2

$y = (b-x)^{n-1} u(z); \quad z = \ln\dfrac{a-x}{b-x}.$ The transformed equation in

u, z will have constant coefficients; see **1**.

6. THE EQUATION IS NONLINEAR AND OF ORDER GREATER THAN TWO

The most general equation in this section will contain a sum of terms $X_i(x, y, y'', \ldots, y^{(n)})$. At least one term must have a derivative of third order or more. The arrangement is according to increasing rank, starting with the term containing the highest derivative. See 1, 2, and 4 for further details. Refer to Part I, Introduction-4 and **C2** for description of the notation and general properties of these equations.

Integration constants are $C_1, C_2, \ldots, C_n$. In case the general solution is not given, an integration constant in a first integral may be called C. Singular integrals often occur and an arbitrary constant there will be C_0 or, for a singular solution, other letters may be used for constants. If no singular solution is given, it does not necessarily mean that none exists.

1     $y''' = y'(1+y')$ 2-2
$y' = u(x);$ $u'' = u(1+u);$ see **B2-2-1**.

2     $y''' - yy'' + y'^2 = 0$ 2-4
$y' = p; p(pp'' + p'^2 - yp' + p) = 0;$ see (4-141).

3     $y''' + ayy'' = 0$ 2-4
$y' = p;$ $p(pp'' + p'^2 + ayp') = 0;$ see (4-142).

4     $x^2y''' + xy'' - (1 - 2xy)y' + y^2 = f(x)$ 4
A first integral is
$$x^2y'' - xy' + xy^2 = \int f(x)dx + C; \quad \text{see } \mathbf{B2}.$$

5     $x^2y''' - (1-y)xy'' + xy'^2 + (1-y)y' = 0$ 4
$I(x) = 1/x^2$
$$xy'' - (1-y)y' = Cx$$

6     $yy''' - y'y'' + y^3y' = 0$ 4
$I(y) = 1/y^2$. A first integral is $y'' + y^3/2 = Cy$. See (4-74) for a second integral.
$$4y'^2 = C_1 + C_2y^2 - y^4$$

7     $(a+y)y''' + 3y'y'' = 0$ 4
A first integral is $(a+y)y'' + y'^2 = C$; see (4-165).
$$y(2a + y) = x(C_1x + C_2) + C_3$$

427

8    $x^3yy''' + 3x^3y'y'' + 9x^2yy'' + 9x^2y'^2 + 18xyy' + 3y^2 = 0$ **4**
A first integral is $x^3yy'' + x^3y'^2 + 6x^2yy' + 3xy^2 = C_1$; see (4-229).
$$x^3y^2 = C_1x^2 + C_2x + C_3$$

9    $(x+y^2)y''' + 6yy'y'' + 3y'' + 2y'^3 = 0$ **4**
A first integral is $(x+y^2)y'' + 2yy'^2 + 2y' = C$; see (4-243).
$$2y(3x+y^2) = C_1 + C_2(1+3x^2) + 6C_3x$$

10    $4y^2y''' - 18yy'y'' + 15y'^3 = 0$ **5**
$y = 1/u^2(x)$; $8u^{-7}u''' = 0$;   see (5-1).
$$1/\sqrt{y} = C_1 + C_2x + C_3x^2; \quad y = C_0$$

11    $9y^2y''' - 45yy'y'' + 40y'^3 = 0$ **4, 5**
i. $I(y) = 1/y^{11/3}$; $9y^{-5/3}y'' - 15y^{-8/3}y'^2 = C$; see **2-4**.
ii. $y = u^{-3/2}(x)$; $(27/2)\,u^{-11/2}u''' = 0$; see (5-1).
$$y^2 = 1/(C_1 + C_2x + C_3x^2)^3; \quad y = C_0$$

12    $y'y''' + y'^2 = 2y''^2$ **2-3**
$p^2(pp'' + 1 - p'^2) = 0$;   see (4-127).
$$x = \ln[\sec(C_1 + C_2y) + \tan(C_1 + C_2y)] + C_3$$

13    $y'y'' = axy'^5 + 3y''^2$ **5**
Interchange x and y; $x'''(y) + ax = 0$;   see (5-8).

14    $2y'y''' = 3y''^2$ **5, 2-3**
$y' = u(x)$; $2uu'' = 3u'^2$; $(x+C_2)^2y' = C_1$;   see (4-184) and
A1-1-1.
$$(x+C_2)y = (C_1 + C_3x)$$

15    $(1+y'^2)y''' = 3y'y''^2$ **5**
$y' = u(x)$; $(1+u^2)u'' = 3uu'^2$; $y'\sqrt{1-(C_2+C_2x)^2} = C_1 + C_2x$;
see (4-240) and **A1-1-1**.
$$x^2 + y^2 + 2Ax + 2By + C = 0; \quad y = a+bx$$

16    $(1+y'^2)y''' = (a+3y')y''^2$ **5**
$y' = u(x) = \tan t$; $(1+u^2)u'' = (a+3u)u'^2$;   see (4-241)
$$x = C_1 + C_2e^{-at}(a\cos t - \sin t)$$
$$y = C_3 + C_2e^{-at}(a\sin t + \cos t)$$

17    $y'^3y''' = 1$ **2-2**
$y' = u(x)$; $u^3u'' = 1$;   see (4-260).
$$2y\sqrt{C_1} + C_3 = (C_2 + x)R(x) + C_1^2\ln(C_2 + x + R);$$
$$R(x) = \sqrt{(C_2 + x)^2 + C_1^2}.$$

18    $y''y''' = 2$ **2-1**
$$15y = 8(C_1 + x)^{5/2} + C_2x + C_3$$

19     $y''y''' = a\sqrt{1+b^2y''^2}$ 2-1

$y'' = u(x);$ $uu' = a\sqrt{1+b^2u^2};$ $ab^2x = C_1 + R(u);$

$R(u) = \sqrt{1+b^2u^2};$ see (1-432).

$$y = C_2 + C_3\frac{R}{ab^2} + \frac{u^3}{6a^2b^2} + \frac{u}{2a^2b^4} - \frac{R}{2a^2b^5}\sinh^{-1}bu$$

If $u(x)$ could be eliminated from the last equation, the result would be the general solution, with three integration constants.

20     $2xy''y''' = y''^2 - a^2$ 1-2

$y'' = u(x);$ $2xuu' = u^2 - a^2;$ $u^2 = Cx + a^2;$ see **A1-5**.

   $15C_2y = 4(C_1^2a^2 + x)^{5/2} + C_2x + C_3$

21     $(1-x^2)y'''^2 + 2xy''y''' - y''^2 + 1 = 0$ 1-2

$y'' = u(x);$ $(1-x^2)u'^2 + 2xuu' - u^2 + 1 = 0;$ $u = Cx \pm \sqrt{C^2 + 1};$

see (2-175).

   $6y = C_1x^3 \pm 3x^2\sqrt{C_1^2 + 1} + C_2x + C_3$

22     $(1-y''')\sqrt{1+y''^2} = y''y'''$ 2-1

$y'' = u(x);$ $u'(u+R) = R;$ $R(u) = \sqrt{1+u^2};$ $2u = x + C$

$-1/(x+C);$ see **A1-1-3**.

   $12y = (x+C_1)^3 + C_2(x+C_1) - 6(x+C_1)\ln(x+C_2) + C_3$

23     $3y''y^{iv} = 5y'''^2$ 2-3

   i. An equivalent form is $(y''^{-2/3})'' = 0$.

   ii. $y'' = u(x);$ $3uu'' = 5u'^2;$ see (4-191).

   $(y+C_1x+C_2)^2 = C_3x + C_4.$

24     $3y'y''y^{iv} - 4y'y'''^2 - 3y''^2y''' = 0$ 4

$I(y) = 1/y'''^2.$ A first integral is $(C+y)y''' + 3y'y'' = 0;$ see (7).

   $C_1(x-C_2)^2 + (y-C_3)^2 = C_4$

A singular solution is $y = a + bx + cx^2$.

25     $9y''^2y^v - 45y''y'''y^{iv} + 40y'''^3 = 0$ 1-3, 4

   i. An equivalent form is $(y''^{-2/3})''' = 0$.

   ii. $9I(y) = y''^n,$ for $n = -11/3$ and $n = -13/3$.

   iii. $y'' = u(x);$ $9u^2u''' - 45uu'u'' + 40u'^3 = 0;$ see (11).

   $(y+C_1x+C_2)^2 = C_3x + C_4x^2 + C_5$

26     $y^{(n)} = f(x)$ 1-1

27     $y^{(n)} = f[y^{(n-2)}]$ 2-2

28     $y^{(n)} = f[y^{(n-1)}]$ 2-1

29      $y^{(n-2)}y^{(n)} = [y^{(n-1)}]^2$ **2-3**

$y^{(n-2)} = u(x)$; $y^{(n-1)} = v(x)$; $y^{(n)} = vv'(u)$; $uv' = v$;

$u = C_2e^{(C_1x)}$;   see **1-1**.

$$y = C_2e^{C_1x}(c_0 + c_1x + c_2x^2 + \ldots + c_{n-3}x^{n-3})$$

30      $f(x, y^{(n)}) = 0$ **1-1**

31      $f(x, y^{(n-1)}, y^{(n)}) = 0$ **1-2**

32      $f(y^{(n-2)}, y^{(n-1)}, y^{(n)}) = 0$ **2-3**

33      $f(x, y', y'', \ldots, y^{(n)}) = 0$ **1, 1-3**

34      $f(y, y', y'', \ldots, y^{(n)}) = 0$ **2, 2-4**

INDEX OF EQUATION TYPES

In the following index every equation in Part II is
listed according to the equation types of Part I. If an
explanation of the notation is wanted, see page 223.

431

BIBLIOGRAPHY

The following list of references is not intended to be exhaustive. It contains some of the classical nineteenth century treatises on differential equations; most of the current textbooks, written for an undergraduate college course; advanced texts or monographs, more concerned with theory and special properties of differential equations than with methods of solving them. A number of books on related branches of mathematics have also been included. They were chosen because they were especially helpful to the author, because they are readily available, or because they are generally regarded as the authoritative treatment of that particular field. There are many excellent books describing the use of differential equations in the natural sciences or engineering. Only a few of them have been listed. For more references of that kind or for a more complete bibliography of mathematical works, the reader should consult Parke. His book is very interesting for it also contains informative definitions, historical comments, and summaries of many specialized branches of mathematics.

Two or more books by the same author are distinguished by consecutive numbers so that they can be identified from the text. This bibliography was completed after the rest of the text had been written and, for that reason, some references in the latter lack an identifying number. In such cases, it can be assumed that the first reference in the bibliography is meant.

Abdank-Abakonowicz, Br., *Les intégraphes. La courbe intégrale et ses applications. Étude sur un nouveau système d'intégrateurs mécaniques*, Gauthier-Villars, Paris, 1886.

Adams, Edwin P., *Smithsonian Mathematical Formulae and Tables of Elliptic Functions*, Smithsonian Miscell. Collections, 73, No. 1, Publication 2672, Smithsonian Institution, Washington, 1947.

Agnew, Ralph P., *Differential Equations*, McGraw-Hill Book Company, Inc., New York, 1942.

Andronov, A. A., and C. E. Chaikin, *Theory of Oscillations*, Princeton University Press, Princeton, N. J., 1949.

Bellman, Richard, *Stability Theory of Differential Equations*, McGraw-Hill Book Company, Inc., New York, 1953.

Bennett, Albert A., William E. Milne, and Harry Bateman, *Numerical Integration of Differential Equations*, Dover Publications, Inc., New York, 1956.

Betz, Herman, P. B. Burcham, and George M. Ewing, *Differential Equations with Applications*, Harper & Brothers, New York, 1954.

Bieberbach, Ludwig, *Einführung in die Theorie der Differentialgleichungen im reelen Gebiet*, Springer-Verlag, Berlin, 1956.

436

Bieberbach, Ludwig, *Theorie der gewöhnlichen Differentialgleichungen auf funktiontheoretischer Grundlage dargestellt*, Springer-Verlag, Berlin, 1953.
Bieberbach, Ludwig, *Theorie der Differentialgleichungen. Vorlesungen aus dem Gesamtgebiet der gewöhnlichen und der partiellen Differentialgleichungen*, 2nd edition, Springer-Verlag, Berlin, 1930; Dover Publications, Inc., New York, 1944.
Boole, George — 1, *A Treatise on Differential Equations*, 3rd edition, Macmillan and Co., Ltd., London, 1872. A supplementary volume, 1877, is very rare.
Boole, George — 2, *A Treatise on the Calculus of Finite Differences*, 3rd edition, Macmillan and Co., Ltd., London, 1880; 4th edition, J. F. Moulton, Editor, Chelsea Publishing Company, New York, 1958.
Buckingham, R. A., *Numerical Methods*, Isaac Pitman & Sons, New York, 1957.
Burington, Richard S., and Charles C. Torrance, *Higher Mathematics with Applications to Science and Engineering*, McGraw-Hill Book Company, Inc., New York, 1939.
Burkill, J. C., *The Theory of Ordinary Differential Equations*, Interscience Publishers, Inc., New York, 1956.
Byerly, William E., *Elements of the Integral Calculus, with a Key to the Solution of Differential Equations, and a Short Table of Integrals*, 2nd edition, Ginn and Company, Boston, 1892.
Campbell, G. A., and R. M. Foster, *Fourier Integrals for Practical Applications*, D. Van Nostrand Company, Inc., Princeton, N. J., 1948.
Cayley, Arthur, *An Elementary Treatise on Elliptic Functions*, 2nd edition, George Bell and Sons, London, 1895.
Churchill, Ruel V. — 1, *Modern Operational Methods in Engineering*, McGraw-Hill Book Company, Inc., New York, 1944.
Churchill, Ruel V. — 2, *Fourier Series and Boundary Value Problems*, McGraw-Hill Book Company, Inc., New York, 1941.
Churchill, Ruel V. — 3, *Introduction to Complex Variables and Applications*, McGraw-Hill Book Company, Inc., New York, 1948.
Coddington, Earl A., and Norman Levinson, *Theory of Ordinary Differential Equations*, McGraw-Hill Book Company, Inc., New York, 1955.
Cogan, Edward J., and Robert Z. Norman, *Handbook of Calculus, Difference and Differential Equations*, Prentice-Hall, Inc., Englewood Cliffs, N. J., 1958.
Cohen, Abraham — 1, *An Introduction to the Lie Theory of One-Parameter Groups with Applications to the Solution of Differential Equations*, D. C. Heath and Company, Boston, 1911.
Cohen, Abraham — 2, *An Elementary Treatise on Differential Equations*, 2nd edition, D. C. Heath and Company, Boston, 1933.
Collatz, Lothar — 1, *Numerische Behandlung von Differentialgleichungen*, 2nd edition, Springer-Verlag, Berlin, 1955.
Collatz, Lothar — 2, *Eigenwertaufgaben mit technischen Anwendungen*, Akademische Verlagsgesellschaft, Leipzig, 1949.
Collatz, Lothar — 3, *Eigenwertprobleme und ihre numerische Behandlung*, Becker und Erler, Leipzig, 1945; Chelsea Publishing Company, New York, 1948.
Condon, Edward U., and Hugh Odishaw, Editors, *Handbook of Physics*, McGraw-Hill Book Company, Inc., New York, 1958.
Conkwright, N. B., *A First Course in Differential Equations*, The Macmillan Company, New York, 1934.
Copson, E. T., *An Introduction to the Theory of Functions of a Complex Variable*, Oxford University Press, New York, 1935.
Darboux, G., *Leçons sur la théorie générale des surfaces*, 2nd edition, 4 vols., Gauthier-Villars, Paris, 1894-1915.

Davis, Harold T., *Studies in Differential Equations*, Northwestern University Press, Evanston, Ill., 1956.

Doetsch, G., *Handbuch der Laplace-Transformation*, 3 vols., Birkhäuser Verlag, Basel, 1950, 1955, 1956.

Doetsch, G., *Einführung in Theorie und Anwendung der Laplace-Transformation*, Birkhaüser Verlag, Basel, 1958.

Doetsch, G., *Theorie und Anwendung der Laplace-Transformation*, Springer-Verlag, Berlin, 1937; Dover Publications, Inc., New York, 1943.

Erdélyi, A., (Editor) — 1, *Higher Transcendental Functions*, 3 vols., McGraw-Hill Book Company, Inc., New York, 1953.

Erdélyi, A. — 2, *Asymptotic Expansions*, Dover Publications, Inc., New York, 1956.

Erdélyi, A., (Editor) — 3, *Tables of Integral Transforms*, 2 vols., McGraw-Hill Book Company, Inc., New York, 1954.

Ford, Lester R. — 1, *Automorphic Functions*, 2nd edition, McGraw-Hill Book Company, Inc., New York, 1951; Chelsea Publishing Company, New York, 1951.

Ford, Lester R. — 2, *Differential Equations*, 2nd edition, McGraw-Hill Book Company, Inc., New York, 1955.

Forsyth, Andrew R. — 1, *A Treatise on Differential Equations*, 6th edition, The Macmillan Company, New York, 1929.

Forsyth, Andrew R. — 2, *Theory of Differential Equations*, vol. 1, *Exact Equations and Pfaff's Problem;* vols. 2-3, *Ordinary Equations, Not Linear;* vol. 4, *Ordinary Linear Equations;* vols. 5-6, *Partial Differential Equations*, Cambridge University Press, London, 1890-1906; Dover Publications, Inc., New York, 6 vols. bound in 3, 1959.

Forsyth, Andrew R. — 3, *Solutions of the Examples in "A Treatise on Differential Equations,"* 3rd edition, Macmillan and Co., Ltd., London, 1956.

Fort, Tomlinson, *Finite Differences and Difference Equations in the Real Domain*, Oxford University Press, New York, 1948.

Fox, L., *The Numerical Solution of Two-Point Boundary Problems in Ordinary Differential Equations*, Oxford University Press, New York, 1957.

Franklin, Philip, *Fourier Methods*, McGraw-Hill Book Company, Inc., New York, 1949; *An Introduction to Fourier Methods and the Laplace Transformation*, corrected edition, Dover Publications, Inc., New York, 1958.

Franklin, Philip, *Differential Equations for Electrical Engineers*, John Wiley & Sons, Inc., New York, 1933.

Frazer, R. A., W. J. Duncan, and A. R. Collar, *Elementary Matrices and Some Applications to Dynamics and Differential Equations*, The Macmillan Company, New York, 1947.

Friedman, Bernard, *Principles and Techniques of Applied Mathematics*, John Wiley & Sons, Inc., New York, 1956.

Fry, Thornton C., *Elementary Differential Equations*, D. Van Nostrand Company, Inc., Princeton, N. J., 1929.

Gambier, B., *Acta Mathematica* **33,** 1 (1909).

Gardner, M. F., and J. L. Barnes, *Transients in Linear Systems*, John Wiley & Sons, Inc., New York, 1942.

Golomb, Michael, and Merrill Shanks, *Elements of Ordinary Differential Equations*, McGraw-Hill Book Company, Inc., New York, 1950.

Goursat, Édouard, *A Course in Mathematical Analysis*, 3 vols., vol. II, Part II, *Differential Equations* (bound separately), Ginn and Company, Boston, 1894-1917; Gauthier-Villars, Paris (in French), 5th edition, vol. 1, 1943, vol. 3, 1942; 7th edition, vol. 2, 1949.

Grobner, W., and Nikolaus Hofreiter, *Integraltafel*, 2 vols., Springer-Verlag, Vienna, 1949-1950.

Hartree, Douglas R. — 1, *Numerical Analysis*, 2nd edition, Oxford University Press, New York, 1958.

Hartree, Douglas R. — 2, *Calculating Instruments and Machines*, University of Illinois Press, Urbana, 1949.

Heffter, L., *Einleitung und die Theorie der linearen Differentialgleichungen mit einer unabhängigen Variabeln*, B. G. Teubner, Leipzig, 1894.

Hill, M. J. M., *Proc. London Mathematical Soc.* **19**, 561 (1888).

Hodgman, Charles D. (Editor), *Handbook of Chemistry and Physics*, Chemical Rubber Publishing Co., Cleveland, Ohio, 39th edition, 1957-1958, and later editions published annually. The mathematical sections are available separately, 11th edition, 1957.

Hoheisel, G., *Gewöhnliche Differentialgleichungen*, 5th edition, Walter de Gruyter & Co., Berlin, 1956.

Hoheisel, G., *Aufgabensammlung zu den gewöhnlichen und partiellen Differentialgleichungen*, 2nd edition, Walter de Gruyter & Co., Berlin, 1952.

Horn, J., *Gewöhnliche Differentialgleichungen*, 5th edition, Walter de Gruyter & Co., Berlin, 1948.

Hurewicz, Witold, *Lectures on Ordinary Differential Equations*, John Wiley & Sons, Inc., New York, 1958.

Ince, E. L. — 1, *Ordinary Differential Equations*, Longmans, Green & Company, Inc., New York, 1927; Dover Publications Inc., New York, 1956.

Ince, E. L. — 2, *Integration of Ordinary Differential Equations*, 6th edition, Interscience Publishers, Inc., New York, 1952.

Jahnke, Eugene, and Fritz Emde, *Tables of Functions with Formulae and Curves*, 3rd edition, Dover Publications, Inc., New York, 1948; 5th German edition, F. Losch (Editor), B. G. Teubner, Leipzig, 1952.

Jeffreys, Harold, and Bertha S. Jeffreys, *Methods of Mathematical Physics*, 3rd edition, Cambridge University Press, London, 1956.

Johnson, Clarence L., *Analog Computer Techniques*, McGraw-Hill Book Company, Inc., New York, 1956.

Jordan, Camille, *Cours d'analyse de l'école polytechnique*, 3rd edition, 3 vols., Gauthier-Villars, Paris, 1915.

Jordan, Charles, *The Calculus of Finite Differences*, Chelsea Publishing Company, New York, 1947; 2nd edition, Rottig-Romwalter, Budapest, 1947.

Julia, Gaston, *Exercises d'analyse*, 2nd edition, Gauthier-Villars, Paris, 1950.

Kamke, E. — 1, *Differentialgleichungen, Lösungsmethoden und Lösungen*, vol. 1, *Gewöhnliche Differentialgleichungen;* vol. 2, *Partielle Differentialgleichungen erste Ordnung;* 3rd edition, vol. 1 only, Chelsea Publishing Company, New York, 1948; 4th edition, vols. 1-2, Akademische Verlagsgesellschaft, Leipzig, 1959.

Kamke, E. — 2, *Differentialgleichungen reeler Funktionen*, Chelsea Publishing Company, New York, 1947; 2nd edition, Akademische Verlagsgesellschaft, Leipzig, 1952.

Kantorovich, L. V. and V. I. Krylov, *Approximate Methods of Higher Analysis*, translated from the 3rd Russian edition, Interscience Publishers, Inc., New York, 1958.

Kaplan, Wilfred — 1, *Ordinary Differential Equations*, Addison-Wesley Publishing Company, Inc., Reading, Mass., 1958.

Kaplan, Wilfred — 2, *Operational Methods for Linear Systems*, Addison-Wesley Publishing Company, Inc., Reading, Mass., in preparation.

Kaplan, Wilfred — 3, *Advanced Calculus*, Addison-Wesley Publishing Company, Inc., Reading, Mass. 1953.

Kells, Lyman M., *Elementary Differential Equations*, 4th edition, McGraw-Hill Book Company, Inc., New York, 1954.

Koenigsberger, Leo, *Lehrbuch der Theorie der Differentialgleichungen mit einer unabhängiger Variabeln*, B. G. Teubner, Leipzig, 1889.

Langer, R. E., *A First Course in Ordinary Differential Equations*, John Wiley & Sons, Inc., New York, 1954.

Lefschetz, Solomon, *Lectures on Differential Equations*, Princeton University Press, Princeton, N. J., 1946.

Lefschetz, Solomon, *Differential Equations: Geometric Theory*, Interscience Publishers, Inc., New York, 1957.

Leighton, W., *An Introduction to the Theory of Differential Equations*, McGraw-Hill Book Company, Inc., New York, 1952.

Levy, H., and E. A. Baggott, *Numerical Studies in Differential Equations*, 2 vols., Watts and Co., London, 1934; *Numerical Solutions of Differential Equations*, reprint of vol. 1, Dover Publications, Inc., New York, 1950.

Lie, S., and E. Engel, *Theorie der Transformationsgruppen*, 3 vols., B. G. Teubner, Leipzig, 1888-1893.

Lovitt, W. V., *Linear Integral Equations*, McGraw-Hill Book Company, Inc., New York, 1924; Dover Publications, Inc., New York, 1950.

MacRobert, T. M., *Functions of a Complex Variable*, 4th edition, Macmillan and Co., Ltd., London, 1954.

Madelung, Erwin, *Die mathematischen Hilfsmittel des Physikers*, 3rd edition, Dover Publications, Inc., New York, 1945; 5th edition, Springer-Verlag, Berlin, 1954.

Magnus, Wilhelm, and Fritz Oberhettinger, *Formulas and Theorems for the Special Functions of Mathematical Physics*, Chelsea Publishing Company, New York, 1954.

Martin, W. T., and E. Reissner, *Elementary Differential Equations*, Addison-Wesley Publishing Company, Inc., Reading, Mass., 1956.

McLachlan, N. W., *Ordinary Non-Linear Differential Equations in Engineering and Physical Sciences*, 2nd edition, Oxford University Press, New York, 1956.

Meyer zur Capellen, Walther, *Integraltafeln. Sammlung unbestimmter Integrale elementarer Funktionen*, Springer-Verlag, Berlin, 1950.

Miller, Norman, *A First Course in Differential Equations*, Oxford University Press, New York, 1935.

Milne, William E. — 1, *Numerical Calculus. Approximations, Interpolation, Finite Differences, Numerical Integration, and Curve Fitting*, Princeton University Press, Princeton, N. J., 1949.

Milne, William E. — 2, *Numerical Solutions of Differential Equations*, John Wiley & Sons, Inc., New York, 1953.

Milne-Thomson, L. M., *The Calculus of Finite Differences*, Macmillan and Co., Ltd., London, 1951.

Morris, M., and O. E. Brown, *Differential Equations*, 3rd edition, Prentice-Hall, Inc., Englewood Cliffs, N. J., 1952.

Morse, Philip M., and Herman Feshbach, *Methods of Theoretical Physics*, 2 vols., McGraw-Hill Book Company, Inc., New York, 1953.

Moulton, F. R., *Differential Equations*, The Macmillan Company, New York, 1930; Dover Publications, Inc., New York, 1958.

Murray, Daniel A., *Differential Equations*, 3rd edition, Longmans, Green & Company, Inc., New York, 1953.

Murray, Francis J., and Kenneth S. Miller, *Existence Theorems for Ordinary Differential Equations*, Interscience Publishers, Inc., New York University Press, New York, 1954.

Nelson, A. E., K. W. Folley, and M. Coral, *Differential Equations*, 2nd edition, D. C. Heath and Company, Boston, 1960.

Nemickii, V. V., and V. V. Stepanov, *Qualitative Theory of Differential Equations*, translated from the 2nd Russian edition, Princeton University Press, Princeton, N. J., 1960.

Oberhettinger, Fritz, and Wilhelm Magnus, *Anwendungen der elliptische Funktionen in Physik und Technik*, Springer-Verlag, Berlin, 1949.

Page, James Morris, *Ordinary Differential Equations. An Elementary Text-Book with an Introduction to Lie's Theory of the Group of One Parameter*, The Macmillan Company, New York, 1897.

Painlevé, P., *Acta Mathematica* **25**, 1 (1902); *Compt. rend.* **143**, 1111 (1906).

Parke III, Nathan Grier, *Guide to the Literature of Mathematics and Physics Including Related Works on Engineering*, 2nd edition, Dover Publications, Inc., New York, 1958.

Peirce, Benjamin O., and Ronald M. Foster, *A Short Table of Integrals*, 4th edition, Ginn and Company, Boston, 1956.

Phillips, E. G., *Functions of a Complex Variable with Applications*, 7th edition, Interscience Publishers, Inc., New York, 1951.

Phillips, H. B., *Differential Equations*, 3rd edition, John Wiley & Sons, Inc., New York, 1951.

Piaggio, H. T. H., *An Elementary Treatise on Differential Equations and Their Applications*, 3rd edition, G. Bell and Sons, Ltd., London, 1938.

Picard, E., *Traité d'analyse*, 3rd edition, 3 vols., Gauthier-Villars, Paris, 1922, 1925, 1928.

Pinney, Edmund, *Ordinary Difference-Differential Equations*, University of California Press, Berkeley and Los Angeles, 1958.

Poole, E. G. C., *Introduction to the Theory of Linear Differential Equations*, Oxford University Press, London, 1936 (out of print).

Powell, J. E., and C. P. Wells, *Differential Equations*, Ginn and Company, Boston, 1950.

Rainville, Earl D., *Intermediate Course in Differential Equations*, John Wiley & Sons, Inc., New York, 1943.

Rainville, Earl D., *A Short Course in Differential Equations*, The Macmillan Company, New York, 1958.

Rainville, Earl D., *Elementary Differential Equations*, The Macmillan Company, New York, 1958.

Reddick, Harry W., and Donald E. Kibbey, *Differential Equations*, 3rd edition, John Wiley & Sons, Inc., New York, 1956.

Relton, F. E., *Applied Differential Equations*, Blackie and Son Limited, London, 1948.

Richards, Paul I., *Manual of Mathematical Physics*, Pergamon Press, New York, 1959.

Richardson, Clarence H., *An Introduction to the Calculus of Finite Differences*, D. Van Nostrand Company, Inc., Princeton, N. J., 1954.

Richtmyer, R. D., *Difference Methods for Initial Value Problems*, Interscience Publishers, Inc., New York, 1957.

Sanden, H. v., *Praxis der Differentialgleichungen*, 4th edition, Walter de Gruyter & Co., Berlin, 1955.

Sansone, Giovanni, *Equazioni differenziali nel campo reele*, 2nd edition, 2 vols., Nicoala Zanichelli, Bologna, 1948-1949.

Sansone, Giovanni, and R. Conti, *Equazioni differenziali non lineari*, Ed. Cremonese, Rome, 1956.

Scarborough, J. B., *Numerical Mathematical Analysis*, 4th edition, Johns Hopkins Press, Baltimore, 1958.

Schlesinger, L., *Handbuch der Theorie der linearen Differentialgleichungen*, 3 vols., B. G. Teubner, Leipzig, 1895, 1897, 1898.

Schlesinger, L., *Vorlesungen über linearen Differentialgleichungen*, Walter de Gruyter & Co., Berlin, 1908.

Schlesinger, L., *Einführung in die Theorie der Differentialgleichungen auf funktiontheoretische Grundlage*, 3rd edition, Walter de Gruyter & Co., Berlin, 1922.

Sneddon, Ian N., *Fourier Transforms*, McGraw-Hill Book Company, Inc., New York, 1951.

Sneddon, Ian N., *Special Functions of Mathematical Physics and Chemistry*, Interscience Publishers, Inc., New York, 1956.

Soroka, Walter W., *Analog Methods in Computation and Simulation*, McGraw-Hill Book Company, Inc., New York, 1954.

Spiegel, M. R., *Applied Differential Equations*, Prentice-Hall, Inc., Englewood Cliffs, N. J., 1958.

Steen, F. H., *Differential Equations*, Ginn and Company, Boston, 1955.

Stoker, J. J., *Non-Linear Vibrations in Mechanical and Electrical Systems*, Interscience Publishers, Inc., New York, 1950.

Tranter, C. J., *Integral Transforms in Mathematical Physics*, 2nd edition, John Wiley & Sons, Inc., New York, 1956.

Tricomi, F. G. — 1, *Lezioni sulla funzioni ipergeometriche confluenti*, Cheroni, Turin, 1952.

Tricomi, F. G., *Elliptische Funktionen*, translated from the Italian edition, Akademische Verlagsgesellschaft, Leipzig, 1948.

Tricomi, F. G., *Integral Equations*, Interscience Publishers, Inc., New York, 1957.

Tricomi, F. G., *Equazioni differenziali*, 2nd edition, G. Einaudi, Turin, 1953.

Turnbull, H. W., *Theory of Equations*, 5th edition, Interscience Publishers, Inc., New York, 1957.

Valiron, Georges, *Cours d'analyse mathematique*, 1st edition, 2 vols., Masson et Cie, Paris, 1942-1945; 2nd edition, vol. 1, 1948.

Vallée Poussin, C. J. de la, *Cours d'analyse infinitesimale*, 2 vols., 10th edition, vol. 1; 8th edition, vol. 2, Gauthier-Villars, Paris, 1947, 1949.

Varner, Walter W., *Computing with Desk Calculators*, Rinehart & Company, Inc., New York, 1957.

Wasow, Wolfgang, *Introduction to the Asymptotic Theory of Ordinary Linear Differential Equations*, National Bureau of Standards Report, Washington, 1953.

Watson, G. N., *A Treatise on the Theory of Bessel Functions*, 2nd edition, Cambridge University Press, London, 1944.

Wayland, Harold, *Differential Equations Applied in Science and Engineering*, D. Van Nostrand Company, Inc., Princeton, N. J., 1957.

Whittaker, E. T., and G. Robinson, *The Calculus of Observations*, 4th edition, D. Van Nostrand Company, Inc., Princeton, N. J., 1944.

Whittaker, E. T., and G. N. Watson, *A Course of Modern Analysis. An Introduction to the General Theory of Infinite Processes and of Analytic Functions; with an Account of the Principal Transcendental Functions*, 4th edition, reprinted, Cambridge University Press, London, 1940.

Wilkes, M. V., D. J. Wheeler, and Stanley Gill, *The Preparation of Programs for an Electronic Digital Computer*, 2nd edition, Addison-Wesley Publishing Company, Inc., Reading, Mass., 1957.

Willers, F. A., *Practical Analysis: Graphical and Numerical Methods*, Dover Publications, Inc., New York, 1948; 3rd German edition, Walter de Gruyter & Co., Berlin, 1957.

Yates, R. C., *Differential Equations*, McGraw-Hill Book Company, Inc., New York, 1952.

INDEX

443